THE PETROLEUM HANDBOOK

THE PETROLEUM
HANDBOOK

*COMPILED BY
MEMBERS OF THE STAFF OF
THE ROYAL DUTCH-SHELL
GROUP*

THIRD EDITION

LONDON
THE SHELL PETROLEUM COMPANY LIMITED
1948

Published by

THE SHELL PETROLEUM COMPANY LIMITED
ST. HELEN'S COURT, GREAT ST. HELEN'S
LONDON, E.C.3

First Edition	*1931*
Second Edition	*1938*
Third Edition	*1948*

Printed in Great Britain by
JAMES TRUSCOTT AND SON LIMITED
London and Tonbridge

FOREWORD

by GEORGE LEGH-JONES

TWENTY-FIVE thousand members of the Group's staff acquired copies of the first edition of *The Petroleum Handbook*. Although the second edition was produced in 1938, by the time the Second World War came upon us nearly 30,000 of the 35,000 copies printed were on the desks or bookshelves of "Shell" employees in every part of the world.   That is the measure of the success of this work and the value attached to it as an educational handbook by those engaged in our great industry.

During the last nine years technical developments have proceeded at an unprecedented pace, and a chemical industry based on petroleum is already established.   The anonymous authors of this third edition of the Handbook have therefore had much new material to dwell upon.   Those who have been associated with oil for many years will accordingly find the new volume more than a mere refresher course ; newcomers to our ranks will appreciate that a close study of its pages will reward them with a fund of knowledge which will be of benefit to them whatever may be the duties they are called upon to perform.

This book is the product of collaboration among "Shell" people operating in different parts of the world.   I am sure that the same co-operative spirit and enthusiasm will guide all members of our staffs in their work in the strenuous years that lie ahead so that the continued success of our Group may be judged by the service which we render and the constructive work which we achieve.

St. Helen's Court,
September 1948

CONTENTS

CONTENTS

In addition to the ordinary Index, a Glossary of unusual terms is provided, references to which are indicated by the sign * in the text.

PREFACE

At a period when the petroleum industry is busily engaged in reconstruction and extension, a revised edition of the Group's *Petroleum Handbook* should be very useful. While this edition was in the press, the applications for copies among the Group's staffs exceeded the number distributed in former editions. There is, therefore, no question that the *Handbook* fulfils an important demand.

In this, the third edition, new advances in most branches of the petroleum industry have been incorporated, thus increasing the size of the book by about fifty per cent. The book has been rearranged to bring the information up-to-date, and every effort has been made to make the contents readily understood by the non-technical reader.

The authors are members of the staffs in the United States, Holland and the United Kingdom, and thanks are due to them for giving their assistance in the compilation of this book. Our grateful thanks are also given to those who have spent many hours on work in connection with the preparation of the book and its illustrations.

We also wish to thank Messrs. Alfa Laval Co., Ltd., Avery Hardol, Ltd., Babcock & Wilcox, Ltd., Brown Boveri, Ltd., Chicago Bridge & Iron Works, A. F. Craig & Co., Ltd., Satona, Ltd., Thompson Bros., and Whessoe Foundry & Engineering Co., Ltd., for permission to publish illustrations.

THE EDITOR

THE WORLD PETROLEUM INDUSTRY

PATTERN OF THE OIL INDUSTRY

THE pattern of the oil industry and the nature of its operations are largely governed by the physical and chemical characteristics of oil itself. The fact that oil is a liquid determines broadly the methods used at each stage of the operations of the industry, from prospecting for crude oil to the sale and distribution of its many products. To the complex chemical nature of crude oil we owe the development of elaborate and precise methods of refining, which aim at the production of a continually increasing range of products in the proportions required to meet a changing demand ; to this we also owe the rapid development, in recent years, of a new chemical industry based on petroleum.

The geographical distribution of known underground oil resources—a large proportion of which is in tropical and subtropical zones—divides the countries of the world into two main classes : those producing oil surplus to their own needs and those whose requirements need to be wholly met, or supplemented, by imports. This fact has led to the great growth of the international trade in petroleum, which now exceeds, in value and volume, that of any other commodity. For many countries oil production, or oil importation, is one of the largest, if not the largest, item on their economic balance sheet.

There have been changes from time to time in the relative importance of producing countries in the international oil trade ; these changes are still taking place and may be expected to continue. For example, in the industry's early days Russian oil was exported to many countries, and, with interruptions, this continued, although on a diminishing scale, until 1940, since when the U.S.S.R.'s home demands have absorbed all her production and more—a situation which is likely to obtain for some years to come. Mexico's production in 1921 was about 27 million tons, Mexico being second only to the U.S.A., both in production and exports. To-day Mexico's production is only about a quarter of her peak output in 1921, and her export trade is comparatively small. The later years of the first World War saw the rise of Iran and Venezuela as important oil producers and exporters. Except for brief periods during the economic crisis in 1931–1933 and during the second World War, their production (nearly all of which is exported) has advanced continuously, Venezuela now being the leading oil exporting country in the world. In the past decade or so new important producing countries have entered the lists, notably Bahrein, Iraq, Kuwait and Saudi Arabia, in the Middle East.

Now, a far-reaching change is taking place in the position of the U.S.A. Until recently, the surplus production of that country was large enough to play a major part in supplying the needs of the rest of the world, but for some years past the U.S.A. has had to resort in increasing measure to imports, mainly of heavy fuel oil, in order to balance supplies and total requirements. During the second World War, output in the U.S.A. reached a high level of about $4\frac{3}{4}$ million barrels daily, and has since surpassed it. For some years, however, the rise in domestic consumption has been greater than the rise in domestic production. Moreover, the rate of discovery of new oil resources in the U.S.A. has declined. Failing the discovery of any outstandingly large and extensive new oilfields within the country, it is not surprising that the U.S.A. has become a net importer of petroleum. In view of the progress of industrialization and of the mechanization of agriculture in the U.S.S.R., it seems possible that that country also may need in the future to supplement its own oil production by imports.

Nearly all the other main oil-consuming countries are dependent wholly, or partly, upon other countries for their supplies. The petroleum needs of none of these countries are comparable in total amount with the needs of either the U.S.A. or the U.S.S.R. Consumption of petroleum products in the U.S.A. in 1938 was about 162 million metric tons ; in 1947 it was about 270 million tons. Consumption in the U.S.S.R. in 1938 was about 27·7 million tons, and by 1950 is expected to reach $35\frac{1}{2}$ million tons. By contrast, the United Kingdom, which has the next largest oil consumption, consumed 11¼ million tons in 1938—about one-fourteenth that of the U.S.A., and two-fifths that of the U.S.S.R. The next largest oil-consuming countries in order of their importance in 1938 were France, Germany, Canada, the Japanese Empire, Argentina, Italy, Roumania, Mexico and India.

The inter-dependence of the oil-producing and oil-importing countries has resulted in the evolution of a world-wide oil industry which is essentially international in its character and outlook, and which seeks to provide each country's requirements in the best way from one or more sources of supply. This is a task which calls for the closest co-ordination of the activities of the various branches of the industry. The marketing areas look to the refineries and to the transport sections to fill the demand for varying quantities of different grades of products. The refineries look to the research workers for the new knowledge and manufacturing processes which will enable them to produce in the right proportions, from the various kinds of crude oil available, the products required by the consumer. The production departments must discover and develop sufficient underground reserves to meet demand for many years ahead. At the base of this closely linked chain of effort lies the costly and highly speculative search for new oil-bearing territories in many parts of the world.

The world-wide search for oil-bearing territories goes on continuously and calls for increasing effort in order to satisfy the world's rising needs. Notwithstanding the scientific knowledge and experience that have been brought to bear upon oil prospecting, it is not yet possible to predict with certainty the presence of oil even in an area which may appear geologically promising. The final test is to drill a well. If the test well reveals the presence of crude oil or natural gas, this may not be present in sufficiently large quantities to justify production on a commercial basis ; or the well may fall into the "dry and abandoned" class. Out of a total of 4,518 exploration wells drilled in the United States in 1946, 3,576, or 83%, were dry, which illustrates the speculative character of oil exploration. When the existence underground of oil in commercial quantities has been established, a very large outlay of capital must be undertaken before production can be begun. Experience in one area in Colombia may be cited as an example. There the Royal Dutch-Shell Group expended a sum of more than £8,000,000 over a period of nine years in discovering oil and, afterwards, providing the requisite production and other facilities. The Group has in hand extensive prospecting operations in Netherlands New Guinea and in Ecuador, and is also prospecting in Canada and in a number of other countries. Other oil concerns are also carrying out extensive prospecting work in many parts of the world.

The oil industry embraces four main groups of activities, each of which can, without exaggeration, itself be classified as a major industry. These are :—

(a) Search and production ;

(b) Refining and manufacture (including research upon the chemistry of petroleum and on the application of petroleum products) ;

(c) Transportation by tanker, pipeline, rail and road ;

(d) Distribution.

All these operations are carried out under widely varying conditions and, many of them, by the use of plant and equipment peculiar to the industry. The scientist searches for oil-bearing territory in tropical jungle and uninhabited hinterland, in mountainous country and low-lying swamp, in fertile agricultural areas and beneath coastal waters. When oil is found in commercial quantities wells have to be drilled and all ancillary services may have to be provided by the producing company. Often new townships have to be created, including new roads, transport, living accommodation, schools, hospitals, as well as the power and industrial facilities which modern production efforts require. Pipelines will have to be laid to take the crude oil to the terminal port or refinery. The refined products then go by rail tank-car, pipeline, river barge or tanker to bulk storage and main distribution centres, and they are sold in bulk, or in drums or tins, to consumers and retailers. In this way petroleum products reach every corner of the globe to meet a wide variety of needs, ranging from those of the factories and transport in highly industrialized countries to those of the peasant using kerosine as an illuminant in the interior of Africa or China. Thus, the petroleum industry is, perhaps more than any other, world wide, whilst the oil-importing organizations and the network of distribution facilities established in each country are an essential part of local economic and social life.

Because searching for crude oil is a costly and speculative undertaking and because of the further very large expenditure of capital that has to be made after the oil is found in order to produce and refine it and to place the products in the hands of the consumer, often thousands of miles from the place where the oil is found, it is not surprising that a large part of the international oil trade is done by a comparatively small number of large units. The existence of large organizations is, indeed, inherent in the oil industry in order to achieve the lowest possible overall costs and to provide assured supplies for the future. In this way, also, it is possible for each concern to plan and co-ordinate its operations and to make petroleum products available everywhere in the most efficient way, to the direct advantage of the consumer. In many countries a number of purely local concerns flourish side by side with the companies which trade internationally. However, the need and the value of world-wide oil distributing organizations become more apparent as all means of transport become intensified. Shipowners have for many years had the advantages of a world-wide oil-bunkering service, and, as in the case of ships' bunkers, the Royal Dutch-Shell Group was the pioneer in providing for aircraft, a world-wide refuelling service.

Although the oil industry throughout the world must for many purposes be regarded as a whole, it lends itself naturally to a division into two parts : first, that in the U.S.A., and, secondly, that in the remainder of the world. The oil industry in the U.S.A. is, in some ways, the predominant part, because, of a total world oil production of about 427 million tons, the U.S.A. produces and consumes about two-thirds and also exports and imports considerable quantities. Oil production in the rest of the world is about half that of the U.S.A. and comes from a score of countries, among which Venezuela and Iran are the leading exporters. Together these two countries now (1947) provide about two-thirds of the oil which enters international trade. A large expansion of production in the Middle East during the next few years and the expected large increase in the United States' oil imports will bring a number of changes in the direction and volume of the international oil trade.

THE OIL COMPANIES

Since the oil industry, from its earliest days, had its greatest development in the U.S.A., it is a natural consequence that the majority of the world's large oil companies are of United States origin.

The more important United States oil companies may be divided into two main classes : first, those operating on a worldwide basis through all stages of the industry, i.e., production, refining and distribution ; and second, those embracing any or all stages of the industry but whose operations are wholly within or mainly confined to the North American continent.

The first class includes :—

    Standard Oil Company (New Jersey).
    Socony-Vacuum Oil Co., Inc.
    The Texas Company.
    Gulf Oil Corporation.
    Standard Oil Co. of California.

The foregoing have associated companies formed for the purpose of operating in certain areas outside the U.S.A. These associated companies are in some instances wholly owned by the parent company ; in other cases they are constituted in conjunction with other companies of United States or non-United States domicile.

The second group of United States companies includes the following :—

    Atlantic Refining Co.
    Cities Service Co.
    Continental Oil Co. (Delaware).
    Ohio Oil Co.
    Phillips Petroleum Co.
    Pure Oil Co.
    Shell Union Oil Corporation.
    Sinclair Oil Corporation.
    Standard Oil Co. (Indiana).
    Sun Oil Co.
    Tide Water Associated Oil Co.
    Union Oil Co. of California.

Although these companies' activities are mainly confined to the U.S.A., they have, in some cases, lesser interests in one or more stages of the industry outside the U.S.A.

Three concerns, not of United States origin, which are engaged on a large scale in the international petroleum industry are :—

Royal Dutch-Shell Group,
Anglo-Iranian Oil Co., Ltd.,
Canadian Eagle Oil Co., Ltd.,

the first representing joint British and Dutch capital, and the second a British company, in which the British Government has a large shareholding.

The Burmah Oil Co., Ltd., which is also a British company, in addition to its interests in Burma and India, has shareholdings in the Shell and Anglo-Iranian companies.

The foregoing by no means exhausts the list of large and small concerns engaged in various branches of the oil industry throughout the world. In the U.S.A., the so-called "major" companies are, in fact, vastly outnumbered by the "independent" concerns. In other countries, numerous concerns not associated with the leading oil companies are in operation in one or other of the main branches of the industry, and in the United Kingdom, for example, a large number of independent companies are in normal times engaged in the industry, some having their own sources of production overseas.

In some countries, the State has taken an active part in the industry. For example, in France a proportion of the country's internal petroleum trade is conducted by the government-sponsored Compagnie Française des Pétroles ; in Spain, nearly the whole of the petroleum trade is in the hands of a State monopoly ; in the Argentine, the Government has its own oil-fields, refineries, tankers and distribution system, which it operates in competition with those of the oil companies.

An outline of the organization of the Royal Dutch-Shell Group is given in chapter II.

PROSPECTING AND PRODUCTION

Before prospecting for oil can begin, it is usually necessary to obtain a prospecting licence or concession covering a particular area or territory from the appropriate government or authority. Under the laws of the majority of countries, the minerals contained in the subsoil belong to the State, which is therefore in a position to say who may search for oil and to define the size and conditions of the concession to be granted. In the U.S.A., however, a different position obtains. Under common law, the minerals below the ground belong to the owner of the surface

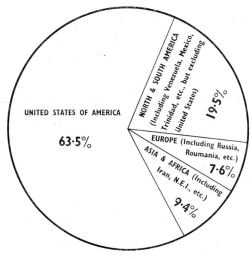

Fig. 1. World crude oil production, 1947.

and, subject to State regulations, the search for oil may be started by the owner of even the smallest plot independently of what others may be doing in the same neighbourhood.

Consequently, in the U.S.A., in contrast to the position in other leading producing countries, there is a very large number of separate oil-producing concerns. Yet about half the country's output is produced by twenty companies. The number of wells in operation is well over 400,000, many of which are owned by large oil companies, and many by smaller concerns and individuals. Small producers seldom have their own refineries and

WORLD CRUDE OIL PRODUCTION 1947 (Prov.) and 1938

Country	Thousand metric tons			
	1947 (Prov.)	%	1938	%
U.S.A.	265,800	62.3	170,700	60.9
W. Hemisphere (excl. U.S.A.)				
Venezuela	63,500	14.9	28,100	10.0
Mexico	7,900	1.9	5,500	2.0
Colombia	3,500	.8	3,100	1.1
Argentine	3,100	.7	2,400	.9
Trinidad	3,000	.7	2,600	.9
Peru	1,800	.4	2,200	.8
Canada	1,000	.2	900	.3
Ecuador	300	.1	300	.1
Others	100(e)	—	—	—
Total W. Hemisphere (excl. U.S.A.)	84,200	19.7	45,100	16.1
Near and Middle East				
Iran	20,400	4.8	10,300	3.7
Saudi Arabia	12,000	2.8	100	—
Iraq	4,700	1.1	4,400	1.5
Egypt	1,300	.3	200	.1
Bahrein	1,200	.3	1,100	.4
Kuwait	2,200	.5	—	—
Total Near and Middle East . .	41,800	9.8	16,100	5.7
Far East				
Brit. Borneo	1,900	.5	900	.3
N.E.I.	1,000	.2	7,400	2.7
India and Burma	300	.1	1,500	.5
Japan	200(b)	—	400(a)	.1
Others	100(f)	—	—	—
Total Far East	3,500	.8	10,200	3.6
U.S.S.R.(c)	25,000	5.9	30,100	10.7
Europe				
Roumania	3,900	.9	6,900	2.5
Austria	800	.2	100	—
Hungary	600	.1	—	—
Germany	500	.1	500	.2
Others	700(g)	.2	800(d)	.3
Total Europe	6,500	1.5	8,300	3.0
WORLD TOTAL	426,800	100.0	280,500	100.0

(a) Incl. Taiwan. (b) Excl. Taiwan. (c) Incl. Sakhalin. (d) Albania, Czechoslovakia, France, Hungary, Italy, Poland, French Morocco. (e) Bolivia, Brazil, Cuba. (f) China. (g) Albania, Czechoslovakia, France, Holland, Italy, Poland, U.K., Yugoslavia, French Morocco.

usually sell their oil to concerns engaged in all branches of the industry, or to concerns who are refiners only. The prices at which would-be purchasers are prepared to buy crude are posted up in the oilfields and are known as ''posted'' prices.

Thus, owing to the legal position in the U.S.A., it is still comparatively rare for an entire oilfield to be developed by a single company upon a rational plan (known elsewhere as ''unit development'') designed to ensure the highest ultimate yield of crude oil from the known underground formations. It is, however, now fairly common for sections of oilfields in the U.S.A.—for example, Kern County, in the San Joaquin Valley in California, or the K.M.A. field in North Texas—to be operated on a unit basis by agreement between the various concerns operating in a particular region and the owners of the land and subsoil. Moreover, in the U.S.A., some of the advantages of unit development are secured by the intervention of the State authorities to prevent uneconomic and wasteful development of the State's oil resources by fixing quotas of allowable production per well. Outside the U.S.A., unit development is more common, and examples are to be found in Iran, Iraq and other Middle East countries, and in Latin America, where concessions are usually granted covering a large and geologically well-defined area. It happens that in these territories the yield per well is usually much above the average in the U.S.A.

Among the major oil-producing countries, the U.S.A. is unique in that it has also a large natural gas industry ; also in that it is industrialized to a pre-eminent degree. In none of the other great oil-producing and refining countries, with the exception of the U.S.S.R., has all-round industrial development yet progressed very far. The local oil industry is consequently one of the main pillars of the economic structure of many producing countries. Thus, in Venezuela, oil is not only the country's most important industry but its oil exports represent over 90% of the value of the country's total exports, and the revenue from oil represents as much as 53% of the national budget. In the N.E.I., oil exports before the war represented 60% of the tonnage of exports and 25% of their value. On the other hand, whilst the oil industry as a whole in the U.S.A., including all operations from discovery to distribution, ranks as the third largest and most important of the country's economic activities, exports of petroleum products, valued at $436 millions for 1946, were only 4·5% of United States total export trade in that year.

The production of oil in the United States is largely confined to seven States, notable among them being Texas and California, which together account for 63% of the country's production. The economic importance of oil production to these States parallels that in the main foreign oil-producing countries, in that oil forms the bulk of their external trade and is their chief source of income.

Naturally enough, the rate of important new discoveries in many of the older-established producing areas is decreasing. In particular, this is true of the U.S.A., where oil has been sought and produced for several decades far more intensively than in any other country. There are extensive known resources, particularly in Middle East territories, which are now being developed or will be developed in future. Other new oil-bearing territories must, however, be found in order to ensure that the world's needs for many decades ahead will be fully met.

REFINING

Two-thirds of the world's oil-refining capacity, representing a potential output of 750,000 tons per day, is situated in the U.S.A., and comprises over 400 refineries of all types and sizes. These range from large plants with a capacity of 25,000 tons daily, equipped with the most modern facilities and capable of manufacturing the whole range of major petroleum products as well as a number of special products, to the old-fashioned small topping plants treating a few tons of crude oil daily.

The refining industry in the U.S.A. is situated principally in the following regions :—

(1) The coast bordering the Gulf of Mexico, the country's largest oil-exporting region.

(2) The Eastern seaboard, particularly the States of New York, New Jersey and Pennsylvania.

(3) The Mid-Continent, particularly the States of Oklahoma Kansas, Illinois and Indiana.

(4) California, on the Pacific Coast.

These locations have been selected, primarily, for their convenient accessibility both to sources of crude oil and to the main home markets ; those on the sea coast have the added advantage of being in a position to compete for export trade.

The siting of a refinery in such a large area as the U.S.A. has to be given most careful consideration. In general, these plants are located either near oilfields (as occurs, for example, in California) or are linked by pipeline systems to the producing areas, so as to ensure an uninterrupted flow of crude oil at a low transportation cost. Where possible, refineries are also located within easy access of main water routes, river, lake or ocean, since shipment by water transport, either river barge or ocean tanker, is very much cheaper than by railway tank-car or road lorry. Most large refineries in the U.S.A. are owned by the integrated companies, the majority of which also purchase a certain proportion of their crude oil requirements. There are other concerns in the U.S.A. which engage only in refining, selling their output to distributors.

In other parts of the world most oilfields are remote from the markets they serve, and under normal conditions refineries are most advantageously erected as near as possible to the sources of crude oil, and usually at the nearest ocean terminal. Thus the refinery centres at Aruba and Curaçao, in the Netherlands West Indies, each with a capacity exceeding 35,000 tons daily, provided, in the past, the nearest developed deep-water facilities for the crude oil from western Venezuela ; and the refinery at Abadan, in Iran, at the head of the Persian Gulf, is the most convenient location in relation to the oil-fields of southern Iran. Similarly, the refinery at Haifa, Palestine, is one of the most convenient places for refining crude oil from the oilfields in Iraq. Incidentally, the refineries at Aruba, Curaçao and Abadan are larger than any in the United States.

A number of countries which do not possess, and are not near any sources of crude oil, have fostered the erection of oil refineries as a matter of national policy. Many of these plants owe their existence to discriminatory import duties or other form of governmental support, and in some cases to positive enactments.

The tendency has, however, been towards large refineries, since it has been proved that they offer operational and economic advantages which cannot be attained with a number of small and scattered units of equal aggregate capacity. Necessarily, a small plant is limited in scope and flexibility ; large refineries, on the other hand, are more easily adapted to supply the changing needs of consumers and can accommodate new plant or facilities for improved technique without the drastic reconstruction and possible complete stoppage of operations that is often unavoidable in the case of small units.

TRANSPORTATION

Since the first oil pipeline was laid in 1875 from Oil City to Pittsburgh, in Pennsylvania, U.S.A., a distance of 60 miles, it has become the practice to use pipeline systems as the connecting links between oilfields and refineries ; also for moving oil overland to consuming centres, where the demand is sufficiently large and continuous to justify the capital outlay and the operating and maintenance expenditure. In general, pipelines have proved the most convenient as well as the most economic means of overland oil transportation.

Long-distance pipelines are peculiar to the oil and natural gas industries. They are usually from 6 to 30 inches in diameter, with capacities ranging upwards from 1,000 tons per day. Frequently these lines extend for hundreds of miles ; for example, the portion of the Iraq pipeline running from Kirkuk, in Iraq, to Haifa, on the Palestine coast, is over 600 miles long ; another portion terminating at Tripoli, in Syria, is 560 miles long. In the U.S.A. there are a number of connected systems which cover considerably greater distances. During the second World War, when enemy submarines threatened shipping off the east coast of the U.S.A., the United States Government built two giant pipelines, known as the ''Big Inch'', about 1,300 miles long, and the ''Little Big Inch'', about 1,500 miles long, to curtail to a minimum the use of ocean tankers in what had become a danger area and to ensure the regular supply of crude oil and petroleum products by the safe overland route. The diameter of the ''Big Inch'', a crude oil line, is 24 inches, and that of the ''Little Big Inch'', a refined products line, is 20 inches (*vide* chapter XIX).

The construction of these lines followed soon after the completion of the Plantation Pipe Line Co.'s 8 to 12-inch pipeline, which runs 1,236 miles from Louisiana to North Carolina and is partly owned by Shell Union Oil Corporation. Two others, in which Shell has a major interest, are the 500-mile 20 to 24-inch line from New Mexico to Oklahoma, and the 440-mile 20-inch line on to Wood River, Illinois. The total length of crude oil and finished products lines in the U.S.A. alone is now approximately 140,000 miles, while the natural gas pipeline system is even longer. Included in the outstanding pipeline constructions in recent years outside the U.S.A. are one line in Colombia, over 365 miles in length, which reaches the seaboard after crossing the Andes, the war-time lines laid down from Assam into China, some 2,000 miles in length, and that in Alaska and Canada, 577 miles long. A war-time development was the portable pipeline, devised by a Shell engineer, used in the campaigns in North Africa and Europe.

From the point of view of international trade, the most important means of transportation employed is the ocean-going tanker. It is designed solely for carrying crude oil or petroleum products and is usually a one-way carrier only. Shell tankers returning to Curaçao frequently carry fresh-water supplies to meet the shortage of water in the island for human needs and for refinery working.

Before the war, the typical ocean-going tanker had a carrying capacity of between 8,000 and 12,000 tons and a speed of 10 to 12 knots. But in the years immediately preceding the war, and since, some tankers have been built, of which a number are now in service, with a capacity of about 16,000 tons and of about 17 knots. Shell is now building tankers of 28,000 d.w.t.

The table on page 15 gives an indication of the sizes of the tanker fleets of the principal countries in 1939 and 1947. The reduced percentage accounted for by the British, Norwegian and Dutch fleets is due to the severe losses suffered by these countries during the war years. The United States also suffered very severe losses, but was able during the war to build many more vessels than she lost.

Tankers now represent about 24% of the world's ocean-going shipping. All ocean tankers are oil driven.

WORLD TANKER FLEETS

Ocean-going Vessels of 3,000 Dead Weight Tons (D.W.T.) and over

	September 1st, 1939			October 1st, 1947			Building and Orders for Owners in Countries named at July 1st, 1947	
	No.	D.W.T.	% of Total	No.	D.W.T.	% of Total	No.	D.W.T.
WESTERN HEMISPHERE								
United States	383	4,434,100	26.0	744*	11,171,400	47.4	4	45,200
Panama	53	732,800	4.3	132	1,688,500	7.2		
Others	56	338,000	2.0	77	577,800	2.4		
Total Western Hemisphere	492	5,504,900	32.3	953	13,437,700	57.0	4	45,200
EUROPE								
Great Britain	442	4,704,000	27.8	436	4,789,500	20.3	39	475,615
Norway	263	3,125,400	18.3	195	2,517,300	10.7	51	839,050
Netherlands	105	740,000	4.3	80	570,700	2.4	6	44,300
France	44	462,300	2.7	33	410,500	1.7	13	211,180
U.S.S.R.	17	162,500	1.0	25	266,800	1.1		
Germany	34	387,700	2.3	4	50,400	.2		
Italy	80	618,700	3.6	35	374,000	1.6		
Sweden	20	257,000	1.5	36	491,100	2.1	6	54,845
Others	50	458,000	2.7	57	556,000	2.4	5	57,900
Total Europe	1,055	10,915,600	64.2	901	10,026,300	42.5	120	1,682,890
FAR EAST								
Japan	47	612,500	3.5	9	68,500	0.3		
China				4	46,000	0.2		
Total Far East	47	612,500	3.5	13	114,500	0.5		
Egypt				1	7,300			
TOTAL WORLD FLEET	1,594	17,033,000	100.0	1,868	23,585,800	100.0	124	1,728,090

* Includes tankers laid up. A number of these have since been recommissioned and some transferred to other flags.

c

DISTRIBUTION

The chain of distribution of petroleum products in the various consuming countries takes different forms, according to geographical conditions, to the product offered for sale and to the character of the market. There are usually one or more main ocean installations which receive products from the refinery. The products are then sent in bulk or packages by rail, road, coastal vessel or river barge to depots and sub-depots, and to selling agents throughout the country. In the more developed countries gasoline, for example, is delivered in bulk by road or rail tank-wagon to large users, and is usually retailed through the familiar pumps installed at retailers' premises, garage or service station. These stations may be owned by the oil-distributing companies or by the retailer. In the U.S.A. there are company-owned and company-operated stations, but most stations are operated by independent owner-dealers, who retail the gasoline under some form of sales contract, and many purchase their supplies from jobbers. In the United Kingdom, virtually all retail gasoline trade is done through dealer-owned garages and service stations. In the less developed countries, gasoline is sold in returnable or non-returnable steel drums, usually containing 44 Imperial gallons, or 200 litres, which can be emptied by a portable pumping outfit. It is also sold in a few territories in 4-gallon non-returnable tins, two tins being often packed together into one wooden case. The non-returnable 4-gallon (Imperial) tin is also widely used for kerosine trade, which in a number of countries, e.g., China, Egypt and India, is considerably larger than the trade in gasoline. Used non-returnable 4-gallon tins are of very high utility in many countries and, like non-returnable drums, often have a comparatively high secondhand value.

Gas oil and fuel oil are usually sold by the oil companies direct to the consumer, whether for inland consumption or for use as ships' bunkers. A feature of the trade in these products in some countries is the large tonnage delivered in bulk to a comparatively small number of customers. In many countries, however, the use of small corn-grinding mills and other small power-driven plants, including diesel-engined tractors, calls for small deliveries of one or more 40 to 50-gallon drums.

For "black oils" trade, as well as for trade in lubricants, chemicals and other products for specialized uses, the leading oil companies offer expert advice and guidance in the choice and use of the various grades of products, grounded upon extensive research work both in the laboratory and in the various fields of application. All staff engaged in sales work require to have some knowledge of the technical characteristics of the products they are selling and of the way in which the products are used.

EMPLOYMENT

The extensive scope of the activities covered by the various branches of the oil industry is accompanied by a corresponding diversity in the types of employment that it offers. The personnel falls naturally into two main classes : (1) technical ; (2) commercial ; and these classes are themselves split into a great number of sub-divisions.

In oil-producing areas the industry is often the largest, if not the only large, employer. Where local conditions require it, the oil companies provide social services of various kinds, and in some areas may provide houses for employees and their families, also medical, educational and recreational facilities. Employees at refineries and in marketing centres often have their own sports and cultural organizations. In general, the oil industry in each country is regarded as among the best employers in respect of both wages and working conditions.

On the commercial side, the oil industry touches economic life at so many points that there is opportunity for using almost every variety of commercial knowledge and experience. In addition, there are specialized branches peculiar to the industry which call for the services of considerable numbers of professional staff, such as those with engineering and accountancy qualifications.

In the technical group are employed geologists, chemists, physicists, metallurgists, engineers and research workers of various kinds and of different degrees of specialization. The need for scientific workers of all kinds is continually growing. In the early days of the industry, haphazard methods sufficed ; now planning and scientific methods are applied in every department. For example, geological and geophysical survey, as a preliminary to drilling and production, have supplanted the old time "wild-catting", i.e., testing by trial and error, of an earlier age. (The term "wildcat"*, however, is still applied to test wells drilled in territory whose oil-bearing possibilities are unknown.) The production of oil has become a highly scientific business, calling for the scientific and technical knowledge of a new profession, the exploitation engineer. Simple distillation, once the only known process for obtaining petroleum products from crude oil, is to-day but the initial step in refining and manufacturing operations, the complexity of which demands the attention of highly trained research workers and specialist engineers in the chemical and technological fields.

RESEARCH

The constant search for new and better products and for the better utilization of crude oil and natural gas has given research a high place in the activities of the major oil companies, particularly in recent years, during which the value of petroleum as a base material for the chemical industry has been given greater emphasis. Research within the oil industry is often highly competitive, and there exist also several independent specialist petroleum research undertakings.

Twenty-five years ago, the industry had to work within the limits which the simple distillation of the varying types of crude imposed. To-day there is a wide choice of processes available, whose versatility in producing the desired products is only restricted by considerations of money cost. Much important work is carried out in association with technologists and others working in different spheres of activity. Examples are to be found in the research carried out in conjunction with the automobile, aviation, chemical and plastics industries ; also in conjunction with public health bodies and agricultural institutions—the latter work now being done to a great extent, in the case of our Group, in our own farms in California and in the United Kingdom.

This co-operation between units within the oil industry and other industries is the natural and logical outcome of their interdependence ; indeed, there are few technical developments in which oil does not directly or indirectly play some part. Improvements in plant design and new types of engines have created a demand for new and improved oil products ; the existence of these products has facilitated further technical research and development by plant and engine designers. Each step forward in design has always been met, and sometimes anticipated, by a further technical advance or changes in the qualities or characteristics of oil products. To quote a few examples : higher octane gasoline manufactured to meet the needs of the modern motor car was a stepping stone towards the demands of aviation, which have been met by the manufacture of high-duty aviation fuels ; the advent of jet propulsion for aircraft has been met by the production of a suitable ''jet'' fuel, calling for expert knowledge of combustion problems, which experience in the use of furnace oils has provided. Research into problems of refinery operation led to utilization of petroleum gases for the production of synthetic rubber—a whole new industry which sprang up during the war— and the development, also from petroleum gases, of feedstocks for the plastic and chemical industries.

LOOKING FORWARD

The revolutionary changes in land, sea and air transport that have taken place in this century owe much to the vision and foresight of the oil industry, and to its versatility in evolving and producing fuels and lubricants for rapidly changing needs. In this work, however, it has been encouraged by the constantly expanding demand for its products. The simultaneous growth of the use of the motor vehicle, the use of oil fuel in ships, and the output of crude oil, and also the changing proportion of the gasoline yield from crude oil in the U.S.A. are shown in the table on page 20.

Other important new fields for the use of petroleum products are now rapidly developing, e.g., aviation, agriculture and chemicals. None would venture to predict the extent to which demand in each of these fields might grow.

The supply of the products of the right qualities and in the desired quantities is, however, only part of the task ; the creation of transport and distribution organizations, the provision of bunkering installations and chains of air fuelling services have to be organized, not merely abreast of, but in anticipation of the consumer's requirements. Because many of the oil industry's important customers operate on a world-wide basis, they expect to be able to enter into global contracts and to find a uniformity of products and of services in whatever part of the world their business activities may take them.

GROWTH IN THE APPLICATION OF OIL

	WORLD				U.S.A.
	Motor Vehicle Registrations (excluding Motor Cycles and Tractors)	Ships using Fuel Oil		Crude Oil	Percentage yield Gasoline from Crude Oil
		Gross Tonnage	Percentage of Merchant Marine	Production. Metric Tons	
1914	(1917) 4,232,000	1,544,000	3·4	53,400,000	18·2
1920	8,852,000	10,315,000	19·0	96,900,000	26·1
1930	34,975,000	27,954,000	41·0	200,000,000	42·0
1935	35,087,000	31,190,000	49·0	227,000,000	44·3
1938	42,678,000	35,291,000	52·0	280,500,000	44·2
1946	44,892,000	58,300,000	75·0	390,300,000	39·6

No large unit in the oil industry could have reached its present stage of development without bold enterprise, large-scale organization and the co-ordination of its efforts in widely separated localities. The fruits of the experience thus gained in a variety of conditions and in many different spheres of operation have resulted in advantages to the consumers of petroleum products everywhere. These advantages can perhaps best be illustrated by the quotations for gasoline f.o.b. United States ports in the Gulf of Mexico, a region which constitutes a recognized market for petroleum products and which, in general, determines the value of petroleum products everywhere. Quotations decreased by about 45% between 1929 and 1939, while the quality of the product had improved out of all comparison ; 70 octane gasoline, which in 1939 was quoted at 5·4c. per American gallon, was far superior to the best grade available ten years earlier at 9·5c. per American gallon. Also, the wholesale price index (1926 : 100) for petroleum products in the U.S.A. has, during the past twenty years, been consistently lower than that for other commodities. Often, however, the consumer has not been able to derive the full benefit of the reduction in the costs of products because of the high taxes which, in most countries, have been imposed on petroleum products, particularly gasoline.

Financial resources of a high order are needed to sustain the operations of a large oil company, and must provide not only for the day-to-day operation of its business but also for the discovery and development of new oil-fields to replace fields which become exhausted and to supply new needs ; also for the renewal of refining and other equipment when this becomes out of date. The search for oil, as has already been pointed out, is both costly and liable to be attended by disappointment. In an industry which is in such constant change and development, plant becomes obsolete in a relatively small number of years.

It is the practice, therefore, of all prudently conducted oil companies to put to reserve a considerable proportion of the profits earned. It was this alone which enabled the Group to face with relative equanimity the very heavy losses suffered during the second world war through the destruction of oil wells, refineries and equipment.

Vision, enterprise and efficient technical and commercial organization, applied to such a valuable raw material as crude oil, have brought to the modern world the boon of abundant supplies of petroleum products. The stage is set for both greater abundance and yet greater variety of products in the future.

II

THE ROYAL DUTCH-SHELL GROUP

HISTORY

THE Royal Dutch-Shell Group is forty years old. Its main constituents, the ''Royal Dutch'' and the Shell Transport and Trading Co., Ltd., are, however, both considerably older, and the Group came into being enjoying the advantages of the goodwill and experience already gained by its two parent companies. These two companies, first brought together in 1903, established in 1907 the full partnership which has since existed. By then, the world's oil production had reached 37 million tons a year and the motor car was hardly any longer a novelty. The subsequent rapid growth of the oil industry and the great changes within it have had their effect in the rapid expansion of the Group, which can justly claim to be a pioneer not only in time but in many of the notable developments within the industry.

The formation, in The Hague, of the Royal Dutch (full title translated from the Dutch : '' Royal Dutch Company for the Working of Oil Wells in the Netherlands Indies'') goes as far back as 1890. It had an initial capital of 1,300,000 guilders (then about £100,000). It was formed to acquire, from a Dutch planter, a concession granted by the Sultan of Langkat covering an area in north-eastern Sumatra which included the site of the present oilfields and refinery at Pangkalan Brandan. It is interesting to note that one of the earliest successful wells, Telaga Toenggal No. 1, drilled in this area in the year 1885, was producing oil until 1942, when the country was overrun by the Japanese.

In due course, additional concessions in Sumatra were obtained and the Royal Dutch set about not only producing crude oil but also refining it, and itself transporting and distributing the refined products to the nearby markets throughout the Far East. This comprehensive vertical organization was a new departure for concerns engaged in the international oil industry at that time. In the U.S.A., each operation was usually carried out by separate concerns, whilst in Russia, although all operations within the country were integrated, all export trade was done through merchants. Although having begun by selling in tins and cases, the Royal Dutch soon adopted bulk transportation, and its first shipment was made from Pangkalan Brandan to Hong Kong with considerable competitive advantages over imports from the U.S.A. and Russia, then the main sources of supply for the Far East. At that time, kerosine was the most important refined product sold, not only in the Far East but elsewhere. Until the war disturbances of recent years, the demand for kerosine in India, China, Netherlands East Indies and Egypt still remained larger than that for any other petroleum product.

A decline in the production from its Sumatran fields led the Royal Dutch to buy kerosine from Russia, which, for a few years around 1900, was the world's foremost oil-producing country. It also bought oil from other producing concerns in the Netherlands East Indies and acquired concessions in Borneo. Thus, it was able to compete in the expanding markets of the Far East, using the bulk ocean installations which it had established as far afield as Bombay, Madras, Calcutta, Bangkok, Hong Kong and Shanghai.

Concurrently, the London merchant banking firm of Samuel Brothers was also engaged in the kerosine export trade, buying its supplies mainly from Russia and transporting them in its own tankers to its own bulk installations in the Far East. In 1897, the Shell Transport and Trading Co., Ltd., was formed to take over this growing activity. It had an initial capital of £1,800,000 and its headquarters were in London. This company also acquired oil concessions in Borneo. At this period the Paris Rothschilds' interests, controlling oilfields in Russia, were also important competitors in the oil export trade. Thus, the Shell Transport and Trading Co., the Royal Dutch and the Rothschilds were competitors working on almost parallel lines, and were all faced with strong competition throughout the Far Eastern markets from the Standard Oil interests. It was consequently not surprising that the three concerns should have decided in 1903 to merge their marketing organizations by the formation, in London, of the Asiatic Petroleum Co., Ltd. (now Shell Petroleum Co., Ltd.). The issued capital was £600,000, held equally by the Royal Dutch,

Shell Transport and Trading Co., Ltd., and the Rothschilds. Mr. H. W. A. Deterding (later Sir Henri Deterding), who had succeeded Mr. J. B. A. Kessler as managing director of the Royal Dutch upon the latter's death in 1900, became managing director of the Asiatic Petroleum Co., Ltd., and moved his headquarters from The Hague to London.

The success of this association in the marketing sphere led to the full partnership, in 1907, of the Royal Dutch and Shell Transport and Trading Co. In that year, the Anglo-Saxon Petroleum Co., Ltd., was formed with a capital of £4,000,000, and with head offices in London, to undertake all transportation and storage operations, and N.V. de Bataafsche Petroleum Maatschappij was formed, with a capital of 80 million guilders and with head offices at The Hague, to undertake oil production and refining activities. To each of these companies the Royal Dutch contributed 60% of the capital, and the Shell Transport and Trading Co., Ltd., 40%. These proportions have been maintained and are also applicable to the Shell Petroleum Co., Ltd., the Rothschilds' interest included in the former Asiatic Petroleum Co., Ltd., having been acquired by the Group many years ago.

The early years of the twentieth century brought greatly increased demand for kerosine, and a new demand for gasoline, which had hitherto been a waste product and a nuisance to the refiner. The use of oil fuel for marine purposes was also beginning. Between 1900 and 1913, the world's annual oil production rose from 20 million to 50 million tons. The latter part of this period was one of great expansion for the Group, during which new interests were acquired in Rumania, Russia, U.S.A., Mexico, Venezuela, Egypt and Mesopotamia (Iraq). Also, the interests in the Netherlands East Indies and British North Borneo were extended and the Group's marketing organization spread throughout Europe.

Shell's entry into the domestic oil industry of the U.S.A. was regarded, at the time, as a very bold step. A preliminary geological survey had been carried out in Oklahoma in 1908, and trading began in 1912 as a result of the acquisition of a marketing company in California, and soon afterwards oil-producing properties were also bought in that State. Simultaneously, activities spread to the mid-West, and in 1922 Shell Union Oil Corporation was formed to consolidate the Shell interests in the U.S.A. with those of the Union Oil Co. of Delaware. In 1929 Shell's marketing activities spread to the Atlantic coast, thus providing a country-wide distribution.

The increase in the demand for petroleum products brought about by the first World War led to a rapid expansion of the Group's business. Its production rose from 2 million tons in 1910 to over 4¼ million tons in 1915. The oilfields in Russia were lost in 1917, and in 1919 the Group's production was still only little more than 4 million tons. There were, however, great developments in Mexico and Venezuela in the early '20s, and by 1929 the Group's production had risen to over 25 million tons, Venezuela becoming in that year, as it is now, the Group's most important source of supply.

The world economic crisis of 1930–1933 brought a recession, which was overcome in 1935, and at the outbreak of the second World War the Group's production was about 30 million tons a year, out of a total world production of about 280 million tons. This comparison, however, masks the importance of the Group in the international oil trade. This is appreciated better if one compares production figures, excluding the U.S.A. and the U.S.S.R., in which countries output is used predominantly for inland consumption. Thus, the Group's output in 1938, excluding that in the U.S.A., was over 22¼ million tons compared with world production, excluding that in the U.S.A. and the U.S.S.R., of 80 million tons.

The second World War involved the Group in the destruction and temporary loss of its extensive interests in the Netherlands East Indies and British North Borneo, which accounted for nearly 6½ million tons of its pre-war annual production. It also involved loss of access to the Group's fields in Roumania, which accounted for a further 1½ million tons a year. During 1938 the group had already suffered by the expropriation of the properties in Mexico of the Mexican Eagle Oil Co., Ltd., which in 1937 had yielded over 4 million tons. Compensating increases in other areas during the war years resulted, however, in the Group's total production in 1945, including that in Roumania, still amounting to 29½ million tons, coming, in order of importance, from Venezuela, U.S.A., Roumania, Egypt, Iraq, Trinidad, Argentine, Colombia and a small initial production from the Netherlands. Some of the changes which have taken place in sources and volume of oil production since 1919 until 1947 are shown in the following table :—

GROUP'S CRUDE OIL PRODUCTION

Metric Tons

Countries	1919	1929	1934	1938	1947
Venezuela ...	41,000	8,799,000	8,168,000	11,310,000	20,304,000
U.S.A. ...	1,348,000	7,584,000	5,549,000	7,680,000	10,302,000
Roumania ...	241,000	852,000	1,701,000	1,515,000	1,043,000
Egypt ...	226,000	272,000	215,000	226,000	1,329,000
Iraq	—	—	215,000	978,000	1,012,000
Trinidad ...	38,000	103,000	149,000	387,000	750,000
Argentina ...	—	15,000	477,000	544,000	565,000
Colombia ...	—	—	—	—	703,000
British Borneo	79,000	760,000	674,000	914,000	1,826,000
N.E.I. ...	2,093,000	4,746,000	4,479,000	5,407,000	945,000
Austria ...	—	—	—	7,000	92,000
Netherlands ...	—	—	—	—	106,000
Germany ...	—	—	—	2,000	31,000
Mexico ...	2,518,000	2,053,000	2,451,000	954,000	—
TOTAL ...	6,584,000	25,184,000	24,078,000	29,924,000	39,008,000

At the outbreak of the second World War, the Group had a sales organization in nearly every country in the world. Notable exceptions were the U.S.S.R. and Mexico. In Burma, Iran, Ecuador and Peru, where the Group has no established production, the local market is served mainly, if not entirely, by the locally established producing companies.

A feature of the Group's development has been its provision of world-wide services, first for the bunkering of oil-burning vessels, and later for the fuelling of aircraft. In both these fields it was a pioneer, and, as a result, it enjoys a large proportion of the world's bunkering trade outside the U.S.A. and can claim to be the world's leading supplier of aviation fuels for civilian aircraft.

The Group's sea-going tanker fleet at the outbreak of the second World War consisted of 179 vessels and aggregated nearly 1,500,000 tons deadweight, owned as follows :—

British flag :   The Anglo-Saxon Petroleum Co., Ltd.
Netherlands flag : N.V. Nederlandsche-Indische Tank Stoomboot Maatschappij.
                N.V. Petroleum Maatschappij "La Corona".
                N.V. Curacaosche Scheepvaart Maatschappij.

During the second World War, seventy-two of the Group's vessels were lost, aggregating 660,000 tons. These losses were made good by new tonnage by the end of 1946.

The Group manufactures and sells every kind of petroleum product : all grades of gasoline, for motor vehicles and aeroplanes ; various grades of fuel oil—heavy fuel oil for burning under ships' boilers, diesel fuel for motor vessels and industrial compression ignition engines, a special grade of diesel fuel for use in high-speed compression ignition engines (sometimes called "automotive gas oil"), and the various grades of fuel oils which are used for domestic heating and for many industrial purposes ; tractor fuel ; lubricating oils and greases of all kinds for the innumerable purposes which modern transport and industry demand, as well as special oils for electrical, medicinal and other uses ; kerosine, for lighting, cooking and domestic heating ; asphaltic bitumen in its various forms, for road-making and for many industrial purposes ; paraffin wax, for candles and for a great variety of other purposes. Not only are new applications for existing products frequently developed, but many new products are introduced to meet new and potential demands.

In recent years the Group has made very great strides in the manufacture of chemicals, solvents and plastics from petroleum-base materials, also in the manufacture and application of other special products for use in industry and agriculture.

ORGANIZATION

The three companies already mentioned—The Shell Petroleum Co., Ltd., The Anglo-Saxon Petroleum Co., Ltd., and N.V. de Bataafsche Petroleum Maatschappij—are the core of the Group, and most of its physical operations are carried out directly by these three companies or their subsidiaries, or by companies in which they participate.

The Shell Petroleum Co., Ltd. has marketing subsidiaries in many countries, usually with the title "Shell Co. of (country), Ltd.," and is responsible for the supply of products to them. It is also responsible for managing the Group's ocean bunker trade throughout the world, and for co-ordinating sales policy and aviation refuelling services.

The Anglo-Saxon Petroleum Co., Ltd. is responsible for managing the Group's tanker fleet and is the owner of a fleet of British flag tankers. It manages a number of British oil-producing companies associated with the Group and holds shares in various companies.

De Bataafsche Petroleum Maatschappij (B.P.M.) has its offices at The Hague and is responsible for the technical side of all operations connected with oil discovery, production and refining. It also manages the Group's interests in the Netherlands East and West Indies. It is the owner of a large number of valuable patent rights.

Upon the German invasion of Holland in 1940, the head-quarters of the B.P.M. (like those of the Royal Dutch) were temporarily transferred to Curaçao, in the Netherlands West Indies ; however, a skeleton staff from the B.P.M. office at The Hague worked in England during the war years.

The Group has close links with Canadian Eagle Oil Co., Ltd., and, through it, with Eagle Oil and Shipping Co., Ltd., which owns a fleet of tankers. The Group and Canadian Eagle are both interested in marketing, and in oil exploration and producing companies in various South and Central American countries and in Cuba. They are also associated, together with the Anglo-Iranian Oil Co., Ltd., in Shell-Mex and B.P., Ltd., a joint distributing company for the United Kingdom.

The Group is financially interested in, and is the manager of, the Mexican Eagle Oil Co., Ltd. (Compania Mexicana de Petroleo "El Aguila" S.A.), whose properties in Mexico were expropriated in 1938.

The Group is also a partner to the extent of 50 % with the Anglo-Iranian Oil Co. in Consolidated Refineries, Ltd., which owns a refinery at Haifa, Palestine, and in the Consolidated Petroleum Co., Ltd., which controls the various marketing companies in some Near East countries, also in Egypt, Sudan, Aden, East and South Africa, Rhodesia, Mozambique and Ceylon. The Group is associated with the Anglo-Iranian and other interests in the Iraq Petroleum Co., Ltd., and sister companies, and is a partner with the Burmah Oil Co., Ltd., in "Burmah-Shell", which undertakes marketing of the two parent companies' products in India and Pakistan. The Group and Trinidad Leaseholds, Ltd., have formed joint companies for marketing in Trinidad and other West Indies territories. The Group has an interest in various companies dealing with technical processes and research. An outline of the Group's interests and organization throughout the world is given below.

EUROPE

United Kingdom. The head offices of the Shell Petroleum Co., Ltd., and the Anglo-Saxon Petroleum Co., Ltd., are at St. Helen's Court, in the City of London. During the second World War these offices were almost completely evacuated and the staffs accommodated partly at Lensbury, the staff sports club at Teddington, Middlesex, and partly at other, often widely dispersed, places throughout the country.

The head office of Shell Transport and Trading Co., Ltd., is at 13 Austin Friars, London, E.C.2.

Shell-Mex and B.P., Ltd., markets in the United Kingdom the full range of Shell products with the exception of chemicals, which are handled by a separate organization.

In addition, the Group owns specialized refining plants at Shell Haven, in the Thames Estuary, at Stanlow, on the Manchester Ship Canal, and at Ardrossan, on the Firth of Clyde, from which lubricants and special products are exported to many parts of the world. During the second World War a new and large research laboratory was built at Thornton, Cheshire, with special facilities for research work on aero engines and on their fuels and lubricants. More recently, other research laboratories have been erected at Thornton (*vide* chapter III).

France. The Group's main company is Shell Française, formerly " Jupiter'', which was formed in 1922 to carry on the business of Les Fils de A. Deutsch de la Meurthe et Cie, in which the Group had for some time been interested and which had always been a large buyer of the Group's products. There are two refineries, one at Petit Couronne, near Rouen, and the other at Pauillac, near Bordeaux. An interest is also held in a refinery at Berre on the Mediterranean coast.

Holland. The head offices of the Royal Dutch and B.P.M. are at The Hague. The marketing organization in Holland is Shell Nederland N.V., with headquarters at The Hague. There is a refinery at Pernis, near Rotterdam. B.P.M. has large research laboratories at Amsterdam and at Delft, and has recently discovered, and is producing oil at Schoonebeeck, in the north-eastern part of the country.

Germany. The Deutsche Shell A.G., formerly Rhenania-Ossag Mineraloelwerke A.G., is the principal subsidiary company of the Group. It has its head office in Hamburg and engages in marketing all petroleum products sold in Germany.

It has refining plants at Harburg, Grasbrook and Wilhelmsburg, near Hamburg, and at Monheim and Reisholz, near Dusseldorf.

Apart from being represented by Deutsche Shell A.G., the Group participates in various German marketing and refining companies and plays a part in German indigenous crude oil production by participating in the Gewerkschaft Brigitta.

All the refining plants and much of Deutsche Shell's distributing facilities suffered heavy damage during the recent war. At the present time (September, 1948) reconstruction and rehabilitation work, as sanctioned by the Occupying Authorities, is in progress.

Italy. Nafta Societa Italiana pel Petrolio ed Affini is the Group's marketing company in Italy and in Libya. The head office is in Genoa. There is a refinery at Spezia, owned by the Societa per l'Industria del Petroleo ; in addition, a small company known as the " Filta " (Fabbrica Italiana Lubrificanti en Affini) owns a refining plant for white oils at Zivarola.

Roumania. The Group has a majority interest in Astra Romana S.A., which is the largest producing and refining company in the country. The head office is in Bucharest, and the refinery is in the Ploesti district. It participates with three other leading producing and refining companies in "Distributia", a country-wide marketing organization.

Other European Countries. Elsewhere in Europe the Group has small refineries in Austria at Floridsdorf, near Vienna, in Hungary at Budapest, and in Belgium near Ghent. In Austria it has an interest in local oil production through R.A.G. (Rohöl-Gewinnungs A.G.). The Group has full-scale marketing organizations in these and most other European countries, including Turkey but excluding Spain, Poland and Czechoslovakia, in which countries only lubricants and special products are sold by the Group. There are also separate marketing companies for Gibraltar, Malta and Iceland. The Group had marketing subsidiary companies in the Baltic States when these territories became a part of the U.S.S.R. in June, 1940.

NORTH AMERICA

U.S.A. The Group has a majority financial holding in Shell Union Oil Corporation, whose main subsidiaries are :—

Shell Oil Co., Inc., with main offices in New York and San Francisco ; undertakes production, refining and marketing in the United States.

Shell Oil's main fields are in the States of Texas, California, Oklahoma, Kansas, Louisiana, New Mexico and Illinois. Its crude oil production in 1945 was 9,866,000 tons, and its net purchases of crude oil amounted to about 5 million tons. It has six refineries : Coalinga, Martinez and Wilmington, on the Pacific Coast, Houston and Norco (New Orleans), on the Gulf of Mexico, and Wood River, in the Mid-Continent.

Shell Oil also has its own pipeline system on the West Coast, and operates its own refined products pipeline in the region east of the Rocky Mountains.

Shell Chemical Corporation, a subsidiary of Shell Oil, with head

D

offices at San Francisco, is responsible for manufacturing and marketing in the U.S.A. fertilizers and chemicals from petroleum base materials, also for export trade in these products.

Shell Development Co., an affiliate of Shell Union, carries out research and technical development work in the U.S.A., mainly at its laboratory at Emeryville, California, but also in conjunction with Shell Oil Co.'s research laboratories attached to the various refineries of that company. The company owns a considerable number of patents.

Shell Pipeline Corporation owns and operates Shell's crude oil pipeline systems east of the Rocky Mountains.

In total, the Shell companies in the U.S.A. operate over 6,500 miles of pipelines. They do not own any ocean-going tankers.

The Asiatic Petroleum Corporation in New York functions independently of the Shell Union group of companies, being mainly concerned with the purchase in the U.S.A. of petroleum products and stores and equipment for shipment overseas.

Canada. Shell Oil Co. of Canada, Ltd., an affiliate of Shell Union, markets Shell products in the provinces of Ontario and Quebec, and has a refinery at Montreal. Shell Oil Co. of British Columbia, Ltd., owned by Shell Oil Co. of Canada, markets Shell products in British Columbia and has a refinery at Vancouver, B.C.

Shell does not produce crude oil in Canada, but extensive exploration work has been carried out for several years in the province of Alberta.

CENTRAL AMERICA AND WEST INDIES

The Group does not trade in Central America except in Panama, and in Guatemala and British Honduras in association with Canadian Eagle. It is a partner with Canadian Eagle Oil Co., Ltd., in Cia Petrolera Shell-Mex de Cuba, Ltd., and both the Group and Canadian Eagle have a holding in Compania Estrella de Cuba, which operates exploration concessions in Cuba.

United British Oilfields of Trinidad, Ltd., controlled by the Group, now produces about 700,000 tons of crude oil a year, which is treated at its Point Fortin refinery, considerably enlarged during the recent war. U.B.O.T. has an equal third interest with

Trinidad Leaseholds, Ltd., and D'Arcy Exploration Co., Ltd. (Anglo-Iranian), in Trinidad Northern Areas, Ltd., which recently received a licence to search for oil under certain territorial waters of the island and in the Gulf of Paria, between Trinidad and Venezuela. Shell Leaseholds Distributing Co., Ltd., is a marketing company for Trinidad, owned jointly by Trinidad Leaseholds and U.B.O.T.

The Group's products are marketed in Jamaica, Haiti, San Domingo (also in Panama) by the Shell Co. (West Indies), Ltd., and in Porto Rico by Shell Co. (Porto Rico), Ltd. Petroleum Marketing Co. (West Indies), Ltd., is owned jointly by Trinidad Leaseholds and the Group and is the marketing company for the remaining West Indian islands, also for British, Dutch and French Guiana.

The Group's largest refinery is at Emmastad, on the island of Curaçao, in the Netherlands West Indies. It has a capacity of 10 million tons a year and treats most of the Group's crude oil production in Venezuela and Colombia. It has a staff totalling over 9,000. The Group owns, through N.V. Arend Petroleum Maatschappij, a refinery on the neighbouring island of Aruba, with a capacity of one million tons a year.

SOUTH AMERICA

The Group has extensive oil producing and exploration areas in Venezuela and Colombia, and a large exploration concession in Ecuador. It also has oilfields and a refinery in Argentina.

Venezuela. The main producing companies in Venezuela in which the Group is interested are :—

Caribbean Petroleum Co., Ltd., which also undertakes marketing in Venezuela.

Colon Development Co., Ltd.

Venezuelan Oil Concessions, Ltd.

N.V. Nederlandsche Olie Maatschappij, responsible for the Group's share in the production of the Mene Grande Oil Co.

Apart from the last-mentioned, the Group's production is at present all obtained from the Maracaibo Basin in Western Venezuela, V.O.C. contributing by far the greater proportion. Exploration work is being started in Eastern Venezuela. There is a small refinery at San Lorenzo, which caters for local market needs. A new refinery with a capacity of over 7,000 tons a day is now being built by Shell Co. of Venezuela, Ltd., at Cardon, on the Paraguana Peninsula in Western Venezuela, together with berthing facilities for ocean-going tankers.

The Group's head office in Venezuela is at Caracas, the capital. There is a main office at Maracaibo controlling operations in Western Venezuela.

Colombia. Both the Group's and Canadian Eagle's interests in Colombia are represented mainly by Compania de Petroleo Shell de Colombia (which also undertakes marketing) and by Compania Colombiana de Petroleo ''El Condor'' S.A. There are a number of other Group companies holding exploration concessions.

The Group's production began in 1945, in the newly discovered Casabe field. Exploration wells have been, or are being, drilled at various other points and oil has been discovered at Dificil, in the lower Magdelena Valley.

Ecuador. Shell Co. of Ecuador, Ltd., owned by the Group and by Canadian Eagle, has an exploration concession in the Oriente province, covering 32,000 square miles east of the Andes. A feature of the extensive search for oil being carried out in this remote part of the country is that, for the first time in the history of the Group, all material for drilling the test wells has had to be conveyed to the sites by air.

Argentina. The Group's oil producing company is Diadema Argentina S.A., with fields in the Comodoro Rivadavia area and a refinery at Buenos Aires. The refined products are sold locally through Shell-Mex (Argentina), Ltd., jointly owned by the Group and Canadian Eagle.

Brazil, Chile, Uruguay. The Group's products are marketed in these countries by joint Group-Canadian Eagle companies : Shell-Mex Brazil, Ltd., Shell-Mex Chile, Ltd., and Shell-Mex Uruguay, Ltd.

Peru. The Group and Canadian Eagle Co., Ltd. have established a local company (Shell del Peru) to market mainly lubricating oils and chemical and technical products.

NEAR AND MIDDLE EAST

Syria, Lebanon, Palestine, Transjordania. Marketing is carried out by Shell Co. of Syria, Ltd., in Syria and Lebanon, and by Shell Co. of Palestine, Ltd., in Palestine and Transjordania, all subsidiaries of Consolidated Petroleum Co., Ltd.

Iraq and Arabian Coast. The Group holds $23\frac{3}{4}\%$ of the capital of the Iraq Petroleum Co., Ltd., now producing about 4 million tons of oil annually from the Kirkuk oil-field, on the eastern side of the Tigris. The crude oil is sent by pipeline to Tripoli (Syria) and to Haifa. Most of the crude oil reaching Haifa is treated in a refinery there owned by Consolidated Refineries, Ltd. Production from the Kirkuk field will be trebled from 1948 onwards.

The Group similarly holds $23\frac{3}{4}\%$ of the capital of a number of sister companies of the Iraq Petroleum Co., Ltd., which have concessions at various places along the Arabian coast and in the Near East.

Similar participations in Iraq Petroleum and sister companies are held by Anglo-Iranian, Compagnie Française des Petroles, Near East Development Corp. (representing Standard of New Jersey and Socony Vacuum Groups) ; the remaining 5% is held by Participations and Investments, Ltd.

The Group's products are not marketed in Iraq.

Egypt. The Group is a shareholder in Anglo-Egyptian Oilfields, Ltd., an oil producing and refining company, managed by the Anglo-Saxon Petroleum Co., Ltd. Shareholdings are also held by Anglo-Iranian, the Egyptian Government and the public.

The fields are at Ras Gharib and at Hurghada, on the western shore of the Red Sea, and exploration concessions are held covering areas in the Sinai Peninsula and in other parts of Egypt. The refinery is at Suez. Products consumed within the country are marketed by Shell Co. of Egypt, Ltd., a subsidiary of Consolidated Petroleum Co., Ltd., with head offices in Cairo.

AFRICA

Sudan, East and South Africa. Marketing in the Sudan and in East and South Africa is carried out by various Shell companies, all subsidiaries of Consolidated Petroleum Co., Ltd.

North Africa.   There are separate Shell marketing companies for the French territories of Algiers, Tunisia and Morocco. Before the war, Shell products were marketed in Libya by the Group's Italian company, "Nafta". Shell products are marketed in Tangier and Spanish Morocco through local agents under the control of the Group's office in Madrid.

West and Central Africa.   The Group's main office for this region is at Lagos, in Nigeria. Bulk coastal installations at Dakar (Senegal), Takoradi and Accra (Gold Coast) and at Apapa and Port Harcourt (Nigeria), are operated by storage companies owned jointly by the Group and Socony Vacuum Oil Co., Inc. These companies are managed by the Group. Marketing is carried out throughout the area, including the Belgian Congo and Angola, almost entirely through trading agents.

Canary Islands.   The Group has an important bunkering installation at Las Palmas, and Shell products are marketed throughout the Canary Islands by the Sociedad Petrolifera Española, whose head office is in Madrid.

Cape Verde Islands.   The Group has a bunkering installation at St. Vincent, which comes under the control of the Shell Co. of Portugal, Ltd., Lisbon.

Azores, Madeira.   The Group's products are sold through local agents under the control of Lisbon office.

THE FAR EAST AND AUSTRALIA

India and Pakistan.   The Group's trade in the Dominions of India and Pakistan is handled by "Burmah-Shell", which is an amalgamation of the marketing facilities of the Group and The Burmah Oil Co., Ltd.

Netherlands East Indies.   The Group owns, through B.P.M., exploitation rights in Sumatra, Java, Tarakan, Ceram and Netherlands Borneo.   There are refineries at Pangkalan Brandan and Pladjoe, in Sumatra, at Tjepoe and Wonokromo, in Java, and at Balikpapan, in Netherlands Borneo.   A sales organization is maintained throughout the East Indies.   All these facilities suffered severely from the denial measures carried out at the time of the Japanese invasions, and also by the subsequent destruction during their evacuation by, and recapture from, the Japanese forces. Extensive plans for the rehabilitation of these areas are being carried out with great vigour by B.P.M., as rapidly as difficulties concerning the supply of materials, transport and skilled labour can be overcome. By the end of 1946 production had been resumed at Balikpapan, Tarakan and Sourabaya.

B.P.M. manages N.V. Nederlandsche-Indische Aardolie Maatschappij (N.I.A.M.), which holds a concession for working the Djambi oilfields in Sumatra. The Government of the N.E.I. and the Group each holds 50% of the capital.

B.P.M. manages N.V. Nederlandsche Nieuw Guinee Petroleum Maatschappij, which holds a very large exploration concession in Netherlands New Guinea. The Group and the Standard-Vacuum Oil Co. each holds 40% of the capital of this company ; the remaining 20% belongs to the Standard Oil Co. of California and the Texas Company.

British Borneo. The Group owns producing fields at Seria, in Brunei, and Miri, in Sarawak, the operating companies being British Malayan Petroleum Co., Ltd., and Sarawak Oilfields, Ltd., respectively. There is a refinery at Lutong, in Sarawak, where the crude oil from both fields is treated. A new refinery is planned for erection on Muara Island, in Brunei Bay. As in the case of the Netherlands East Indies, severe damage to all property was inflicted by denial measures taken in 1941 and, again, subsequently by the Japanese when they were driven out in 1945. However, by the end of 1947 the production from the Seria field was about three times the pre-war level.

Malaya, Siam. The marketing of the Group's products in these territories is directed from Singapore, which is also the headquarters of the Far-Eastern division of the Marine Department of the Anglo-Saxon Petroleum Co., Ltd., by whom all the Group's ocean tankers in the Far East are controlled.

The bulk storage plants on the British island of Bukom and on the Dutch island of Samboe, both near Singapore, are the main installations supplying Malaya. Owing to the absence of deep-water facilities at the refineries in Sumatra, they also serve as transhipment centres for supplies from these refineries to other countries in the Far East.

China, Indo-China, Philippine Islands.   Group marketing companies operate in these territories, with head offices at Shanghai for China (also, before the war with Japan, Hong Kong for South China), Saigon and Manila.

Japan.   The Group markets its products in Japan through the Rising Sun Petroleum Co., Ltd., with head offices at Yokohama. The Group has not engaged in oil production or oil refining within the country.

Australia.   Shell Co. of Australia, Ltd., with its head office at Melbourne, Victoria, and with branch offices in each of the six States, markets the Group's products throughout the Australian Commonwealth, in the Australian mandated territory of New Guinea and in Papua, where the Group has also carried out exploration.   The company owns a refinery at Clyde, near Sydney, which treats imported crudes and manufactures bitumen ; however, the major part of the Company's sales consists of imported refined products.

Exploration work in Queensland is now being undertaken by the Group.

New Zealand.   The Shell Company of New Zealand, Ltd., with head office at Wellington, markets the Group products in both North and South Island.   The Group has undertaken exploration work in South Island.

Pacific Islands.   British and French marketing subsidiary companies and agents, working under the direction of Melbourne office, distribute the Group's products throughout these territories.

III

THE LABORATORY

THE great industrial developments of the present day depend to an ever-increasing extent on the application of scientific knowledge and of scientific methods of control to the operation of manufacturing processes. Indeed, new industries often owe their existence entirely to the results of scientific researches which, in many cases, at the time they were carried out, gave no indication of their future great commercial value. The makers of high-pressure steel vessels now use powerful X-ray equipment to detect flaws in welds up to four inches thick. The North Sea fishermen sell their halibut oil on a test carried out by measuring the absorption of ultra-violet light with a spectrograph. Cigarettes are arranged for packing in proper order, and boxes passing on a conveyor are counted by the help of a photo-electric cell. But for the discovery of the rare gases of the atmosphere in the laboratory of Sir William Ramsey there would be no red neon lights on Broadway to-day. The scientific work of Bækeland gave rise to the great synthetic plastics industry, the far-reaching effects of which can hardly be visualized ; its effect on the paint industry has given rise to a great demand for special organic solvents, which the new petroleum chemical industry based on the gases made by cracking, is successfully supplying.

In the early days of the petroleum industry, when crude oil worked up by simple rule-of-thumb methods readily yielded an illuminant which was far superior to any of its competitors, laboratory control methods were practically unknown. Nowadays, the industry is quite in the forefront in this respect.

The Group early realized the value of laboratory control and also of research. Before the complete amalgamation in 1907, research into the chemical nature of the Company's raw materials had already been inaugurated, and research to improve the quality of products and to be ready to meet new market possibilities has been the rule ever since.

The functions of the laboratory may be divided into three main classes, which are usually carried out in separate establishments.

(1) Work in connection with the control of the refinery and its operations, carried out in the works laboratory.

(2) Control of the products sold, investigation of their applications, advice to selling organizations and service to customers carried out in the marketing laboratories of the local company.

(3) Research proper carried out only in the Group's well-known laboratories in Holland, England and the United States.

THE WORKS LABORATORY

The works laboratory is an essential part of the refinery. Its chief function is that of control. The actual operating control of a modern plant is, to some extent, effected by automatic instruments based on the measurement of temperatures, pressures, the maintenance of levels and steady rates of flow and pumping. The points at which these automatic controls are to be set are largely determined by laboratory work on the analysis of the various products obtained at different points in the plant. The accuracy and regularity of operation of these instruments is ensured by regular inspection and calibration. The works laboratory, or part of it, works night and day to examine the numerous samples which are sent in regularly from many sections of the plant in order to ensure constancy of quality of the various products. For this purpose, special methods, which can be quickly carried out, are sometimes used in place of the more accurate methods used to check the quality of the final products before they are pumped to the storage installations. The apparatus used is often complicated, and in some cases special apparatus is made so that a number of similar tests can be carried out simultaneously by one operator, and, when possible, automatic recorders are used. The laboratories are equipped to examine all products made in the refinery, ranging from gases to the hardest asphaltic bitumens. The works laboratory may also control the qualities of the materials, such as acid and fuller's earth, used in the refinery, but such material, whenever possible, is bought on suppliers' guarantee of quality.

The quality of the intake of crude oil must be regularly examined as any variation in quality affects the details of the plant control. If new types of crude oil are to be handled, the laboratory must investigate their properties so that a decision as to the best way of working them up may be taken. It also carries out investigation work on the improvement of the methods of treatment in use, on the reduction of refinery losses and the working up of by-products, and it must develop the application of new methods of treatment and manufacture which have been worked out by the research laboratories. Work of this nature, particularly that dealing with the development of new processes, is usually carried out in a so-called pilot plant. This small plant, which represents the intermediate stage between laboratory and full-scale plant, is a model plant rather than a magnified piece of laboratory apparatus. Several of the major installations also have laboratories of this type to control the blending operations which are carried out on a large scale in connection with the shipping programme.

THE MARKETING CONTROL AND SERVICE LABORATORIES

The various marketing companies maintain one or more service laboratories according to the needs of the country and the trade. The functions of these laboratories are twofold :—

(1) The control of the quality of the products sold and purchased.

(2) Service to customers.

Uniformity of quality of a product is essential, and the laboratory must ensure that this is always maintained.

In order to ensure uniformity of testing so that all departments, technical and selling, understand each other, the laboratories must employ standardized methods of analysis and prescribed and standardized apparatus, as, otherwise, identity of results on a definite sample of oil cannot be obtained. The arrangements to ensure this are centred in the chief control laboratories of the Group in Amsterdam, Emeryville (California) and London. Details of all important testing methods are issued in loose-leaf book form by the Emeryville laboratory. The most important and efficient routine and research tests are selected by the Central

Standardization Committee (Europe) and the Shell Standardization Committee (United States) and incorporated, after joint discussion, in the Shell Method Series* as the official Group tests. These two Standardization Committees keep in close contact with such official bodies as the American Society for Testing Materials and the Institute of Petroleum, who see to the publication of various standard methods covering petroleum and its products. As it is highly desirable not to swell the great number of petroleum tests unnecessarily, it is always the Group's policy to adopt such official tests when possible.

The arrangements necessary for the control of the quality of products are often surprising. Complicated automatic and semi-automatic electrical apparatus, spectroscopes, micro-photographic apparatus, intricate glass distilling columns and many other such pieces of equipment are required.

In order to control the quality of fuels for internal combustion engines, standard anti-knock engines are used, often necessitating the provision of special engine-testing rooms. The staff in charge of these engines co-operate with members of other organizations, particularly in the United States, in order to ensure uniformity of testing methods, without which comparable results cannot be obtained.

To ensure that all apparatus for testing is up to standard, it is purchased, against specifications, from reliable manufacturers— with whom the Group's Central Laboratories are in close contact—checked, and, when advisable, tested before issue. Particular care is also taken to see that such apparatus as thermometers and hydrometers, used in oil measurement operations, are in accordance with the specifications which the Standardization Committees issue in their Apparatus Catalogue and Apparatus Specification Book, after consulting the Oil Measurement Section, located in London.

A most important function of the marketing laboratory is the giving of service to customers, especially to manufacturers who use the Group's products in their works processes. For this purpose, it is necessary that the laboratory staff should be men who are acquainted with the applications and uses of the products, so that they may be in a position to visit customers' works and, with

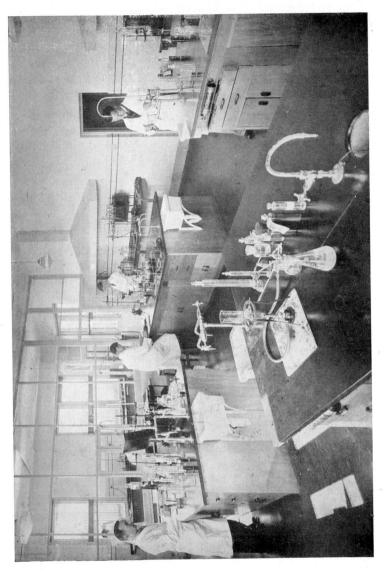

Fig. 1. Interior view of a marketing laboratory.

their co-operation, intelligently study the works operation, in order that they may, and often do, offer valuable advice. These laboratories study the practical applications of the Group's products, and their men keep in touch with the industries of the country so that they may always be awake to the possibilities of new outlets and new applications for these products. They must anticipate new demands, not wait for them to arise. They must study carefully the possibilities of our products and also co-operate with the manufacturers of appliances which make use of petroleum products.

A useful function of the laboratories is that of controlling the quality of the diverse materials, such as solder, chemicals, paint and tinplate, to mention only a few, which the Group purchases in very large quantities. In this respect, the laboratories act as advisers to the purchasing and stores departments.

Still one more function of the service laboratory is that of providing educational facilities for members of the staff who are likely to hold positions where some knowledge of the properties and applications of the Group's products is highly desirable. In the large marketing areas, laboratories generally co-operate with the staff department in making special arrangements for giving instruction to a limited number of the sales staff, particularly to those who have to work in distant centres where direct contact with the laboratory is not so readily obtained.

THE RESEARCH LABORATORY

The research laboratories are engaged in work of a different nature. Their work falls into three categories :—

(1) The complete study of the chemical and physical characteristics of the products which are manufactured, with a view to understanding thoroughly their behaviour in relation to their applications, not only to complete our knowledge in this respect, but also to extend their uses in other directions.

(2) Applied or service research relating to specific problems which arise in connection with manufacturing methods and applications of the manufactured products. There is always room for improvement in the refining methods in general use, and there is often need for the development of entirely new methods for re-

fining some new type of product. There are also the problems of utilizing by-products resulting from the refining or treating processes. There is always scope for investigating the products in relation to their application in industry. The research laboratory thus gives service to the refineries and works laboratories, and also to the marketing and service laboratories.

There is necessarily some overlapping of the functions of the above two types of laboratories. This is unavoidable, and is in fact desirable, provided that co-operation and close contact between the various laboratories is ensured.

(3) Fundamental research in directions which are of great scientific interest, but which may not, at the time, have any obvious bearing on the problems of manufacture and applications.

Laboratories of this kind are found within the Group in Amsterdam, Thornton near Liverpool, and Emeryville near San Francisco. Certain limited fields of research may be delegated to specially equipped research laboratories, such as the Motor Research Laboratory at Delft (Holland), which investigates problems of motor fuels and lubrication, the Agricultural Laboratory and experimental station in Modesto (California), and the laboratory for research on geology and crude oil production situated at Houston (Texas).

As examples of type (1) can be cited the study of the chemical and physical properties of gases, both natural and cracked, such data being needed for the design of stabilizers and distillation plant ; the study of the chemical properties of the numerous hydrocarbons produced by the cracking process, these being mainly of a type unknown in crude oil. The splitting of crude oil emulsions on the fields, and the making of emulsions of oils and asphaltic bitumens afford problems which can only be attacked by sound scientific methods, often involving the use of ingenious electrical and chemical apparatus.

Examples of the applied research work of the laboratories are numerous and far-reaching in their effects. The laboratory work on solvent extraction resulted in the basic patent on the furfural extraction method as well as on the back-wash principle, and also patents relating to the Duo-sol process (*vide* chapter XII). The Shellperm process (which was used in connection with the exten-

Fig. 2.   The B.P.M. Research Laboratories at Amsterdam.

sion of the Assiut dam, *vide* chapter XXXI), and the process of making bituminous paper by incorporating a stable bituminous emulsion into the paper pulp, were worked out in the Amsterdam Laboratory. The use of asphaltic bitumen for pipe coating, in the lining of canals and the revetments of dykes and dams has also been promoted by the Group's research work. An outstanding example is the development of a manufacturing process for iso-octane to the extent that there is now a commercial process producing, at a commercial price, an aviation fuel which previously was made only by laboratory methods at a cost of several pounds per gallon, for use as a standard laboratory test fuel (*vide* chapter XVI).

Research on the gases evolved when paraffin wax is cracked led to the development of the production of detergents, which are now manufactured by the Group to alleviate the present soap shortage (*vide* chapter XVII). Further work on cracked gases led to the production of polyvinyl chloride and a range of plastics with important industrial applications. Other fundamental research, such as the study of bituminous mixes under load, shock and vibration, has led to the proper formulæ for road mixes and other compounds in which bitumen, stone and sand are used in civil engineering.

Fundamental research work tackles scientific problems which are of great interest but which may not, at the moment, appear to have any bearing on the problems of manufacture and use. But the industrial history of the past fifty years affords numerous examples of the surprising developments which have arisen out of discoveries which, at the time they were made, appeared of purely scientific interest only. The importance of fundamental research is now generally recognized and most large industrial firms now carry out much work in their own laboratories and encourage it in universities in various ways.

BIBLIOGRAPHY

Discovery. Sir Richard Gregory. (Macmillan & Co., London.)
Research. T. A. Boyd. (D. A. Appleton-Century Co., New York.)

E

IV

EXPLORATION

GEOLOGY

SINCE accumulations of petroleum are governed by geological factors, a short account of the different types of rocks which are found in the earth's crust, and of the types of structures in which oil deposits are likely to be found, will be of general interest.

TYPES OF ROCKS

The rocks which compose the earth's crust can be divided into three broad classes :—

(1) **Igneous Rocks,** which are formed by solidification as a result of the cooling of the molten magma* within the earth's crust. This molten magma may cool on the surface (extrusive* types) as lava or pumice when erupted by volcanoes, or before actually

Fig. 1.   Laccoliths.

Fig. 2.   Sills.

reaching the surface (intrusive* types), as a result of its being forced up into contact with cooler rocks, thus forming buried intrusions which may take various forms such as laccoliths* (fig. 1), sills or horizontal sheets, dykes* or vertical sheets, and irregular veins (figs. 2 and 3).

These diagrammatic sections may represent hundreds or even thousands of feet in reality.

Common igneous rocks of the extrusive types are lava and tuff* ;

of the intrusive type, granite and gabbro*. Inasmuch as most of them, with the exception of tuff, are compact and not porous, it is clear that they can rarely function as oil-bearing rocks. These igneous intrusions, however, sometimes have an influence on oil accumulations, as dykes, for example, may have walled off, to

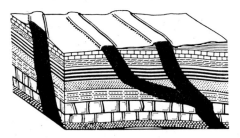

Fig. 3. Dykes.

some extent, different blocks of oil-bearing formations, thereby localising the accumulation of oil.

(2) **Metamorphic Rocks,** which are sedimentary (*vide inf.*) or igneous rocks, the texture and mineral composition of which have been altered by heat, great pressure, or a combination of both. Examples are slate (a modified form of clay) and marble (altered limestone). The process of metamorphism* usually results in such changes to igneous rocks that they still remain unsuitable for oil reservoirs, while sedimentary rocks, which were originally suitable as reservoirs, are generally adversely changed to such an extent that they lose their oil-storing capacities. Metamorphic rocks are, therefore, valueless as potential oil reservoirs.

(3) **Sedimentary Rocks.** Rain, streams, wind and ice are constantly weathering away the surface of the earth, this process being called "denudation" or "erosion". The products of this erosion in the form of mud, sand, pebbles, etc., are carried away by wind, water or ice and deposited elsewhere. These agencies, though slow in action, judged by man's standards, produce immense changes during the millions of years of geological time. The gorge of Niagara has been carved out by the river, and

the falls still recede at the rate of one foot a year. The whole area of the Ganges basin is lowered about a foot in a thousand years. The removal of the chalk which once covered the Sussex Weald between the North and South Downs was effected, according to the calculations of Darwin, in about eighty million years. Water played the most important part in this process, the eroded material being borne down the streams, thence to rivers, and eventually to open water. As the speed of a water current diminishes, for instance, in the estuary of a river, the larger particles settle out first, and as the speed is further reduced so smaller and smaller

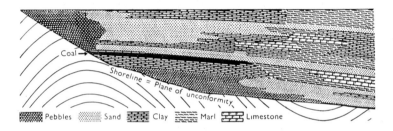

Coal

Shoreline = Plane of unconformity

Pebbles   Sand   Clay   Marl   Limestone

Fig. 4.   Sketch showing vertical and lateral changes in sedimentation.

grains settle, until at last, more or less far out to sea, the finest suspended particles are deposited, the continuation of this process resulting in the deposition of beds which may attain a very considerable thickness and which may occupy an enormous area.

The sedimentary rock beds deposited in this manner are rarely uniform in texture or character throughout their extent. The variations may be slight or very considerable, according to climatic conditions, to the incidence of floods or droughts—which resulted in the sedimentation of larger or smaller grains—to fluctuations of sea level and varying currents, or to many other causes which altered the kind of material brought down by the streams and thus caused different kinds of beds to be deposited.

As a consequence of the modifications brought about by these various factors, a section through a sedimentary series may show fine and coarse sands, sandstones, shales, limestones, coal, etc., and these layers may alternate or be repeated in a multiplicity of ways both vertically and laterally (fig. 4). Sedimentary rocks are of importance from the point of view of storage of oil as well as of origin of oil deposits.

EARTH MOVEMENTS

Rocks may be folded, bent, distorted or crushed in an extra-ordinary variety of ways as a result of earth movements. It is not possible to go into this question here in any detail, but the two sketches (figs. 5 and 5a) and the two pictures (figs. 6 and 6a) will serve to illustrate, in an idealised manner, two of the principal groups into which these disturbances can be classified.

Fig. 5.   Symmetrical Anticline and Syncline.

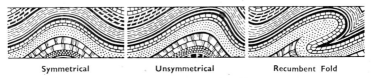

Symmetrical   Unsymmetrical   Recumbent Fold

Fig. 5a.   Types of Folds.

The faults or breaks (fig. 7) which result when rocks are bent or stressed beyond their breaking limit are of very frequent occurrence in Nature, and a knowledge of their existence is of importance to the oil geologist. Such faults often result in the vertical displacement of strata to the extent of hundreds and sometimes thousands of feet.

The great surface upheavals and alterations resulting from such earth movements will, of course, be subject to the weathering processes previously mentioned, so that eventually the surface of

Fig. 6. Anticline near Pasadena, California.

the earth may present a picture very different from that which it had soon after the folding took place.

An excellent example of these weathering processes, or denudation, on a large scale, which will be well known to many readers, is afforded by the Weald area of Kent, Surrey and Sussex, as is

Fig. 6a.   Syncline near Gebo Dome in Mesaverde.

so clearly seen on the roads from London to the south coast. London lies in a syncline* filled by the London clay.   As the road runs southward it climbs up a comparatively gentle slope to the top of the North Downs (chalk) and then suddenly descends to the Weald, on to the softer strata—the Gault, Greensands and the

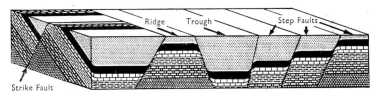

Fig. 7.   Diagram of Fault types.

Weald Clays—which underlie the chalk. As it proceeds further southward, the road crosses another range of hills (Hindhead and Blackdown), forming the centre of the Wealden anticline*, composed of sandstone, which lies beneath the Weald clay. Further southward the same effect is found again ; the comparatively bold escarpment* of the South Downs faces northward, and the gentle dip slope (*vide* fig. 12) extends from the top of the Downs to the sea (fig. 8).

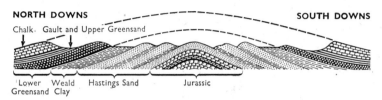

Fig. 8.   Diagrammatic Section of the Weald.

A key to the geological history of this south-east corner of England is afforded by the peculiar gaps in the Downs through which flow the rivers Mole, Medway, Arun and Adur. The strata, originally laid down horizontally, were pressed into a series of folds, one of which took the form of an anticline running from Hastings to Haslemere. When the unfolded arch was exposed to erosion, rivers formed which flowed north and south down the flanks, gradually cutting valleys for themselves as they flowed over the chalk. In course of time the central area was denuded of its original chalk cover ; the rivers, however, kept pace with the recession of the escarpments and continued to flow in their original north and south direction, cutting down through the chalk ridges and producing the curious gaps through which the present-day much smaller streams run.

UNCONFORMITY

The geological history of the earth is an often-repeated cycle of deposition, folding (usually accompanied by igneous activity) and erosion, sometimes on a minor scale, but sometimes embracing areas of continental extent. The deposits of each new cycle rest horizontally on the folded and eroded members of the previous cycle, until they, in their turn, are involved in later folding movements. This discordant relationship is termed ''unconformity'' (figs. 9 and 9a), the folds of the younger formation being unconformable to those of the older series (see also fig. 4).

Fig. 9.   Unconformity.

OIL GENERATION AND MIGRATION

Of the many theories of the origin of oil, the most generally accepted and supported by practice is that which considers marine and possibly brackish water sediments rich in organic matter as its mother formation.   It is believed that, under certain circumstances, the remains of marine organisms (foraminiferæ*, diatoms*, etc.) are preserved and finally sealed by fine-grained sediments deposited upon them after they have sunk to the bottom.   Such favourable conditions would be afforded by the stagnant waters of lagoons, gulfs and inland seas, where it is likely that animal and vegetable life would be abundant.

By reason of heat and the pressure produced by the weight of overlying sediments, assisted probably by the action of anærobic* bacteria, the organic remains are, in some way not yet fully understood, transformed into oil and gas.   Under the pressure of the overburden, and particularly under folding pressure, the oil and gas, together with the salt water originally sealed with the organic material, will be forced out of the fine-grained so-called ''mother formation'', and will migrate to more porous beds, such as sands and cavernous limestones (reservoir rocks).

In consequence of differentiation according to specific gravity and other physical properties, the contents of these reservoir rocks will separate in such a way that the oil and gas will accumulate in the uppermost parts, whilst the salt water will settle in the lower.

SUITABILITY OF ROCKS FOR OIL ACCUMULATION

Oil can be stored underground in crevices, cracks or fissures, but most commonly occupies the pore spaces between the grains of the sedimentary rocks. From the description of the manner in which sedimentary rocks are laid down, it will be clear that the

Fig. 9a. Unconformity near Gera, Germany.
A—Upper Permian (Lowermost Zechstein). B—Unconformity.
C—Mississippian (Kulm).

unevenness of the deposited grains will result in a complete network of small interstices or pores between the grains. Porosity and permeability (that is, the ability to permit the passage of fluids) vary between wide limits and thus play an important part in making a saturated formation easily drainable or otherwise. Shales, for example, although their porosity may be high, are so fine in texture that it is virtually impossible to tap their fluid content by means of wells ; they can be considered impermeable and, therefore, suitable capping rocks for holding oil in a deeper and more pervious stratum. On the other hand, sands, sandstones and sometimes limestones are sufficiently porous to permit a much freer passage of fluids, and, accordingly, these rocks form the best reservoirs.

REPRESENTATIVE TYPES OF OIL STRUCTURES

Accumulations of oil in sedimentary rocks are found in many types of structure, but two factors are essential to hold petroleum in its reservoir :—

(1) a suitable impervious "cap-rock" or seal to prevent its escape into higher layers ;

(2) a "structural" or "stratigraphic* closure" to trap the oil and prevent its further movements within the layer.

The illustration marked W in fig. 10 is a simple anticlinal structure, the oil-bearing sand "B" being capped by the impervious bed "A" and closed, because "A" also covers the sides or flanks and, therefore, prevents the oil from escaping in a horizontal direction.

Figure X illustrates a simple fault structure. Again "A" functions as a cap for the oil sand "B", whilst the fault "CC" acts as a closure on the right-hand (up-dip*) side.

Figures Y and Z show two examples of traps where the upward movement of oil and gas is stopped by a stratigraphic and not by a tectonic* phenomenon. In fig. Y, a tilted and eroded series, including an oil-bearing sand, is unconformably overlain by an impervious formation, which thus acts as a cap-rock. In fig. Z three sand horizons are present : in two of them no oil could accumulate as they open to the surface, whilst the middlemost, a sand lens wedging out in an up-dip direction, represents an excellent trap for oil. Another type of trap, the permeability trap, is provided by a lack of permeability in an up-dip direction in the same stratum. In fig. U the oil is prevented from migrating to

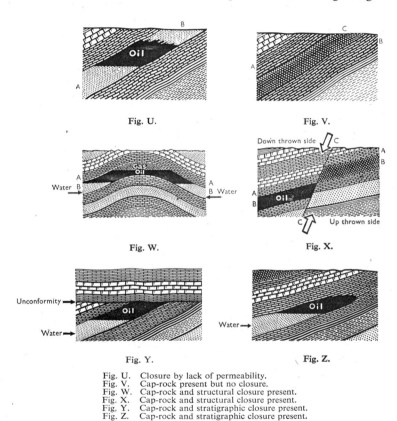

Fig. U.

Fig. V.

Fig. W.

Fig. X.

Fig. Y.

Fig. Z.

Fig. U. Closure by lack of permeability.
Fig. V. Cap-rock present but no closure.
Fig. W. Cap-rock and structural closure present.
Fig. X. Cap-rock and structural closure present.
Fig. Y. Cap-rock and stratigraphic closure present.
Fig. Z. Cap-rock and stratigraphic closure present.

Fig. 10. Sketch sections to show "capping" and effect of closure.

the surface by the lack of permeability in the layer "B" in the up-dip (right-hand) direction.

The mobility of salt under pressure has resulted, in some regions (Gulf Coast of Texas, Mexico, Roumania, etc.) in a modified form of anticlinal structure or dome, in which oil accumulates against the sides of, or above, the salt plug, or in the overlying cap-rock.

If any of the essentials described above are lacking, the oil will invariably leak or seep away, unless the pressure tending to expel the oil through the strata (e.g. the hydrostatic head*) is insufficient to bring it up to the surface, or unless the outcrop* is clogged by asphalt. An example of a seepage* on a large scale is the well-known Trinidad Pitch Lake.

RELATIVE POSITION OF OIL, GAS AND WATER IN A LAYER

As has been described previously, subterranean deposits of petroleum are commonly associated with water and gas, and the water, being the heavier, occupies the lower part of the structure. Since the fluids in the rocks are always under pressure (which may vary from a few pounds to several thousand pounds per square inch), and since gas will dissolve in oil under pressure, the oil in the structure will always contain some gas in solution. Above the oil, at the crest or highest part of the structure, there is sometimes an accumulation of free gas, known as a ''gas cap''. An analogy to the disposition of oil and gas in a stratum is the common soda-

Dotted layers show two oilsands.
A—Gas cap (pores of sand filled with gas).
BB—Oil (pores of sand filled with oil containing dissolved gas).
C—Water (pores of sand filled with water).
Note that sands need not have a gas cap and that the water level in both need not be the same.

Fig. 11.   Sketch to show occurrence of gas, oil and water in layers.

water siphon. The space above the water in the siphon is occupied by gas under pressure (the gas cap), and the fluid in the lower part of the siphon consists of water with gas dissolved in it, although this dissolved gas cannot be seen when the siphon is not in use. On pressing the trigger, the soda water is squirted out under pressure, the reduction of which, as it leaves the siphon, permits the gas to come out of solution, and the gas can then be seen rising in the tumbler and in the siphon in the form of tiny bubbles. If the siphon had been filled with sand before charging it with water and gas, the analogy of producing oil and gas from a porous bed would be complete (fig. 11).

EXPLORATION METHODS

The task of the petroleum geologist is not, as is so often thought, to find oil, but to discover conditions under which oil may accumulate.

Geological Surveying of a country unknown as far as its oil possibilities are concerned can be divided into two parts. It is first necessary to know if geological, especially stratigraphical, conditions are such as to have favoured the generation of oil. This entails regional examination of the exposed rocks and a search for oil or asphalt seepages, oil impregnations, gas emanations, and deposits of natural wax, and sometimes sulphur. Then, if it is considered that conditions are favourable, the region must be examined for structures in which oil could accumulate, and the delineation of these structures constitutes the geologist's most exacting task.

Briefly, the method followed is to map as accurately as possible the outcrop of a "bed" (a rock layer) or series of beds. At all points where observations are possible (such as in banks of rivers, in quarries or on cliffs) careful measurements are made of the inclination of the beds (the "dip") and also the direction in which the beds extend (the "strike") (figs. 12 and 12a), whilst, at the same time, the physical character of the rocks is carefully observed in order that correlation may be effected with beds exposed elsewhere.

In areas where exposures are frequent the field work is comparatively straightforward, although the influence of a great variety of factors calls for skill and experience in the interpretation of the results.

With the continued search for new oil accumulations, regions have to be explored where superficial evidence is obscure or absent, as is the case where alluvium* or laterite* occurs, and then other methods have to be called into use to supplement the deficiencies of the surface picture. Thus pits and trenches have to be dug or auger holes drilled down to bedrock. When the cover is too thick for pits, etc., to be successful, the use of hand or light-powered

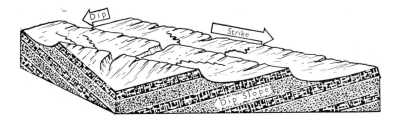

Fig. 12.   Dip and Strike.

Fig. 12a.   Limestone Strata at Ingleton, Yorkshire.

drilling outfits, by which a cored section of the hidden rocks may be obtained, is coming into more general use.

Photographic mapping from the air is rapidly becoming one of the geologist's chief aids, as, not only do the photographs provide a reliable topographic* base, but, by the use of the stereoscope, a surprising amount of geological evidence is made visible even in densely wooded county. With the development of this aerial aid

A—East plunging anticline.
B—Syncline rising to the west.

Fig. 13. Air photograph (scale approximately 1 : 40,000).

the time is passing when a geologist, working in unknown regions, must depend on local guides to plan his field work, as, with the help of photographs, he can now see at a glance how best to arrange his traverses* to obtain the maximum of geological data.

Whilst direct observation of the geology is the ideal to be hoped for, physical features of the landscape may often, by reason of having been originated by geological causes, provide valuable clues to the underlying structural conditions. This study of geomorphology* is naturally enormously facilitated by the use of aerial photographs. A working knowledge of botany is also of value to the geologist, as under suitable conditions the distribution of plants reflects the geology.

Geophysical Methods. Other methods of geological investigation must be adopted when the structure of rocks underground cannot be mapped by geological work on the surface, as is the case either where the surface rocks are covered by alluvial deposits, swamps, river deltas and water, or where the structure of the prospective oil-bearing rocks is obscured by unconformities. The methods most frequently in use may be grouped into gravimetric, seismic, magnetic, electrical and geochemical. These methods are covered by the term "geophysical exploration".

The *gravimetric method* depends on measurements made by highly sensitive instruments known as gravimeters, torsion balances and pendulums. These instruments measure with great precision the slight variations in the attraction of gravity at the surface of the earth, which is influenced in magnitude and direction by the distribution of rocks having different densities and underlying the area. The presence and magnitude of these slight variations in the force of gravity can be subjected to mathematical analysis, which may afford evidence of the presence of concealed geological structures which, under certain favourable conditions, may even be defined with considerable accuracy.

Seismic methods offer the most direct evidence of geological structure thus far achieved by geophysical prospecting. In this method artificial earthquakes produced by charges of explosives generate energy waves in the surface of the earth which are recorded by sensitive instruments known as seismographs placed at varying distances from the explosion. One method of seismic

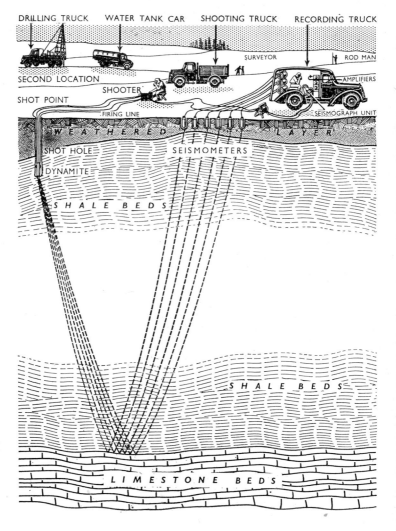

Fig. 14.   Diagrammatic scheme for Reflection Shooting.

exploration, known as refraction shooting, makes use of the fact that energy waves travel more rapidly in hard compact formations such as limestones and salt, and less rapidly in relatively soft rocks, thus making it possible by measuring the speed of these waves to infer the type of rocks through which the waves have travelled and compute their depths from the data. A second, more widely used method, known as reflection shooting, makes use of the fact that energy waves return a reflection or echo when they encounter hard beds such as limestones. The time taken by this wave to travel from the source of energy (explosion) at the surface down to the reflecting layer and back to the surface can be interpreted to give a measure of the depth to the reflecting layer. The illustration (fig. 14) shows graphically the equipment and process of reflection shooting.

The *magnetic method* depends upon measuring the intensity and direction of the earth's magnetic field and inferring from local variations in this field the distribution of rocks having different magnetic properties. Magnetic surveys suitable for this type of prospecting can now be made with instruments mounted in an aeroplane, which affords a very rapid method of mapping.

The resistance of various rocks to the passage of electrical current varies very greatly, and this property can be used to disclose the type of rock lying buried beneath relatively thin mantles of surface soil. By this means useful geological information can occasionally be obtained.

The geochemical method makes use of the inference that in areas overlying accumulations of oil and gas under high pressure small quantities of gas may be expected to permeate to the surface. Samples of the gaseous content of surface soils are analysed for the presence of minute quantities of such gas. Other geochemical methods utilize analyses of surface soils for the presence of liquid or solid petroleum derivatives, which it is surmised may be carried to the surface by escaping gases.

Subsurface Geology. In countries where many wells have been drilled very valuable information can be obtained by compiling the geological data revealed by these wells. This type of work, called "subsurface geology", is particularly well developed in the Mid-Continent and Texas Gulf areas of the United States.

Outcrops are generally poor in these areas, and the structures as exposed at the surface do not sufficiently reflect those of the deeply buried oil-bearing formations on account of the many unconformities present.

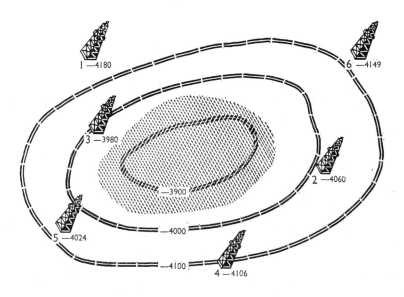

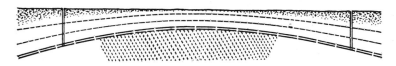

Fig. 15. Anticlinal Structure mapped by Subsurface Geological Data.

The method consists of plotting on a map the depth (with reference to some convenient datum plane, usually sea-level) of a selected subsurface marker ; for example, a distinctive fossil zone or a top of a well-recognized limestone. If the depth to the marker in well no. 1 in fig. 15 is 4,490 feet and the surface elevation is 310 feet, the marker lies 4,180 feet below sea-level ; this point, —4,180, is then plotted on the map. In like manner the depths below sea-level of wells nos. 2, 3, 4, 5 and 6 are plotted on the map. Contours (lines connecting points of equal elevation) are then drawn and the configuration of the top of the marker is depicted. Thus, in fig. 15 an anticlinal structure is interpreted with the shaded area having a higher elevation than the five dry holes. The shaded area would be likely territory to explore for oil and gas possibilities.

The subsurface method is also employed in the search for stratigraphic traps. Pertinent information—for example, the thickness of a sandstone or data on the permeability of a limestone—is plotted on a map and used to localize areas which hold promise for stratigraphic type accumulation of oil and gas.

Correlation of the Formations. For subsurface geology, core drilling and all geological investigation, correlation of the formations of the same age is of primary importance. The study of the type and character of the rocks (petrology*) and the determination of the nature of the contained fossils (palæontology*) are the principal means of establishing correlation. Methods of investigation are being more and more refined and have been greatly improved by the study of small fossils (micro-palæontology) and by an analysis of the nature and relative abundance of the mineral constituents of the rock (heavy mineral investigation). Furthermore, certain physical properties of the beds penetrated by the drill can be used for correlation purposes, as is done by the Schlumberger method (*vide* chapter V) of determining the electrical resistivity and permeability of the formation. This latter method also indicates the production possibilities of the porous beds and is now widely adopted in the development of oilfields.

PROCEDURE AND DEVELOPMENTS FOLLOWING EXPLORATION

Oil geologists and geophysicists explore enormous tracts of land in their search for prospective oil structures and make preliminary surveys which usually give sufficient information to enable a distinction to be made between those areas which are worth the expense of exploring in detail and those which can at once be rejected. It may be said that, generally speaking, only a small proportion of all the areas examined justifies further consideration.

Even when a structure of highly promising appearance has been mapped and fully investigated at the surface there is no guarantee that it will be oil bearing, and it is certainly impossible to say that it will be capable of yielding commercial quantities of petroleum. This can only be determined by the drilling of test wells in the most likely places, a proceeding which is invariably very costly. The first few exploration wells drilled on a structure may give such positive results that the area can at once be considered as proven territory, or they may give such negative results and further geological information that it is possible to condemn the structure ; they may give, on the other hand, small but promising shows of oil and geological information encouraging enough to warrant the drilling of additional wells before a final judgment is formed as to the value of the structure.

If the test wells indicate that the structure is suitable for development as a commercial proposition, the exploitation wells drilled on it are carefully checked and controlled for geological information by means of cores, etc., and this process is carried on throughout the life of the field. The accumulation of detailed data, including the nature of the oil, permits of further elucidation and more accurate interpretation of the structure, thereby enabling its more economic development by the minimizing of wasteful dry holes.

THE RELATION OF OIL TO GEOLOGICAL AGE

Crude oil may be found in sedimentary strata of almost any geological age. About half the world production, however, comes from rocks of the younger geological formations, those of the tertiary system (*vide* table on p. 69).

A few examples will illustrate the great diversity of character which crude oils display. The oils of the Eastern United States fields are geologically very old, being found in "palæozoic" strata ; they are of the paraffin base type and yield a poor gasoline, good kerosine, lubricating oils, paraffin wax, but no asphaltic bitumen. Those of Western United States (California)

are of tertiary age, yielding good gasoline, fair kerosine, lubricating oils, and some asphaltic bitumen, but no wax. The heavy
crude oils of Mexico, of cretaceous age, yield little gasoline but
a very large percentage of asphaltic bitumen. The tertiary crude

TABLE OF GEOLOGICAL GROUPS (ERAS) AND SYSTEMS (PERIODS)

Time-Eras and Rock-Groups	Time-Periods and Rock-Systems	Approximate age in millions of years (very hypothetical)
Quaternary	Recent	—
	Pleistocene	1
Tertiary ...	Pliocene	—
	Miocene	30
	Oligocene	—
	Eocene	60
Secondary or	Cretaceous	100
Mesozoic	Jurassic	150
	Triassic	180
Primary or	Permian	200
Palæozoic	Carboniferous	300
	Devonian	400
	Silurian	450
	Ordovician	500
	Cambrian	600
Eozoic ...	Pre-Cambrian (Algonkian)...	1,200
Azoic ...	Archæan	1,500

oil of Tarakan, in East Borneo, is a natural liquid fuel, while the
gasolines from Borneo and Sumatra crude oil, of similar age,
need no refining.

There seems no obvious relation between the type of crude oil and its geological age.

BIBLIOGRAPHY

Principles of Physical Geology, 1945. Arthur Holmes. (Ronald Press, New York.)

Geologic History of North America, 1944. Russell C. Hussey. (McGraw-Hill, New York and London.)

Field Geology, 1942 (4th edition). Frederick H. Lahee. (McGraw-Hill, New York and London.)

Geophysical Prospecting for Oil, 1940. L. L. Nettleton. (McGraw-Hill, New York and London.)

Textbook of Geology, 1931. Lake and Rastall. (E. Arnold, London.)

Oilfield Exploration and Development, 1925. A. Beeby Thompson. (Crosby, Lockwood & Son, London.)

V

DRILLING

THE art of well drilling dates back to 221 B.C., when it was first practised in China, where brine wells as deep as 3,500 feet have been drilled with equipment of a surprisingly primitive nature (fig. 1 and 1a). Ancient illustrations of the tools then used show that they bore a striking resemblance to those used in modern cable tool drilling, especially those for retrieving articles left in the hole. The Chinese drilled their wells by means of drilling bits which were moved up and down, a method which was the precursor of the percussion system of drilling. The latter method was at one time used almost exclusively in oil well drilling, but has now been almost entirely superseded by the rotary system of drilling.

The birth of the petroleum industry is marked by Colonel

Fig. 1. Early Chinese Drilling Rig.

Drake's famous well drilled at Titusville in 1859, the first well sunk with the definite object of obtaining oil. As is to be expected, the methods used for drilling salt and water wells at that time influenced those applied in drilling for oil, but as the petroleum industry grew, the methods employed in drilling for oil took on a character of their own. In the early days of the petroleum industry, drilling was a comparatively simple process, as the wells were very shallow. At the famous Petrolea Field of Canada, for example, which yielded oil at depths of 200 or 300 feet, wells were drilled during a long week-end by means of a string of drilling tools suspended from a tripod made of wooden poles.

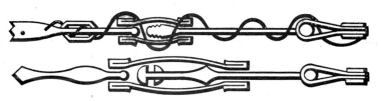

Chinese Boring Bits

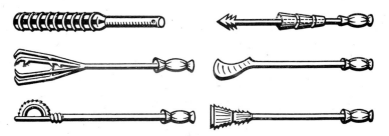

Fishing Tools used in recovering broken Bits

Fig. 1a.

The ever-increasing demand for petroleum and its products led, however, to the exhaustion of the shallow oil sands, so that deeper productive measures had to be introduced. Rapid advances have been made in deeper drilling techniques during the last few years, accelerated by improvements in steels and other hard metals. This is strikingly illustrated by the fact that in 1919 rotary drilling equipment could penetrate only the softer formations, and then to depths not exceeding 3,000 feet. In 1933, when the first edition of this Handbook was published, the deepest well in the world had reached 10,944 feet ; this depth has since been exceeded by a number of wells, the deepest at present being over 17,000 feet. For deep drilling of this kind the hydraulic rotary system is invariably used.

PROSPECTING

After the geologists and geophysicists have found what appears to be a favourable location for drilling, this prospect is sometimes further checked by drilling a number of small-diameter wells, usually with a very light portable drilling rig called a core drill. Under other conditions, depending upon the depth at which the geologists expect to reach the objective and the types of formations which are likely to be encountered, different types of equipment may be required. Where troublesome or badly caving formations are expected, wells are drilled of such a size that emergency casing strings may be inserted to protect that part of the well already drilled. "Slim holes" are sometimes drilled primarily for the purpose of gathering information. Completion of such slim hole wells as producing wells is always desirable, should satisfactory oil "pay zones" be encountered.

All wells drilled with the object of discovering a new structure, a new pay zone, or of extending the productive area of known pay zones, are "exploratory"* wells. The first well in a field is usually known as a "wildcat" well. Those wells extending a known field are "extension" or "outstepping"* wells. Wells drilled for deeper pay sands in the same field are "vertical exploration" wells. Those wells drilled within the known boundaries of a proven field are known as "exploitation"* or "development" wells.

After the drilling of several exploratory wells in a newly discovered field, the characteristics of the formations, pay zones and drilling requirements are determined. The development department then organizes its skill and ingenuity to enable the exploitation wells to be drilled as economically and simply as possible.

Since old-time "wildcat" wells were often located by pure guesswork or superstition, the term "wildcat" gained its present colloquial meaning of "highly speculative ". The present-day wildcat well is still not by any means certain of discovering oil. It is usually backed, however, by geological, geochemical, gravimetric, seismic or electric surveys, by aerial mapping, core drilling or other work, and often by several of the above. This preliminary work, however, only locates structures which have oil-bearing possibilities. No way has yet been found to determine whether oil is actually present, except by drilling wells.

That drilling wildcat wells is still a venturesome business is shown by the fact that, of the 3,636 such wells drilled in the U.S.A. during the first eleven months of 1945, only 433, or 1 in 8·4, were successful commercial producers.

DRILLING MACHINERY

When the location of the wildcat well has been decided, the site of the well is cleared for operations. For wildcat wells in remote countries, houses and quarters must first be built for the drilling crews. The crew, which usually works in three shifts, consists in all of between 15 and 24 men, including engineer, tool pusher, drillers and crews. Personnel concerned with the machine shop, materials and spare parts, warehouse, transportation and office may sometimes raise to over 100 the staff required to serve the wildcat. Among the special services which may be required in addition are : electric power, electric and acetylene welding, radio or telephone facilities and automotive, boat or even aircraft transportation.

Depending on the type or depth of well, the drilling machinery itself varies from a " light rig", using perhaps 200 horse-power for the drilling operations and capable of 3,000-foot drilling, to a "heavy rig" using 1,200 horse-power. The heaviest engine-driven electric rig just assembled for 15,000-foot drilling in the U.S.A. employs almost 2,000 horse-power at the rig.

Depending on available fuel, drilling rigs are powered by steam, using locomotive-type portable boilers, or by internal combustion engines. The wildcat well of to-day is most often powered by either diesel, butane or gas engines because of the greater fuel economy obtained in remote locations. A heavy steam rig can consume an average of 200 barrels of fuel daily, whereas a heavy diesel rig may average only 20 barrels per day.

The first structure of the rig itself to be built is the derrick, which is either a structural steel tower such as shown in fig. 2 or a portable derrick, shown in fig. 3—the latter being moved from well to well. The former type is used for medium to deep drilling, and the latter type for light to medium drilling.

Let us assume that our wildcat is to be drilled with a heavy rig, with its objective below 10,000 feet. In this case the derrick will be installed on top of a steel "substructure" 8 to 14 feet high, which raises the machinery off the ground a sufficient height to permit the drilling control valves to be installed beneath the derrick floor. The derrick itself is 136 feet high plus about 13 feet for the "gin pole", which is installed over the top to facilitate installation of the drilling crown block. The 30-foot square derrick floor, which is surfaced with boards and stands 8 to 14 feet off the ground, is the working platform for the crews. The whole structure, including a structure for the engines, is mounted on a foundation to support the drilling loads. The derrick load capacity is about 500 tons.

Fig. 4 shows a diagrammatic sketch layout of the essential parts of a typical drilling rig operated by internal combustion engines.

The hoisting winch or "draw-works", by which the drill pipe, casing and tubing is handled, weighs about 30 tons, and consists of two main pieces which are taken apart for transporting. The hoist includes a drum for holding the wire-hoisting rope and several chain-driven shafts comprising a multi-speed chain transmission capable of from four to eight hoisting speeds. The controls for the hoist are placed at the right-hand side of the front of the hoist, where the driller can see clearly all operations of "coming out of the hole" and "going in the hole".

The hoist is driven by three or four engines installed behind it, and these are coupled to each other and to the hoist by additional chain drives. The hoist speed changes are usually made

Fig. 2.   Heavy Rotary Drilling Derrick.

Fig. 3. Portable Drilling Derrick.

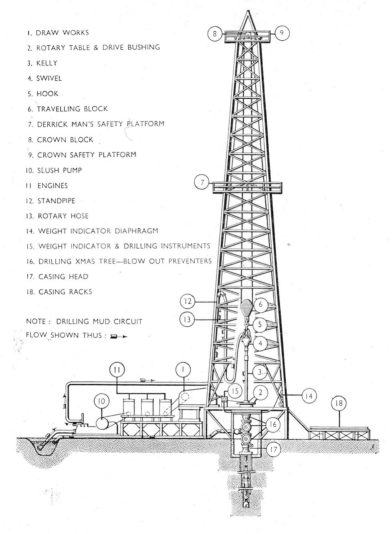

1. DRAW WORKS
2. ROTARY TABLE & DRIVE BUSHING
3. KELLY
4. SWIVEL
5. HOOK
6. TRAVELLING BLOCK
7. DERRICK MAN'S SAFETY PLATFORM
8. CROWN BLOCK
9. CROWN SAFETY PLATFORM
10. SLUSH PUMP
11 ENGINES
12. STANDPIPE
13. ROTARY HOSE
14. WEIGHT INDICATOR DIAPHRAGM
15. WEIGHT INDICATOR & DRILLING INSTRUMENTS
16. DRILLING XMAS TREE—BLOW OUT PREVENTERS
17. CASING HEAD
18. CASING RACKS

NOTE : DRILLING MUD CIRCUIT
FLOW SHOWN THUS :

Fig. 4.   Diagrammatic View of Rotary Drilling Rig.

by jaw type clutches, while the drum is placed in and out of operation by friction clutches, much as in the transmission of an automobile. The hoist drum is equipped with powerful friction brakes to control the heavy loads involved, and additional assistance is given, and brake life greatly increased, by the use of a "water brake" which absorbs a large part of the braking horse-

Fig 5. Front View of Heavy Hoist, showing Controls.

power. The brake rims are water cooled to help dissipate the heat of braking and give longer life.

Figs. 5 and 5A illustrate a modern steam-driven hoist without a driving engine, and show the water, or hydromatic* brake at the far end of the hoist. The spools on each end of the lineshaft, or upper shaft of the hoist, are termed "catheads". Of an automatic type, controlled by the driller, they are used to pull on the end of the large pipe wrenches, or "tongs", when "breaking out" (unscrewing) or "making up" the drill pipe as it "comes out of the hole" or "goes in the hole".

The rotary table, set over the centre of the well, rotates the drill pipe. It consists of a heavy steel table, mounted on ball or roller bearings, and equipped with a bevel gear under its outer rim. It is turned by a bevel pinion on a shaft, which is driven in turn either by a chain drive from the draw-works or by an independent engine drive. The rotary table is also equipped with a heavy steel bowl in which removable toothed wedges or "slips" are placed to prevent the pipe from slipping when coming out of, or going into the hole.

Cathead

Fig. 5a.   Rear View of Heavy Steam-driven Hoist.

The hoisting equipment consists of a crown block (pulley) on top of the derrick and travelling block, which moves up and down the derrick by means of the hoist and multiple cable arrangement. The block is equipped with a heavy hook at its lower end, and on this hook the "elevator", or special quick-latching clamp, is attached by heavy steel links as shown in fig. 6.

While drilling, a "swivel" is placed on the hook. This device encloses a heavy roller bearing which enables the upper half, or housing, to remain stationary while the "kelly"—a square or

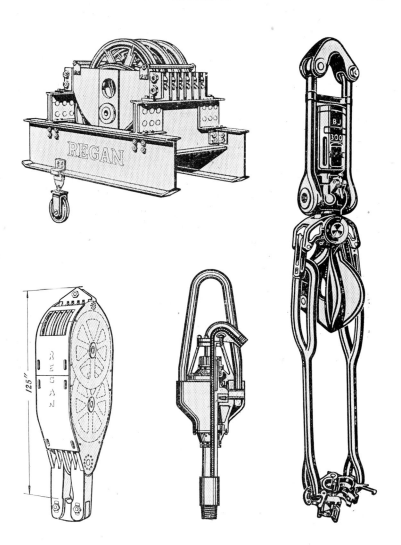

Fig. 6. Crown Block, Travelling Block, Hook and Elevators.

hexagon shaped hollow steel bar—can rotate, turning the drill pipe. The kelly is rotated by the rotary table, through which it is to feed the bit into the formation. To the upper end of the swivel, which is hollow, is attached the rotary hose, made of steel-wrapped rubber, or of all-steel pipe, equipped with ball-bearing swivel joints. Through this hose, heavy hydraulic pumps force drilling fluid or "mud", which goes through the kelly, down the drill pipe, through the bit (to keep it cool and clear of cuttings) and thence back up to the surface around the outside of the drill pipe, carrying with it the cuttings.

Heavy wrenches or tongs are suspended in the derrick for tightening up and unscrewing the drill pipe and other pipe in the well. These wrenches are suspended on steel wire cables, and their weight is counterbalanced by steel or concrete weights, which, for the safety of the crews and for convenience, are usually suspended under the floor.

To permit the lifting of heavy articles of up to two or three tons around the derrick floor, an auxiliary steel cable or manila rope, about $1\frac{1}{2}$ inches in diameter, called the "catline", is usually suspended over a pulley fastened to the derrick top. This is operated from the cathead on the driller's side of the hoist, power being obtained by wrapping the rope around this rotating cathead and pulling on the free end.

The drill pipe itself is a special grade of steel pipe equipped with "tool joints" at each end, either welded on or threaded and shrunk on. These tool joints are a special tapered-thread coupling designed to screw together quickly and shoulder tightly.

At the lower end of the drilling "string"*, as the connected drilling pipes are called, are a number of "drill collars", extra heavy sections of alloy steel pipe. In this way, the great weight needed to push the bit downward into the formations is concentrated at the bottom of the drill string, thus reducing the chance of crooked wells or drill pipe failures.

If a steam rig is used, the boiler plant normally consists of four 150-h.p. locomotive boilers with 350 lb./sq. in. working pressure, and with specially built and quickly-connected unitized pipe and valve manifolds designed for quick breakdown and assembly. The boiler auxiliaries, including feed-water pumps, fuel controls, electric turbo-generators and accessories, are mounted as one unit on long steel beams or skids. After moving the boiler plant into position, all that is required is to assemble a few quick-connecting steel unions and the plant is ready to produce steam. Under good conditions a heavy boiler plant of this type can be placed in operation in as little as eight hours from the time all the material has reached the site.

In remote countries a cementing outfit, consisting of two small duplex pumps, a jet type cement-mixing hopper, suction box and water-measuring tanks, is supplied as part of the rig for cementing the casing. In the U.S.A. these services are normally supplied from a mobile unit by a contracting company.

In view of the importance to the safety of the well of properly controlled drilling mud, the rig is also equipped with means for mixing and otherwise handling a proper supply of the correct type of drilling mud needed. Most wells ''make mud'' as part of the cutting process, and part of this can sometimes be made into suitable ''reserve'' mud to be held ready in case of emergency.

In some fields where high bottom hole pressures or caving formations are encountered, the mud requires expensive ''weighting'' or treating materials, and an elaborate system of making, distributing and collecting new and spent mud is justified.

DRILLING THE WELL

After the equipment is assembled and inspected, the well is ready for ''spudding in'' or starting. As a rule, a large bit of perhaps 20 inches diameter is screwed on to the end of the kelly. The kelly is held in a vertical position by the rotary table and temporary guides below the floor, to get the well started vertically. The pump and rotary table are started and the bit is lowered until it starts drilling. While drilling the surface hole the mud returns are usually conducted back to the mud pit through a ditch.

After drilling in this manner for a distance of from 50 to 300 feet, the conductor pipe—perhaps of 16-inch casing—is set and cemented up to the surface, often by pumping cement alongside the outside of the casing through 1 or 1½-inch pipe. The conductor pipe usually projects several feet above the ground, and through it the mud returns are conducted back to the mud pit.

From there they go by a pipe to a vibrating mud screen, which screens out cuttings. After passing through the screen the mud is carried by an open flume, or ditch, to the pump pit once more, the gas or vapours escaping *en route*.

When operating the rig, each member of the crew has certain specific duties. The driller is in full charge of the operation under the general direction of the drilling foreman or "tool pusher". The driller operates the hoist, controlling the speed of drilling by his judgment of the correct rotary speed, weight on the bit and rate of fluid flow. The "derrick man", from a platform about 80 feet up in the derrick, unhooks the elevators from the drill-pipe "stands" (two or three lengths of pipe) as they are pulled from the well. He also stacks the pipe in place in the derrick. When going into the hole he latches the elevators back on to the pipe lengths. Usually the no. 2 man on the rig, the derrick man, is also in charge of the operation and maintenance of the pumps. Two floor men generally work at the rotary table, handling the tongs and slips when making "round trips" with the drill pipe. The fifth man is the fireman on a steam rig or, on a power rig, the mechanic in charge of the engines.

When coming out of the hole, the drill pipe is raised in "stands" consisting of two or three joints of pipe each 30 feet in length. When a stand has been raised until a tool joint is about 3 feet above the rotary table top, "slips" or toothed wedges are placed in the rotary table and the pipe lowered until the slips grip the pipe. The break-out tongs, which have been rough-closed around the pipe while it is being raised, are set. Other tongs, which have been placed by the second floor man, are set to hold against the pull of the break-out tongs, and the automatic cathead is then engaged by the driller. This "breaks" the tool joint. The "back-up" tongs are then removed and, while the break-out tongs are held in position by the floor man, the rotary table is engaged, thus unscrewing the joint. The broken-out stand is then lowered to its position on the pipe rack.

The travelling block is then lowered again until the elevator is in position to be latched around the portion of pipe which projects above the rotary table. The elevators are latched, the driller starts the hoist on its upward travel, the floor men pick out the slips as the pipe rises, and the whole process is repeated. On a 10,000-foot well it must be repeated over a hundred times, once for each 90-foot stand.

When going into the hole, the above operation is approximately reversed. The drill collars, with bit attached, are lowered into the well and the pipe set in slips with the top about 3 feet above the rotary table. As the empty elevator hook is hoisted the derrick man latches in a stand as it passes his level. The stand is picked up and "stabbed" into the tool joint at the rotary table. While the blocks have been rising the floor men have placed the make-up tongs in position and installed the "spinning line", which consists of a few wraps of chain or rope, around the pipe. When the new joint is stabbed, the spinning line is raised on to the loose pipe and the line is pulled by means of the spinning cathead. This tightens or "spins" the tool joint until it nearly shoulders, at which point the cathead pulls on a cable attached to the tong handle and makes up the joint tightly. The rotary table meanwhile is locked against rotation by a special locking latch, which avoids the necessity of using both sets of tongs.

A good crew in action is a perfect example of co-ordination of men and machines in a complex task. On a 10,000-foot well such a crew can handle a 90-foot stand going into the hole in about 45 seconds ; coming out of the hole, in an average of about 60 seconds.

The casing programme of a typical wildcat well may be as follows :—

$$20\text{-inch hole} \quad \dots \quad 0\text{--} \quad 100 \text{ feet} \quad \dots \quad 16\text{-inch conductor casing}$$
$$14\tfrac{3}{4}\text{-inch hole} \quad \dots \quad 0\text{--} 3,000 \text{ feet} \quad \dots \quad 10\tfrac{1}{2}\text{-inch casing}$$
$$9\tfrac{7}{8}\text{-inch hole} \quad \dots \quad 0\text{--}10,000 \text{ feet} \quad \dots \quad 5\tfrac{3}{4}\text{-inch casing}$$

An emergency string of $7\tfrac{5}{8}$-inch casing may be kept at the well in case unexpected formation difficulties make it imperative to set casing, by cementing, to preserve the existing hole and continue drilling to the objective zone.

Other wildcat casing schemes can be used, depending upon the depth and other conditions involved.

DRILLING MUD

The upper formations, which usually include fresh water-bearing sands, are frequently comparatively soft and unconsolidated, so that they are easily drilled through. The drilling fluid plasters off the walls of the hole by forming a filter cake. The porous rocks act as a strainer, holding the clay particles at the walls, and the water in the mud filters through. Much research has been done to improve the properties of drilling mud, so that now it is possible to form an almost impervious cake very quickly, thus allowing little water or filtrate from the mud to enter the formations. It is very important not to contaminate or "invade" the porous rock with water, as well as to avoid a thick cake from forming which may cause the drill pipe to stick, resulting in a "fishing job" (*vide inf.*). Muds having a great degree of fluidity when in motion, but which assume a gel (jelly-like) condition at rest, can be made by using bentonite*, soda ash, quebracho*, etc. A very effective drilling fluid can be made by adding ordinary starch. This material is useful because it will not settle out when very salty water is used. A highly alkaline mud made by the addition of caustic soda, is used when the presence of anhydrite* and gypsum would cause the mud to settle out or flocculate. An oil base mud, which employs oil rather than water, is used to drill through "pay" sands so that any filtrate that enters the formation is oil rather than water. An oil base mud, using diesel fuel as the base, mixed with asphalt, pine oil, and caustic soda for the body of the mud, has been found to plaster off porous formations without losing any filtrate to the formations. This may be called a perfect plastering mud. When fractured formations are encountered, the mud fluid itself may enter the layers and mud circulation may be lost. The addition of mica flakes, cellophane or fibrous material will help to plug these holes, thus restoring proper circulation.

As a rule, the pressures in water, oil and gas sands are about equal to the pressures exerted by a column of water of a height equal to the depth at which the sand is encountered. A mud of specific gravity somewhat greater than that of salt water (say, 1·2) should keep such sands under control. Friable formations, which are apt to cave in, and shales, which are liable to heave*, have to be contended with at times, and then very heavy muds are required. Weighting materials, such as hæmatite* and barytes*, in

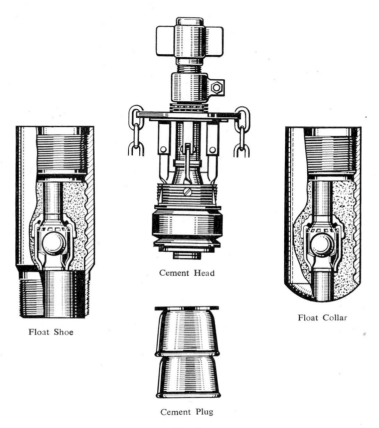

Cement Head

Float Shoe

Float Collar

Cement Plug

Fig. 7.

very finely powdered form, are then used and, by suitable chemical treatment, may be kept in suspension in the mud indefinitely.

CEMENTING THE WELL

Each string of casing is set by a special cementing method. When the hole is ready for setting casing, the last trip of the drill pipe is accompanied by a thorough conditioning of the drilling mud to be sure it is of the proper quality to prevent caving while the casing is being run, or building up of extra heavy filter cakes which make the casing have a tendency to stick.

The casing string is equipped at its lower end with a cement guide shoe or, more generally, a float guide shoe containing a ball valve such as shown in fig. 7. At the top of the first casing joint a float collar is used. The use of dual ball floats is advisable since, in case the lower ball valve becomes fouled up with deposits, the upper ball valve will act as a check valve and hold the cement in place when it is setting.

The float shoe, float collar and several lower casing joints are tightly screwed up and firmly spot-welded together so that, in case of failure of the cement to set around the bottom, the drilling operation will not later on unscrew the bottom joints and drop them in the well.

The casing is usually set with the lower end in some firm rock or shale section. When bottom is reached, a cement head such as that shown in fig. 7—a device which can quickly be attached and detached from the casing head—is attached and connected to the mud pumps and cement pumps. After mud has been sufficiently circulated to establish free circulation, a slurry of neat cement containing about 40% by volume of water is pumped into the casing. The amount of cement is calculated to fill up to the desired height on the outside of the casing, usually with a reasonable excess to fill up cavities. This excess allowance depends on the type of formations which have been experienced.

The cement having been pumped into the casing, the cement head is quickly removed. A plug designed to separate the mud from the cement is dropped in the casing. The head is closed and the slush pump is once more applied to pump the cement to its place as rapidly as possible. When the calculated number of minutes of pumping has elapsed, indicating that the plug should be close to bottom, the pressure should start to rise as the heavy cement goes around the shoe and overbalances the lighter mud column. Just before the plug is due to hit "bottom" (the float collar in this case), the pumps are slowed down to avoid heavy impact pressures. The operator watches for the sudden pressure rise,

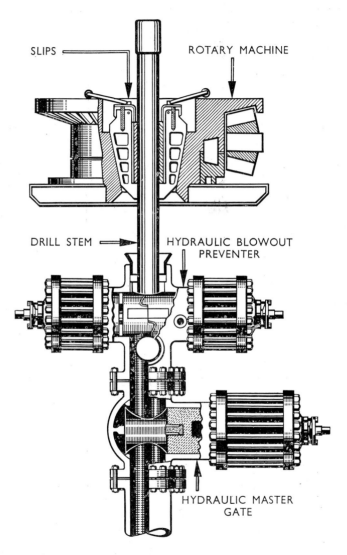

Fig. 8.   Blowout Preventer and Drilling Control Valve.

which indicates that the plug is down. The pumps are then shut down and the surface valves are then closed off until the cement is set, 24 to 48 hours later. After the cement has set, the casing can be suspended at the proper point in the casing head support at the surface and the drilling "Christmas tree"* (*vide* fig. 16) can be installed preparatory to continuing to drill ahead.

The drilling "Christmas tree" consists of rubber-sealed high-pressure valves, or "blow-out preventers" (fig. 8), and other fittings, usually of 3,000 lb. per square inch working pressure on deep wells, and usually not less than 2,000 lb. per square inch even on shallow wells. These valves can be hydraulically closed from a distance and are vital to the safety of the well in case of blow-outs.

The cemented casing is not only relied on to protect the well, but it must prevent any sudden blow-outs from leaking between the casing and formation, causing "cratering" outside the casing. After the cement has been in place for a sufficiently long period to permit it to harden, the cement plug inside the casing, the float collar and the float shoe are drilled out with a bit to a point immediately below the casing. A pressure test is made at this point to be sure that there is no leak around the outside of the casing to the surface. The well is then drilled ahead in the normal manner.

SAMPLING THE FORMATIONS

As the well is drilled ahead, every precaution and effort is made to determine the characteristics of each of the formations penetrated. This is done not only to detect an oil or gas reservoir, but to correlate the formations penetrated in the well with the formations found in nearby wells. The structure of the rocks in the vicinity may thus be determined, and the limits and type of reservoir estimated.

The circulated mud brings pieces of the formations to the surface. These are screened out and samples taken every few feet, to be examined under a microscope. A complete description of the lithology* can be obtained ; shells or fossils present indicate the age of the formations penetrated. When it is desired to determine the porosity and oil saturation in the cuttings with accuracy,

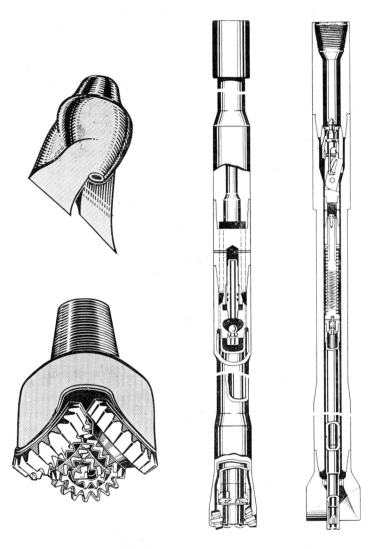

Fig. 9.   Core Drills and Bits.

they are sealed in cans at the well and sent to a laboratory, where the fluoroscope detects minute amounts of hydrocarbons.

When oil or gas first shows up, the drill pipe may be removed from the hole and a core barrel put on in place of the regular drilling bit so that actual small cylinders of the rock can be brought to the surface for examination. The core barrel and attached cutter head consists of two concentric tubes about 20 feet long, with a hollow bit or core head at the end (fig. 9). As the hollow core head drills through the formation, a core, a few inches in diameter, is left intact and passes into the inner tube, where it is retained at the bottom by means of a catcher. Where a core head can drill more than 20 feet without getting dull, a retractable or "wire line" inner-core barrel is used. After a core has been cut, the inner barrel containing the core can be brought to the surface with a wire line lowered inside the drill pipe, the core is removed and the inner barrel simply dropped back into the drill pipe. On reaching bottom it automatically locks in place. In this way, as long as the bit remains sharp, the cores can be

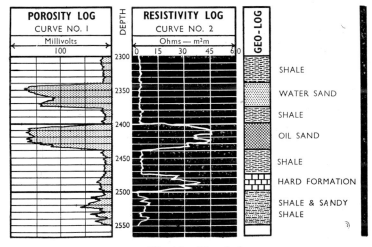

Fig. 10.   Electric Log.

taken continuously, or at intervals, without withdrawing the drill pipe. This is especially advantageous in deep holes.

LOGGING THE FORMATIONS

An electric log of the formations penetrated is made at suitable intervals by lowering a conductor cable into the hole after withdrawing the drill pipe. The electrodes at the end of the cable make electrical contact with the conductive mud in order to convey the electricity into the formations and to record the electrical field set up by the formations themselves. A theoretical log is shown in fig. 10. The self- or natural-potential curve on the left is a record of the electrical field produced by the formations themselves, and it is found to be related to the permeability of the formations and the salinity of the water in the formations. An increase to the left indicates a permeable sand whose contained-water is salty. The curve on the right is a measure of the ease with which electricity flows through the formation. The more water a formation contains and the saltier the water, the lower will be the resistance curve. Therefore, high values are shown opposite formations whose pores are filled with oil or formations having little or no pore space (hard formations).

The electrical log accurately defines the limits of the various formations and is, therefore, a record or log that can be easily used for correlation and also serves as a check on cuttings and cores for detecting and evaluating penetrated oil reservoirs. The electrical log must be run before too much time has elapsed : otherwise the filtrate of the mud may have contaminated the permeable zones to such an extent that the logs will not be representative. The record must also be made before casing is run, for casing "shorts" out the electric fields.

The radio-active log of a drill hole consists of two curves. One curve reflects the amount of radioactive minerals contained in the formations. It is called the "Natural Radioactivity" or "Gamma Ray" curve. The second curve, the "neutron curve", results from bombarding the formation with neutrons. The response to this bombardment is found to be related, among other things, to the porosity of the formations, and, therefore, to the storage capacity for oil, water or gas, of the rocks penetrated.

FISHING

While drilling wells every precaution is taken to see that only first-class materials are purchased, and that they are kept in good condition before being run into the well. In spite of these precautions, drill pipe does occasionally break from fatigue of long running or wears thin by too long usage.   Bit cones become worn off, and, occasionally tools are accidentally dropped down the well. Sometimes drill pipe becomes stuck in the well.

In order to solve these problems a large number of special tools have been devised for recovering the ''fish''—broken or stuck parts—from the hole. Fig. 11 illustrates some of the most common types of fishing tools, designed generally either to go over

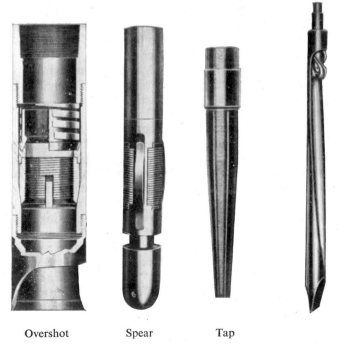

Overshot   Spear   Tap

Fig. 11. Fishing Tools (Outside and Inside Cutter).   Fig. 12. Whipstock.

the outside of the ''fish'' or to go inside it, take hold of it and pull it from the well. Other tools shown, cut off stuck pipe like a lathe from the inside or from the outside, the latter after as much

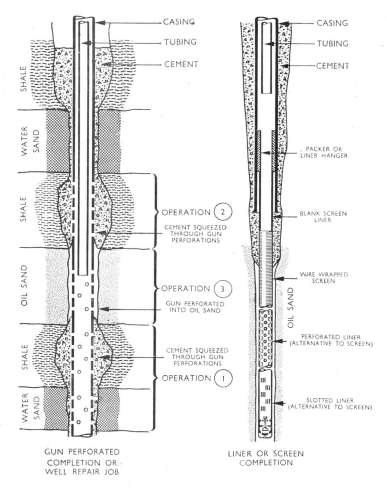

Fig. 13.   Completion Methods.

H

as several hundred feet of larger pipe has "washed over" the fish.

Blind fishing involves a high degree of imagination and intimate knowledge of the tools and character of the fish involved. If the fish cannot be recovered, a cement plug is pumped around the fish and for some distance above it and a metal wedge or "whipstock" is set to guide the bit out of the old hole (*vide* fig. 12). Drilling is then started with the fish effectually " sidetracked".

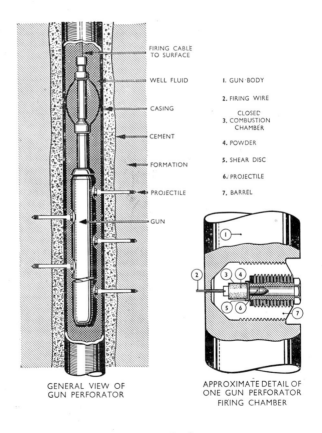

FIRING CABLE TO SURFACE

WELL FLUID

CASING

CEMENT

FORMATION

PROJECTILE

GUN

1. GUN·BODY

2. FIRING WIRE

3. CLOSED COMBUSTION CHAMBER

4. POWDER

5. SHEAR DISC

6. PROJECTILE

7. BARREL

GENERAL VIEW OF GUN PERFORATOR

APPROXIMATE DETAIL OF ONE GUN PERFORATOR FIRING CHAMBER

Fig. 14.   Gun Perforator.

well is generally the spick-and-span painted Christmas tree with a small fence around it—in many cases to keep animals or vehicles from damaging the well head.

STRAIGHT AND DIRECTIONAL DRILLING

It may appear to the casual observer that a well would naturally tend to keep to the vertical path when being drilled. This is far from the case, as can be understood when it is considered that the push exerted on the bit by the drilling string tends to bend the pipe into various arcs, and thus to tend to guide the bit in directions other than vertical. Most wells are required to be as vertical as possible, since such wells are simpler to operate for oil production, wear out fewer pumps and tools and are generally more satisfactory. In strata which are inclined at angles up to about 45°, a bit will naturally dig into the strata, and the well tends to become more or less normal to the strata. In formations dipping over 45°, the bit tends to slide down the strata and the well may deviate parallel to the strata. Good "straight-hole" drilling practice has been developed to reduce these tendencies, and consists, first, of using the heavy-weight drill collars sufficiently long and large so that the bending action near the bit is reduced. Reduced weight on the bit itself tends to keep the well straight, and guides or reamers are also of help in this connection. Special delicate instruments are used to survey the course of the well. Most companies arrange that routine checks of the vertical direction of the hole are taken—say, every 500 feet—and that not over 4° from the vertical is permissible without "plugging back" with cement and straightening the well.

On the other hand, on many marine tideland locations, where the cost of drilling foundations is enormous, wells can be deliberately drilled in any required direction. Several wells may be drilled from the same foundations and their bottoms be as far apart as desired, as long as the angle is not too steep to permit of reasonably economical drilling. In order to start wells in a desired direction, a whipstock, usually of the removable type (fig. 12), is oriented into the well and a pilot hole is started in the desired direction. After drilling this and surveying its course, further deflection is made as needed by setting additional whipstock. The pilot hole is reamed to full size as drilled. The hole is kept going in the desired direction by the judicious use of special bits, control of weight or use of more flexible drill collars.

A number of wild wells have been brought under control by drilling directional relief wells to strike the wild well at the oil sand and pump mud into this well. Almost unbelievable accuracy has been obtained, since the relief well must hit the target within perhaps 10 feet, sometimes two miles or more below the ground.

Directional drilling in fields, such as salt domes, with steeply dipping formations is an invaluable method of drilling, and many dry holes have been converted into successful producers by plugging back and drilling into the producing horizon at a different position from the same well bore.

SHUTTING OFF WATER

Intrusion of water into oil wells is one of the chief bugbears of operators. This water may be present with the oil as part of the fluid in the pay horizon, it may be water from other sands in the section open to production, or it may be water which leaks past the cemented casing from above and contaminates the oil. It may also come through holes eaten in the casing by corrosion, especially in old wells, or those producing corrosive liquids.

A number of methods have been devised for locating the source of the intruding water and of attempting to seal off the troublesome liquid. Study of well logs, producing data and water analysis are of considerable assistance in locating the possible sources of water, especially in an old producing field. Electrical measurements of the resistance of the column of fluid in the well at various points can indicate the location of water intrusion in flowing wells. Oil having a high electrical resistance, the column resistance chart enables the operator to pick out the point of water or oil intrusion in most cases. If the leak is from behind the casing, the water will usually show up immediately below the casing shoe and, if from holes in the casing, it will show the point of entry to be inside the casing.

If a large number of leaks are found, a casing liner is sometimes cemented in the well to seal the leak. Another method is to set a "bridging plug" of easily drillable metal just below the leak

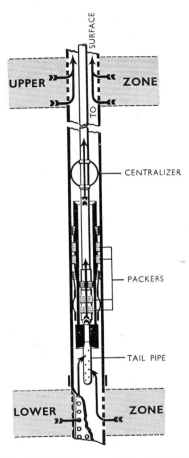

Fig. 17.   Multiple Zone or "Dual" Completion.

and then to "squeeze" cement through the leak by setting a packer on the tubing string just above the leak, and pumping cement down the tubing so that its only outlet is through the leak. The upper packer is then released and the cement washed out of the tubing. After the cement sets, the casing is tested to be sure it does not leak. The bridge plug is then drilled out and the well placed back on production.

MULTIPLE-ZONE COMPLETIONS

During the recent war, largely due to the shortage of steel for use as casing and partly because of the shortage of manpower, a considerable number of multiple-zone wells were drilled. In these wells, oil is obtained from two different producing sands, sometimes widely separated, simultaneously in the same well, firstly through the tubing, and secondly through the annular space between tubing and casing. Packers are set to separate the two zones and isolate the two producing channels. A typical view of the dual completion method is shown in fig. 17.

Two-zone producers are subject to serious troubles under certain producing conditions, but the method has been responsible for production of many needed barrels of petroleum at a time when men and materials were critical war shortages. The economy of being able to have two wells for only slightly more than the cost of one will probably cause this method of well completion to continue to develop.

BIBLIOGRAPHY

Rotary Drilling Handbook. J. E. Brantly. (Russell Palmer, New York and London, 1936.)

Petroleum Production. W. F. Cloud. (University of Oklahoma Press, Norman, Oklahoma, 1937.)

Petroleum Production Engineering—Oil Field Development. L. C. Uren. (McGraw-Hill Book Co., New York and London, 1939.)

Practical Petroleum Engineers' Handbook—Chapter V. J. Zaba and W. T. Dogerty. (Gulf Publishing Company, Houston, 1939.)

Elements of the Petroleum Industry—Chapters IX and X. J. E. Brantly and John R. Suman. (American Institute of Mining and Metallurgical Engineers, New York, 1940.)

VI

THE PRODUCTION OF CRUDE OIL
AND NATURAL GAS

THE term "petroleum production", in its restricted sense, refers to the processes of raising crude oil from the wells to ground level, measuring the quantities of oil and gas produced, and piping the crude oil to refineries or shipping points. In its broader sense, it includes a knowledge of the laws governing the movement of gas, oil and water through the underground reservoirs. This chapter is necessarily confined to the simplest possible explanation of the principles governing the underground movements of oil, gas and water, and their production from wells.

TYPES OF OIL DEPOSITS

The flow of fluids within a reservoir generally occurs toward the points of lowest pressure, i.e., the producing wells. The movement of oil can be due :—

(a) To the propulsive action of the gas liberated from solution in the oil, expanding continuously as lower pressures are encountered, and always providing a force on the oil flowing through the pore spaces in the producing reservoir.

(b) Entirely to the displacement action of water from the adjoining portions of the sand. In such cases, the underground volume of the oil produced is completely taken up by the expansion of the remaining oil and water in the formations.

These forces are frequently found to be present simultaneously depending on the nature of the sand, the structural features of the accumulation and the rate of production. However, it is often observed that free gas, due to its lower specific gravity compared to that of the surrounding mixture of oil plus dissolved gas, follows a path of its own and tends to collect in the highest part of any accumulation. From the above simplified description of the fluid flow within a reservoir, the type of pools encountered can be classified as follows :—

(a) *Gas-Drive Fields* are reservoirs where the oil accumulations are overlain by a gas cap. The movement of the oil is primarily due to the pressure of the gas within the gas cap supplemented in part by the expanding gas liberated from solution in the oil.

(b) *Water-Drive Fields,* in which the space voided by the oil produced is refilled almost entirely by water from the adjoining portions of the sand. No free gas is present in the reservoir as long as formation pressures are maintained above the saturation point, i.e., above the pressure at which dissolved gas escapes from the oil. A small fraction of the space voided by the produced oil is taken up by the expansion of the oil plus dissolved gas still present in the reservoir. It is computed that after the East Texas Field had produced two billion barrels of oil and the pressure had stabilized at around 1,000 lb./sq. in., only 1% of the oil produced was replaced by the expansion of oil still present in the reservoir ; the remainder of the void space was taken up by water.

(c) *Depletion Type Reservoirs* are oil traps from which the oil is produced by gas liberated from solution in the oil helped by gravitational force, the latter being the only source of energy remaining after the gas originally present in the oil is depleted.

Reservoirs producing by water-drive are recognized as being very efficient, since displacement of oil by water will yield a greater ultimate recovery per unit volume of pore space than is obtainable when gas, or gas and gravity, are the driving forces in the accumulations.

In practice, no sharp line of demarcation can be drawn between gas-drive, water-drive and depletion type reservoirs, as most depletion and gas-drive fields are also influenced to some extent by a water drive. Hence, classification of an accumulation as one of these three types merely shows that under the prevailing rate of production the accumulation shows predominantly one or other of the characteristics enumerated above.

In a **gas-drive** field the underground conditions resemble those outlined on page 59, and follow the soda-water siphon analogy given therein. If the reservoir is exploited in a wasteful manner —that is, if large quantities of gas are produced per unit volume of oil—the energy will soon be expended and a large quantity of oil will be left in the formation which only gravity can bring to a well. Since, in general, this force is small compared to the forces originally present in the reservoir, the oil remaining after the gas pressure has been dissipated is often considered as irrecoverable, although water-flood or re-pressuring (see page 109) may be effective in promoting the recovery of some portion of it.

In pursuance of the idea that use can be made of the natural energy present in the reservoir, it is clear that the first step will be to shut in wells producing solely gas, and wells which are producing a disproportionately large volume of gas with their oil. In the first case the gas is doing no useful work in propelling oil to the well, and in the second case it is working inefficiently and, therefore, wastefully.

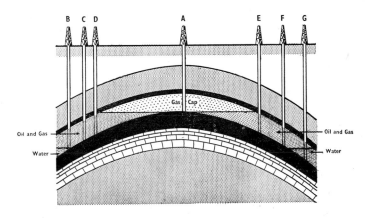

Fig. 1.   Gas-drive Field—Early Life.

The following diagrams illustrate the mechanics of a gas-drive field in idealized form. Fig. 1 shows the condition in the early life of the field with well A producing only gas, wells B, C, D, E and F producing oil and gas on the same principle as the soda-water siphon, and well G (because of the fact that it has been drilled too far down the flank of the structure) producing only water. In normal circumstances, well G would be closed in and abandoned as useless, while well A would also be closed in, since letting it produce would result in unnecessary dissipation of the gas in the formation, thereby reducing the energy available for driving oil to the good wells B, C, D, E and F.   Fig. 2 shows the changed condition after the field has been in production for some considerable time.   It will be noted that the gas cap has expanded, in the same way as the gas cap of a soda-water siphon expands ; therefore, well E has to be closed in, as it has changed from a normal oil producer to a pure gasser, and well D will also probably be making an abnormal quantity of gas. Furthermore, the extraction of a large quantity of oil has allowed the ''edge water'' to encroach up the structure, filling the pores formerly occupied by oil, so that well B will have been nearly ''drowned out'', while wells C and F will probably be producing water with their oil.

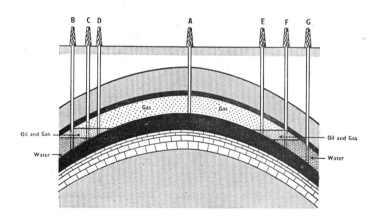

Fig. 2.   Gas-drive Field—Later Life.

In **water drive** fields the relative position of the oil, gas and water in the reservoir can be essentially the same as in a gas-drive field ; however, many water-drive fields are known in which no free gas caps are present.   In this type of reservoir gas plays only a minor part in propelling oil through the formation, the bulk of the work being done by the water, which can flow so freely through the porous rock that its pressure forces the oil ahead of it. The extent to which the energy stored in the water will be utilized to move the oil depends largely on the permeability and the thickness of the sand, and on the rate of production. Thus, if the formation has considerable thickness and is highly permeable, the reservoir pressure will remain close to the original value even at high rates of production. On the other hand, the reduction in pressure in thin blanket sands of low permeability can be appreciable even for restricted rates of production, and the water drive will not appear as strong. In the first case, the pressure decline caused by the production of oil is immediately offset by movement of the water, which tends to keep the pressures high. In the second case, the entrance of water is retarded and, as a result, the pressure decline in thin, tight sands exceeds that occurring in the more permeable thick sands.

In truly **depletion type** reservoirs the total decrease in pressure depends on the cumulative oil production. When the pressures have declined to the saturation pressure, this type of reservoir produces with increasing "gas-oil ratios". If all wells producing from one reservoir do not exhibit this increase in gas-oil ratio to the same degree, it is good policy to produce from those that have the lowest ratios, as the amount of gas produced has a greater influence on the total pressure drop of the reservoir than the amount of oil produced.

CHARACTERISTICS OF OIL DEPOSITS

The principal characteristics which distinguish gas-drive and depletion type reservoirs from water-drive fields are the following :—

1. **Gas-drive and Depletion Type Field.** Since the amount of energy available for moving oil to the wells and lifting it to the surface is limited and, therefore, constantly declining during the life of the field, the production of the wells will also decline until finally no more fluid can be produced. Newly drilled wells will flow for a time, but the quantity produced per day will steadily decline as the formation pressure is reduced. Eventually, a stage will be reached when there is no longer sufficient energy to lift the oil to the surface, and this must then be accomplished by artificial means (e.g., pumping the well). Finally, there will not be even sufficient energy to move oil through the formation to the bottom

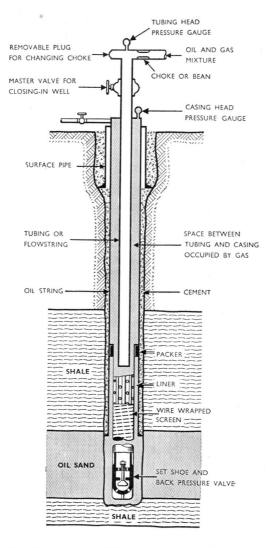

Fig. 3. Arrangement of Component Parts of a Flowing Well.

of the well. When this occurs, there is still a quantity of oil left in the formation, and it may then be possible economically to extract some of this oil by :—

(a) *Repressuring*. The operation of pumping back substantial quantities of compressed gas into the formation in the hope that at least a part of the original gas energy can thus be restored.

(b) *Water-flooding*. The operation of pumping appreciable quantities of water into wells situated down the flanks of the structure in the expectation that this injected water will create an artificial drive and wash the inert oil out of the sands to wells situated "up dip". This method of increasing the recovery from an oil sand has found a wide field of application in several places.

2. **Water-drive Fields.** In view of the fact that the supply of underground water can sometimes be inexhaustible, wells situated on structures which have a strong water-drive often show no decline in the rate of production throughout their life. The water follows the oil up the slope (or dip) of the structure as fast as fluid is produced from the wells ; it washes the oil out of the sands and drives it ahead until, finally, the level of the water ("water table") reaches the wells, which thereafter will produce both oil and water. The proportion of water to the total fluid produced by the well will steadily increase until finally the yield consists entirely of water, when the well is stated to be flooded or " drowned out", and is of no further use.

Water-drive fields are easiest and cheapest to operate when the water pressure is great enough to lift the oil to the surface, thereby saving the capital and operating expenditure which is normally required for lifting services and equipment in gas-drive fields. Repressuring and water flooding are likewise unnecessary where a strong water-drive prevails. Well-known examples of fields under strong water-drive are the Tampico Field, in Mexico, and East Texas.

PRODUCTION OF OIL FROM WELLS

Fig. 3 shows, in a generalized way, the arrangement of a flowing well, with the casing cemented at the top of the producing sand and equipped with a liner and a screen to exclude sand. The screen and liner can be withdrawn in case it becomes necessary to work the well over, to plug back to exclude water, to drill deeper, or to replace the screen. The screen may be perforated with a large number of small round holes or slots or one of the several kinds of wire-wrapped screen (fig. 13, page 95). Oil sands are usually made up of grains of different size, and each sand has its own characteristics, which are determined by means of a sieve analysis. The screen which will keep out 2 to 5% of the sand grains is usually selected, and all sand is excluded after sufficient large particles have accumulated on the screen. The entry of sand into the well is also controlled by back-pressure, by reducing the rate of flow of oil at the well head by means of the choke or "bean"*. The screen serves to support the walls of the hole, which might otherwise tend to cave in, particularly if the producing sands are friable and unconsolidated.

In reservoirs where the producing sand is firm, and the sand grains are well cemented together, wells may be completed in "open hole", with the casing cemented at the top of the sand, but with no screen. This is also true for some limestone reservoirs. Whether the producing sand is loosely consolidated or firm, the casing is sometimes cemented through the reservoir rock, then gun-perforated* opposite the oil sand for production with a device which shoots steel bullets through the casing and its surrounding sheath of cement at the depth selected. The well is then brought into production either with or without a screen which can be hung inside the perforated casing. The gun perforator is illustrated in fig. 14 on page 96.

Flowing Wells. Normally there is little or no free gas at the bottom of a flowing oil well, and the gas comes out of solution in the oil in the form of bubbles, with the resulting reduction in pressure as the fluid column rises in the well. At the well head, the mixture of oil and gas may be a foam or a spray of oil and gas, and means are then provided for separating the oil from the gas.

The well is usually provided with a "flow string" or tubing, which is ordinarily 2 or $2\frac{1}{2}$ inches in diameter and normally extends to near the bottom of the hole. The reason for using a comparatively narrow tubing is to obtain the proper velocity and efficient flowing conditions which give steady, continuous flow.

The tubing string is also needed for introducing mud or water in order to "kill" the well when it becomes necessary to replace the screen or to work the well over for other reasons.

A recent development in completion practice, which is being widely used in certain areas, is the "dual completion", in which the well is equipped so that oil or gas production can be secured from two separate producing layers simultaneously through the same well without intermingling of the fluids. A common arrangement is to cement the casing string through the two productive layers and gun-perforate opposite each. The tubing and a packer are then run into the well. The packer set in the casing acts as a seal between the perforated intervals. It is then possible to produce the upper of the two reservoirs through the annular space between the tubing and casing, and the lower through the tubing. Fig. 17 on page 101 illustrates the arrangement for dual completion. At the surface, the products of the two reservoirs are handled through separate lines and tanks. There are even cases of "triple completions" being made in order to exploit three separate oil or gas reservoirs simultaneously through a single well without commingling of the products. A triple completion involves the setting of another casing string, packed off at the bottom, below the uppermost producing layer.

Artificial Life. After natural flowing conditions stop it is usually necessary to install additional equipment to lift the oil. Lifting methods fall into two general classes : (a) gas-lift methods and (b) mechanical pumping.

Just before natural flow stops and the well begins to flow by "heads" due to periodic accumulations of water in the flow string or to lack of gas, which causes slugs of dead oil in the flow string, the installation of an automatic choke at the well head may, under the proper conditions, greatly extend the natural flowing life of the well. The automatic choke installed on the well head, in addition to the regular fixed choke, is a sensitive back-pressure regulator, the diaphragm of which is connected to the tubing head so that, when the tubing pressure declines, due to the well loading up with a slug of water or dead oil, the choke will be opened in addition to the fixed choke already in use. The resulting increase in production rate washes out the obstruction, giving an increase in tubing pressure. When the tubing pressure has recovered to a predetermined point, the choke regulator closes, the rate is again reduced, and the cycle is complete. The regulator can be adjusted for suitable opening and closing pressures, so that the cycles may be repeated at frequent or infrequent intervals automatically to fit the individual well conditions. In this manner, the need for installation of gas-lift or mechanical pumping equipment may be delayed for a period of months or even years under some conditions.

This heading condition could be corrected by replacing the tubing string with a string of smaller diameter, or even with several different diameters, to simulate a tapered string, in order to maintain the necessary velocity to give steady continuous flow. However, in practice, tubing diameters of less than 2 inches are not generally workable for several reasons, such as difficulty of swabbing to start the flow, the running of sub-surface pressure instruments and mechanical tubing scrapers to remove wax accumulations.

(a) *Gas-Lift*. This artificial lift method makes possible flowing conditions more nearly like natural flow than any other method. When sufficient gas and pressure are no longer available from the reservoir to maintain natural flow, due to depletion or because the flow column loads up with water, the necessary additional volume of extraneous gas to maintain flow is introduced to the tubing string at the proper depth. This gas is injected at the well head, usually into the space between tubing and casing or oil string. Gas-lift flow is usually accomplished with the aid of flow valves placed at calculated intervals on the tubing, and which can be opened or closed, depending on the fluid level in the well and the gas input pressure. The volume of extraneous gas used is kept to a minimum by control of the flow valves, which for some types is automatic, and also by control of the input gas pressure, or by a combination of both.

One of the most economical gas-lift arrangements now in common use is to run a string of 1-inch or 1¼-inch tubing inside the tubing string already in the well. This small tubing, or "macaroni", is equipped with flow valves at intervals and with a device for anchoring it at the bottom to the inside of the larger

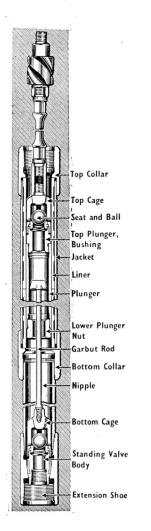

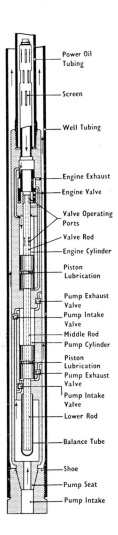

Fig. 4. Reciprocating Pump for Mechanical Pumping.

Fig. 5. Common Type of Pumping Unit.

tubing. The necessary volume of high-pressure gas is introduced down the space between the tubing strings and the fluid is then produced through the small tubing, or the gas can be injected down the small tubing and the fluid then flows up the annular space between the two tubing strings. With the weight of the small tubing resting on the anchor, the normal position of the valves is open, but they can be closed in turn, starting with the topmost valve, by simply raising the anchored small tubing a few inches with a hand-operated screw-jack or a small hydraulic hoist mounted on the well head. In this manner, the necessary gas can be introduced at the required level in the flow string so as to maintain steady continuous flow at the required production rate. There are a number of advantages in this gas-lift method : (1), it can be installed in a heading or intermittently flowing well without the necessity of killing the well with mud or water in order to pull the tubing ; (2), in many cases, after the fluid column is once unloaded, the well will again flow naturally due to the greater velocity obtained in the small tubing ; and (3), the small tubing and positive control of gas injection level make it simple and economical to operate.

Compared with mechanical pumping methods, gas-lift has not a very wide application. Ordinarily gas-lift methods can be applied only as an intermediate stage between the natural flowing stage and the mechanical pumping period in the productive life of the well. One of the most important exceptions to this may occur in water-drive fields, where the fluid level in the well remains high, and under these conditions gas-lift may be the best method of producing the well to depletion. A plentiful supply of inexpensive high-pressure gas is a prime requisite for successful gas-lift installations.

(b) *Mechanical Pumping*. Probably the most widely known and most extensively applied method of artificial lift is the common reciprocating pump, which is simply a suction pump with a hollow moving piston. There is an inlet valve at the lower end of the pump cylinder, which is attached to the tubing and a discharge valve at the top of the plunger (see fig. 4). A type of pumping unit commonly used to impart the reciprocating motion to the rods to which the pump plunger is attached is shown in fig. 6. Oil well pumps vary in diameter from 1¼ to 6 inches, pumps from 2 to 4 inches being most common. Pump strokes range from 2 to 10 feet, and speeds from 5 to 25 strokes per minute. The pump is lowered on the tubing to the desired depth and, after suspending the tubing from the tubing head, the plunger is run into the pump cylinder on the so-called "sucker rods" (pumping rods), which at the upper end are provided with a heavy

Fig. 6. Common Type of Pumping Unit.

polished rod and stuffing box. After connecting the outlet from the tubing to the production tank, the pumping unit, which is usually driven by a gas engine or electric motor, is put into operation. The oil, sometimes accompanied by water, is thus pumped into the production tank. These individual pumping units are used mainly for pumping one well, although it is sometimes found economical to pump more than one well from such a unit. When the pump has to be pulled to the surface for overhaul, this is done by suitable mobile hoists.

In fields where the wells are not very deep, the well spacing not too wide apart, the topography favourable, and few or no obstructions exist, the use of a ''central pumping power'' may result in considerable savings. The central pumping power is simply a machine to which a number of rods can be attached ; it imparts a reciprocating motion by means of eccentrics or cranks. In this way only one prime mover and transmission is required to serve a number of wells, and thus the first cost as well as the running costs can be reduced materially.

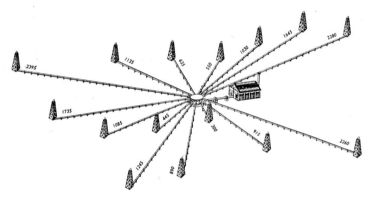

Fig. 7.   Central Pumping Power.

The sub-surface arrangement of wells on a pumping power is similar to that for individual pumpers. The perspective view (fig. 7) shows a central pumping power with the pull rods radiating to the different wells. Each well is provided with a jack to convert the reciprocating motion of the pull rods into an up-and-down motion for the sucker rods. Means are provided for disconnecting wells which have to be serviced without stopping the central pumping power.

Another type of centralized pumping is the electric pumping power, in which a group of wells equipped with pumping units are powered with electric motors, the necessary current being supplied from a centrally located generating plant. In some cases groups of two to four wells equipped with pumping jacks may be pumped from a single motor and unit.

A relatively new and radically different type of centralized pumping is the "hydraulic" pumping system, in which all of the conventional "beam pumping" equipment, both on the surface

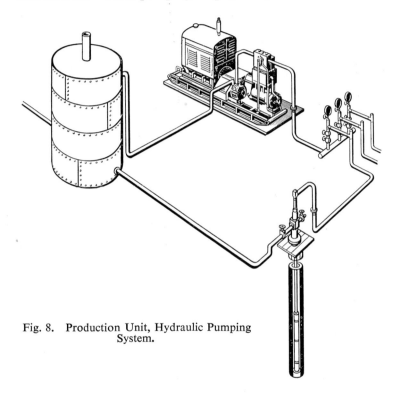

Fig. 8.   Production Unit, Hydraulic Pumping
                        System.

and in the well, is replaced by a central motor-driven "power oil" pump, a piping system to serve each well, and the power oil tubing in the well to deliver the power oil to the sub-surface production unit.

Fig. 8 is a schematic drawing showing the general layout of the hydraulic pumping system, and fig. 5 (page 113) is a sketch of the sub-surface production unit. The power oil used to actuate the double-acting hydraulic engine is exhausted into the production fluid from the pump, and together they are carried to the surface between the pressure tubing and the production tubing.

The operator at the central pumping plant has control of the individual well performance as to the number of strokes with the aid of pressure gauges and valves on the manifold from which the power-oil supply lines radiate to the wells. Unique operating features which have been developed in connection with this system of pumping include a sub-surface production unit which can be pumped to the surface when working parts need replacement without the necessity of pulling the tubing, and a method of removing wax deposits from the surface lines, tubing and the production unit with solvents injected periodically into the system.

The applicable range of the hydraulic pumping system as compared with others is not yet established, although it is coming into general use in certain areas, and plants now in service are operating groups of from two to twenty-four wells, ranging from a few hundred to 8,700 feet in depth. Simplicity, flexibility, low installation and operating costs are some of the advantages claimed for this modern pumping method.

SEPARATION, MEASUREMENT AND COLLECTION OF OIL AND GAS

After passing through the choke on the well head which controls the rate of flow, the mixture of oil and gas is piped to the oil and gas separator or gas "trap", a cylindrical vessel 2 to 5 feet in diameter and 10 to 20 feet in height. The entrained gas is separated from the fluid, which may be clean oil, a simple mixture of oil and water or an emulsion*. The separator is provided with a safety valve and usually has three outlets : (*a*) a drain valve for washing out accumulations of solid matter, (*b*) an oil outlet located near the bottom from which the fluid is taken through a liquid level controlled valve, and (*c*) a gas outlet, at or near the top of the trap, from which the "casinghead" or "natural" gas is piped to an orifice meter, where the volume is measured.

Gas separator pressures may vary widely depending upon local conditions, but for ordinary oil wells the pressure is usually maintained at from 10 to 100 lb./sq. in.

A. *Gas Rich in Gasoline*, irrespective of whether it is at high or low pressure, can be piped to gasoline extraction plants, where it is stripped of its liquid hydrocarbons and can then be used in the same way as lean gas.

B. *Lean Gas*, at low trap pressures, may be used as follows :—

(i) Local fuel requirements (firing field boilers, fuel for gas engines, or for domestic purposes).

(ii) Supplying compressor plants to be compressed for gas-lift work, for reservoir repressuring or pressure maintenance, or for piping to distant fuel-consuming points.

(iii) Burning to make carbon black.

Waste gas for which no use can be found is sometimes blown off into the atmosphere or burned, but, as a matter of conservation, this practice is, wherever possible, being replaced by plans to return the unwanted gas to a sub-surface reservoir, either to assist in producing more oil or simply as gas storage.

Gas is sometimes available at high pressures, in which case a high-pressure gas-oil separator supplies high-pressure natural gas directly, thus reducing or eliminating the installation and operating costs of a compressor plant.

TREATMENT OF "WET OIL"

As already mentioned, wells may produce water with the oil, and it is usually necessary to separate the water from the oil in the field in order to avoid the necessity of handling this unwanted product in the pipelines. It is also frequently necessary to dispose of the water, usually a strong brine, so that it will not damage growing crops or pollute streams in the vicinity of the field.

Separation of oil and salt water, where there is no emulsification, takes place in a settling tank, the water being drained off at the bottom of the tank. The breaking down of emulsions in order to separate oil and water is often a more difficult matter and may be accomplished in a variety of ways.

Fig. 9 shows a typical oil field tank battery. The liquid production from the gas-liquid separator is received in the larger tank, known as the wash tank or "gun-barrel". Delivered at the bottom of this tank, separation of the two liquids takes place due to the difference in specific gravity, the clean oil rises in the column of water, accumulates at the top, then goes over the top to the adjacent storage tanks for gauging and shipping, the water being taken off at the bottom. A constant water level is maintained in the wash tank with an automatic water siphon. A water heater is usually needed in addition to this equipment in order to maintain

Fig. 9. Typical Field Tank Battery.

the necessary temperature to make possible the breaking down of oil and water emulsions. Moreover, the addition of chemicals is also frequently needed to assist in breaking difficult emulsions. Another method is to subject the emulsion to the action of a high-tension alternating electric field (10,000 volts or more). Under the influence of this electric field the water droplets cohere and settle out.

BIBLIOGRAPHY

The Flow of Homogeneous Fluids through Porous Media. M. Muskat, Ph.D. (McGraw-Hill Book Co., New York, 1937.)

Petroleum Production. W. T. Cloud. (University of Oklahoma Press, Norman, Oklahoma, 1937.)

Petroleum Production Engineering — Oil Field Exploitation. L. C. Uren. (McGraw-Hill Book Co., New York, 1939.)

Volumetric and Phase Behaviour of Hydrocarbons. Bruce H. Sage and William N. Lacey. (Stanford University Press, 1939.)

Practical Petroleum Engineers' Handbook. J. Zaba and W. T. Doherty. (Gulf Publishing Co., Houston, 1940.)

Elements of the Petroleum Industry—Chapters XI, by C. V. Millikan, and XIII, by Paul D. Torrey. (The American Institute of Mining and Metallurgical Engineers, New York, 1940.)

Secondary Recovery of Oil in the United States. The Subcommittee on Secondary Recovery of the American Petroleum Institute. (American Petroleum Institute, New York, 1942.)

Petroleum Production (2 vols.). Park J. Jones. (Reinhold Publishing Corporation, New York, 1946.)

VII

GENERAL NATURE OF PETROLEUM

PETROLEUM is the name given to an oily liquid which exists at various places in the earth's crust. In some places it is found at the surface in the form of seepages, in others it occurs trapped at greater or lesser depths in rocky formations. It is usually a dark coloured or black liquid with a characteristic odour imparted by small quantities of compounds such as those containing sulphur or nitrogen.

It is common to find a gas associated with liquid petroleum, and in some cases wells are drilled solely for the production of this Natural Gas, which is classified as one of the forms of petroleum found in nature. There are cases where seepages and oil wells exist side by side ; for example, in Southern California, the Los Angeles basin contains oilfields in which liquid crude petroleum and natural gas are produced alongside the famous La Brea asphalt pits, which contain a sticky, thick liquid form of asphaltic bitumen*.

HYDROCARBONS

All materials found in nature consist of combinations of atoms of the various chemical elements, and in the case of petroleum the elements predominating are carbon and hydrogen. Petroleum consists of mixtures of hydrocarbons, which is the name given to those compounds in which the molecules consist solely of atoms of carbon and hydrogen. There exist a great variety of these hydrocarbons, depending upon the number of carbon and hydrogen atoms in each molecule and the way in which the various atoms are linked one with the other. Fortunately, as we shall see, they fall into several distinct groups or series, which helps greatly in studying them. Hydrocarbons exist in liquid, solid or gaseous form, and very frequently all three forms are found together but in completely different proportions in different localities. Thus, the petroleum found in the Burma fields has a very high proportion of solid hydrocarbons, and the result is that, while the oil as it comes from the ground is liquid, on cooling it becomes solid due to the separation of solid hydrocarbons. In many of the fields in the United States, on the other hand, there is very little of the solid type of hydrocarbon, and the crude oil remains fluid down to quite low temperatures.

Valency. Before going on to discuss the various types of hydrocarbons which make up petroleum, it is useful to discuss a property of matter which is a key to its chemical behaviour. The characteristic referred to is known as "valency", and in general terms describes the power of the various types of atoms to combine with other atoms.

The elements fall into classes, and in each class the elements have the same valency or combining power. The alkali metals —for example, sodium, potassium, lithium—all have a valency of one, which means that they can combine with one atom of chlorine or with one atom of any other element having a valency of one. Oxygen, on the other hand, has a valency of two, and therefore one atom of oxygen can combine with two atoms of hydrogen, hydrogen itself having a valency of one. An atom of nitrogen can combine with three other monovalent atoms, thus having a valency of three ; ammonia, for example, is a compound containing one atom of nitrogen and three of hydrogen.

Carbon has a valency of four, and it can, therefore, combine with four other monovalent atoms. For example, methane, the simplest of the hydrocarbons, is a molecule consisting of one atom of carbon and four atoms of hydrogen. This can be represented as follows :—

$$
\begin{array}{c}
\text{H} \\
| \\
\text{H---C---H} \quad \text{or } CH_4 \text{ (methane)} \\
| \\
\text{H}
\end{array}
$$

This is not the whole story but gives sufficient information to follow the discussion of the various hydrocarbon series.

An atom of an element may combine with other atoms of the

same element, and in particular hydrocarbons can be built up consisting of numbers of carbon atoms uniting together, with hydrogen occupying the remaining carbon valencies. Thus :—

$$
\begin{array}{cccc}
& \text{H} \quad \text{H} & \text{H} \quad \text{H} \quad \text{H} & \text{H} \quad \text{H} \quad \text{H} \quad \text{H} \\
& | \quad\; | & | \quad\; | \quad\; | & | \quad\; | \quad\; | \quad\; | \\
\text{H}-\text{C}-\text{C}-\text{H} & \text{H}-\text{C}-\text{C}-\text{C}-\text{H} & \text{H}-\text{C}-\text{C}-\text{C}-\text{C}-\text{H} \\
& | \quad\; | & | \quad\; | \quad\; | & | \quad\; | \quad\; | \quad\; | \\
& \text{H} \quad \text{H} & \text{H} \quad \text{H} \quad \text{H} & \text{H} \quad \text{H} \quad \text{H} \quad \text{H} \\
& \text{ethane} & \text{propane} & \text{butane}
\end{array}
$$

Saturated Hydrocarbons. The hydrocarbon methane will be seen from the formula given above to consist of carbon with all its valencies combined with separate hydrogen atoms. Similarly, the other hydrocarbons shown consist of carbon and hydrogen atoms whose valencies are all filled separately by links to carbon or hydrogen. This type of compound is known as a "saturated" compound, since there are no possibilities of further combination of the molecule with anything else. A series of these saturated hydrocarbons exists in which chains of carbon atoms are linked together with hydrogen occupying the remaining carbon valencies. At each end of the chain will be CH_3 groups, and in between the remaining groups will be CH_2 groups. Thus one can write :—

$$\text{propane } CH_3\text{—}CH_2\text{—}CH_3$$
$$\text{or butane } CH_3\text{—}CH_2\text{—}CH_2\text{—}CH_3.$$

The whole series of such hydrocarbons is known as the "paraffin"* series, and when the carbon atoms form a straight chain, so to speak (as above), the series is known as the "normal paraffin" series.

Radicles. It will be noted that in the foregoing formulæ we have written groups of carbon and hydrogen atoms as "CH_3", "CH_2", etc., treating such groups as if they were single entities. This is a universally adopted "shorthand" in chemistry, since such groups have in fact an identity of their own and influence the properties of compounds in which they occur. To take an example, in the case of two acids, HCl (hydrochloric acid) and

H_2SO_4 (sulphuric acid), the chlorine atom in hydrochloric acid and the SO_4 group in sulphuric acid both behave in many respects like single elements. Thus, one can derive from these acids chlorides and sulphates respectively, e.g. :—

NaCl Na_2SO_4

sodium chloride   sodium sulphate

Such groups are referred to as "radicles", and in hydrocarbon molecules one may have CH_3, the methyl radicle, C_2H_5, the ethyl radicle, etc., from which one can derive all sorts of compounds by adding on other atoms or radicles to saturate the molecule, e.g. :—

C_2H_5 . OH ethyl alcohol, C_2H_5 . H (or C_2H_6) ethane.

In the ethyl alcohol formula the OH portion is itself a radicle having a valency of one ; in sulphuric acid the SO_4 radicle has a valency of two.

Isomers. In the foregoing graphic formulæ the carbon atoms have been shown joined together in a continuous chain ; but it is also possible to have side chains attached to a main chain, or to have several chains linked together through a common carbon atom, thus :—

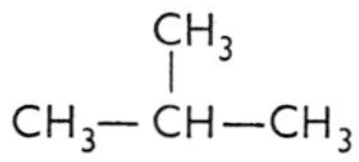

$$CH_3—\underset{\underset{CH_3}{|}}{CH}—CH_3$$

iso-butane

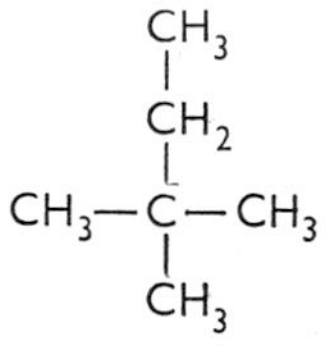

$$CH_3—\underset{\underset{CH_3}{|}}{\overset{\overset{CH_3}{|}}{\overset{\overset{CH_2}{|}}{C}}}—CH_3$$

iso-hexane

Forms of hydrocarbons in which any of the carbon atoms are represented as having more than two other carbon atoms joined to it are known as "iso" forms, and the different hydrocarbons which have the same numbers of carbon atoms but which can be represented as straight-chain or branched compounds are called "isomers".

As the number of atoms in the molecule increases, so the

number of possible isomers of the compounds increase. We can only have two butanes, thus :—

$$CH_3 . CH_2 . CH_2 . CH_3$$

normal butane

and

$$CH_3 - \overset{\displaystyle CH_3}{\underset{\displaystyle CH_3}{|}}$$

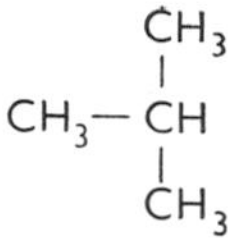

iso-butane

but in the case of octane there are many possible forms, e.g. :—

(1) $CH_3-CH_2-CH_2-CH_2-CH_2-CH_2-CH_2-CH_3$ normal octane

(2) 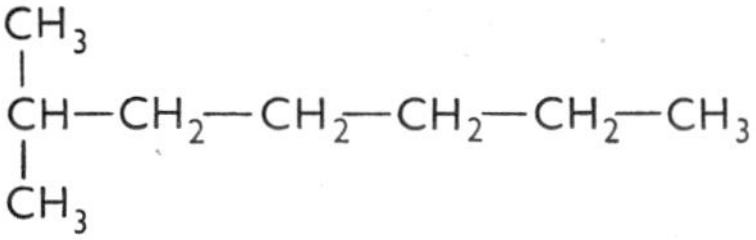 $\overset{\displaystyle CH_3}{\underset{\displaystyle CH_3}{\overset{|}{\underset{|}{CH}}}}-CH_2-CH_2-CH_2-CH_2-CH_3$ 1 : 1 dimethyl hexane

(3) $CH_3-\overset{\displaystyle CH_3}{\overset{|}{CH}}-\overset{\displaystyle CH_3}{\overset{|}{CH}}-CH_2-CH_2-CH_3$ 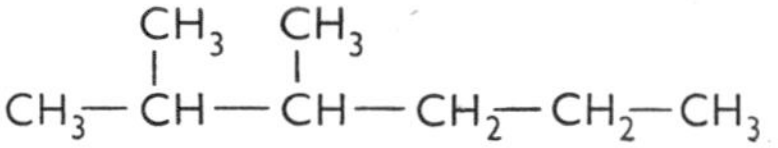   2 : 3 dimethyl hexane

(4) 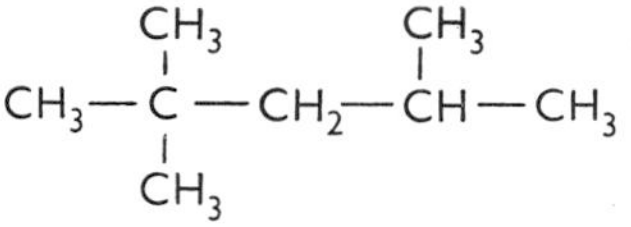 $CH_3-\overset{\displaystyle CH_3}{\underset{\displaystyle CH_3}{\overset{|}{\underset{|}{C}}}}-CH_2-\overset{\displaystyle CH_3}{\overset{|}{CH}}-CH_3$ 2 : 2 : 4 trimethyl pentane

etc.

In the nomenclature shown the numbers refer to the carbon atoms in the longest chain.

Unsaturated Hydrocarbons. In addition to the hydrocarbons in which every valency or bond is satisfied by a separate atom, there are hydrocarbons in which carbon is linked to carbon by two or more of the carbon valencies. In this case the number of hydrogen atoms that can be linked to the carbon atoms is reduced. For example, in the hydrocarbon C_2H_4 or $H_2C=CH_2$ the carbon atoms are linked together by two bonds, and only two additional hydrogen atoms can then be linked to each carbon atom. It will be noticed that each carbon atom still has four valencies, but they are not all used up in separate combination with other atoms. Such a hydrocarbon is called an "unsaturated" hydrocarbon, and the one referred to above is known as ethylene. We could thus have an unsaturated series as follows :—

$$H_2C=CH_2 \qquad H_2C=CH-CH_3 \qquad H_3C-CH=CH-CH_3, \text{etc.}$$
ethylene $\qquad$ propylene $\qquad$ butylene

Hydrocarbons of this class, known as "olefins"*, are not found in natural crude petroleum, but they are formed in the cracking process, which is described in chapter X. Being unsaturated they can readily take part in chemical reactions and can combine with each other (polymerize), both of which facts form significant bases for some of the processes which will be discussed in later chapters.

RING HYDROCARBONS

The hydrocarbons so far discussed have been all of the "chain" variety. There are, however, other series of hydrocarbons in which carbon atoms form closed rings. Two of the principal series found in petroleum are (a) the naphthenes or cyclo-paraffins, and (b) the aromatics.

(a) **Naphthenes* or Cyclo-paraffins.** These compounds are hydrocarbons in which the carbon atoms forming a ring are fully saturated. This means that, in addition to the bonds connecting the carbon atoms with each other, the remaining two bonds on each carbon atom are linked to separate atoms of hydrogen or an equivalent group. The ring may contain various numbers of carbon atoms, though those most frequently found in petroleum contain 5, 6 or 7, thus :—

cyclopentane $\qquad$ cyclohexane $\qquad$ cycloheptane

K

Naphthenes may, like the paraffins or other hydrocarbons, contain side-chains consisting of groupings of carbon and hydrogen, thus :—

methyl cyclopentane   propyl cyclohexane

Similarly, two or more positions in the rings may contain like or different side-chains, and some of these may be isomers of each other, thus :—

are two isomers of dimethyl cyclohexane.

(b) **Aromatics*.**   The second important series of ring hydrocarbons is the series whose simplest member is benzene.   This is a six-carbon ring hydrocarbon in which each carbon atom in the ring has only one hydrogen atom attached :—

benzene or benzol, C_6H_6

Each carbon atom is shown to be linked to one neighbouring carbon atom by two bonds, and the molecule therefore has the appearance of being unsaturated. The series of hydrocarbons of this type is known as the "aromatic" series.

Other members of the aromatic series are obtained by substituting the hydrogen atoms by carbon/hydrogen groups or radicles, thus :—

toluene   xylene

Here again it will be seen that with more than one substituent radicle, isomers can exist. Thus, there are three isomers of xylene :—

ortho-xylene   meta-xylene   para-xylene

A fourth isomer is ethyl benzene :—

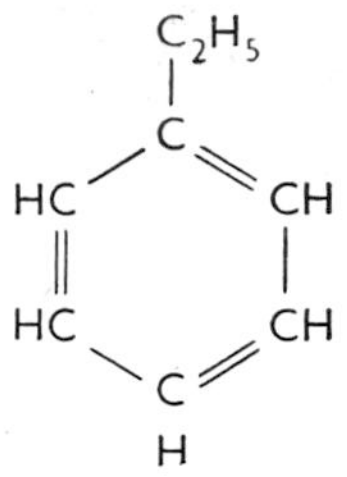

An interesting type of aromatic hydrocarbon which occurs in many crude petroleums is the naphthalene type. This form of hydrocarbon consists of aromatic rings linked together through two common carbon atoms, thus :—

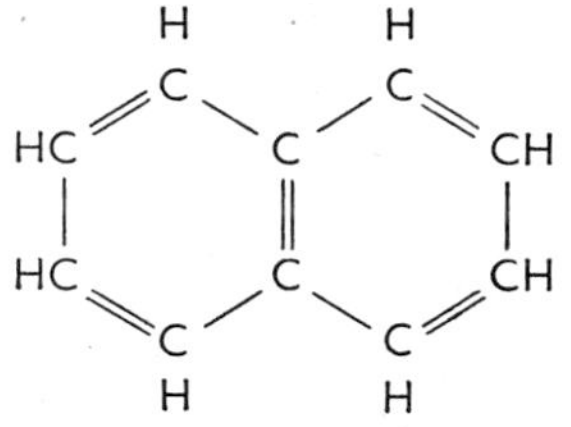

naphthalene

Additional hydrocarbon types contain more than two rings linked as above, e.g. :—

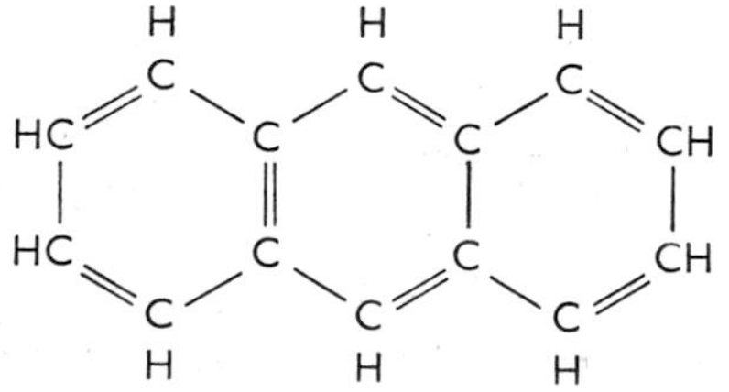

anthracene

OTHER TYPES OF COMPOUNDS IN PETROLEUM

At the outset it was pointed out that petroleum consists predominantly of hydrocarbons. In addition, all natural crudes contain small quantities of compounds containing sulphur, nitrogen or other elements. Some crudes also contain appreciable quantities of complicated organic compounds containing certain metals in the molecules.

Of particular interest are sulphur compounds, which, due to their bad odour, corrosive and other objectionable characteristics, make it essential to adopt processes in the refinery for their removal. Chief of these sulphur compounds is a series known as mercaptans*. These compounds can be considered as hydrocarbons in which a hydrogen atom has been replaced by a grouping of an atom of sulphur and an atom of hydrogen, thus :—

$$CH_3 . CH_3 \quad\text{------}\quad CH_3 . CH_2 . SH$$

| ethane | ethyl mercaptan |

Such compounds can react with many metals as do acids, and are therefore corrosive to such metals.

TYPES OF CRUDE OIL

Although all crude oils consist mainly of hydrocarbons of the various series discussed above, oils from various sources differ widely in the proportion of the different hydrocarbon series which they contain. Thus, one type of crude oil may contain more of the paraffins, including the solid paraffin waxes, while another may contain more of the naphthenes. The products that are worth producing will therefore vary from crude to crude, and economic factors, such as market demand and accessibility, often have a determining influence on the products made. Thus, from some crude oils useful yields of lubricating oils and waxes may be obtained, while others may yield insignificant quantities of wax but may contain asphaltic bitumen together with lubricating oil of a different character due to different chemical nature. Others again may contain little lubricating oil but provide excellent stock for cracking.

In a very general way, crude oils may be divided into three classes :—

(1) **Paraffin Base Crudes,** which contain paraffin wax but little or no asphaltic matter. Such crude oils consist mainly of paraffin hydrocarbons and usually yield gasoline of low octane value and gas oil of high cetane value. They usually give good yields of paraffin wax and high-grade lubricating oils. An example of crude oil of this type is Pennsylvanian crude oil.

(2) **Asphaltic Base Crudes,** which contain little or no paraffin wax but usually asphaltic matter, often in quite large proportions. The hydrocarbons consist mainly of the naphthene series, and these crude oils yield lubricating oils which can be made equivalent to those obtained from crude oils in Class (1) by special refining methods (*vide* chapter XII.) Examples of crude oils of this type are Venezuelan, Californian, Russian and Roumanian.

(3) **Mixed Base Crudes,** which contain both paraffin wax and asphaltic matter in quantity. Both paraffin and naphthenic hydrocarbons are present together with a certain proportion of aromatic hydrocarbons. Examples of such crude oils are certain oils from the Netherland East Indies, and those of Iran and Iraq.

The above classification of crude oils is a rough-and-ready division into types, and should not be used too strictly. There is considerable overlapping between the types in the case of most crude oils.

VIII

DISTILLATION

THE PRINCIPLES OF DISTILLATION

IT IS a well-known fact that, when water is heated in an open vessel for some time, a temperature is reached at which evaporation becomes intense and vapour bubbles are formed ; the liquid is then said to be at its boiling point. The vapour pressure of the water is, at that moment, the same as or slightly in excess of atmospheric pressure.

As long as boiling continues the temperature of the boiling water remains constant. This constant temperature is called the boiling point of water. This temperature is, however, not the same under all conditions. At sea level, or at standard barometric pressure, the boiling point of water is exactly 100° C. (212° F.) ; at greater altitudes, however, water starts boiling at temperatures below 100° C. This is caused by the fact that the atmospheric pressure is lower and the pressure of the water vapour, which increases with the temperature, will sooner attain the same value as the atmospheric pressure.

When the vapours developed during boiling are cooled, they will condense again into water. The process consisting of the evaporation of part of a liquid followed by the collecting and condensing of the vapours again into liquid is called "distillation"*. The preparation of distilled water may be mentioned as a simple example. Water containing impurities, e.g., salt water, is boiled ; the impurities which do not evaporate remain behind, while the pure water vapours are condensed. The condensate is collected, and this is known as distilled water.

Each of the pure hydrocarbons present in crude oil, when handled separately, behaves in exactly the same way as water. However, they are never produced by nature separately, and the products which we make from the crude oil rarely consist of single components. Therefore, in practice, we are principally concerned with mixtures of a great number of hydrocarbons.

A mixture of two miscible* liquids will start boiling at a temperature lying somewhere between the boiling points of the components, depending on their relative proportions in the mixture. Thus, for instance, by adding alcohol (boiling point 78° C.= 172° F.) to the water in the radiator of a car, to prevent freezing, the boiling point of the mixture is lowered, and the more alcohol is added the lower the boiling point becomes. When such a mixture starts boiling, it is not only the more volatile of the two components which evaporates ; the vapour also contains the less volatile component.

This is clearly demonstrated when boiling vinegar, which is a dilute solution of acetic acid in water, as is often done in the kitchen. Acetic acid has a boiling point of 118° C. (244° F.), and water of 100° C. (212° F.), but, nevertheless, acetic acid vapours spread through the kitchen.

To understand this, it is necessary to understand the subject of partial pressure*. For boiling at atmospheric pressure (as also for distillation) to take place, the pressure inside the still must be equal to atmospheric pressure, so that molecules can move from the liquid to the space above the liquid.

When a liquid consists of two components, each of these contributes its own quotum to the total vapour pressure of the liquid, so that when boiling takes place the pressure in the still is made up of two parts, one exerted by the vapour of the first component, the other by the vapour of the second and, since the sum of these partial pressures of the components is equal to atmospheric, the combined vapours leave the liquid, that is to say, both of the components are able to evaporate at the same time.

The partial pressure of each component is principally dependent on the vapour pressure of the component in a pure state, and on its proportion in the liquid mixture, so that for the same proportion in the liquid the percentage in the vapour will be highest for the component with the highest vapour pressure.

This can be expressed also by saying that the more volatile substance evaporates more readily, so that its percentage in the vapour is greater than in the liquid. Because the evaporated part of the liquid contains a higher percentage of the lighter component than the original liquid, the remainder will necessarily

contain a smaller percentage. Consequently, the boiling point
of the remaining liquid will be higher than that of the original
liquid. This will be true as long as evaporation goes on, so that
the longer the evaporation proceeds the higher the boiling point of
the remainder of the liquid. Thus, for such a mixture there is no
question of a constant boiling temperature.

For petroleum products consisting of many components, with
boiling points covering a great range of temperatures, this phenomenon will be still more pronounced. The boiling temperature
will rise continuously from the temperature at which the product
starts boiling, i.e. the initial boiling point (I.B.P.*), up to the temperature when the last remnant of liquid evaporates, i.e. the final
boiling point (F.B.P.*). This boiling range will, of course, be a
function of the boiling points of all components present and their
respective percentages in the mixture, but for a long series of
components the initial boiling point will be principally determined
by the components with the lower boiling points, while the final
boiling point is more exclusively a function of the heavier hydrocarbons. Thus, the boiling range can be very wide. There are
special standardized apparatus for measuring the boiling range
(*vide* chapter XXV).

In the distilling of mineral oil, just as has been explained for
water, the vapours are collected and condensed into liquid, and
this condensate is called the distillate*.

From what has already been said regarding the composition of
the vapours, it is evident that the distillate is again a mixture of
various components, so that it has no constant boiling point. As
the more volatile components are present in a larger concentration, the I.B.P. will be lower than that of the original product,
while also the F.B.P. will be lower, because the higher boiling
hydrocarbons will, at first, hardly be present in the vapours.

Consequently, by means of distillation we can separate a mixture consisting of components of different boiling points into
different fractions.

FRACTIONAL DISTILLATION

By simple distillation one cannot avoid considerable overlapping
of the boiling ranges of the fractions, because the lightest com-

ponents remain partly in the residue, while much heavier constituents are in the vapours. Consequently, the I.B.P. of the residue is well below the F.B.P. of the distillate ; moreover, the boiling ranges of the products are by no means narrow.

To obtain narrow fractions, a more complicated process is required, based principally on repeated distillation. Suppose a distillate is again partly evaporated ; the more volatile components, which were already more concentrated in the distillate than in the original, will again be still more concentrated in the second distillate. By repeating this procedure several times, eventually a fraction can be produced consisting of the lightest constituents in a concentrated form. However, the efficiency of

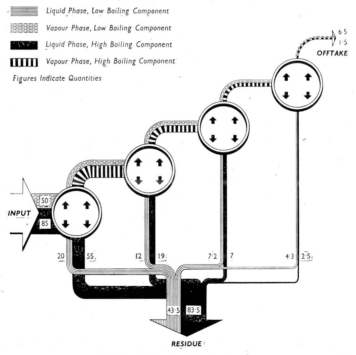

Liquid Phase, Low Boiling Component
Vapour Phase, Low Boiling Component
Liquid Phase, High Boiling Component
Vapour Phase, High Boiling Component
Figures Indicate Quantities

Fig. 1.   Fractional Distillation.

separation is very low ; only a small part of the light fractions is obtained in this way, because, at each evaporating stage, part of them is left behind in the liquid. This can be seen from fig. 1, showing a two-component mixture.

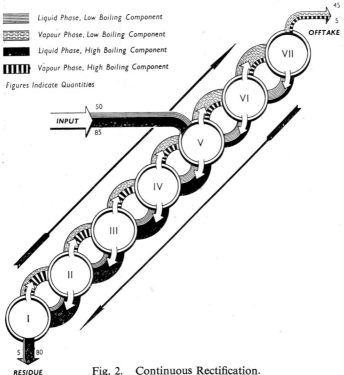

Fig. 2. Continuous Rectification.

In order to get a quantitative separation between the desired fractions, it is necessary not only to effect evaporation in many successive stages but, moreover, to return the residue of each stage into the preceding one, in which it is again partly evaporated for the purpose of driving out light fractions once more. As this goes on continually, the final residue will eventually be freed from light fractions. This process is called "rectification" and enables the separation of a product into two fractions, of which the one consists only of the low-boiling constituents, and the other only of the higher boiling ones. The principle can best be understood from the diagram in fig. 2, which, for the sake of simplicity, has been again drawn for a two-component mixture and shows a continuous rectification process.

The consecutive stages in which the evaporation is carried out are numbered I–VII. The input, consisting of 50 parts low and 85 parts high-boiling components, is fed into V, in which part is evaporated. The distillate is again partly evaporated in VI, while the residue from VI is returned into V for partial evaporation. The residue from V flows into IV, while the distillate from IV is introduced into V, and so on. What is returned from VII to VI, and further from each higher to the next lower stage, is called the "reflux", and it will be clear that without reflux no rectification is possible.

In actual practice, all stages except bottom and top (I and VII) are combined into one rectifying tower or column, made as a high column containing many trays, which function like the stages in the diagram. Thus, the reflux overflows from tray to tray downwards, while the vapours formed on each tray will rise to the next higher one, where they are mixed with the liquid on that tray, from which mixture new vapours are again developed, as indicated in the diagram for the different stages. For constructional details of the trays or plates, reference should be made to the section on "Fractionating Columns" later in this chapter.

The bottom stage (I) is called the "reboiler" and consists of a separate vessel, which is heated in order to obtain the required amount of evaporation. These vapours supply the heat required for the evaporation of the liquid in the lowest tray of the tower ; these latter vapours for the liquid in the tray immediately above, and so on. The uppermost stage (VII) is built as a separate so-called "reflux condenser", in which the vapours from the highest plate of the tower (stage VI) are partly condensed to form the reflux.

The product to be rectified is introduced at an appropriate place in the column (stage V), and the remaining vapour from the condenser (which as a rule is further condensed into liquid) and the residue from the reboiler are the two products obtained, representing the low and the high boiling fractions respectively.

VACUUM AND PRESSURE DISTILLATION

The heaviest fractions of crude oil would require such high temperatures to evaporate them that cracking would occur. In order to avoid this, distillation is carried out under vacuum, because the boiling point is thus lowered.

For the very lightest fractions, condensation of the vapours cannot be obtained at atmospheric pressure and temperature, so that distillation is carried out under pressure, which increases the boiling point and, consequently, the temperature at which condensation can be obtained.

STEAM DISTILLATION

If steam is continuously blown into the oil in the still, steam vapours are mixed with the oil vapours, so that the total pressure is obtained from both together. Thus, when the joint pressures are equal to the pressure of the surrounding atmosphere, the oil having to supply only part of the pressure boils at a lower temperature. The more steam is used, the lower the boiling temperature, since the steam supplies a greater portion of the pressure required. Steam distillation is applied, just like vacuum distillation, for the higher boiling point components, and also often in combination with vacuum distillation.

DISTILLATION OF CRUDE OIL

From the foregoing it will be clear that, if a crude oil is gradually heated in a laboratory still connected to a condenser, the constituents which have the lowest boiling point or which, in other words, are the most volatile, will distil off first and be condensed, giving a light volatile product such as gasoline. As the temperature is increased, components of higher boiling points will distil over and, after condensation, products such as kerosine, gas oil and lubricating oils are obtained, leaving, when the distillation is stopped, a heavy residue such as fuel oil, asphaltic bitumen or waxy residue, according to conditions and the type of crude oil.

The distillates come over continuously and are arbitrarily divided into fractions or "cuts"* as the operator pleases.

The same principle as the laboratory still shown in fig. 3 was followed in the earliest plants for distillation of crude oil. This plant, known as a "batch still", consisted of a cylindrical boiler set horizontally in brickwork over a firebox. The vapours formed left the still through a vapour line and were led to a water-cooled condenser. The fractionation of the different cuts was improved by placing a simple fractionating column on top of the still.

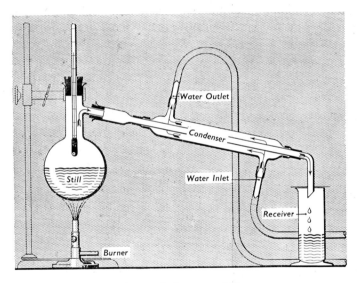

Fig. 3.   Laboratory Still.

The batch process is still used for the production of special boiling point fractions when the amount required is small.

As the batch distillation of crude oil was inefficient and expensive, it is not surprising that this system was abandoned in favour of a continuous process.

The next step in the history of crude oil distillation was the continuous ''bench'' of stills, an arrangement of several stills side by side in cascade at different levels, so that the oil could flow continuously from one still to the next. The temperature was kept slightly higher in each still so that in this way the crude oil was split up into fractions until, finally, in the last still a residue was left which was continuously drawn off, through a cooler, to storage. Although this system had many advantages over the batch distillation system, there were still many drawbacks, the most important being that large quantities of oil are always under treatment at one time, as these benches often consisted of about fifteen stills, each holding 25 tons of oil. This made any adjustments in operation very sluggish and also constituted a grave fire risk.

The fractionation was far from perfect, there being still a great deal of overlapping of products which necessitated redistillation of certain cuts in order to obtain correct separation ; moreover, the oil was at high temperatures for a relatively long time, which led to decomposition due to cracking.

TUBULAR OR PIPE STILLS

About 1912, completely new ideas were introduced into the practice of distillation. In place of the so-called fractional distillation as described above, the fractional condensation system was adopted. Instead of gradually heating the oil to higher and higher temperatures, so that the distillate which was being distilled off gradually became heavier and heavier, the whole of the oil was heated right up to the highest temperature necessary to drive off all the distillate and then was cooled down gradually, so that the successively condensed fractions became lighter and lighter (''flash distillation''*). The heating was carried out in what is known as a ''pipe still'', i.e. a series of tubes of about 4 inches diameter connected together, so that the oil inside travels back and forth over the fire until it reaches the required temperature.

MODERN FURNACE DESIGN

Much attention has been paid to the type of furnace which is used in these pipe stills. When the pipe still was first designed it consisted merely of a number of pipes placed in a furnace space, and little or no thought was given to the design of this furnace so long as the oil was heated up. The result was that the whole space tended to become overheated and, as the flames actually licked the tubes, tube burning was frequent. Furthermore, the furnace gases left the plant at a very high temperature, with, consequently, a great loss in efficiency.

The first advance made in furnace design was to increase the space in which the burning of the fuel was allowed to take place, so that the tubes were only heated by the combustion gases and not by the flames themselves. The gases, having passed between

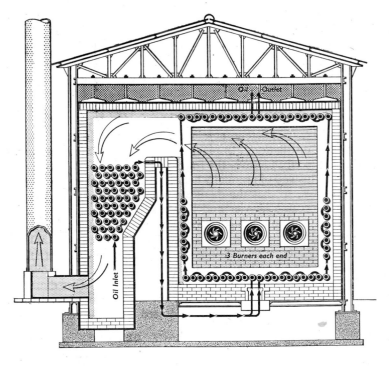

Fig. 4.   Diagram of Modern Double-end-fired Furnace.

the tubes, left the furnace through a flue to the chimney, the temperature of the gases being still very high. This heat, which was carried away in the flue gases, was a definite loss. To meet this, the latest furnace designs have two sections, one of which is known as the "radiant section", where the tubes are heated by radiant heat, and the other the "convection section", where the tubes are heated by the gases immediately before they enter the chimney (fig. 4).

FRACTIONATING COLUMNS

The heated oil leaving the pipe still passes to the fractionating columns, where the separation into fractions or "cuts" takes place. These columns are long cylindrical vessels set up on end and fitted with a large number of trays of a special type (figs. 5 and 6).

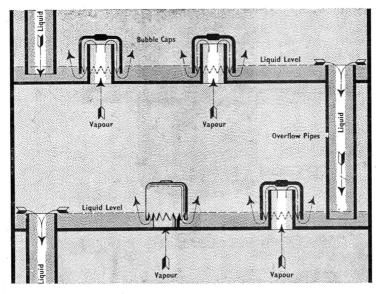

Fig. 5.   Trays and Bubble-caps of Fractionating Column.

L

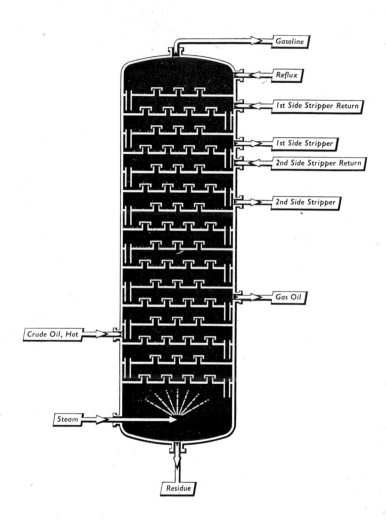

Fig. 6.   Diagram of Modern Column.

The mixture of vapour and liquid leaving the pipe still is led in at a point near the bottom of one of these fractionating columns, where it rises gradually through the vapour uptakes shown. As it rises it cools and a certain amount condenses on each tray, until the tray is full of liquid up to the level of the over-flow. This level is kept just above the holes in the bubble-caps*, so that all the vapour has to pass through liquid, but has not any great head of liquid through which to force its way. It will be apparent that each tray is a little cooler than the one below it and that, therefore, lighter and lighter products will be present on each tray as the vapour passes up the column. As the vapours bubble through the liquid on these trays, that part of the vapour will condense which has the same boiling point as the liquid on the tray, and in addition any light fractions present in the liquid on the tray will be re-evaporated. The temperature throughout such a column is controlled at the bottom by the temperature of the crude oil leaving the pipe still, and at the top by pumping back a certain amount of the material which leaves the top of the column after condensing it (this distillate pumped back is termed "reflux").

In this way, by controlling the temperature at the top and the bottom, the temperature variation throughout is kept under con-trol, so that the temperature of each tray varies gradually from the bottom of the column to the top. The amount of liquid which is pumped back to the top of the column can be varied as required, in order to give the correct temperature at the top of the column, which, in turn, controls the final boiling point of the gasoline leaving at the top.

In most cases, improvement in fractionating efficiency is ob-tained by supplying additional heat to the product in the bottom part of the fractionating column. This is done by pumping the oil at the bottom of the column either through a furnace or through a heat exchanger (see below), where it is heated, and then back again over some stripping trays in the column. Such an arrangement is referred to as a "reboiler".

Side-strippers*. Although each tray has the tendency to collect liquid of a small range of boiling points, yet, on account of the complete range of vapours bubbling through any one tray, a certain amount of material will condense which has a lower boiling point than the bulk of the liquid on that tray. It is customary, therefore, to draw the liquid from a selected tray out of the main column into a small subsidiary column called a "side-stripper" and allow it to flow down through several bubble trays. While passing over these trays, it meets an upward stream of steam, injected at the bottom of the stripper, which boils off the lightest components and thus narrows the boiling range. The vapours thus boiled off, together with the steam, re-enter the main column.

Other means of supplying heat to side-strippers employ the reboiling principle, hot residue being used as heat medium.

By using two or more of these side-strippers in conjunction with one main column, streams of white spirit, kerosine and gas oil can be obtained direct from the plant, without further distillation. This arrangement considerably simplifies the production of the various grades of distillates and places the refiner in a position to manufacture gasolines and the other products mentioned above of the correct distillation range, without the necessity of redistillation. If, however, still closer boiling point ranges are needed, as, for example, in special boiling point spirits, where a range of only 10° or 20° C. is sometimes specified, fractions from the trays are subjected to further distillation in order to improve the boiling range.

HEAT EXCHANGERS

Simultaneously with the improvement in the efficiency of furnaces and fractionating columns, other improvements were also being made. The main cost of running a distillation unit is the cost of the fuel, so that it was natural that attempts to improve efficiency should be concentrated on the conservation of heat. This was achieved by the installation of heat exchangers in which the crude oil was heated up by the outgoing residue and also by the hot vapours.

A heat exchanger is a cylindrical vessel into which a nest of tubes is fitted. The cold crude oil passes down one half of the tubes and back through the other half, the hot residue circulating round the tubes. In order to avoid strains set up by the different expansions of the heater and the outside wall, the nest of tubes is free to expand somewhat as it is fixed rigidly only at one end. This arrangement is called a "floating head" (fig. 7).

OPERATION OF A MODERN DISTILLATION PLANT

Modern units are controlled throughout by means of instruments. Temperatures, quantities of intake, liquid levels, etc., are controlled at every point where necessary. The result of this is, not only a reduction in the amount of labour necessary for the opera-

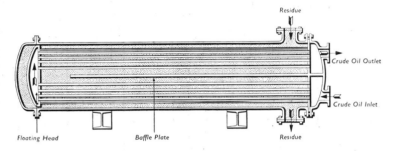

Fig. 7.   Diagram of Heat Exchanger.

tion of the plant, but also a considerably increased efficiency due to the much steadier running which can be obtained in an instrument-controlled plant as against one which depends on the human factor.

The flow diagram of a modern distillation plant is shown in fig. 8.

The crude oil generally contains a small amount of water, which is unavoidably drawn from the well with the oil. This water contains some dissolved salts which are injurious to process equipment and must be removed. This is done in large tanks before the crude oil is charged to the plant ; for instance, by scrubbing (desalting) with a weak water solution of caustic soda.

The crude oil which is being pumped to the furnace first passes through heat exchangers, where it picks up heat from the outgoing

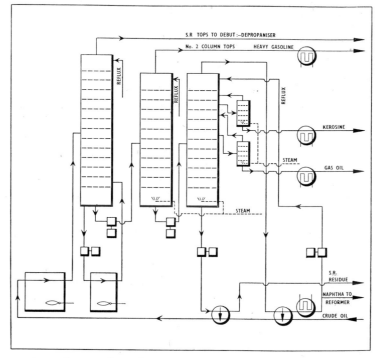

Fig. 8.   Flow Diagram of Modern Distillation Unit.

vapours and residue.   Before it reaches the furnace, its temperature has risen to, say, 150° C. (302° F.).   In the furnace, the crude
oil is heated to 300°–350° C. (572°–662° F.), depending on the
crude oil and on the residue needed.   The foam of liquid and
vapour now enters fractionating column no. 1, as shown, and the
liquid flows down over the trays, meeting an upward stream of
superheated steam and of vapours.   These take up with them any
light oil present in the descending liquid.

The top product is partly condensed and pumped back over the
top of the column as reflux ; the remainder is transferred to the
straight run depropanizer and debutanizer (*vide* chapter IX),

where the lightest constituents, ethane and methane, are passed into the refinery fuel gas system and most of the other products are separated as straight-run components for aviation spirit or are the basic products for the manufacture of aviation spirit (alkylation*, isomerization*, polymerization*, cumene manufacture, *vide* chapter XVI).

The bottom of the no. 1 column is fed to column no. 2, where a top product is a motor gasoline component. The bottoms of column no. 2 are charged to column no. 3 to produce a heavy gasoline as top product, which is cracked to re-formed gasoline in the re-forming units (*vide* chapter X). Side streams are taken from intermediate points in the no. 3 column and stripped in the small stripping columns to produce kerosine or white spirit and gas oil. The straight-run residue from the bottom of the no. 3 column passes through the heat exchangers and can be used as cracking stock for the thermal crackers or feed stock for the manufacture of lubricating oils, depending on the nature of the crude processed.

It will, of course, be realized that the unit described is only one of the many types of modern crude oil distilling units which employ various combinations of furnaces, columns and heat exchangers to obtain the highest efficiency of operation, the greatest possible yield of the desired products and, in addition, such flexibility of operation that the products being made can be varied to meet market requirements.

MISCELLANEOUS DISTILLATION PROCESSES

Sometimes the usual distillation processes are unsuitable for the separation of a mixture, e.g., when the boiling points of the components are too close together, or when the components form constant boiling mixtures (azeotropes). In such cases, other distillation processes can often be used successfully.

Component Azeotropic Distillation. When a mixture of two components cannot be separated by normal distillation, addition of a third component, which forms a low constant boiling mixture with one or both components, can change the apparent relative volatility in such a way that separation by distillation becomes possible. As an example we can take the system isopropyl alcohol-water, which forms a constant boiling mixture, boiling at 80° C. and containing 87·7% isopropyl alcohol and 12·3% water. It is, therefore, impossible to obtain isopropyl alcohol with less than 12·3% water by normal distillation processes. When benzene is added to the system, an azeotrope boiling at 66·5° C. and containing 18·7% isopropyl-alcohol and 7·5% water, balance benzene, is formed. The proportion of water to alcohol in the first case amounts to $\frac{12\cdot3}{87\cdot7}=14\%$, and after addition of benzene it amounts to $\frac{7\cdot5}{18\cdot7}=40\%$.

The mixture can be distilled in a normal distillation column and the 3-component azeotrope can be obtained as a top product, leaving pure isopropyl alcohol as a bottom product. The isopropyl alcohol lost in the top product can be recirculated to the column.

Azeotropic distillation processes find wide application in the petroleum chemical industry (*vide* chapter XVIII).

Extractive Distillation. In the extractive distillation process a third component is used, which does not evaporate during the distillation but reduces the vapour pressure of one of the components by dissolving it. The distillation is carried out in a normal type fractionation column, but a third liquid component is pumped over the upper tray, washing down one of the components which can be recovered by stripping the bottom product in a second column. A typical example of this process is the production of pure toluene from a hydrocarbon mixture of narrow boiling range. In this case phenol is used as a third component, paraffins and naphthenes are obtained as top product of the primary fractionation tower, while pure toluene is obtained as top product of the stripper.

BIBLIOGRAPHY

The Scientific Principles of Petroleum Technology. Gurwitsch. (Chapman & Hall, Ltd., London.)

Distillation Principles and Processes. Sydney Young. (Macmillan & Co., Ltd., London.)

The Science of Petroleum, Vol. II, Section 25. (Oxford University Press, London.)

American Petroleum Refining. H. S. Bell. (Constable & Co., Ltd., London.)

Petroleum Refinery Engineering. W. L. Nelson. (McGraw-Hill Book Co., New York and London.)

IX

MANUFACTURE OF PRODUCTS FROM NATURAL GAS

THE term "natural gas" is applied only to those gases which originate from, and are associated, directly or indirectly, with crude petroleum. In some cases, gas is found in strata which do not contain oil, the gas having been separated from its mother oil in past geological ages by some process of migration ; in other cases, it is found associated with and dissolved in crude oil, in which case it is termed "casinghead gas"*.

Natural gas is composed almost entirely of hydrocarbons of the paraffin series, the lightest member, methane, predominating. The lower members of the paraffin hydrocarbon series are :—

Name	Chemical formula	Boiling point at atmospheric pressure (Barometer reading 760 mm.)	
Methane	CH_4	$-161 \cdot 5°$ C.	gaseous at
Ethane	C_2H_6	$- 88 \cdot 5°$ C.	ordinary
Propane	C_3H_8	$- 42 \cdot 2°$ C.	atmospheric
Isobutane	C_4H_{10}	$- 12 \cdot 1°$ C.	temperature
Butane (normal)	C_4H_{10}	$- 0 \cdot 5°$ C.	and pressure.
Isopentane	C_5H_{12}	$27 \cdot 9°$ C.	liquid at
Pentane (normal)	C_5H_{12}	$36 \cdot 1°$ C.	ordinary
Hexane (normal)	C_6H_{14}	$69 \cdot 0°$ C.	atmospheric
Heptane (normal)	C_7H_{16}	$98 \cdot 4°$ C.	temperature
Octane (normal)	C_8H_{18}	$125 \cdot 6°$ C.	and pressure.

Members with higher boiling points may also be present, and in addition others, such as isohexanes and so on, which, however, occur in smaller proportions and which, for the present, may be neglected. Other components, such as carbon dioxide, nitrogen and sulphuretted hydrogen, are sometimes present in varying proportions, but these may be regarded as impurities or as undesirable components.

It will be clear from an inspection of the boiling points that methane, ethane, propane and the butanes are gases at ordinary temperature and pressure, but that pentane, hexane, heptane and octane are liquids, pentane being about as volatile as ether and heptane having a boiling point nearly equal to that of water. Just as air at ordinary temperatures will hold much water in the form of vapour, so also will natural gas contain, as vapour, hydrocarbons with boiling points above atmospheric temperatures, in, of course, decreasing proportions the higher the boiling points.

PROPERTIES OF HYDROCARBONS

Methane. The boiling point of methane is very low, indeed so low that it can be considered purely as a gas ; air, which can also be liquefied, and which has a boiling point at atmospheric pressure of −182° C. (−296° F.), is certainly considered by everybody as a gas.

Ethane has such a low boiling point that it can also be considered as a gas.

Propane and the Butanes. These are used either separately or in admixture, as gaseous fuels for domestic as well as for industrial purposes, but are stored and transported as liquids. This has led to the general name of liquid gases for these products.

As has been explained in chapter VIII, the liquid state exists at or below the boiling point, and the boiling point increases with pressure. Consequently, in order to keep these gases in the liquid state, the pressure under which they are stored and transported must be increased to such an extent that their boiling points rise to the normal surrounding temperature. For instance, for a boiling point of 20° C. (68° F.) the pressure should be :—

Propane	...	...	7·2 atm. above atmospheric pressure.		
Iso-butane	...	...	3·0 ,,	,,	,,	,,
Butane	...	...	1·04 ,,	,,	,,	,,

Consequently, these pressures are the minima at which these hydrocarbons must be stored in order to keep them liquid at a temperature of 20° C. (68° F.).

The advantage of storing these substances as liquids rather than as gases is apparent when we consider that a volume of 1 litre can contain about 500 grams of liquid propane, but only 12 grams of propane vapour compressed to a pressure of 7 atm.

Besides serving as gaseous fuel, butane can also be incorporated to a certain extent in ordinary motor gasoline. At first sight, this appears extraordinary, in view of the low boiling point of butane. However, it should be noted that when blended with much larger quantities of heavier components (in this case, ordinary motor gasoline), the latter will keep the butane in solution, so that the boiling point of the mixture will be only slightly lower than that of the original gasoline. The amount of butane to be added must, of course, be kept within certain limits, to avoid trouble due to vapour lock* (*vide* chapter XXV).

Pentane and Heavier Hydrocarbons. These are normal constituents of gasoline. Their boiling points lie above the normal surrounding temperature, so that when stored at atmospheric pressure they remain in liquid form. When extracted from the gas, together with some butanes, they form the so-called "natural gasoline", or, as it is also sometimes called, "casinghead gasoline", a product with excellent qualities as a blending agent for motor fuel.

The fact that the pentanes and heavier paraffins are liquids has led to the terms "wet" gas, for indicating gas which contains these components, and "dry" gas for natural gas with none, or only a slight content, of these fractions. The gases from wells which yield no oil are "dry", whilst gases produced in contact with oil can be either "dry" or "wet", depending on the nature of the crude oil and the method of separating the gas from the oil.

MANUFACTURE OF NATURAL GASOLINE

Natural gasoline and liquid gas can be extracted from the wet gases by one of the following methods, which can also be used in combination with each other :—

   (*a*) compression and cooling,
   (*b*) absorption,
   (*c*) adsorption.

Although it had long been known that gasoline could be

extracted from natural gases, some time elapsed before the oil industry realized that very valuable material was being lost by allowing the wet gases to go to fuel, or to waste, without treatment. It was not till about 1910 that gasoline extraction was put into practice. Since then this industry has very much developed, the production of natural gasoline in the U.S.A. in 1945 being 4,650,000,000 U.S. gallons.

THE COMPRESSION PROCESS

Natural gas can be considered, for the sake of simplicity, as consisting of methane (gas) containing pentane, etc. (liquid) in a vapour state, just as air contains water in a vapour state.

If a dish of water is exposed to a continuous draught of air it will soon evaporate away ; but if the same dish of water is put under a glass cover, it will not. This can be explained by the fact that a certain volume of air can only contain a limited amount of water vapour. As soon as the air under the cover is saturated, no further evaporation of water takes place. People sitting in a closed car on a cold day will notice how the windows become steamed on the inside ; the air in the car, which contains abundant water vapour from their breath, is cooled down by the glass and deposits liquid water on it. This shows that the amount of water vapour which the air can contain also depends on the temperature. The fact that a certain volume of a gas can only contain a fixed amount of a vapour of a liquid, which amount is dependent on the temperature, is the fundamental principle on which gasoline extraction by compression and cooling is based. If a certain volume of methane+pentane is compressed to a smaller volume at the same temperature, there is no room to accommodate all the pentane in a vapour state so that part of it will settle out in a liquid state. If the remaining gas is refrigerated, more pentane will settle out.

The gases are conducted from the oil-gas separators on the field (*vide* chapter VI) into one main suction line, which leads them to the compressors, either *via* a gasometer or one or more large liquid catchers, in order to prevent crude oil which might be entrained by the gases from entering and damaging the compressors.

The gases which are saturated at the pressure and temperature of the crude oil separators are now compressed so that, at the original temperature, the correspondingly much-reduced volume could only accommodate part of the heavier hydrocarbons originally present. However, as a result of the compression, the gases are also heated (as in pumping up a bicycle tyre), and this, as explained above, counteracts the effect of the reduction in volume. Therefore, after compression, the gases are cooled so that the heavier constituents condense and can be collected in separators.

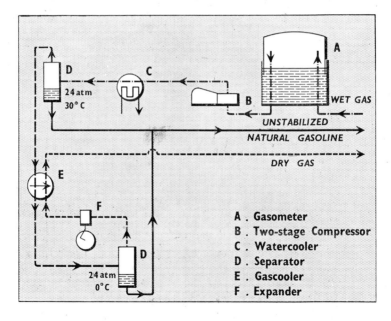

Fig. 1.   Compressor Plant with Expander.

The gases are generally compressed to about 24 atm., the compression being effected in two stages.

The compressed gases are cooled in water-coolers in which the water passes as much as possible in counter-current* to the gases.

In this way, very efficient cooling can be obtained down to a temperature only slightly above that of the cooling water. From the coolers, the mixture of gases and liquid enters the separators, from which the condensate is drained separately.

When the residual gas is not required at a high pressure, a further cooling can be obtained by the expansion of the gas. Just as compression of a gas causes its heating, expansion will cause its cooling. Therefore, the gases from the compressor plant under, say, 24 atm. pressure are made to drive an engine in just the same way that steam drives a steam engine, the power so obtained being utilized for various purposes. The exhaust gases of the "expander" engine are very cold and are used to cool the compressed gas before it enters the expander. As this is still under the full compression pressure, this refrigeration will cause gasoline to settle out. The dry gases remaining are used to drive the expander.

Another method is to effect cooling by means of a refrigerating plant, using ammonia or any other suitable medium. With this method, the dry gases are available at the full compression pressure.

THE ABSORPTION PROCESS

This is essentially a solution process. Gases and vapours can go into solution in a liquid. Air dissolves in water and enables fish to get their necessary oxygen, and carbon dioxide is dissolved in water to make soda-water.

When natural gas is brought into contact with absorption oil (which is, in practice, a fraction lying generally somewhere between heavy gasoline and light gas oil, according to circumstances), some of the gases go into solution in the oil. The heavier the hydrocarbons the more easily they dissolve, so that there is a tendency for the heavier components to go into the oil. This is just exactly what is desired, because in such a way the heavier natural gasoline constituents can be removed, leaving the lighter parts in the gas.

The rate of absorption depends on the pressure of the gas ; a quantity of oil can absorb more when the gas with which it is in contact is under high pressure than when it is at low pressure. The soda-water bottle again affords a good example. In the bottle there is an increased pressure; as soon as the bottle is opened, the excess pressure is let off and the carbon dioxide gas cannot now all remain in solution—the excess comes off as gas bubbles.

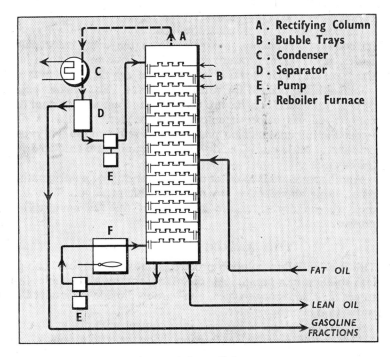

Fig. 2. Stripper Column.

Therefore, the absorption process is seldom practised at atmospheric pressure, because then the amount of absorption oil required in order to obtain a reasonable extraction would be so large.

The gas is brought into intimate contact with the oil in the absorber, which is a column in which there are several "bubble trays". The absorption oil is introduced at the upper part of the column and runs down from tray to tray. The wet gas enters at the bottom of the column and bubbles through the liquid on the trays until it escapes as dry gas at the top. The absorption oil with the heavy components of the gas in solution—the so-called "fat" oil—is collected from the bottom of the tower.

The dissolved gasoline is now distilled off. The apparatus in which this is done is called a "stripper". This also consists of a column with several bubble trays (fig. 2). The fat oil is introduced about half-way up the column and, in running to the bottom, is gradually heated up, either by introduction of steam at the bottom or by direct-fired heaters for the bottom product. In the latter case, the bottom is pumped through a furnace, the re-boiler furnace, where the required amount of heat is supplied. The fractions absorbed from the gas are driven out by the heat.

It may be said, in general, that for very wet gases the compression process is the more economical, unless a very high recovery of butanes is desired, in which case compression followed by absorption is the usual procedure. For less wet gases, the absorption process is more economical. Of course, in all those cases where the gases must be transported under pressure or used for repressuring (*vide* chapter VI), compression is required in any case, so that the compression gasoline is obtained without additional cost.

THE ADSORPTION PROCESS

This process makes use of the fact that certain highly porous materials have the power of condensing on their surfaces large amounts of vapours ; this effect is generally called "adsorption". The substance generally used is activated charcoal, a special charcoal which is also used in gas masks, where it adsorbs poisonous constituents from the air. Like absorption oil, charcoal has the property of extracting, preferentially, the heavier hydrocarbons from the gas.

A charcoal plant consists of several large vessels filled with activated* charcoal. The gas is passed through a vessel until the charcoal is saturated and is then switched into another vessel. The saturated charcoal is steamed, to drive out the adsorbed components, which are again collected and condensed. After drying

M

Fig. 3.   Absorption Plant.

Fig. 4.   Charcoal Adsorption Plant.

with hot gas and cooling, the charcoal is again ready for a new adsorption cycle.

The use of the adsorption process is not so general as that of oil absorption because charcoal cannot be used for all gases. Sulphuretted hydrogen, if present, is adsorbed by the charcoal, which then loses its capacity to adsorb hydrocarbons.

THE STABILIZATION PROCESS

Although the extraction processes all show a preference for capturing the heavier components, some of the lighter undesirable fractions will be captured too, so that the total product extracted from the gases will be a mixture of all components present in the gas, the heavier components predominating. Therefore, the liquid product obtained will have a very low initial boiling point and will boil at atmospheric pressure ; it is a "wild" product. Such unstable liquid is not suitable for blending into motor gasoline, as it would make the gasoline very gassy, causing carburettor troubles and vapour lock. A process must, therefore, be applied to separate out the stabilized natural gasoline containing all the pentanes and heavier hydrocarbons, and also so much of the butanes as can be incorporated in the motor gasoline.

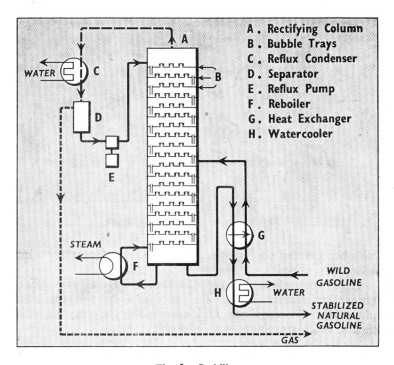

A . Rectifying Column
B . Bubble Trays
C . Reflux Condenser
D . Separator
E . Reflux Pump
F . Reboiler
G . Heat Exchanger
H . Watercooler

Fig. 5.   Stabilizer.

The stabilizing is carried out by rectifying under pressure, which makes it possible to obtain a sharp cut between the fractions, so that only the undesired light components are eliminated. The rectifying installations for this purpose are called "stabilizers"* (fig. 5), and have become a regular part of modern gas plants. A stabilizer is essentially a rectifying column working at considerable pressure, containing bubble trays. The wild product is introduced somewhere in the middle of the column. At the bottom, heat is supplied to the reboiler, in which vessel the liquid flowing from the column is brought into indirect contact with steam, which causes it to boil, the vapours being reintroduced into the column.

Fig. 6. Stabilizer Plant.

At the top, a water-cooled reflux condenser is installed, which condenses part of the vapours which are returned as "reflux" into the column. The continuous contact between the reflux descending the column and the rising vapours generated in the reboiler results in the heavier fractions being washed out of the vapours by the liquid leaving the bottom of the column and the lighter fractions being evaporated from the liquid and taken along by the gases leaving the top of the column. In such a way, a clean separation is obtained between heavy and light components.

Stabilizer plants were originally designed only to produce a suitable motor gasoline component from the natural gas, and a single stabilization process was sufficient to deliver the stabilized natural gasoline as a bottom product.

From the foregoing it is evident that a stabilizer splits its intake into two fractions, a top and a bottom fraction. Each of the two fractions can, if desired, again be split up into two, so that, by installing more stabilizers in series, several sharply rectified products can be obtained from the original unstabilized product. Such a series of stabilizers is used nowadays for making the liquid gases, propane and butane. Any butane which cannot be used in the gasoline fraction is produced *tel quel*, and propane is also separated as such.

For purposes of distinction, the various stabilizers are often called de-butanizers, de-propanizers, de-ethanizers, indicating the product which is separated from the bottom fraction.

BIBLIOGRAPHY

The Science of Petroleum, Vol. II, Sections 23 and 25. (Oxford University Press, London.)

Handbook of Casinghead Gas. Henry Westcott. (Metric Metal Works, Erie, Penn.)

Gas Engineers' Handbook. (McGraw-Hill Book Co., New York and London.)

X

THERMAL CRACKING

The cracking process plays an important part in the modern petroleum industry, not only as a process for obtaining a higher yield of gasoline from crude oil, but also for improving the quality of the gasoline.

Cracking is essentially a high-temperature treatment which breaks up heavier or larger hydrocarbon molecules into smaller ones, often at the same time altering their internal structure. There is not sufficient hydrogen in the large molecules to supply the needs of the small molecules into which they crack. Cracked molecules are, therefore, mainly unsaturated (*vide* chapter VII) and because of this they polymerize to some extent as soon as they are formed ; the result is that heavier molecules are also formed at the same time. The total product of the cracking of a heavy oil (residue), therefore, contains gases, light hydrocarbons (gasoline) and hydrocarbons with large molecules, heavier than the original oil, as well as fractions boiling within the range of the oil which has been cracked.

When the automobile industry was in its infancy, it became obvious that the production of large quantities of straight-run* gasoline would involve the production of much larger quantities of residual fuels than the market could absorb. The demand for gasoline thus spurred on scientists to look for means of obtaining a higher yield of this product from crude oil. The cracking process brought the desired solution. About 35 years ago, cracking was begun on a commercial scale in the U.S.A., the resulting products being usually referred to as cracked gasoline, cracked fuel, etc. Cracked gasoline was, however, considered as an inferior product ; it had a very unpleasant odour, soon turned yellow and readily formed resinous products (gum), which led to serious fouling of engines. Fortunately, however, improvements in the cracking process, and perfected refining methods, removed the above-mentioned drawbacks.

It was noticed that the cracked gasoline had a better engine performance (anti-knock* value) than that of a straight-run gasoline. This property of cracked gasoline rendered it possible to design engines with a higher compression ratio and, as a result of the building of such engines, the demand for cracked gasoline increased. As some straight-run gasolines have very poor anti-knock properties, the process of cracking gasoline itself (known as "reforming"*) was also developed.

LIQUID-PHASE CRACKING—THE DUBBS PROCESS

By keeping the oil to be cracked under a high pressure, complete vaporization is prevented and the oil is thus kept in the liquid phase. In this so-called "liquid-phase" process, the material to be cracked, known as the "cracking stock", can be ordinary residue, gas oil, kerosine or, in the case of reforming, gasoline.

There are a number of different liquid-phase cracking processes, the better-known being : the Dubbs process, Holmes Manley process, Tube and Tank process, Cross process. They are all based on the same principle, and merely differ in the arrangement of the various sections of the plant and in some engineering details.

The Dubbs process is widely used by the Group ; a flow sheet of a Dubbs cracking unit is given in fig. 1.

The cracking stock is pumped into the lower part of the fractionating column, where it runs downwards over bubble trays in counter-current with the cracked vapours. The cracking stock is thus pre-heated by the ascending hot vapours, these latter, on the other hand, being thereby cooled. The heavier cracked and non-cracked hydrocarbons are partly condensed and flow to the bottom of the column. The hot-oil pump conveys the bottom product through one heating coil of the furnace. The latest heater design developed is the so-called "equiflux" furnace, in which the heavy oil is heated to 900° F.–1,000° F. (482°–538° C.) with a minimum of coke formation, on account of the high velocity achieved in such furnaces. A lighter fraction is withdrawn from the side of the fractionating column by means of a hot oil pump which discharges the oil to a second heating coil of the furnace, where it is subjected to higher temperature and pressure conditions than are maintained within the first bank of heating

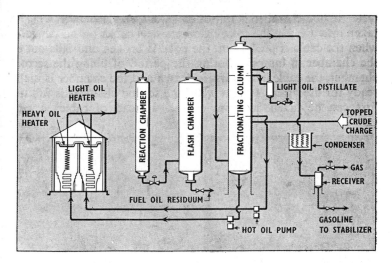

Fig. 1.   Two Coil Selective Dubbs Cracking Unit.

tubes, as the lighter hydrocarbons are more resistant to cracking. The light oil discharges into the same reaction chamber as the heavy oil.   The hydrocarbon mixture from the reaction chamber is discharged from the bottom and flows into a flash chamber at reduced pressure, where a segregation into vapours and liquid residuum takes place.   The hot vapours pass to the fractionating column, where separation into gasoline and light oil fractions takes place.

The selective cracking process described above is only one way of operating this process, several modifications and alternatives being possible.   If there is, at the time, a shortage of gas oil this side cut is not cracked, but runs separately through a cooler to storage.

The process may be operated either by the non-residue method, producing only gasoline and coke, or by the residue method, where a cracked residue is produced.   With the non-residue operating method, the plant is usually provided with several coke chambers having a diameter of 10 feet and a height of 30 to 40 feet. If one chamber is full of coke, a second chamber can be taken into use. In the coke chambers steel cables are suspended; when the cable is pulled out, the coke is broken and falls out of the chamber in lumps. During the period of filling the second chamber, the cable in the first is drawn and the chamber is made ready for use again, so that when the second chamber is full the first can be taken into use again. Instead of cables a new

Fig. 2.   Modern Thermal Cracking Plant.

"hydraulic decoking method" was developed recently by the Group, where reaction chambers are cleaned by means of water jets, a stream of water under high pressure being used to cut the coke out of the chamber.

Coke also deposits in the tubes of the furnace and the transfer line, and the cycle of switching chambers can go on until the plant has to be shut down for cleaning of the furnace. This can be done by passing turbine cutters through the tubes or by the so-called steam-air decoking method, in which the coke is burned out of the tubes, using heat together with steam and air alternatively.

With the residue operating method great care has to be taken to prevent the formation of sludge in the cracked residue. Therefore a low level in the reaction chamber is kept to decrease the cracking time. For the same reason, the mixture of oil and gas leaving the furnace is often cooled by the injection of cold oil ("quenched"). The yield of cracked gasoline is lower by this kind of operation ("low-level"), but the unit can be kept much longer in operation before it has to be cleaned.

Recent developments in thermal cracking have been in the direction of the use of alloy steels (such as 4–6% chromium + $\frac{1}{2}$% molybdenum steel) for resistance to corrosion and to high temperatures. The use of alloy furnace tubes which will withstand higher temperatures and pressures than ordinary steel tubes has permitted a greater intensity of cracking than could be formerly practised. Improvements in furnace design, mainly directed towards higher heat intakes per unit of tube surface and higher velocities, have also favoured deeper thermal cracking. The use of alloy furnace tubes, pipelines and alloy-lined steel vessels has also greatly reduced the corrosion menace, which formerly made thermal cracking a hazardous process. As a result, longer runs can be made with safety on the units, and higher gasoline yields can be achieved than, in general, was possible in the early days of thermal cracking.

REFORMING

A straight-run gasoline which has poor anti-knock properties can be split by fractional distillation into a light fraction which has excellent anti-knock properties and a heavy fraction, which is very bad in this respect. The heavier fraction is then cracked or "reformed". The lighter hydrocarbons demand a much higher cracking temperature than the heavier ones.

With modern furnace construction it is possible, without there being danger of too intense local overheating of the tubes, to obtain a uniform heating of the gasoline fraction to be cracked and to keep this fairly constant at the cracking temperature. In the convection tubes of such a furnace the temperature is increased from about 124° C. (255° F.) to about 400° C. (752° F.). In the radiant heat tubes, the temperature increases to about 530° C. (986° F.). In the remaining radiant heat tubes the temperature increases only about 20° C. (36° F.). These last tubes are called the "soaking" section of the furnace.

The high temperature and the light character of the cracking stock necessitate the pressure in the tubes being kept high for reforming operation, as it is desired to crack as much as possible in the liquid phase. Pressures of 84–91 atm. (1,200–1,300 lb. per square inch) are used. In the transfer line of the furnace there is a pressure reducing valve, so that the remainder of the apparatus is not under this high pressure. Quenching is common practice with the reforming operation.

During the war the so-called "Avaro" process was developed in Curaçao, which yields a valuable component for 100 octane aviation gasoline. This process consists mainly of reforming again the heavy fractions of an already reformed gasoline (100°–200° C. boiling range), in the presence of light fractions. Preferably, a quantity of propane-propylene is used as the light fraction, and is injected into the feed before entering the furnace. The process, on this account, has been termed the "co-reforming" process. The 100°–200° C. fraction from the products of this second stage is called "Avaro" distillate.

All cracked and reformed distillates have to be refined ; this is described in chapter XI under Refining or Treating Processes.

VAPOUR-PHASE CRACKING

In vapour-phase cracking, the hydrocarbons to be cracked are first brought into vapour form. These vapours are then cracked by exposing them for a short time to a very high temperature. This can be done in various ways. The vapours can be led through intensely heated tubes (Gyro process) or the vapours to be cracked can be mixed with gas which has been so intensely heated that the mixture attains the desired cracking temperature ("True Vapour-Phase" [T.V.P.] process).

In the Gyro process (fig. 3) the oil vapour is heated in a pipe still, C (converter), to about 593° C. (1,100° F.). The cracked vapour is passed to an arrester, A, where it is quenched

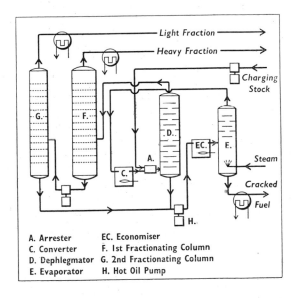

A. Arrester   EC. Economiser
C. Converter   F. 1st Fractionating Column
D. Dephlegmator   G. 2nd Fractionating Column
E. Evaporator   H. Hot Oil Pump

Fig. 3. Gyro Process.

by part of the incoming charging stock. Cracked vapour and the charging stock are then passed on to a dephlegmator, D, where they are split up into cracked distillate, leaving at the top, and charging stock and heavy fractions, leaving at the bottom. The latter are taken to a pipe still, EC, called an "economiser", where the oil is heated to about 370° C. (698° F.). This hot oil is passed to an evaporator, E, where the oil is allowed to vaporize, and the vapours, together with steam, are then passed to the converter mentioned above. The bottom product of the evaporator goes to cracked fuel storage. The cracked distillate leaving the top of the dephlegmator is split up in two fractionating columns, F and G, into a light and a heavy fraction, which are condensed and refined separately, the residue from the second column being recycled through the economiser.

In the T.V.P. process the oil vapours are superheated to about 455° C. (851° F.), which temperature is not high enough for cracking in the vapour phase. This vapour is then mixed with gas, which has been heated in another part of the plant in a tube still. The mixture of cracking stock vapours and heated gas is kept in a reaction chamber at 500°–540° C. (932°–1,004° F.), according to the nature of the vapour to be cracked. At this temperature, the vaporized charging stock is cracked and the vapour mixture is passed to a tower, called a "scrubber", where the cracked vapour is quenched by fresh charging stock. In the scrubber, most of the charging stock is vaporized by the heat of the cracked vapours, the heaviest fraction leaving the bottom of the scrubber as fuel oil. The vapour from the scrubber is passed to a bubble tower (fractionating column), where the cracked distillate is taken off at the top and the charging stock leaves the bottom of the tower to be passed to a pipe still, where it is heated and vaporized. This charging stock vapour then goes through the cycles already described.

A disadvantage of the vapour-phase process is its poor flexibility. Only such products as can be brought into vapour form without decomposition (kerosine, gas oil) can be cracked with this process, whereas with the liquid-phase process residues also can be cracked. One of the former advantages of vapour-phase cracking—that it produced a good yield of valuable unsaturated hydrocarbons—is now better achieved by the recently developed catalytic cracking processes (*vide* chapter XVI). As a result, vapour-phase cracking has fallen recently into disfavour and is being displaced by catalytic cracking.

BIBLIOGRAPHY

The Principles of Motor Fuel Preparation and Application.
Alfred W. Nash and Donald A. Howes. (Chapman & Hall,
Ltd., London.)

Conversion of Petroleum. A. N. Sachanen. (Reinhold Publishing
Corp., New York.)

Gasoline and Other Motor Fuels. Carleton Ellis and Joseph V.
Meigs. (Van Nostrand Company, New York.)

*Composite Catalog of Oil Refinery Equipment, including Process
Handbook.* (Published by The Refiner and Natural Gasoline
Manufacturer, Houston, U.S.A.)

XI

REFINING OR TREATING PROCESSES

SOME petroleum products, such as gasoline, kerosine, paraffin wax and lubricating oil, are not marketable without chemical treatment being applied in the course of their production. Without such treatment, they have a bad smell or colour or they deteriorate during storage, forming gum or resin. Chemical treatment improves the appearance and the odour of the oils as well as their stability.

LIGHT HYDROCARBONS

Propane to be used for "liquefied petroleum gas" (LPG) (*vide* chapter XXIV) requires complete removal of hydrogen sulphide and mercaptans, followed by complete removal of moisture. Hydrogen sulphide can be efficiently removed by treatment with potassium phosphate (Shell Phosphate Process). The light mercaptans occurring in propane and butane can be completely removed by treatment with caustic soda solution. Moisture can be removed by passing over calcium chloride.

GASOLINE

Refining of straight-run gasolines is seldom carried out nowadays ; the reduction of the sulphur content constitutes the principal motive for doing so. In this case, the common method is treating with concentrated sulphuric acid, which removes substances that may discolour during storage and which also very often carry the sulphur. The mixing of the gasoline with sulphuric acid is carried out in batches of from 10 to 300 tons of gasoline, in vessels known as "agitators". After some time, the acid sludge is drawn off, and the gasoline is further freed from acid by washing first with water and then with a dilute caustic soda solution. The refined gasoline is then drawn off into rundown or settling tanks, where the last traces of water settle out.

Continuous Treating Process. In modern practice the treating process is generally carried out in a continuous manner by pumping the gasoline together with the requisite amount of acid through pipes containing suitable baffles, which cause the gasoline and acid to mix thoroughly. The mixture is then passed into a settling tank, where the acid tar settles to the bottom and is drawn off, while the gasoline is taken off continuously from the top and is passed through another mixing device with water. The water is drained off in another settling tank and the gasoline is passed through a third mixer, where caustic soda solution is introduced to neutralize any remaining traces of acid. A continuous treating plant of this type is shown in fig. 1.

There is better contact between the gasoline and the chemicals in the continuous treating process, resulting in a considerable saving in chemicals, while less labour is required. This method is more economical than batch treatment, especially when large quantities of gasoline have to be refined.

In another continuous process, the settling tanks are replaced by centrifuges, which separate the acid tar from the gasoline much more rapidly than ordinary settling by gravity. This method is not important for gasoline, however, centrifuges being oftener applied in the refining of lubricating oils.

Pressure Distillate. The unrefined gasoline obtained in thermal cracking operations is called pressure distillate (P.D.) and requires elaborate refining before it can safely be used as a motor spirit. This refining can best be carried out on the following lines :—

The P.D. is distilled to obtain the following fractions :—

(1) A light gasoline distilling up to about 100° C.

(2) A heavy gasoline distilling about 100°–200° C.

(3) A gas oil fraction. This fraction is separated mainly with a view to economizing on chemicals.

In modern cracking units, this distillation is combined with the cracking operation, the distillation being carried out in a number of distilling columns working on surplus heat from the cracking operation (*vide* chapter X).

The light gasoline normally does not require an acid treatment as it is sufficiently stable against discoloration and gum formation, and, moreover, acid treatment would result in heavy losses, both in yield and in valuable properties. However, it contains a

N

Fig. 1.   Continuous Treater.

considerable quantity of sulphur compounds of relatively simple composition, the so-called mercaptans, whose odour is very bad ; they have to be removed. The mercaptans have weak acidic properties ; when the light gasoline is treated with concentrated caustic soda solution the greater part of the mercaptans passes into the caustic soda. After separation, the caustic solution can be regenerated by prolonged boiling, the mercaptans gradually distilling off, after which the caustic solution is once again ready for use.

The solubility of mercaptans in the caustic solution can be improved by the addition of certain compounds, such as iso-butyric acid (forming salts with the caustic soda). By this method, (the "Solutizer process"), the mercaptans are removed from the gasoline to a much higher degree. The regeneration of the caustic solution was formerly carried out by stripping with steam, but recently it was found that the addition of a small quantity of tannin has made it possible to use oxidation by air for regeneration, thus saving considerable quantities of steam and reducing the capital cost of the plant required.

The heavy gasoline is treated with sulphuric acid in the same way as described above. The unstable products are either dissolved in the sulphuric acid or they combine with each other (polymerize), forming products in the gas oil and lubricating oil ranges. The acid-treated gasoline is, therefore, a dark brown liquid, which has to be redistilled for the production of water-white gasoline. The polymers are obtained separately as a gas oil fraction.

Other chemicals than sulphuric acid are in use for refining purposes, one of the best known being a concentrated solution of zinc chloride (Lachmann process). In this case, also, polymerization of the very unstable products takes place.

Vapour-phase treatment by means of clay is often used. All the vapours leaving the cracking unit are passed through vessels filled with clay, thus polymerizing the most unstable components of the gasoline. This process is known as Gray vapour-phase treating.

Doctor Treatment and Allied Processes. The light and heavy gasoline fractions are recombined and are then ready for use,

except that they usually still contain a certain amount of mercaptans. The gasoline is "sour" and must be "sweetened".

To remove this residual mercaptan content several processes
are in use, which all operate on the common principle that the
mercaptans are oxidized to heavier products without the nauseous
mercaptan smell. The oldest, and still the best known of these
processes, is the "doctor" treatment, whereby the gasoline is
mixed with "doctor solution", a solution of lead oxide (litharge)
in caustic soda, with the addition of sulphur. Other processes
serving the same purpose are carried out with copper chloride or
sodium hypochlorite.

Gasoline obtained by catalytic cracking (*vide* chapter XVI)
requires only a light "sweetening" treatment.

Inhibitors. Although it is essential to remove the most unstable
portions of the pressure distillate, as they form gummy compounds
and discolour the gasoline during storage, it is sometimes more
economical to effect this refining to the least possible degree only,
stabilizing the gasoline further through the addition of small
quantities of certain substances. These substances are known as
"inhibitors"*. In this way, a somewhat higher yield of gasoline is
obtained, while valuable properties such as the octane number,
are less adversely affected by the refining process.

KEROSINE

The refining of kerosine is carried out in practically the same
way as that of gasoline, sulphuric acid and caustic soda again
being used for the purpose. When treatment in batches is applied,
the mixing is still often effected by blowing with air. Sometimes
the treatment is followed by a further refining with decolorizing
earth. Kerosine sometimes remains in stock for a long time, so
careful refining is required.

Kerosines containing high percentages of naphthenic, and
especially aromatic hydrocarbons, are suitable as power kerosines
for use in tractors, etc. They have a comparatively high anti-
knock value, but they are not suitable as illuminating kerosines,
owing to their tendency to smoke. Paraffinic kerosines are far
more suitable for this purpose. Kerosines containing aromatic
hydrocarbons can be split into paraffinic and aromatic fractions

by treating at low temperature with liquid sulphur dioxide. This process is known as the Edeleanu process and is described fully in chapter XII.

Kerosine distillates containing a high proportion of sulphur can be desulphurized by treatment at elevated temperatures in the presence of a suitable catalyst.

GAS OIL

In the United States, domestic fuel oils, which may be derived either from straight-run gas oil or light gas oil from catalytic cracking, are usually given a treatment to eliminate impurities which would cause screen clogging in domestic burners. Treatment may also be required to improve stability on storage and to remove substances which cause corrosion of copper parts in the domestic burners. The usual treatment is with sulphuric acid and caustic soda in continuous treaters, followed by filtration through clay.

LUBRICATING OIL

The refining of lubricating oil is necessary chiefly to obtain a good colour, and to keep the colour stable during long periods of storage. Here again sulphuric acid is used, but in order that the lubricating oil may mix thoroughly with the acid and the acid tar settle out readily, it is usual to reduce the viscosity of the oil by warming it. The temperature at which the acid treatment is carried out depends on the grade of oil, the more viscous grades being treated at higher temperatures.

The mixing with acid is effected either by the batch method, in agitators, or by the continuous method, using a centrifuge to separate the acid tar from the oil. The agitator used for the acid refining of lubricating oils is usually fitted with a tubular heater, through which the unrefined oil is fed, or with a steam coil in its interior, or it is double-walled, the space between the walls being steam-heated (*i.e.* the agitator is steam-jacketed).

The acid refining is usually followed by a treatment with decolorizing earth, which has the effect of removing the dark colouring matter from the oil. It is usual to add a small proportion of lime to the decolorizing earth in order to neutralize any acid left

Fig. 2.   Battery of Centrifuges.

in the oil from the previous acid treatment. The oil is also kept
heated during this process in order to ensure thorough mixing,
and the earth is removed after treatment by passing the mixture
through a filter press (*vide* chapter XV). The product on its way
to storage is passed through a "blotter" press (containing filter
paper), which removes traces of fines, such as clay, rust scale, or
moisture. This step assures a bright and polished appearance
for the finished product.

Certain grades of lubricating oil, usually the most viscous
grades, such as those used for the manufacture of bright stock
(*vide* chapter XIII), are not given an acid treatment but are refined
with decolorizing earth. In such cases, the oil is thinned down by
dissolving in heavy gasoline or naphtha and the solution is passed

through a column of coarse decolorizing earth, the process being known as "percolation", in contrast with the "contacting" process described in the previous paragraph. The filtered solution is then distilled at a temperature just sufficient to boil off the heavy gasoline, leaving a residue of filtered bright stock.

Other methods of treating lubricating oils have been introduced, such as solvent extraction and solvent dewaxing, which are described in chapters XII and XV.

SPECIAL OILS

There are certain fractions in the lubricating oil range which are used for purposes other than lubrication. Examples of such oils are transformer or switch oils, medicinal oil or liquid paraffin, and oils which form the basis of spray oils or miscible oils used as insecticides and fungicides for horticultural purposes. Transformer oils should have the least possible tendency to form sludge during use, and horticultural oils should not contain any reactive constituents which might injure the plants under treatment. For these reasons, oils of this type are refined with large quantities of fuming sulphuric acid or oleum*, that is, sulphuric acid containing excess of sulphur trioxide. This acid reacts more energetically than ordinary sulphuric acid with the constituents of the oil which are undesirable for these special applications.

As an example of the extent of refining necessary for special oils, medicinal oil is produced by treating a distillate of suitable viscosity with about 40% to 50% by weight of fuming sulphuric acid applied in portions of about 5% to 10% at a time. The use of such large quantities of fuming sulphuric acid gives rise to the formation of sulphonic acids which are soluble in oil. In order to remove these oil-soluble acids, the acidified oil is neutralized with caustic soda solution containing alcohol. This solution, after the treatment, contains sodium salts of sulphonic acids, which are recovered as such, or from which the acids are obtained. Both salts and acids are valuable by-products, as they can be used as emulsifying agents for the production of various industrial emulsions. After neutralization, the medicinal oil is treated with decolorizing earth and filtered. The final product is the water-white, odourless, tasteless oil known as liquid paraffin.

PARAFFIN WAX

The refining of paraffin wax, which is necessary chiefly to improve its colour, is also sometimes effected by means of mixing hot wax with sulphuric acid and, after drawing off the acid tar, with decolorizing earth. Generally, however, percolation through a column of coarse earth is sufficient. In the case of wax there is no need to add a solvent to thin down the liquid, as the viscosity of melted wax is sufficiently low to ensure rapid filtration. The molten wax leaving the percolator is passed through a steam-jacketed filter press, and the clear water-white wax emerging is run into moulds, where it is allowed to cool down in the form of slabs. If the wax is required in flakes, the molten wax is allowed to pass over a rotating drum which is internally cooled with water. A scraper removes the wax as it solidifies in a thin layer, causing the solid wax to break up into thin flakes.

BIBLIOGRAPHY

The Scientific Principles of Petroleum Technology. L. Gurwitsch and H. Moore. (Chapman & Hall, London.)
Chemical Refining of Petroleum. V. A. Kalichevsky and B. A. Stagner. (Chemical Catalog Comp., Inc., New York.)
American Petroleum Refining. H. S. Bell. (D. Van Nostrand Comp., Inc., New York.)
The Science of Petroleum, Sections 26 and 27. (Oxford University Press, London.)

XII

SOLVENT REFINING

THE refining processes described in the previous chapter were, until recently, employed almost exclusively, and are still largely used. They are chemical methods in which the deleterious products in the oils are destroyed. The constituents so removed are changed in nature and are refinery waste products, the disposal of which often presents a difficult problem.

Difficulty was encountered in former years, when kerosine had to be continually improved by severe acid refining to meet market requirements, particularly in those countries where the available crude oil had a pronounced aromatic character, resulting in a kerosine of poor illuminating quality.

However, a Roumanian chemist, Dr. L. Edeleanu, found that liquid sulphur dioxide has the power of extracting the aromatic compounds responsible for the bad illuminating qualities of the kerosine. Thus, Edeleanu opened the field of solvent extraction processes. Although the first Edeleanu plant was started in 1907 with kerosine as the feed stock, it was not until 1926 that solvent extraction (Edeleanu) was first applied to lubricating oils.

EDELEANU PROCESS

Once the principle of solvent extraction had made its appearance in the oil industry many other processes were patented, and nowadays solvent extraction is among the most widespread methods in modern refinery practice. By these solvent extraction processes the desired and the undesired components are separated by taking advantage of their different solubility in a solvent (which is therefore called a "selective" solvent), from which they can be recovered subsequently, so that the solvent is again obtained ready for use. In this way, the undesirable components are not destroyed by chemicals but are separated and later recovered unaltered, in the form of oils which can be used, perhaps only as fuel, but in many cases for special purposes.

As stated above, Edeleanu found that aromatic hydrocarbons and certain other components in some kerosines were the cause of their poor illuminating qualities and that the removal of these by sulphuric acid, i.e. by chemical treatment, the only method applied at that time, could be advantageously replaced by an extraction with liquid sulphur dioxide, a relatively cheap chemical. When, for instance, Roumanian kerosine was shaken up with liquid sulphur dioxide and allowed to settle, two layers were formed, the lower one consisting of the bulk of the sulphur dioxide in which most of the harmful constituents and also some of the good components were dissolved ; the upper one consisting of the good kerosine components together with a small quantity of the harmful constituents and the rest of the sulphur dioxide in solution in this kerosine. The lower layer is called the ''extract''* or solvent layer, the upper one the ''raffinate''* or oil layer. These two layers could be separated and the sulphur dioxide boiled off from them, so that the kerosine was then obtained in two parts, one a good illuminant and one a bad illuminant, but neither had been destroyed as had been the case when the sulphuric acid treatment was used. In this case, the bad illuminant was found to be useful as a fuel for motor tractor engines, as it had good anti-knock properties ; this product is now well known as ''Edeleanu Extract''. The Shell Group erected a small plant in 1911 to carry out this process in Rouen, and later—in 1916—erected its first commercial Edeleanu plant at Balik Papan. There are now some fifty or sixty of these plants in existence, many of them being operated mainly for the part extracted by the sulphur dioxide rather than the part left undissolved.

The solvent layer obtained in such a process will also contain paraffinic oil, because the solvent does not dissolve the non-paraffinic (aromatic) oils exclusively. On the other hand, part of the non-paraffinic constituents will remain in the raffinate layer, so that there is not a very sharp separation between the two groups of components. But the raffinate layer is again mixed with solvent and allowed to settle out in two layers ; the new raffinate layer therefore contains a lower percentage of non-paraffinic material than previously. By repeating this process the raffinate will be still further improved. Therefore, in actual practice a multi-stage treatment is always effected nowadays. However, instead of adding fresh solvent in each stage, this is usually done only at the end, where the last impurities have to be removed ; this solvent is further used, successively, in the other stages, in such a way that the solvent is running in counter-current with the oil.

Fig. 1.   Edeleanu Plant for Kerosine.

Fig. 1 is a view of the Wilmington (California) Edeleanu plant for treating kerosine.   Fig. 2 is a simplified flow sheet of the same plant.   In this plant, the effect of a succession of separate stages, in each of which mixing and separating into two layers takes place, is obtained by carrying out treatment in a tower filled with material which serves to bring the kerosine and liquid sulphur dioxide into close contact, a so-called "packed tower".   The kerosine is pumped into the tower near the bottom, and the sulphur dioxide near the top.   The kerosine, owing to its low specific gravity, moves up the tower and meets the heavier sulphur dioxide descending, the latter dissolving the aromatic constituents

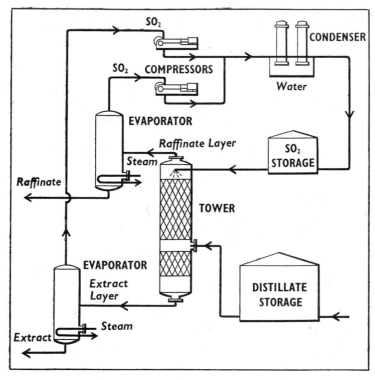

Fig. 2.   Flow Sheet of Edeleanu Process.

of the kerosine.   By the time the paraffinic raffinate reaches the
top of the tower it is nearly free of the aromatic constituents and
leaves the tower together with a small amount of sulphur dioxide,
while the bulk of the sulphur dioxide leaves the bottom of the
tower together with the aromatic extract.   The rest of the plant
consists of evaporators for distilling off the sulphur dioxide from
the raffinate and extract and returning it to the system for re-use.

All counter-current plants of the type just described, whether
they use packed towers or separated mixers and settlers, have
essentially the same features.   The raffinate can be obtained in

a high degree of purity, but the extract is not free from paraffinic material because, as is apparent from the flow sheet and the description, the extract is produced from the incoming material direct, so that it takes part of the raffinate constituents away in solution.

Gasolines, kerosines, gas oils and lubricating oils may all be treated by the Edeleanu process, the extracts being known as Benzex*, Kerex*, Gasex* and Lubex* respectively.

Benzex is produced by extraction of gasoline because of the high anti-knock value of this extract ; the kerex obtained by extraction of kerosine may be further separated by distillation into a light fraction with good anti-knock properties, also known as benzex, and a residual fraction, resex. All these extracts, being of a pronounced aromatic character, may constitute valuable base materials for the synthesis of chemical products.

SOLVENT TREATMENT OF LUBRICATING OIL

Solvent treatment of lubricating oils was developed in order to produce oils with greater resistance to oxidation in an engine and having good viscosity indices* (*vide* chapter XXIX). Oxidation causes the formation of sludge and also induces other undesirable properties in the oil. The manufacture of special oils such as turbine oils, transformer oil, white oils and medicinal oils generally involves a severe acid treatment, and for reasons of economy, a solvent treatment generally precedes the final refining. As, however, the higher-boiling aromatics in lubricating oils are not very soluble in sulphur dioxide, even at higher temperature, and so tend to be left in the refined portion instead of being dissolved out by the solvent, other solvents, superior to sulphur dioxide in this respect, were sought for treating lubricating oils.

Thus, processes using organic liquids such as phenol, nitrobenzene, furfural, etc., were developed, and the Edeleanu process itself has been improved by the use of a mixture of sulphur dioxide and benzene as a solvent. All these solvents function in the same way as does liquid sulphur dioxide in that they all dissolve the non-paraffinic constituents much more readily than the paraffinic constituents.

Temperature has a considerable influence on the separation of both components, and each case requires its own most suitable extraction temperature or, in case of multi-stage treatment, its temperature gradient or range. The temperature at which the extract leaves the extraction system is all-important, and more than any other factor determines the yield and quality of the raffinate.

The boiling point of the solvent must differ considerably from that of the oil to be extracted, in order to enable their separation by distillation. For this reason most of the lubricating oil process solvents would never be suitable for white products, sulphur dioxide being one of the few exceptions.

All the solvents mentioned above are so-called single solvents ; they are specially suitable for the extraction of distillates. They are unsuitable for the extraction of residual feedstocks containing high molecular weight resins and asphaltenes, unless these have been previously removed by de-asphaltizing with liquid propane (*vide infra*).

RECTIFLOW EXTRACTION PROCESS

Since recovery of the solvent is the biggest item in the cost of running an extraction plant, it is obviously desirable to produce the required product with a minimum of solvent. The value of lubricating oil extract is relatively low and the loss of valuable components must be reduced to a minimum. With these ends in view, the Rectiflow process has been developed. In this process, the extract formed from the intake material is not allowed to leave the system but is further treated, again in successive stages, in order to separate the paraffinic material out of it. This will be further elucidated in the following description.

Fig. 3 illustrates such a process diagrammatically and also serves to show how a solvent process operates using mechanical mixers and settlers instead of a tower.

The plant, as illustrated, has seven stages, each stage consisting of a pump, a mixing tee, and a settler. The solvent is fed into stage 7, is mixed with the raffinate layer from the no. 6 settler and is then led to no. 7 settler. In this settler, as also in the other settlers, two layers separate, the raffinate layer rising to the top and the extract or solvent layer settling to the bottom. This latter layer contains, besides paraffinic components, the greater part of the non-paraffinic substances still contained in the raffinate of settler no. 6, so that the raffinate layer is now sufficiently pure and can leave the system, and is afterwards freed from solvent by distillation. The extract layer is mixed with the raffinate layer from no. 5 settler and passes to no. 6 settler, where, again, the

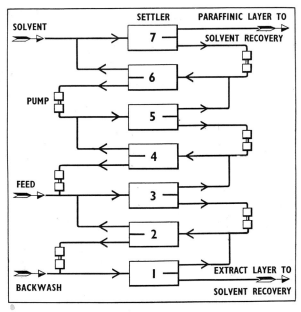

Fig. 3. Flow Sheet of Rectiflow Process.

extract layer takes away part of the non-paraffinic constituents of no. 5 raffinate, and the raffinate layer, on the other hand, regains some of the paraffins dissolved in no. 7 extract layer. Thus the paraffinic components move to the top, whereas the extract moves to the bottom. Until stage 3, where the warm feed enters, this portion of the plant corresponds to the tower described above, the extract leaving settler 3 corresponding to the extract leaving the bottom of the tower.

The Rectiflow system includes several stages (two in the diagram) beyond this point, and consists in pumping into the final stage (no. 1) a certain amount of extract almost free from solvent which is called the "backwash"*. When this backwash is mixed with the extract layer from settler no. 2 and allowed to settle in settler No. 1, a raffinate layer is formed which contains the greater part of the paraffins still present in the extract from settler no. 2, so that the extract layer from no. 1 can flow substantially freed from paraffinic components. The raffinate layer is pumped back to no. 2 settler, where it again takes away part of the paraffins contained in extract from no. 3, and so on. The extract to be used as backwash is usually obtained from the distillation section, where the solvent is distilled off from the raffinate and extract and returned for re-use.

Fig. 4.   Furfural Extraction Plant Settlers.

Fig. 4 is a photograph of the Rectiflow plant at Shell Haven, where furfural is used as a solvent. The vertical cylindrical vessel shown in the photograph consists of seven compartments one above the other, in each of which the layers are allowed to settle. In fig. 5 the flow from compartment to compartment is shown diagrammatically. The extract layer from the bottom of compartment A is mixed with the raffinate layer from compartment C, pumped through a cooler into compartment B, the same procedure being followed for each stage.

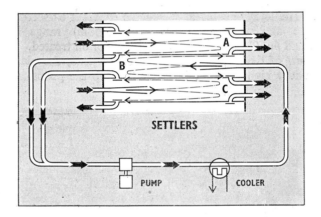

Fig. 5. Flow Sheet of Rectiflow Settlers.

Because the selectivity of the solvent is dependent on the temperature, coolers are installed in order to be able to keep each compartment at its most desirable temperature.

DUO-SOL PROCESS

Thus far, only single-solvent systems have been described, but there are also two-solvent systems, in which two different solvents flow in counter-current to each other. The best known of these processes is the Duo-Sol process, where propane and ''selecto'' (phenol-cresol mixture) are used. The Duo-Sol process is undoubtedly the most versatile of the solvent extraction processes. It is particularly suitable for the extraction of residues, whereas single-solvent processes can only be applied to distillate fractions.

Fig. 3 also serves to illustrate diagrammatically a Duo-Sol plant, as, in flow, it resembles the Rectiflow system very closely. The raw oil is admitted near the middle of the system, the selecto at the top, and, instead of the backwash, liquid propane is pumped in. The propane dissolves the paraffinic components. The non-paraffinic constituents (also asphaltenes* and resins) are extracted by the selecto. The greater part of the selecto goes into the extract layer. The temperatures at which the different extractors work (propane maximum, selecto-stage minimum) range between 24° C. and 66° C., depending on the kind of oil treated.

In view of the low boiling point of propane, the plant must work under high pressure in order to keep the propane liquid.

Fig. 6.   Settler of Duo-Sol Plant.

As each layer contains both solvents, and the solvents must be recovered separately, each layer must be distilled in at least two stages.

In fig. 6 a photograph is shown of the settlers in the Duo-Sol plant at Wood River Refinery. The oil and the solvents are intimately mixed and then led into the settling vessels. These have been built together into one long horizontal tank divided into different compartments, each compartment being one settling stage, in much the same way as in fig. 5. Fig. 7 shows a complete Duo-Sol plant, which consists mostly of equipment for the recovery of solvents.

Thus, the method originally discovered by Edeleanu has been extended successfully to the treatment of lubricating oils, and the treatment of oil in such a way as not to destroy any part of it has a very strong appeal. A great deal of work is being done to find ways of removing other unwanted constituents of crude oil,

Fig. 7.   Complete Duo-Sol Extraction Plant.

such as sulphur, and this physical method of treatment will probably be of more and more importance in the future.

REFINING WITH LIGHT HYDROCARBONS (DE-ASPHALTIZING)

Another process is de-asphaltizing by means of liquids such as propane under pressure, which has the property of dissolving oils but not asphaltic bitumens. The process is again one of separation, taking advantage of properties other than the boiling points of the hydrocarbons. The commonly known method of separating oil from asphaltic bitumen consists in distilling the oil off until nothing is left but bitumen. In the solvent de-asphaltizing processes everything is dissolved except the asphaltic bitumen. It is not surprising that the asphaltic bitumens obtained by the two processes differ in certain respects, the product obtained by propane treatment resembling more closely coal-tar pitch, but, by suitable treatment, it can be used as a road asphaltic bitumen.

In practice the process is a simple one. The oil to be de-asphaltized is mixed with liquid propane or a similar solvent by passing both into a tower similar to a normal extracting tower. The asphaltic bitumen is continuously drawn off at the bottom, and the oil layer at the top, the solvent associated with them being recovered by distillation.

If the relative powers of hydrocarbon solvents to throw down asphaltic bitumen are compared, it is found that propane throws down a larger amount of a softer asphaltic bitumen than does butane, and that butane throws down more than does pentane or ordinary gasoline. If still lighter hydrocarbons, such as ethane or methane, are added to the propane (under pressure) more and more asphaltic bitumen is thrown out of solution, together with the more viscous oil fractions.

Use of this principle is made in the Pilat process. Here, a mineral oil residue is first treated with propane and the asphaltic bitumen drawn off. Gaseous methane is then dissolved under pressure in the resultant solution. This causes the separation of oil fractions, starting with a heavy fraction that consists mostly of resinous material, and continuing with less and less viscous oil fractions. In this way, a kind of fractionation of the oil without distillation is effected. Whether this method will be developed as a commercial application still remains an unanswered question.

BIBLIOGRAPHY

The Refining Process with Liquid Sulphur Dioxide. L. Edeleanu. (J. Inst. Petr. Techn., **18**, 900. 1932.)

Solvent Extraction of Lubricating Oils. S. W. Ferris, E. R. Birkhimer and L. M. Henderson. (Ind. Eng. Chem., **23**, 753. 1931.)

A summarizing article will be found in : The Oil and Gas Journal, issue 31st March, 1945.

The Science of Petroleum, Volume III, pages 1817–1928. (Oxford University Press, London. 1938.)

Oel und Kohle, **11**, 655. S. von Pilat. 1935.

XIII

MANUFACTURE OF LUBRICATING OILS AND GREASES

LUBRICATING OILS

In the primary distillation of crude oils, the lighter fractions, gasoline, kerosine and gasoil, are removed and the remainder, called "straight-run residue", contains a large variety of high-boiling components of the crude oil. As the crude oils are of widely different origin and constitution, it follows that the residues from various crude oils are also widely different, and that some may contain hydrocarbons which will not be present in others, so that some are suitable for lubricating oil manufacture, while others are not.

A further separation by distillation is usually carried out on the residue, but in this case the distillation is performed under low pressure to decrease the boiling temperature, in order to prevent decomposition of the hydrocarbons (cracking). As the boiling point of the hydrocarbons increases, the size of the molecules increases, and other characteristics of the hydrocarbons also change. One which is of special interest is the viscosity, which increases considerably for certain groups of hydrocarbons. Residues which contain those groups of hydrocarbons which have a high viscosity form the main source for the production of lubricating oils. Formerly, lubricating oils were mainly classified according to viscosity. However, as a result of the practical application of lubricating oils, more restrictive specifications have been demanded of them. For instance, due to the development of higher temperatures in engine operations, the lubricating oils quickly deteriorated and it was necessary to select special lubricating oils from certain residues, or to refine lubricating oils differently, in order to remove undesirable components which caused the rapid deterioration.

The residues, as such, often contain, besides the lubricating oil fractions, other products, such as asphalt and wax. Various types

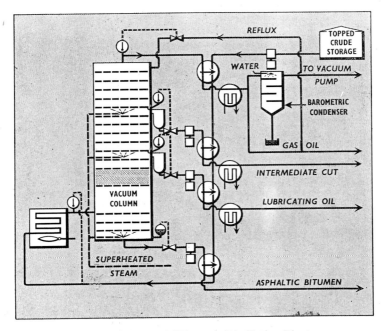

Fig. 1.   Diagram of Vacuum Distillation Plant.

of residues are known which contain all or only one of these main groups of fractions, and therefore the different residues require various methods of processing. The separation of lubricating oil fractions from asphaltic residue is mostly performed by vacuum distillation, that is, distillation under reduced pressure.

VACUUM DISTILLATION

Fig. 1 shows a flow diagram of a vacuum distillation unit. Asphaltic type residue, or topped crude oil as it is sometimes called, is pumped from a storage tank, maintained at a slightly raised temperature to keep the oil fluid, through a series of heat exchangers, where heat is picked up from condensing vapours, hot condensed distillates and the asphaltic residue (bitumen). Thence,

Fig. 2.   Vacuum Distillation Plant.

at a temperature of 150° C. to 200° C. (302° F. to 392° F.), it passes through a tubular heater of the same design as that used for crude oil distillation. The temperature is raised to such a degree that when the oil issues into the vacuum column, the volatile constituents which it is desired to distil off in order to obtain the correct grade of asphaltic bitumen, will flash into vapour. This temperature will be of the order of 320° C. to 440° C. (608° F. to 824° F.).

Superheated steam is introduced into the bottom of the distillation column so that any remaining volatile constituents are removed by this steam as the asphaltic bitumen flows over the steaming trays (shown below the inlet of the feed). The steamed asphaltic bitumen is pumped away from the plant through a heat exchanger, the flow being regulated by a level controller, which maintains a steady asphaltic bitumen level in the bottom of the column.

The amount distilled off is determined by the distillation temperature. As in all modern plants, this temperature is automatically controlled. There are various methods of effecting this. One method is to keep the fire in the tubular heater as steady as possible, the oil temperature then being kept steady by regulating the amount passing through the heater by means of a regulating valve automatically controlled by the heater outlet temperature.

The vapours leaving the flashing section of the column pass into the upper part of the column, which contains a series of bubble trays and one or more distillate collecting trays, being in this respect very similar in design and principle of operation, to the type already described for crude oil distillation. One or more side streams can be collected, but all distillates must be pumped away, as the column is under vacuum. The superheated steam injections under the so-called collecting trays serve the same purpose as the strippers in former distilling columns.

Nowadays, bubble trays are often replaced by "shower decks"*, consisting of perforated plates allowing the reflux stream to divide itself in a shower in counter-current with the rising vapours. Thus, the resistance of the vapours is lower than in the case of bubble plates, which means a better vacuum in the whole of the column.

The quality of the top product, which is a gasoil, is automatically controlled by a temperature controller, which maintains a steady temperature at the top of the column by regulating the amount of condensed gasoil that is refluxed. In a similar manner, the quality of each side stream is controlled by a temperature controller regulating the relative amounts of product withdrawn and overflowing as reflux in the liquid down-take of the next section of the column.

The oil vapours and steam from the top of the column pass, in succession, through the vapour heat exchanger and distillate condenser, where practically all the oil vapour is condensed, leaving only the steam, which, because of its low boiling point under vacuum, is not condensed in the comparatively warm oil condenser. The steam is finally condensed in a vessel called a ''barometric'' condenser. This is simply a vessel into which water can be introduced in such a manner as to become intimately mixed with the vapour to be condensed. The vapour, entering by a large connection at the top of the vessel, is brought into very intimate contact with cold water, which is sprayed into the upper part through a series of jets. The distillation steam and all other vapours condensable at the temperature of the cooling water are thereby condensed, and only uncondensable gases, such as dissolved air from the topped crude oil, air from plant leakage and a little cracked gas, pass away through the baffled vapour outlet in the side to the vacuum equipment. In order to allow the mixture of condensate and cooling water to flow away from the vessel without pumping, it is placed at a height above ground level greater than the barometric height of water ($33\frac{1}{2}$ feet), and the liquid outlet from the bottom carries a barometric leg or pipe, the bottom end of which is sealed by the water in an overflow sump. The whole arrangement, therefore, acts like a huge water barometer.

The necessary vacuum may be obtained by means of either a displacement type vacuum pump or a two- or three-stage steam ejector.

PREPARATION OF LUBRICATING OILS BY DISTILLATION OF ASPHALTIC RESIDUE

As the asphaltic residue (topped crude oil) contains naphthenic acids* which are distilled over together with the different lubricating oil fractions, it is customary to collect all the lubricating oil from the first distillation as one bulk distillate ; at the same time a gasoil fraction and straight-run asphalt is obtained. The bulk distillate is neutralized with caustic soda solution or with milk of lime and, without separating the naphthenic acid soaps formed, the oil is redistilled, leaving the soaps together with small quantities of asphaltic bitumen as a residue. Such a residue is commonly referred to in the Group as " Ados ".

Alternatively, the redistillation is carried out in the same plant as the one used for the first vacuum distillation. The neutral lubricating oil distillates are then obtained as side streams. These distillates need a further treatment with chemicals, which is described in chapter XI.

Recently a new method of neutralizing the lubricating oil distillates has been developed. The process consists in circulating a strong caustic soda solution in the vacuum column over the first tray above the hot oil inlet. Fresh soda is injected into the soda stream to the column and spent solution withdrawn from the column. The amount of injected soda is regulated in such a way that the distillates obtained are neutral and so that the asphalt does not contain any soda. The advantage of this method is that the production of neutral distillates is possible in one distillation, simultaneously yielding a straight-run asphaltic bitumen free from soda.

The lubricants from asphaltic base stock have, as a rule, low viscosity indices*, that is, their viscosities are more susceptible to temperature changes than are those of the oils derived from paraffin base crude oils. These oils have, however, excellent lubricating properties and, in consequence, they are used as lubricants wherever no extremes of temperature are met. Most of the grades of industrial lubricants used for general machinery lubrication are made from such oils.

PREPARATION FROM PARAFFINIC RESIDUES

The lubricating oil contained in a typical paraffinic residue is associated with gasoil and paraffin wax, and the amount of asphaltic bitumen present is small or negligible. By further distillation it is possible to obtain from such a residue a waxy lubricating oil residue of high viscosity. If the wax is removed from this residue by one of the methods described in chapter XV and the dewaxed oil given a filtering treatment, a so-called ''bright stock'' will result. The distillation is carried out in the same kind of plant as that described above. Bright stock is a valuable blending agent used largely in the production of motor oils.

The manufacture of high-grade and special oils is described in chapter XII, under ''Solvent Refining ''.

GREASE   MANUFACTURE

Greases are made at a number of Group-owned plants. The major production consists of greases based on calcium, sodium and aluminium soaps, but there are a number of special products which use barium and lithium soaps. No generally applicable manufacturing conditions can be laid down, since these will depend to a great extent on formulation and the properties required in the finished product.

In the conventional method of production the fatty material, alkali and a portion of the mineral oil are charged into an autoclave* (a closed vessel under pressure) or an open kettle, and heated until the formation of soap (''saponification''*) is complete. The concentrated soap solution, if made in an autoclave, is blown down into an open kettle, where the processing is continued. The remainder of the mineral oil is added, the whole stirred until homogeneous and adjusted by necessary additions of water, alkali or acid. The mix is then cooled with continual stirring and eventually filled into packages. Quality is maintained by close attention to manufacturing conditions and by careful laboratory examination at various stages of the process.

Lime and soda greases are, in general, made by the above type of processing. Certain kinds of grease, however, cannot be manufactured in this way. Aluminium- and lithium-base greases, for example, must be cooled in a more or less static condition. To prepare these greases, the pre-made soaps are dissolved in the mineral oil at an elevated temperature. Cooling until recent years was always effected by pouring the molten mass into trays, where it remained until cool enough for removal and subsequent plasticizing. This method is somewhat laborious and handling costs may be high.

The Shell Group has devised several methods for improving on this process. In one such method the molten grease is fed on to a moving belt in thin layers. Cooling and plasticizing produces high-quality products by a truly continuous process.

In another newly-developed method the hot grease is fed into a series of horizontal tubes, where it remains until gelling is complete. A fresh charge of hot grease then forces out the cooled material, which is ready for the plasticizing treatment.

"Cold sett" greases form a class of cheap lubricants suitable for the lubrication of open-type bearings such as are fitted to railway or tramcar axles. They are made at slightly above atmospheric temperature, usually from rosin oil, alkali and mineral oil, and, in general, compare unfavourably with the "boiled greases".

BIBLIOGRAPHY

The Science of Petroleum. (Oxford University Press, London.)

Petroleum Refinery Engineering. W. L. Nelson. (McGraw-Hill Book Company, New York and London.)

The Scientific Principles of Petroleum Technology. L. Gurwitsch, translated by H. Moore. (Chapman & Hall, London.)

Modern Petroleum Technology. (Institute of Petroleum, London.)

Lubricating Greases : Their Manufacture and Use. E. N. Klemgard. (Reinhold Publishing Corp., New York.)

XIV

MANUFACTURE OF ASPHALTIC BITUMEN

THE asphaltic bitumen contained in an asphaltic residue (from the distillation of crude oil) is usually separated from the other constituents by a further distillation in vacuum, from which it is then obtained as a residue. The plant used for this purpose is the same as that shown in fig. 1, chapter XIII, where it is described for the manufacture of lubricating oils. The penetration* (*vide* chapter XXXI) of the resulting asphaltic bitumen depends on the amount of distillate which has been removed ; a hard asphaltic bitumen of low penetration is one which has been distilled further than a soft one of high penetration. The amount distilled off is in turn determined by the distillation temperature.

BLOWN ASPHALTIC BITUMEN

The asphaltic bitumen prepared by straight distillation, as described above, is often referred to as straight-run or steam-refined bitumen. It consists of the unchanged asphaltic compounds of high boiling point originally present in the topped crude oil. Heavy distillates or soft asphaltic bitumens may be oxidized under suitable conditions. By the air oxidizing or ''blowing'' process, some of the hydrogen present in the distillate or bitumen molecules is combined with oxygen from the air to form water. These molecules, robbed of hydrogen, then combine with one another to form the larger and heavier molecules of the asphaltic variety. The oxidation is carried out by blowing air through a heated topped asphaltic crude oil or soft asphaltic bitumen. The resulting product is consequently referred to as a ''blown''* asphaltic bitumen. As the oxidation reaction gives rise to a large amount of heat, the blowing operation must be controlled very carefully to allow this heat to be carried away as fast as it develops, otherwise there is danger of spontaneous combustion occurring owing to the overheating of the charge in the presence of a large amount of air.

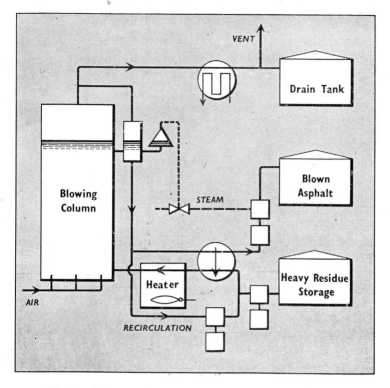

Fig. 1. Diagram of Plant for Blowing Asphaltic Bitumen.

Fig. 1 shows, diagrammatically, a continuous blowing plant. The charging stock is fed, continuously, through a heat exchanger and oil heater into the bottom of a tall reaction column which has a series of small air inlets at the bottom. This column may be some 20 or 25 feet high and is operated nearly full of asphaltic bitumen. Thus, the air has to travel a long distance in contact with the bitumen, so that its oxygen is almost completely used. From the top of the column, the charge passes by way of a level control tank to a circulating pump and also to a product pump. The former maintains a circulation of liquid through the heater and column, whilst the latter continuously draws off a small quantity of asphaltic bitumen and pumps it away through the heat exchanger to a storage tank.   A level controller regulates the amount leaving this pump.   The penetration of the asphaltic bitumen made is regulated by the degree of blowing, which depends upon the average time the charge stays in the system.   This, in turn, is regulated by the rate at which fresh charge is fed to the plant.   The spent gas (mainly nitrogen), light oil vapour and steam (from the combination of oxygen with hydrogen from the oil molecules) pass from the top of the column into a condensing system.

The oil heater is used mainly to supply the initial heat required to get the oxidation started ; after that, the heat of reaction is almost sufficient to heat the incoming charge to the required reaction temperature.

CUT-BACK ASPHALTIC BITUMEN

When asphaltic bitumens are used for road making or repairing they have to be heated to a temperature of some 190° C. (374° F.) to make them sufficiently fluid for easy application.   If they are to be mixed with stone aggregate, this also has to be heated to dry it in order to ensure its being properly "wetted" by the bitumen.   It is, therefore, not surprising that means were sought to simplify the use of asphaltic bitumen in road work.   One method is to thin down the asphaltic bitumen at the refinery, while it is still hot and liquid, with a solvent or flux consisting of light kerosine or gasoil.   When stones are coated with the resultant "cut-back"* bitumen and then spread on the road, the kerosine or gasoil evaporates, leaving the asphaltic bitumen in intimate contact with the stones in its original form.   The cut-back is made sufficiently fluid with the flux to be handled easily from ordinary steel drums. It is still necessary, however, to heat it to a moderate temperature (about 120° C. = 248° F.) before use to ensure good fluidity and adhesion to stone.

The manufacture of a cut-back is carried out either by the batch or the continuous method.   In the batch method, an ordinary blending tank is charged with asphaltic bitumen and the required amount of flux is pumped into the bottom, preferably through a perforated distributing pipe. Thorough mixing is ensured either by air blowing or, if the flux is fairly volatile, by circulating the contents of the tank rapidly by means of a pump sucking from the bottom and discharging back into the top. In the continuous method, the hot asphaltic bitumen and flux are pumped together in the required proportions through a suitable mixing device, such as a centrifugal pump or mixing nozzle, into storage tanks.

ASPHALT EMULSIONS

Another method of simplifying the application of asphaltic bitumen consists in using it as an emulsion in water, heating then being no longer necessary. The simplest type of emulsifying plant, and one which is still used to some extent, consists of a vertical vessel containing a propeller stirrer. Into this agitator is run a charge of water containing a small quantity of emulsifier in solution. This is necessary to stabilize the finished emulsion by preventing the microscopic particles of asphaltic bitumen from merging with one another during storage, thus causing the emulsion to "break" prematurely. Such an emulsifier may consist of a fatty acid soap made by neutralizing olein or liquid rosin with a 25% excess of caustic soda, the quantity used being about 1% calculated on the finished emulsion. The dilute soap solution is heated in the agitator to about 90° C. (194° F.) and asphaltic bitumen at the same temperature is run slowly into it, with the stirrer in operation, until the required amount has been added. In the case of an emulsion used for road spraying, the asphaltic bitumen content will be about 55%, and for grouting about 62%.

A continuous plant employing a colloid mill is, however, more generally used. A typical form of this device consists of two metal discs placed very close to one another and arranged to rotate rapidly in opposite directions, inside a closed metal casing. The shaft on which one of the discs rotates is hollow, and the soap solution and asphaltic bitumen, in the required proportions, are pumped into it together at about 90° C. (194° F.). When the rough mixture is discharged between the two rotating surfaces, the asphaltic bitumen is subjected to a hydraulic shearing force, tearing it into extremely small particles, which are immediately dispersed in the soap solution.

P

A typical emulsion has a viscosity not very much higher than that of water and can be mixed cold with road-making material. Traces of soluble salts, normally present in the latter, have the property of counteracting the effect of the emulsifier, thus causing the emulsion to break slowly and the coagulated asphaltic bitumen to be deposited on the stones. Special types of emulsions have been developed, mainly for the purpose of soil stabilization or consolidation. These do not coagulate readily when mixed with stones or soil, this property being obtained by the use of special emulsifiers.

BIBLIOGRAPHY

The Science of Petroleum. (Oxford University Press, London.)

Asphalt and Allied Substances. H. Abraham. (D. van Nostrand Co., New York.)

Bituminous Substances. P. Spielmann. (Benn, London.)

XV

MANUFACTURE OF PARAFFIN WAX

PARAFFIN waxes occur in some proportion in most crude oils, but in appreciable proportions only in those of the paraffinic or waxy, and mixed-base types. The paraffin wax is dissolved in the oil so that its presence is not obvious at ordinary temperatures. As the solubility decreases with fall in temperature, the wax will begin to separate out in the solid form when a waxy crude oil is cooled. The temperature at which the wax will begin to separate out will depend on the amount present in solution in the crude oil ; the greater the wax content, the higher the temperature at which it will begin to settle out. The lower the temperature to which the oil is cooled, the greater the amount of wax which will separate out. Paraffin wax melts readily, and on being heated eventually distils at about the same temperature as do lubricating oil fractions. It would obviously, therefore, be desirable to de-wax a crude oil which was to be worked up into lubricating oils, as otherwise the wax would distil over with the lubricating oils. On cooling to low temperatures, the wax would then separate out, causing the oils to appear dull, and perhaps even causing them to become semi-solid.

The obvious way to separate out a solid from a liquid is by filtration. The rate of filtration depends on the size of the particles which are to be filtered out, as the smaller the particles the more difficult the operation. Unfortunately, there are also present in crude oils certain heavy constituents which inhibit the separation of the wax in nice, easily filterable crystals. When a crude oil containing wax is distilled, these undesirable inhibiting agents remain in the residue, whereas the wax, or at any rate a good deal of it, distils over with the lubricating oil fractions. From these fractions, wax separates out on chilling in a readily filterable form. In practice, therefore, the wax is generally separated from the distillate fractions rather than from the crude oil itself. The extraction of paraffin wax from crude oils is thus generally associated with the manufacture of lubricating oils.

The first step, therefore, is the distillation of the oil, which is effected in the ways described in chapter VIII. Those fractions which, on taking a sample and chilling it, are found to contain wax, are segregated. The actual selection of the distillates to be segregated will depend on considerations of viscosity, wax content and the desired pour points of the lubricating oils to be made.

CHILLING

The wax distillate obtained in this way is chilled to a low temperature so that the wax will crystallize out. The temperature to which the oil must be chilled will depend on the character of the lubricating oils to be made. These oils must contain so little wax that, on cooling to the lowest temperature they are expected to meet, they will remain clear without separation of wax.

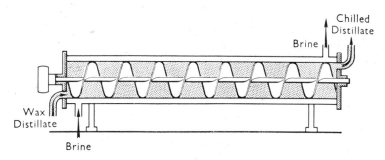

Fig. 1.   Line Diagram of Chiller.

The distillates must, therefore, be cooled to such a low temperature that, when the wax has been removed by filtration, the filtered oil will contain so little still in solution that lubricating oils of the required quality can be made therefrom. In practice, the distillates may be cooled to temperatures as low as —30° C. or —40° C. (—22° F. or —40° F.). However, if the lubricating oils are to be used in warm climates, such deep cooling is not needed. In the case of distillates rich in wax, the cooling of which to such low temperatures would produce a waxy mush too thick for easy filtering, the operation may be conducted in two or even more stages. After one chilling, the wax is filtered off and the clear oil is then chilled further and again filtered.

The chillers used are of various types, the simplest consisting of one tube placed concentrically in another of greater diameter. The inner tube through which the wax distillate passes is fitted with a worm conveyor, and the annular space between the inner and outer tubes is filled with the refrigerating liquid, which is usually brine. This chilled brine is produced by an ammonia refrigerating plant such as is in general use for refrigeration and which is in no way special to the petroleum industry.

FILTRATION

The chilled wax distillate issuing from the chillers is a thick slurry, due to the presence of the wax crystals. A separation of wax (solid) and oil (liquid) is obtained by a simple filtration process by pumping the wax slurry through large filter presses. Each press consists of a number of frames packed between plates covered with filter cloth (fig. 2). The surfaces of the plates are grooved so as to allow the oil which filters through the cloth to run away to a channel cut in the edge of the plate. Each frame, with a cloth-covered plate on either side, forms a compartment into which the chilled distillate is pumped via the central openings in the plates. As the filtration proceeds, the pressure at which the distillate slurry is pumped into the frame of the press is increased up to as much as 350 lb. per square inch. Eventually, when the filtration is complete, each frame contains a cake of crude wax, which, when the press is opened, drops out into a trough beneath.

The filter presses are kept in a room refrigerated to a temperature just above that of the slurry as it comes from the coolers. The reason for this is to prevent any further crystallizing of wax inside the filter press which might clog the pores of the filter cloth with minute crystals of wax.

The filter cakes are removed from the cool-house by a conveyor for further treatment. At this stage the crude wax still contains between 10% and 40% of oil, depending on the nature of the wax

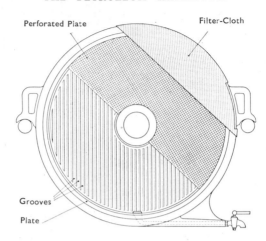

Fig. 2.   Cut-away Section of Filter Press Plate.

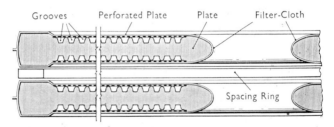

Fig. 3.   Cross Section of Filter Press Plates.

and the pressure applied for the filtering.   This oil has to be removed from the wax by a ''sweating''* process.

The filter oil, which contains very little wax, is passed on to the lubricating oil plant.

SWEATING

The filter press cakes are next melted and the liquid wax-oil mixture passes on to the next stage, which is that of ''sweating''.

Fig. 4.   Modern Filter Press.

This is carried out in a variety of types of plant, the underlying principle of which is, however, the same in every case. The molten crude wax is allowed to cool slowly into a cake, either by floating on the surface of water in a series of horizontal vessels or by being pumped into the tank of the Alanmor type of sweating stove (fig. 5), and being allowed to cool there. The rate at which the wax cools is of importance, as the slower the cooling the better the development of the crystalline structure and the more

Fig. 5.   Tray of Alanmor Sweating Stove.

easily can the oil flow away from the interstices between the crystals in the sweating process. During the crystallizing, the wax crystals form an interlocking fibrous mesh, the oil remaining suspended between the crystals. As commercial paraffin wax is not a simple compound of constant melting point, but a mixture of components of melting points ranging from 45° C. to 65° C. (113° F. to 149° F.), it follows that when such a cake of wax is very slowly warmed, the oil, because of the lowering of its viscosity by the increase of temperature, will drain away and at the same time carry with it those portions of the wax which have the lower melting point. The sweating, or fractional melting, as it really is, is stopped at the point when the wax is free from oil or, alternatively, when a sample drawn from the stove shows the wax has reached the melting point desired.

In one method, the sweating of the cakes is effected in a Henderson sweating stove, which consists of a number of horizontal flat vessels with wire gauze false bottoms, on which the wax cakes rest so that the oil can drain away, a number of these being placed one above the other in a room the temperature of which can be slowly raised. The control of the sweating is effected by the determination of the melting points of the wax remaining on the gauze and the setting points of the oil which sweats off.

In the more modern plants, however, such as that depicted (fig. 5), the wax cake may be several feet thick. As this cake has been formed by cooling in a tank containing a large number of spiral pipes, the wax cake is really built round, and contains these pipes in such a way that no portion of the cake is distant more than $2\frac{1}{2}$ inches or so from a pipe. Through these pipes, water at steadily but slowly increasing temperature is circulated, so that the raising of the temperature of the cake as a whole may be very carefully controlled.

When the sweating has been carried sufficiently far, steam can be passed through the pipes, or, in the other case, the temperature of the sweating room may be raised sufficiently high so that the wax completely melts and passes to storage. The processes in actual practice are much more complicated than outlined here. The runnings from the sweating stoves also contain much wax, so that these must be re-sweated, or sometimes even re-chilled and pressed.

REFINING

The sweated wax, which should now be free from oil, is still not quite colourless and is, therefore, subjected to a refining process. This may be a treatment with sulphuric acid followed by fullers earth, or may be a treatment with fullers earth or some similar decolorizing powder only. In the former case, the molten wax is agitated in a mechanical agitator with the required amount of strong sulphuric acid. When the reaction is complete, the acid tar is allowed to settle out and is drawn off. The wax is then mixed with fullers earth in an agitator and the fullers earth is subsequently removed by filtration through a steam-heated filter press. The fullers earth filter cakes still contain wax, which may be recovered, if desired, by means of a solvent or by steaming, but in many cases, however, it does not pay to recover this wax. The melted wax is then cast into blocks, which, when solid and cold, are packed ready for transport.

For most purposes for which it is sold a fully refined paraffin wax, substantially free from oil and of good colour, is required.

MICRO-CRYSTALLINE WAXES AND SOLVENT DEWAXING

Some crude oils, when distilled to the point at which they give heavy viscous waxy distillates, leave a residue which still contains highly valuable lubricating oil components and, at the same time, high molecular weight waxes of a special type, called "micro-crystalline" waxes. They contain also a certain amount of asphalt and resins, which have to be removed by a special process before the two other products can be prepared. The manufacture of the highly viscous residual oil (called "bright stock") requires, as in the case of waxy distillates, removal of the wax. In this case, however, the high viscosity of the oil and the special nature of the micro-crystalline wax present in the residue, make the method of simple chilling inapplicable, as the filtration of such a material would present very great difficulties.

If the waxy bright stock is dissolved in a suitable solvent, it is possible to chill the oil to the low temperature required without the viscosity of the mixture becoming too high. The solvent should be capable of dissolving the oil, but not the wax, at low temperature. As in the case of a distillate the wax can now be separated from the oil (dissolved in the solvent) by a simple filtration process.

This method of separating wax from oil is called the "solvent dewaxing" process. It has been applied for many years for the manufacture of bright stock lubricating oil of low cold test from waxy base oils, but nowadays it is also widely used for dewaxing of distillate lubricating oils by applying special solvents. It has the further advantage that, after a second filtration of the wax cake with fresh solvent, a practically oil-free wax can be obtained.

A pair of solvents is now often used, such as benzol and acetone, since, by adjusting the relative proportions of these it is possible to obtain a mixed solvent which has improved properties of dissolving the oil and throwing the wax out of solution. It must be remembered, in this connection, that oil is a solvent for wax, although its solvent power falls off quickly with fall of temperature. The oil is dissolved thoroughly in the solvent and then cooled down to a temperature low enough to remove the wax, which would cause difficulties with the lubricating oil in cold weather. The mixture is cooled down by passing it through a chilling plant of the type already described. In cases of low boiling solvents, such as propane, the mixture may be cooled by allowing some of the solvent to evaporate off, this being recompressed and condensed and returned to the mixture. The evaporation of the solvent lowers the temperature, as the heat required for this evaporation, not being supplied from outside, must be obtained from the liquid itself. This is a well-known principle much used in refrigeration. The wax solidifies at these lower temperatures and the mushy mixture of oil, solvent and wax, still kept cold, is pumped to the filters. The filters may be of several types, but the old filter press type, which operated on the batch system, is giving way to the continuous filter shown in section in fig. 6. The filter consists of a large cylindrical receiver in which is slowly rotating a large drum. The outside of this drum is made of strong coarse-mesh gauze, covered with strong filter cloth, through which oil can easily pass into the interior sections when the drum is in operation. The space inside is divided up into several sections from each of which there is a pipe leading to the centre of the drum. The end of the pipe slides over the openings A, B and C. Openings A and B are connected to a vacuum pump which is sucking the whole time, whilst opening C is connected to a blower which is blowing gas in under a gentle pressure. In the sketch one of the pipes is shown connected to the opening A so that oil and wax are being sucked through the cloth continuously. The oil passes through this pipe to the centre, whilst the wax is held up on the filter cloth. As the drum rotates the pipe slowly passes from A to B, still under suction, at which point the wax is being washed free of oil by a spray of cold solvent. The oil, with this fresh solvent, passes into opening B, leaving the wax on the filter cloth washed quite free from oil.

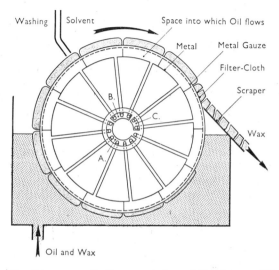

Fig. 6.   Diagrammatic Representation of Continuous Filter.

When the pipe is over opening C, a slight pressure of inert gas forces the wax off the cloth so that it slides on to the scraper down to the trough from which it is pushed out by a conveyor. The oil and the wax are then passed through separate distillation plants to recover the solvents. The solvent-free oil is passed on to the lubricating oil plant.

In some cases the separation of wax and oil is carried out with centrifuges instead of filters. In this case a solvent is chosen with a specific gravity higher than that of the wax ; such a solvent is dichloroethylene. The oil to be dewaxed is dissolved in the solvent and the solution is then cooled to a low temperature, at which the wax separates out as a cloud of small crystals. The oil remains dissolved in the heavy solvent at this temperature, and the slurry is now separated by passing through a centrifuge, an apparatus like a cream separator. The oil solution, being much heavier, behaves like the milk, and the wax slurry as the cream. The solvent has to be removed, by distillation, after the separation.

BIBLIOGRAPHY

Petroleum Refinery Engineering, chap. 25. Nelson. (McGraw-Hill Book Co., New York and London.)

Chemical Refining of Petroleum, pp. 233 *et seq.* Kalichevsky and Stagner. (The Chemical Catalog Company, Inc., New York.)

XVI

MANUFACTURE OF COMPONENTS
FOR HIGH OCTANE GASOLINE

THE phenomenal developments in petroleum refining during the past few years are the direct outgrowth of progressive and far-reaching research programmes carried out by the industry during the past ten or fifteen years. At the time these research pro-grammes were undertaken there was little prospect of the results finding immediate application, and under normal conditions it would have taken from ten to twenty years before the work of the laboratory would have found its way to full-scale utilization in the refineries.

The demands of global warfare, however, for such products as 100 octane gasoline, butadiene for synthetic rubber, and toluene, required the industry to draw on every resource at its command. Such new techniques as alkylation*, isomerization*, aromatiza-tion* and superfractionation were literally picked from the laboratory bench and adapted to large-scale operation in the refineries. Some idea of the magnitude of these developments can be gained from the aviation gasoline programme. A total of $900,000,000 was expended for the erection of new plants and the conversion of existing facilities, to produce aviation gasoline alone ; of this amount, $760,000,000 was invested in plants located in the United States.

CATALYTIC CRACKING

In chapter X we have seen how thermal cracking was introduced in 1912 for the purpose of obtaining a higher yield of gasoline from crude oil as well as for improving the quality of the gasoline. It was not until 1936 that a commercial process was developed which was superior to thermal cracking for breaking up straight-run distillate into simpler molecular structures of superior quality. This was the Houdry fixed-bed catalytic cracking process, which was soon to be followed by the Thermofor, Cycloversion and

Fluid processes, all of which depend upon the principle of catalysis.

A catalyst* is defined by chemists as a substance which by its presence can either accelerate or inhibit a chemical reaction without being changed itself. Catalytic phenomena are ever present and catalytic reactions are taking place all about us, but they are so subtle that it is only comparatively recently that we have become conscious of them. One of the most important catalytic mechanisms is that associated with the green pigment or chlorophyll in plants. With the aid of chlorophyll, plants can synthesize sugars and carbohydrates from atmospheric carbon dioxide and water. The enzymes produced by living cells are catalysts that promote the vital metabolic processes.

Industrial catalysis dates back to 1868, with the introduction of the Deacon and Hunter process for the production of chlorine from hydrochloric acid and air, using cupric chloride as the catalyst. Since then, catalysis has been used widely in the manufacture of such chemicals as ammonia, nitric and sulphuric acids, etc. In cracking petroleum, the catalyst in general use is a combination of silicon and aluminium oxides. Other combinations, such as silica-magnesia and alumina-boria, have been used on an experimental scale. The catalyst may either be made synthetically or be a natural combination of these elements found in certain clays. The remarkable thing is that these compounds of silica (SiO_2) and alumina (Al_2O_3) accelerate the decomposition of the complex chemical structures in the feed and at the same time promote the formation of high-quality gasoline and valuable gaseous fractions. The primary advantages of catalytic over thermal cracking may be summarized as follows :

1. Production of motor gasoline of 79–81 A.S.T.M.* octane number* (unleaded) compared with 69–71 by the thermal method.

2. Less degradation of the feed stock to gas and residuals.

3. Increased gasoline yields (from heavy feed stocks).

If the present trend towards high-compression engines continues, the advantages of catalytic cracking are undeniable. Another feature of catalytic cracking is the simultaneous production of a butane-butylene cut in excess of that required for blending in the gasoline to meet vapour pressure specifications, and, moreover, rich in isobutane and olefins. By adjusting operating conditions, it is often possible to produce sufficient butylenes for polymerization* purposes, which is a very convenient method of augmenting the yield of high-quality components for gasoline blends. In addition, it is possible to use the butane-butylene cut for alkylation plant charging stock.

In opposition to these advantages, direct operating cost of the catalytic units is higher than that of the thermal units at the present time, and we are unable to use residual straight-run stocks as feed for the catalytic processes, for which purpose distillates must be used.

Fluid Catalyst Cracking. Although not the first commercial process, the Fluid Catalyst Cracking Process is by far the most widely used. The Shell Group co-operated in the development of this process, which represents the first industrial use of a new chemical engineering tool—the principle of using a fluidized solid

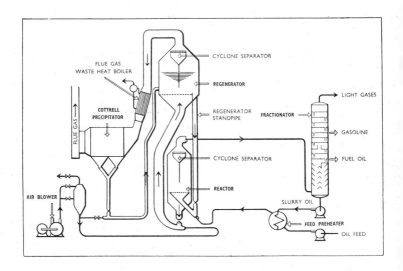

Fig. 1.   Flow Diagram of Fluid Catalyst Cracking Plant.

as a catalyst and heat transfer medium. The catalyst is in the form of a very fine powder that circulates through the plant by the action of oil vapours or air, much like dust in a windstorm. In some plants, circulation of this catalyst dust is at the rate of 35 tons a minute. Contrary to the usual practice in so-called "thermal" or non-catalytic cracking, the operations in fluid catalyst and other catalytic cracking processes are usually carried out at pressures of 15 lb. per square inch or less (i.e., at between 1 and 2 atmospheres).

The charging stock is first heated by either heat-exchange or in a direct-fired furnace, and then fed to the bottom of a vertical reactor approximately 25 feet in diameter and 50 feet high (fig. 1). Before it enters this reactor, where the temperatures range from 800° F. to 1,000° F., it joins with a stream of hot powdered catalyst, which completes the vaporization of the oil. The powder is then carried into the reactor by the oil vapours, where it is in intimate contact with the molecules of oil. The catalyst is continuously withdrawn from the bottom of the reactor and stripped of hydrocarbon vapours by contact with steam. It is then transferred to the regenerator by an air stream, where the carbon deposit is burned off at a temperature of 1,000° F, to 1,150° F. Cracked oil vapours leave the top of the reactor and are fed to a fractionator where light hydrocarbons are recovered as gases, and gasoline and fuel oil are the liquid products. A residue, called slurry oil, containing catalyst carried over into the fractionator, is removed from the bottom of the fractionator and re-cycled to the cracking plant. The gas oil fractions from the fractionator can also be re-cycled if maximum gasoline production is sought. In the regenerator, flue gases are formed as a result of the combustion of the carbon. These are fed through cyclone separators and a Cottrell precipitator to remove any catalyst fines, and are then vented to the atmosphere.

In the production of aviation gasoline, somewhat higher temperatures are employed than for the production of motor fuel, and the gasoline is rich in aromatics such as toluene, xylenes and higher aromatics. These components are extremely valuable in increasing the rich mixture performance of fuels in aircraft (*vide* chapter XXV).

Q

Fig. 2.   Fluid Catalytic Cracking Plant, Wood River, Ill., Refinery.

The Thermofor Catalytic Cracking Process. In the Thermofor Catalytic Cracking (TCC) Process the catalyst is in the form of pellets or beads about 0·2 inch in diameter. They are continually circulated from the bottom of the reactor to the top of the regenerator, and from the bottom of the regenerator to the top of the reactor, by an arrangement of elevators which are designed to operate at approximately 1,000° F. and transport 100 tons of catalyst per hour. Normally, the vaporized feed stock is admitted near the bottom of the reactor and flows upward against the downward movement of the catalyst. Because of the large size of the catalyst, there is no need for Cottrell precipitators, although cyclone separators are used to collect dust ground from the catalyst pellets. Temperatures in the reactor are from 750° F, to 950° F., and pressures are comparable with those used in the fluid process. Regeneration of the catalyst is accomplished by air at temperatures of 900° F. to 1,200° F.

The Houdry Process. The Houdry Catalytic Cracking Process is of the fixed-bed type, which means that the catalyst is not transferred to a regenerator. Three reactor chambers are used in these units ; while one is operating as a cracking chamber, the other two are used to regenerate the catalyst—usually pellets of natural clay—by burning the carbon off. In some instances six reactors may be used, synchronized to operate in sets of two. During both the reaction and regeneration periods heat is controlled by circulation of a molten salt mixture in finned tubes extending through the reactors. Since temperatures higher than 1,000° F. may impair the activity of the catalyst, the regeneration temperature is limited, and cracking temperatures do not normally exceed 900°F. Otherwise excessive coke would be formed, which could not be removed without materially increasing the heat used in regeneration. In the reaction step, pressures may go up as high as 75 lb. per square inch. Flue gases from the regeneration step are used to drive gas turbines, which in turn compress the air used for catalyst regeneration.

Cycloversion Cracking. The chief difference between the Houdry process and the Cycloversion Catalytic Cracking Process is in the control of the heat in the catalyst chambers during the regeneration period. In the Cycloversion process, control of the catalyst bed temperature is accomplished by the injection of a diluent gas such as flue gas or steam. It is quite a flexible process, in that processing conditions can be varied—in temperature from 850° F, to 1,200° F. ; in pressure, from virtually atmospheric pressure to several hundred pounds per square inch ; and in time, from one-hour to twelve-hour cycles. The light hydrocarbon fractions resulting from Cycloversion cracking are rich in olefins, particularly in the C_4 and C_5 range.

Catalytic Hydrogenation Process—Hydro-treating. The fraction of the catalytically cracked product which distils in the aviation gasoline boiling range can be used as a component in aviation gasoline blends, provided it is treated in some manner to reduce the quantity of unsaturated hydrocarbons it contains and thereby improve both its stability during storage and its susceptibility to tetra-ethyl lead (*vide* chapter XXV).   These unsaturated hydro-carbons can be removed by sulphuric acid treatment or by re-running through either a catalytic cracking unit (re-passing) or a thermal reforming unit (after-treating). However, from the standpoint of quantity production, it is better to convert the un-saturated olefins into paraffins of the same boiling range by reaction with hydrogen than to remove them, and such a process was developed by the Shell Group during the last war.

This hydrogenation process provides a method for the catalytic reaction of unstable, unsaturated compounds with hydrogen. At the same time, a large amount of the undesirable sulphur com-pounds present in the catalytically cracked aviation fraction is removed by converting these sulphur compounds to paraffins and hydrogen sulphide (H_2S). The resulting product is a valuable aviation blending component, since it has supercharged engine ratings greatly superior to straight-run fractions (*vide* chapter XXV).

The process utilizes a pelleted catalyst in a fixed-bed reactor into which the base stock fraction is introduced in the vapour state at temperatures of 800°–900° F. and pressures of 700–800 lb. per square inch. Hydrogen gas obtained from de-hydrogenation processes or manufactured for the purpose, is introduced with the vaporized charge and consumed in the process. The total amount of hydrogen required to saturate all undesirable olefins present need not be supplied from outside sources, however, since there is an appreciable dehydrogenation of cyclic compounds to aromatic hydrocarbons (*vide* chapter VII) during the treating process, and the hydrogen thus removed is available for olefin saturation.   The catalyst used is a mixed catalyst containing both nickel sulphide and tungsten sulphide in the most advantageous proportions.   It is relatively active over long periods, but after 2,000–3,000 hours of operation it is regenerated by burning off the slowly formed carbonaceous deposits with air and re-sulphiding with hydrogen sulphide to replace any sulphur lost in the air-burning step.   The activity of the catalyst can be fully restored by this procedure.

The octane rating of the hydrogenated material obtained from this process is 91–93 when 4.6 c.c.* of tetra-ethyl lead is added per American gallon.   This so-called "hydro-petrol" was produced during the last war from gas oil imported into the United Kingdom for this special purpose.   The hydro-petrol was blended with iso-octane and other high octane components for the manufacture of 100 octane aviation gasoline.

AVIATION GASOLINE COMPONENTS

Aviation gasoline is manufactured by blending a base stock (which may be either a straight-run or specially treated cracked gasoline of 70–80 octane number) with high octane components such as alkylate (*vide infra*) and iso-pentane, to which is added tetra-ethyl lead.   In many cases, straight-run gasoline of 65–80 octane number is used in combination with catalytic cracked gasoline to form the base stock.   Other high octane components are aromatics such as toluene and cumene ; the extent of utilization of these depends on the aromatic content of the base stock.

The basis for the volatility or vaporization range is provided by the base stock.   Many pure hydrocarbons and synthetic fuel components, while having excellent anti-knock ratings, could not be used alone in modern internal combustion engines because they have a very narrow boiling range and, therefore, do not possess the range of volatility necessary.   From an economic point of view, too, the use of a base stock is advantageous because it allows the production of aviation gasoline at lower cost than would be possible if the gasoline consisted entirely of materials made by relatively expensive chemical or catalytic processes. A typical 100 octane gasoline may have the following composition :

Catalytically cracked gasoline (base stock) ...	40–60%
Iso-pentane (90–95 octane number)	10–20%
High octane components (alkylates, polymers) ...	30–40%
Tetra-ethyl lead, c.c. per American gallon ...	4·0

In some cases aromatics are added to increase performance under take-off conditions. Usually these are of the substituted aromatic type, the principal agent used being cumene or iso-propyl benzene.

HIGH OCTANE COMPONENTS

The octane number of the base stock is raised to that called for in the finished fuel by the addition of synthetic hydrocarbons or hydrocarbon mixtures, which, because of their chemical structure, have inherently high octane ratings or blending values of their own. In addition, tetra-ethyl lead is also used to the extent of about 3 to 4 c.c. per American gallon. High octane components are made either by the combination of suitable small hydrocarbon molecules to form larger molecules of the desired structure, or by the re-arrangement of the structure of the original hydrocarbon molecules without changing their molecular size. Methods for combining molecules include polymerization and alkylation, while methods for re-arranging the molecular structure can be classified as isomerization, aromatization or cyclization.

Polymerization. Polymerization is the combination of two or more unsaturated molecules to form one large molecule. When used for the manufacture of gasoline components, the reaction is adjusted to give highly branched molecules that possess high octane ratings. The Shell Companies developed the first commercial process for polymerizing iso-butylene in forming iso-octane. Known as the Cold Acid Process, this method uses as feed the C_4 fraction from the cracking units. This contains butanes, normal (straight chain) butylenes and the branched-chain isomer, iso-butylene. The charge is contacted with 60% to 70% sulphuric acid which is a catalyst for the reaction at temperatures of 68° to 95° F. Two liquid phases are formed, an acid and a hydrocarbon phase.

The iso-butylene is literally taken up or absorbed by the acid phase, leaving the remaining hydrocarbons in the oil phase. After separation of these phases, the acid phase, containing the absorbed olefins, is passed into a polymerization unit which consists of coils heated to 212° F. After about one minute in this zone, the iso-butylene molecules combine to form a mixture of di-isobutylene (75%) and tri-isobutylene (25%). Separation of the polymer from the acid is followed by caustic washing and distillation to separate the two types of polymer. Finally, the di-isobutylene is changed to substantially pure iso-octane by the addition of hydrogen over a catalyst. These reactions may be illustrated by the following formulæ

$$2 \begin{array}{c} CH_3 \\ \diagdown \\ CH_3 \diagup \end{array} C{=}CH_2 \xrightarrow{\text{polymerization}} H_3C{-}\underset{\underset{CH_3}{|}}{\overset{\overset{CH_3}{|}}{C}}{-}CH_2{-}\underset{}{\overset{\overset{CH_3}{|}}{C}}{=}CH_2$$

iso-butylene   di-isobutylene

$$\xrightarrow[+H_2]{\text{hydrogenation}} H_3C{-}\underset{\underset{CH_3}{|}}{\overset{\overset{CH_3}{|}}{C}}{-}CH_2{-}\overset{\overset{CH_3}{|}}{CH}{-}CH_3$$

iso-octane

A direct outgrowth of the Cold Acid Process is the Hot Acid Process, in which the temperature at which the reaction takes place is 140° F. to 194° F. At this temperature the steps of absorption and polymerization are combined. Increased yields of product are obtained, since the formation of the higher polymers (tri-isobutylene) is inhibited to a great extent. Furthermore, some of the normal butylenes also react to form unsaturated C_8 compounds. Octane rating of the hydrogenated octanes from this process is about 97, compared with 100 for the polymer from the Cold Acid Process.

Other catalysts used for polymerizing unsaturated C_4 hydrocarbons are phosphoric acid deposited on a carrier, copper pyrophosphate and a water solution of phosphoric acid. The unsaturated octylenes resulting from the polymerization reaction are hydrogenated either at a low temperature and pressure in the presence of nickel catalyst (Shell Process) or at high pressures and temperatures in the presence of a sulphur-resistant catalyst such as molybdenum sulphide.

Alkylation. Closely related to polymerization is the process known as "alkylation". It first came into use in 1940 for the manufacture of high octane components. The alkylation reaction most commonly used in the petroleum industry involves the combination of a saturated branched chain hydrocarbon with an unsaturated hydrocarbon to give a larger, saturated molecule. Generally, iso-butane is combined with normal butylene, in the presence of a catalyst, to give a saturated C_8 product known as alkylate. This reaction can be represented as follows:

$$H_3C-\overset{\overset{\displaystyle CH_3}{|}}{\underset{\underset{\displaystyle CH_3}{|}}{C}H}+CH_2=CH-CH_2-CH_3 \longrightarrow H_3C-\overset{\overset{\displaystyle CH_3\,CH_3}{|\quad|}}{\underset{\underset{\displaystyle CH_3}{|}}{C}}-CH-CH_2-CH_3$$

iso-butane + normal butylene $\longrightarrow$ alkylate (an octane)

However, the reaction is not confined to these two compounds, for the reacting hydrocarbons may have two, three or four carbon atoms.

The sulphuric acid alkylation process is used by the Shell Group, who were instrumental in its development. Feed for the production of butane-butylene alkylate consists of iso-butane and butylene, usually in the ratio of 7 : 1, though this proportion may be varied all the way from 4 : 1 to 15 : 1. The higher ratios are preferable, for in this way polymerization of the olefins and other undesirable side reactions are kept to a minimum. This high ratio is accomplished by re-cycle of unreacted iso-butane. The net consumption of reactants is about 1·3 volumes of iso-butane to 1 volume of butylene.

The feed is first chilled to from 30° F. to 50° F. and then mixed with 98% sulphuric acid (fig. 3). After the reaction has taken place, the mixture of hydrocarbons and acid is separated from the acid catalyst in a separating chamber. The crude product is then neutralized in a caustic scrubber and fractionated to remove light gases, including iso-butane, which is re-cycled. The total alkylate may, and usually does, contain hydrocarbons boiling at a higher temperature than that desired for aviation gasoline blending. For this reason, it is fed to an alkylate re-run tower, when it is fractionated into light and heavy alkylate. The octane rating of a typical light alkylate is 95, and of the heavy alkylate 80–85.

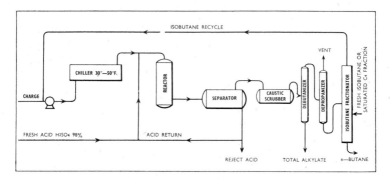

Fig. 3.   Flow Diagram of Sulphuric Acid Alkylation Process.

Another alkylation process employs hydrofluoric acid as the catalyst. It differs from the sulphuric acid process in that refrigeration is not necessary and the used acid can readily be regenerated. Commercial operations are complicated, however, by the poisonous nature of the catalyst and its solubility in the hydrocarbons being processed.

There is at least one alkylation process in commercial operation that, instead of employing a catalyst, uses high pressures and temperatures to unite the iso-paraffin and olefin. Known as "thermal alkylation", it employs temperatures of 900° to 1,000° F. and pressures of 3,000 to 5,000 lb. per square inch. Its principal application has been in the manufacture of neo-hexane (2,2-dimethylbutane) from ethylene and iso-butane. This reaction can be represented as follows :—

$$H_3C-\underset{\underset{CH_3}{|}}{\overset{\overset{CH_3}{|}}{C}}H + \quad \underset{\underset{H_2C}{|}}{\overset{H_2C}{|}} \quad \longrightarrow \quad H_3C-\underset{\underset{CH_3}{|}}{\overset{\overset{CH_3}{|}}{C}}-CH_2-CH_3$$

iso-butane + ethylene ⟶ neo-hexane

(2, 2-dimethylbutane)

Isomerization. In isomerization, the molecular structure of a chemical compound is changed without the loss of any of the atoms that existed in the structure of the original compound. As used in the petroleum industry for the production of high octane fuels, isomerization refers to the re-arrangement of the carbon and hydrogen atoms in a hydrocarbon molecule (*vide* chapter VII).

As has been mentioned before, branched chain hydrocarbons are more desirable as fuel components than those having an unbranched carbon skeleton, because of their superior anti-knock qualities in internal combustion engines of the spark-ignition type. Isomerization has proved extremely valuable in the re-arrangement of the structure of low octane hydrocarbons to high octane hydrocarbons that can be used directly in the fuel. In addition, isomerization has been responsible for augmenting the supplies of iso-butane needed in the alkylation process. The first commercial isomerization process was developed by the Shell Group for the isomerization of normal butane to iso-butane. This is known as the Shell Vapour-Phase Isomerization Process. Another process developed by the Group is the Shell Liquid-Phase Isomerization Process. The liquid-phase process is applicable to the isomerization of n-pentane and hexane as well as to butane, while up to the present the vapour-phase process has been confined to the isomerization of n-butane for alkylation purposes.

All commercial isomerization units at the present time use aluminium chloride ($AlCl_3$), promoted with anhydrous hydrogen chloride, as the catalyst. A "promoter"* is a substance which when present, even in very small quantities, increases the activity of a catalyst.

Fig. 4.   Alkylation Plant, Norco, Louisiana.

Different units employ different methods of operation. In the reactor (fig. 5), the catalyst may be in the form of a liquid pool of catalyst sludge, or the catalyst may be supported on a porous structure of granular aluminium oxide or some other inorganic material. The hydrocarbon feed is dried, split into two streams and passed through pre-heaters. One stream is used for adding catalyst to the reactor either continuously or intermittently. The other stream is introduced to the reactor at the same point as the hydrogen chloride re-cycle. After passing through the catalyst

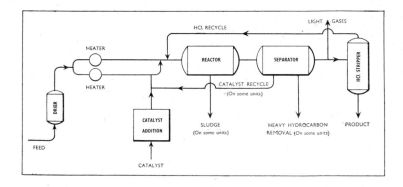

Fig. 5. Simplified Flow Diagram of Paraffin Isomerization.

zone, the effluent is sent to a catalyst separation chamber. The stream from the separator contains the hydrocarbon and hydrogen chloride. It goes to a stripper, where the hydrogen chloride is removed and re-cycled to the reactor. The hydrocarbon stream is then neutralized with caustic soda and finally fractionated to remove unreacted hydrocarbons from the isomerized product.

MANUFACTURE OF AROMATIC BLENDING AGENTS

Aromatic hydrocarbons are compounds of carbon and hydrogen having a closed or ring-type carbon skeleton (*vide* chapter VII). The simplest aromatic is benzene, and all other aromatics are considered as derivatives of this key member of the series :—

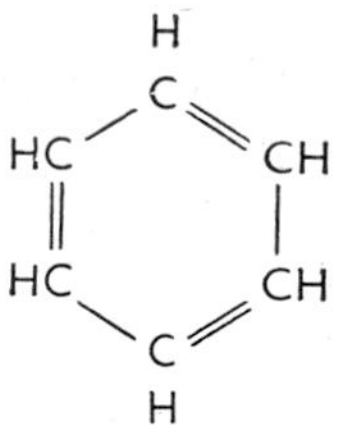

benzene

The substitution of a methyl group, CH_3, for one of the hydrogen atoms gives toluene, while the substitution of an iso-propyl group, $(CH_3)_2CH$, gives isopropyl benzene or cumene.

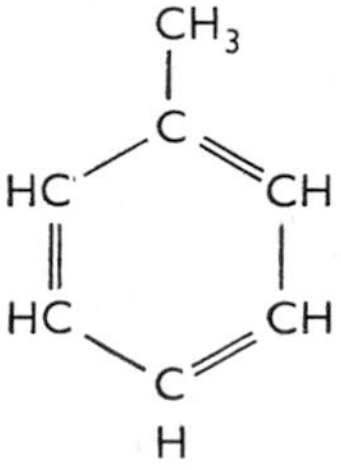

toluene

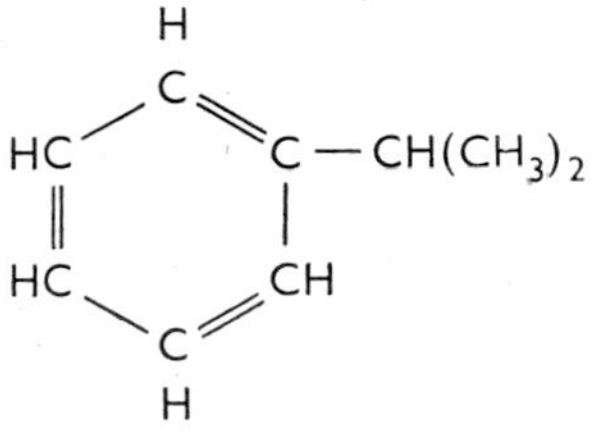

cumene

There are countless other aromatic compounds of increasingly complex structure. While aromatics do occur in crude oil, the concentration is usually very low, and methods for their synthesis have been developed in recent years because of their importance as blending agents in aviation fuel. Toluene has been made in large quantities from petroleum, primarily for use in the manufacture of high explosives.

Hydroforming*. Hydroforming is a process introduced in 1941 for converting low octane gasolines into high octane fuels by partially converting a large portion of the naphthenes to aromatics by de-hydrogenation, and incidentally converting a small percentage of the paraffins to aromatics through cyclization. The process employs a metallic oxide catalyst and takes place in an atmosphere

Fig. 6.   Butane Isomerization Plant, Wood River, Ill.

of hydrogen ; the octane number of the charging stock may be increased by as much as 30–40 units. In actual practice, about half of the final hydrocarbons are aromatic, but the content can be increased to 80%. In wartime operation, the product was separated into a toluene fraction, a light fraction rich in benzene ordinarily used for blending in motor gasoline, and a heavy fraction of high octane rating which was blended in aviation fuels.

Cumene. Early in 1942, it was recognized that cumene, or iso-propyl benzene, was a valuable addition to aviation gasoline, since it could deliver great power under full throttle or ''take-off'' conditions. The first commercial plant for cumene manufacture was put on stream in the middle of the year in the Norco (New Orleans) Refinery of Shell Oil Company. At one time there were approximately twenty plants turning out cumene to tide the aviation gasoline programme over a difficult situation. Use of this agent alone accounted for almost 23% of the increase in 100 octane fuel output in the United States in 1942–43. It is prepared by the alkylation of the aromatic, benzene, with the unsaturated hydrocarbon, propylene, in the presence of a phosphoric acid-on-carrier catalyst. Cumene is no longer of importance now that alkylation and catalytic cracking capacity can more than supply the demands of aviation for high octane fuels.

SUPERFRACTIONATION

Until quite recently, fractionation of petroleum distillates on a commercial scale has been confined to columns of about 30 plates, and reflux ratios of 1 : 1 or less (*vide* chapter VIII). Laboratory techniques of superfractionation have now been adapted to plant scale use and applied to the separation of iso-butane from the C_4 cut for alkylation feed, iso-pentane for direct blending in aviation gasoline, and higher isoparaffins for further synthesis. In superfractionation, columns of 50 or more plates are used and reflux ratios are up to 10 : 1 or higher. A typical installation for iso-pentane recovery employs three columns. The feed charge is straight-run tops and the overhead product from the alkylate de-pentanizer column. In the first column, the de-butanizer, the C_4 fraction is taken overhead and the C_5 and heavier fractions left as bottoms ; there are 50 trays, and reflux is 3 : 1. The second, or de-pentanizer column, has 70 trays and employs a reflux ratio of 2 : 1. Overhead from this column is a mixture of normal and iso-pentanes. These go to the iso-pentane column which has 69 plates and a reflux ratio of 12 : 1. Iso-pentane of 94–97% purity is distilled overhead and normal pentane is removed as bottoms.

XVII

MANUFACTURE OF SPECIAL BOILING-POINT SPIRITS AND CHEMICAL BY-PRODUCTS OF REFINING

APART from the main products of petroleum refining, such as aviation and motor gasolines, kerosines, fuel oils, lubricating oils, etc., a large number of "speciality" products are manufactured from petroleum. Although the quantities produced are comparatively small, these products are, nevertheless, of considerable importance and are used in a large number of industries. Included in this category are the special boiling-point spirits, or S.B.P's, which find extensive application as solvents ; white spirits, whose main application is as a thinner in paints and varnishes ; and such materials as naphthenic acids*, cresylic acids*, sodium naphtha sulphonates and petroleum coke, which are largely by-products of refining processes.

SPECIAL BOILING-POINT SPIRITS AND WHITE SPIRITS

A large variety of special spirits, obtained by distillation of selected gasoline fractions, are marketed throughout the world. These products very often have boiling ranges of less than 20° C. and vary in volatility from the low-boiling petroleum ethers to the comparatively high-boiling white spirits. The petroleum ethers are usually of narrow boiling range, as, for example, the grades with distillation ranges of 40° C. to 60° C. or 60° C. to 80° C., and are used for such purposes as perfume extraction. They are generally of low aromatic content and substantially free from unsaturated hydrocarbons or sulphur compounds. The most important of the special boiling-point spirits are those intermediate in volatility between the petroleum ethers and white spirits. They are used to a considerable extent in many industries as solvents for such purposes as the extraction of oil from seeds, bones, etc., as rubber solvents and lacquer diluents (vide chapter XXXII.)

SPECIFICATIONS OF SPECIAL BOILING-POINT SPIRITS—
UNITED KINGDOM

GRADE	S.P.B. 1	S.B.P. 2	S.B.P. 3	S.B.P. 4	S.B.P. 5	S.B.P. 6	Rubber Solvent
Nominal Range °C.	35–115	70–95	100–120	40–150	90–105	140–160	100–160
Specific Gravity at 60° F.	0·675–0·695	0·700–0·720	0·735–0·755	0·705–0·730	0·725–0·745	0·770–0·790	0·745–0·770
Colour				Water White			
Closed Flashpoint (Abel).	—	—	—	—	—	73° F. min.	—
Initial Boiling Point °C.	35–45	68–72	98–105	30–50	88–95	137–143	100–120
Final Boiling Point °C.	100–115	90–95	118–122	140–160	105 max.	155–165	155–165

R

They may be of narrow or wide distillation range, and of low or high aromatic content, depending on the uses for which they are required. A great variety of these special boiling-point spirits is marketed throughout the world, many conforming to buyers' own specifications, and many differing only slightly from what may be considered as the main types. In the United Kingdom the number of grades made during the war was reduced in the general interest to a range of six special boiling-point spirits and a rubber solvent, and these were found to be adequate for the basic requirements of industry. It is possible, however, that in the post-war years there may be a trend towards an increase in the number of grades marketed. The specifications of this limited number of grades are shown in the table on page 239.

The selected gasoline fractions from which the special boiling-point spirits are made, and sometimes the products themselves, are refined so that the products are free from unpleasant odour, contain no more than traces of unsaturated compounds, and the sulphur content is negligible.

White spirits usually have an initial boiling point of about 150° C. and a final boiling point of approximately 200° C. They must have a good odour and be free from deleterious or corrosive sulphur compounds. They must also be free from non-volatile residues. Originally introduced as a substitute for turpentine, white spirit has proved the equal of turpentine in most respects.

MANUFACTURE

The manufacture of the narrow boiling range special boiling-point spirits is probably one of the most exacting distillation operations carried out in a refinery. Where the offtake is very small, a common method of producing special boiling-point spirits, and sometimes white spirit, is to re-distil a refined and specially selected gasoline cut, from a main distillation process, in a batch still and column using a large amount of reflux, the distillation being carried out very slowly, to obtain the close fractionation required. A flow diagram of a typical batch still plant is shown in fig. 1. The still consists of a cylindrical shell about 30 feet in length and 10 feet in diameter and having a charge capacity of about 10,000 gallons. The still is well lagged

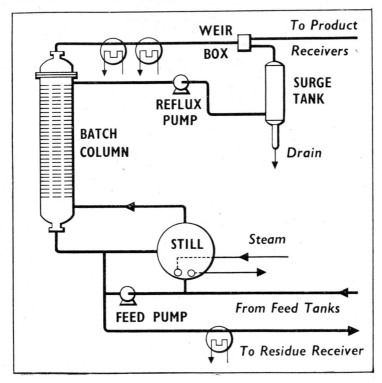

Fig. 1. Flow Diagram of Batch Still Plant.

and provided with closed steam coils of surface area about 650 square feet. An alternative method to the use of closed steam for supplying the necessary heat to the still is by the circulation of hot oil. The still may also be provided with open steam coils, so that open steam may be used to assist in the distillation of the heavier fractions.

The fractionating column is about 60 feet high and 6 feet in diameter, and contains thirty trays with bubble-caps. Alternatively, the column may be packed with rings or other suitable filling. The overhead vapour from the column is condensed in tubular condensers, part of the condensate passing to a reflux surge tank from where it is pumped back to the top of the column to provide the necessary reflux for fractionation, the balance of the condensate passing to the product receivers. The surge tank also separates any condensed water from the spirit. In an alternative arrangement, the whole of the condensate passes to the surge tank, part being pumped back to the top of the column as reflux and the balance overflowing to the product receivers.

The detailed operating procedure for carrying out a run on a batch still plant is worked out on the results of experience with the particular plant concerned and is, of course, also dependent on the properties of the feedstock. In general, the still is charged with a suitable selected gasoline cut and the distillation carried out with careful regulation of the degree of fractionation. The only control test usually employed is that of the specific gravity of the distillate as it comes over. From experience based on laboratory analyses, the operator knows when to change the product over from one receiver to another. The various fractions are collected in separate receivers, and a certain amount of blending of these fractions may or may not be necessary to give the range of special boiling-point spirits required. A complete run in a batch still of the size described will usually occupy about three days. More than one basic feedstock may have to be distilled, particularly if in some of the special boiling-point spirits to be produced a high aromatic content is essential, whereas in others a low aromatic content is required. Since the cost of the re-distillation makes the cost of special boiling-point spirits considerably higher than that of ordinary gasoline, it is very necessary that the selected gasoline cuts for redistillation should give the minimum amount of unwanted fractions which have to be returned to gasoline.

Special boiling-point spirits may be produced in a continuous type of plant, particularly where only a small number of grades are required and the quantities are comparatively large. A flow diagram of a continuous S.B.P. plant for producing the various grades in the United Kingdom is shown in fig. 2. The plant, which has a daily intake capacity of 150 to 160 tons and is very flexible and able to produce the different fractions to accurate

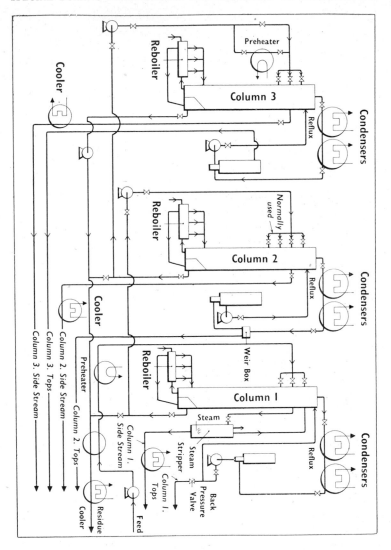

Fig. 2.   Flow Diagram of Continuous S.B.P. Plant.

specifications, consists essentially of three columns connected up in series. The feed is introduced into column no. 1, passing first through a preheater operating on low-pressure steam. The side-stream cut passes through a steaming column, the vapour line of which passes back to the main column, and its flow via a cooler and water separator is controlled by a liquid level controller on the bottom of the steaming column. The main heating in the column is supplied by a reboiler which is operated on high-pressure steam. The feed and feed temperature being constant, the reflux pumped back to the column is fixed to give the required degree of fractionation, and the bottom tray temperature is held constant by an automatic control which regulates the amount of steam to the reboiler. The reflux-product pump takes suction from the overhead product surge tank, the liquid level control of which operates the valve on the product line to storage, so that the excess of requirements for reflux leave the system. The bottoms from this column are pumped continuously as feed to column no. 2, the level in the column being held constant by a liquid level controller.

There is no preheater, and the bottoms from column no. 1 pass directly into column no. 2, the necessary heat being supplied by a reboiler using high-pressure steam, and the bottom tray temperature being held constant by an automatic control which regulates the amount of steam to the reboiler. The amount of reflux pumped back to the column is kept constant, and is regu-lated by a weir box system. The reflux pump takes suction from the reflux surge tank, which is held at constant level by a liquid level controller. The bottoms from the column are pumped con-tinuously as feed to column no. 3, the level in the column being held constant by a liquid level controller. The amount of reflux drawn from the overhead product surge tank is automatically controlled and is kept constant, while any excess merely overflows from the surge tank to storage.

With a feed to the plant consisting of a selected gasoline cut having an initial boiling point of 50° C. to 65° C., about 50% distilling at 100° C., and a final boiling point of 155° C. to 165° C. by the A.S.T.M. Distillation Method, S.B.P. 2 is produced as a top product from column no. 2, while S.B.P. 5 is taken off

as a sidestream from this column.   S.B.P. 3 is produced as a top product from column no. 3, and rubber solvent as a sidestream. Both S.B.P. 1 and S.B.P. 4, being wide-range products, are obtained by suitable blending.   The remaining grade, S.B.P. 6, can be produced by redistilling rubber solvent in a batch type still.

White spirits are also conveniently made in a continuous distillation unit.   A suitable rough cut from a main distillation process is pumped through heat exchangers into a fractionating column, at a point near the bottom of the column.   As in the plant previously described, the necessary heat is supplied by a reboiler at the base of the column.   The reboiler is heated with high-pressure closed steam and is also provided with open steam coils.   Steam and light fractions are taken off overhead from the column, and the main fraction of white spirit is taken off as a sidestream.   The heavy fractions of the feed to the column are run off continuously from the reboiler to storage via a cooler. The vapours from the top of the column pass through a heat exchanger, heating the feed to the column, and then to a condenser. The condensate goes to a surge tank, where water is separated, and a part of the condensate is pumped to the top of the column as reflux, the balance being delivered to storage.   The white spirit fraction is run to a small stripper column, where the light ends are stripped off with open steam so as to obtain the required initial boiling point and flashpoint of the product.   The overhead vapours from the stripper column pass back into the main fractionating column, while the stripped product passes first through a heat exchanger, further heating the feed to the main column, and then through a cooler to storage.   The white spirit produced may then have to be given a chemical treatment.

CHEMICAL BY-PRODUCTS OF PETROLEUM REFINING

Mention has already been made of a number of by-products from petroleum refining processes which find useful applications in industry.   Many of these are recovered from the wastes of the chemical refining of petroleum products and play a by no means unimportant part in the economics of these processes.   The more important of these by-products are now briefly described.

Fig. 3. View of Continuous S.B.P. Plant.

NAPHTHENIC ACIDS

The term ''naphthenic acids'' describes the cyclic carboxylic acids occurring in and obtained from petroleum. They probably occur in small quantities in all crude oils, and have many important technical applications, particularly in the form of their alkali and heavy metal salts. The bulk of the naphthenic acids in crude oils is to be found in the gas oil and light lubricating oil fractions, but for the main part they are extracted only from the kerosine and gas oil fractions, although naphthenic acids from lubricating oil fractions are commercially available.

The manufacture of naphthenic acids is carried out in three stages. The acids are first extracted from the base material by a solution of caustic soda, in which they become fixed as sodium naphthenates. The solution of sodium naphthenates is then acidified with moderately strong sulphuric acid, thus liberating the naphthenic acids, which are insoluble and form a layer above the aqueous solution. Finally, the naphthenic acids layer is separated and dried.

A number of grades of naphthenic acids is marketed, these being distinguished by their acid values, as, for example, the 230 Grade acids, having a minimum acid value (mg. KOH per gm.) of 230, and the 170 Grade, having a minimum acid value of 170. The higher acid value material is obtained from kerosine and light gas oil, and the lower acid value material from heavy gas oil. As would be expected, naphthenic acids are found in the waste lyes from the alkali refining of petroleum products, from which they can be recovered by acidifying with sulphuric acid.

CRESYLIC ACIDS

The occurrence of homologues* of phenol in certain petroleum fractions and in crude oil itself has been known for some time. The term "cresylic acids" is used to cover a wide range of mixtures of these various phenolic compounds, and the cresylic acids from any one source may not have the same composition as the cresylic acids from another source. Commercial cresylic acids, which contain a small amount of phenol, the three cresols and the higher phenols, including xylenols, are being obtained from petroleum and are used for such purposes as disinfectants and for the manufacture of synthetic resins. Cresylic acids are present in most cracked and reformed distillates, from which they are extracted by scrubbing with caustic soda solution. This scrubbing of cracked and reformed distillates with caustic soda solution is incidental to the chemical refining of these products. The caustic soda solution of the cresylic acids is then acidified, and the cresylic acids, which separate and form a layer on top of the aqueous solution, are removed and purified.

MERCAPTANS

Sulphur compounds, in varying amounts, are found in all crude oils, and, as they are objectionable in the majority of the finished products from petroleum, their removal from these products is one of the main problems in refining. Among the sulphur compounds found in the various distillate fractions are the mercaptans, which are of commercial value for a number of purposes. Caustic soda extraction of mercaptans in gasoline and the regeneration of the caustic soda solution for further use in the process, is extensively employed. The sour gasoline and the caustic soda solution are contacted intimately in a continuous counter-current treating system. Such an extraction process takes advantage of the solubility of sodium mercaptides in the caustic soda and subsequent recovery of the caustic. The recovery stage of the process consists of passing the caustic soda solution, which is saturated with sulphur compounds into the top of a bubble tower, the feed to the tower having first been heated by heat exchange with the hot regenerated caustic soda solution leaving the bottom of the tower. The hot solution flows down the tower counter-current to the steam generated in the base of the tower by a steam-heated reboiler. The mercaptans and water vapours pass out of the top of the tower and are condensed. The hot recovered caustic soda solution in the bottom of the tower flows through a heat exchanger and cooler and is returned to the gasoline extraction process.

NITROGEN BASES

The nitrogen content of most petroleum oils is small, the nitrogen usually being present in the form of basic compounds — nitrogen bases* — which find application as pickling inhibitors, insecticides, etc. Nitrogen bases can be extracted from gasolines by treating with an acid which does not form a sludge, for example, with dilute sulphuric acid of not over 50% strength, and then neutralizing the acid with an alkali to free the nitrogen bases. The use of weak acid for the recovery of the nitrogen bases must, of necessity, precede any refining with strong acid.

SODIUM NAPHTHA SULPHONATES

An important group of compounds, known as sulphonic acids, is produced in the course of the sulphuric acid treatment of petroleum products ; particularly in the manufacture of technical white, transformer, and medicinal oils by drastic treatment of suitable base stocks with oleum* (fuming sulphuric acid). Some of these sulphonic acids, known as "mahogany acids", are soluble in mineral oil and remain in the oil layer, while others, the "green acids", are insoluble in mineral oil and are found in the acid layer. In actual practice, these acids are recovered in the form of their sodium salts. The sodium salts of the mahogany acids, called mahogany soaps or sodium naphtha sulphonates A, are more important commercially than the corresponding sodium salts of the green acids, called green soaps or sodium naphtha sulphonates B, because they are effective emulsifiers and help to form stable emulsions of oil and water.

Practically the only oil-soluble sodium naphtha sulphonates that are useful for technical purposes are those resulting from refining spindle oil and light machine oil distillates, the latter being inferior to the former in actual practice. The most suitable sulphonates are not obtained by refining spindle distillates as such, but by refining solvent extracted distillates. Edeleanu raffinates, after the treatment with oleum, contain a considerable percentage of sulphonic acids. These oil-soluble sulphonic acids, in the form of their sodium salts, are recovered during the refining of technical white and transformer oils.

As regards the oil-insoluble sulphonic acids, the green acids, from the oleum sludge, these have been marketed to a limited extent, in the form of their sodium salts, as wetting agents. The working up of suitable oleum sludges, for the manufacture of water-soluble sodium naphtha sulphonates, consists in stirring them with about an equal quantity of water, after which the organic matter forms a cake on top of the solution. The sulphuric acid underneath is discharged, the cake washed with cold water and then dissolved in concentrated solution in hot water, after which it is neutralized with caustic soda solution to form the sodium salts. The neutral solution is evaporated to dryness and the dry material pulverized in a mill.

PETROLEUM RESINS

Because of the rapid growth of solvent refining processes for the manufacture of lubricating oils, the problem of disposing of the extracts has become of considerable commercial importance. While all the extracts can be disposed of as fuel, or in some cases where the extracts are semi-solid, as asphaltic bitumens, some of the more valuable extracts can be employed as raw materials for the manufacture of important by-products. Certain extracts from the solvent refining of lubricating oil distillates, as, for example, furfural extracts, yield, on straight distillation, solid or semi-solid residual products known as "petroleum resins", which are light in colour and find important application, as in the manufacture of bituminous paints. A number of grades of petroleum resins are sold, according to their penetration values at 25° C. These include a very soft grade of penetration 190 to 210, a soft grade of penetration 140 to 160, and a hard grade of penetration 20 to 40.

PETROLEUM COKE

Petroleum coke is produced as a by-product in cracking and destructive distillation processes. As described in chapter X, cracking of petroleum may be carried out either as a residuum process, giving gas, cracked distillate and a cracked residue, or as a non-residuum process, giving gas, cracked distillate and coke. Coke may be obtained in the reaction chambers of cracking units in the residuum process, but only in comparatively small amounts, the main source being from the non-residuum type of operation. Another source of petroleum coke is from the destructive distillation of petroleum. The destructive distillation of crude oils and residues to coke was practised to a considerable extent in the past, but is of little importance at the present time. Although petroleum coke is largely used as a fuel, it has many commercial applications, especially where its low ash content, as compared with coke made from coal, its non-clinkering properties and, in some petroleum cokes, low sulphur content, are an advantage.

ESTER SALTS

In recent years there has been considerable interest in the manufacture of synthetic detergents from petroleum sources. As a result of extensive research carried out by the Group, a process was developed for the production of the sodium salts of higher secondary alkyl sulphates (ester salts) from paraffin wax. A plant was erected at one of the Group's refineries in the United Kingdom where ester salts are being manufactured on a large scale. The product is sold under the trade name of "Teepol" and finds

Fig. 4. View of Ester Salts Plant.

many important applications, both as a detergent and as a "wetting" agent. By vapour-phase cracking of paraffin wax an olefin-rich, cracked distillate is obtained, which is then fractionated to give a special fraction which yields a finished product with an optimum balance of detergent and wetting properties. This olefin-rich fraction is reacted with sulphuric acid, under carefully controlled conditions. The reaction mixture is then neutralized with caustic soda, heated and agitated, after which it is subjected to purification processes to remove any unsulphated organic material and by-products of the reaction which would be deleterious to the finished product. The final product of the process consists of an aqueous solution of sodium alkyl sulphates containing 20% to 22% by weight of the latter. The solution may be spray-dried to produce a "Teepol" powder for certain uses.

XVIII

MANUFACTURE OF SYNTHETIC CHEMICALS FROM PETROLEUM

THE chemical industry based on petroleum is already so extensive, and expanding simultaneously in so many directions, that it will not be possible within the scope of this chapter to achieve more than a broad outline of the subject. Stimulated by the demands of war, the number of chemicals now being obtained from petroleum is about 200, and this is only an insignificant fraction of the number which could be produced, as will be shown by a glance through an up-to-date textbook on organic chemistry.

Strictly speaking, a chemical is a substance produced by, or used in, a chemical reaction. Based on this definition, the modern oil refinery itself is tending to become a gigantic chemical plant in which portions of the crude oil are broken down and built up into more useful products by means of chemical methods ; the production of iso-octane, alkylate, toluene, ester salts (Teepol) and the processes of catalytic cracking, hydrogenation and isomerization are a few examples of the application of chemical technique to petroleum ''refining''. In this chapter we shall deal with the manufacture of some of the more important chemicals derived from petroleum. The properties and applications of these chemicals are fully described in chapter XXXII.

Cracking and reforming plants are by far the most important sources of the light olefins. Originally these gases were burned as fuel, or even wasted entirely, and were universally considered as an undesirable by-product of gasoline manufacture. These gases, however, contain the olefins from which the chemical industry, based on petroleum, has sprung up, and these olefins are worth potentially more than gasoline itself. Only once in the history of the petroleum industry has there been such a startling change in relative values, namely, when gasoline became the most important product of crude petroleum after having been a by-product in the manufacture of kerosine and fuel oil.

The paraffin gases (methane, ethane, propane, and the butanes) which occur in natural gas, crude oil and cracking plant gases, provide the second most important source of raw material for the petroleum chemical industry. Ethane, propane and the butanes may be converted into olefins, but chemicals derived therefrom are, in general, more expensive than those obtained from olefins produced as a by-product of gasoline manufacture. It must be mentioned at this point that industry is making rapid strides in the direct use of paraffins as raw material for chemical manufacture—that is to say, without first converting them to olefins. For example, ethane, propane and n-butane may be converted by direct oxidation into acetic acid, acetone and methyl ethyl ketone respectively ; chlorine or nitric acid will react with these paraffins to give chlorides or nitroparaffins. Natural gas, which consists largely of methane, may be broken down into carbon and hydrogen with either as the main product. Hydrogen, which is an important building brick of the chemical industry, may also be obtained from natural gas by reaction with steam in what is known as the "methane/steam" process (*vide infra*). The products of this reaction are carbon monoxide and hydrogen. Apart from this important source of hydrogen, the gases can also be used for the synthesis of higher hydrocarbons by the Fischer-Tropsch process. By this means gasoline or paraffin wax can be produced depending on the conditions of temperature and pressure used for the process. This gives us a method of producing gasoline from natural gas which is known as the "Synthine" process.

The gaseous mixture of carbon monoxide and hydrogen can also be obtained from the reaction of steam on carbon in the form of coke, and this is one of the chief methods of obtaining oil products from coal. The other important method of producing oil from coal is by direct hydrogenation of coal by the Bergius process, whereby " hydropetrol" is produced.

Where there is no convenient source of either olefin or paraffin gases, it is still possible to produce a full range of olefins for chemical manufacture by the importation and cracking of liquid petroleum fractions, using methods similar to those employed by gas companies for fuel gas enrichment (*vide* chapter XXVIII).

For the manufacture of any particular chemical there is often a choice of feedstocks, and usually several different routes by which the desired product can be obtained from the chosen feedstock. The synthesis of any chemical requires one or more chemical "steps", each of which calls for certain conditions of temperature and pressure, and usually a catalyst for accelerating the desired reaction.

CARBON BLACK

Carbon black is manufactured by the incomplete combustion of natural gas. For many years, untreated natural gas was used for this purpose, but nowadays, the valuable natural gasoline is always extracted first so that only stripped gas, consisting mainly of methane, is used. If this gas is burned with ample air, as in a bunsen burner, the flame will be colourless, but if insufficient air is supplied then the flame will be luminous like that of a candle and, like the candle flame, will deposit soot or carbon on a cold surface on to which it is allowed to impinge.

Several processes have been developed but that most employed is the so-called "channel" process, in which the flames of the burning gas are allowed to impinge on a cool metal surface on which the carbon black is deposited, and from which it is scraped off continuously. All carbon black manufacturing processes are very dirty in that they produce a great deal of smoke and are very wasteful, for, although 1,000 cubic feet of methane actually contains 33 lbs. of carbon, the actual yield of carbon black is less than 2 lb. Higher yields are obtained by other processes, such as the "furnace" process, in which natural gas is burnt in an enclosed system, or the "thermatomic" process, in which hydrocarbon gas is cracked at high temperatures. The carbon black so produced, however, has not the same velvety black appearance as has the carbon black made by the "channel" process, and so is restricted in its uses.

HYDROGEN

Hydrogen may be produced from methane in two ways :—
   (1) By reaction with steam.   (2) By cracking.
   (1) When steam reacts with methane at high temperature, the oxygen of the steam combines with the carbon of the methane to

S

form carbon monoxide, setting free hydrogen ; at the same time, hydrogen is liberated from the steam itself. This process is operated at high temperature and with the aid of catalysts. This method of producing hydrogen is used where methane is available cheaply, as in the form of natural gas.

(2) A second method of producing hydrogen from methane is by cracking the gas into its components, carbon and hydrogen. This is the thermatomic process for the production of carbon black mentioned above. In another cracking process, the methane is passed through a mass of red-hot brickwork contained in a large steel vessel. The brickwork is first heated by burning gas with air in the lower part of the vessel. When the brickwork is sufficiently hot, heating is stopped and the methane is turned in and continuously cracked until the brickwork cools sufficiently to require reheating. At this point, entry of methane is stopped and the air supply is renewed. This process thus works inter-mittently, in the same way as the oil-gas plant described in chapter XXVIII.

AMMONIA

Ammonia was one of the first chemicals associated with the petroleum and natural gas industries ; it is manufactured by com-pressing purified hydrogen and nitrogen and introducing these gases into a reaction vessel containing a catalyst where the pressure is as high as 1,000 atmospheres. Under these conditions the synthesis of ammonia proceeds—2 molecules of ammonia being formed from 3 molecules of hydrogen and 1 molecule of nitrogen :—

$$3H_2 + N_2 = 2NH_3$$

The hydrogen may be produced from natural gas by cracking or reaction with steam. The nitrogen is obtained from the atmo-sphere by either burning the oxygen with hydrogen or natural gas, or by low temperature fractionation.

Ammonia, which is a gas at ordinary temperatures and pressures, may be handled as a liquid under pressure in cylinders or special tank cars, or as an aqueous solution known as "aqua ammonia" ; or it may be neutralized by sulphuric, nitric or phosphoric acids for use as solid fertilizer.

SYNTHESIS OF CHEMICALS FROM OLEFINS

A characteristic reaction of the olefins is their ability, in the presence of sulphuric acid, to add the elements of water and form the corresponding alcohol* :—

$$CH_2{=}CH_2 \xrightarrow{+H_2O} CH_3{-}CH_2{-}OH$$

ethylene   ethyl alcohol

$$CH_3{-}CH{=}CH_2 \xrightarrow{+H_2O} CH_3{-}\underset{\underset{OH}{|}}{CH}{-}CH_3$$

propylene   iso-propyl alcohol (IPA)

$$CH_2{=}CH{-}CH_2{-}CH_3 \xrightarrow{+H_2O} CH_3{-}\underset{\underset{OH}{|}}{CH}{-}CH_2{-}CH_3$$

alpha butylene   secondary butyl alcohol (SBA)

$$CH_3CH{=}CH{-}CH_3 \xrightarrow{+H_2O} CH_3{-}CH_2{-}\underset{\underset{OH}{|}}{CH}{-}CH_3$$

beta butylene   secondary butyl alcohol (SBA)

$$CH_3{-}\underset{\underset{CH_3}{\|}}{C}{-}CH_3 \xrightarrow{+H_2O} CH_3{-}\underset{\underset{OH}{|}}{\overset{\overset{CH_3}{|}}{C}}{-}CH_3$$

gamma or iso-butylene   tertiary butyl alcohol (TBA)

As will be seen from the following brief summary of the manufacture of some of the more important chemicals derived from petroleum, the first step in their synthesis is nearly always the reaction in the presence of sulphuric acid or the reaction with chlorine.

Fig. 1. Plant for Manufacture of Alcohols, Dominguez, California.

Fig. 2.   Plant for Purifying Alcohols, Dominguez, California.

Ethylene Derivatives. Up to the present time ethylene has not been utilized in chemical manufacture to the same extent as propylene and butylene, largely because it is more difficult to obtain in a sufficient degree of purity and because fermentation of molasses and grain has provided a readily available source of ethyl alcohol. Nevertheless, with the improved techniques now available, ethylene ($CH_2{=}CH_2$) can look forward to increasing utilization in the manufacture of *ethyl alcohol* ($CH_3{-}CH_2{-}OH$), *ethyl chloride* ($CH_3{-}CH_2Cl$), *vinyl chloride* ($CH_2{=}CHCl$), *ethylene oxide* $\begin{matrix} CH_2 \\ | \\ CH_2 \end{matrix}\Big{>}O$, *ethylene glycol* $\begin{matrix} CH_2OH \\ | \\ CH_2OH \end{matrix}$ and related chemicals.

Propylene Derivatives

(a) *From reaction with sulphuric acid.* Liquid propane/propylene mixture is contacted with strong sulphuric acid in a reactor, where the temperature is carefully controlled. The propylene is absorbed, giving a material known as "fat acid", but the propane is not absorbed and is ultimately removed. The fat acid is hydrolyzed, which sets the crude alcohol free, and this is stripped from the acid, usually with steam, and condensed. The *iso-propyl alcohol* (IPA) may be dehydrogenated to dimethyl ketone (DMK), otherwise known as *acetone* ($CH_3{-}CO{-}CH_3$). Acetone is the starting point for the manufacture of a large variety of chemicals, of which the following are examples :—

diacetone alcohol (DAA)

$$CH_3{-}\overset{\overset{\displaystyle O}{\|}}{C}{-}CH_2{-}\underset{\underset{\displaystyle CH_3}{|}}{\overset{\overset{\displaystyle OH}{|}}{C}}{-}CH_3$$

mesityl oxide

$$CH_3{-}\overset{\overset{\displaystyle O}{\|}}{C}{-}CH{=}\overset{\overset{\displaystyle CH_3}{|}}{C}{-}CH_3$$

methyl iso-butyl ketone (MIBK)

$$CH_3{-}\overset{\overset{\displaystyle O}{\|}}{C}{-}CH_2{-}\overset{\overset{\displaystyle CH_3}{|}}{CH}{-}CH_3$$

methyl iso-butyl carbinol (MIBC)

$$CH_3{-}\overset{\overset{\displaystyle OH}{|}}{CH}{-}CH_2{-}\overset{\overset{\displaystyle CH_3}{|}}{CH}{-}CH_3$$

acetic acid

$$CH_3{-}\overset{\overset{\displaystyle O}{\|}}{C}{-}OH$$

(b) *From reaction with chlorine.* When chlorine and propylene are reacted together under certain conditions, the products formed are allyl chloride ($CH_2=CH-CH_2Cl$) and chlorinated propylenes ("D—D"). The mixture of chlorinated propylenes is the soil fumigant known as "D—D" (not to be confused with DDT). Allyl chloride is also the starting point for many other important syntheses, one of the best known being the synthesis of glycerine

OH   OH   OH
| | | , which was developed in the Group's research
$CH_2-CH-CH_2$

laboratories at Emeryville, California. A plant for the manufacture of glycerine by this process has been erected at Houston, Texas.

Normal Butylene Derivatives

(a) *From reaction with sulphuric acid.* This reaction is carried out essentially in the same manner as for propylene, except that the temperature is held somewhat lower ; the product is *secondary butyl alcohol* (SBA). Secondary butyl alcohol may be dehydrogenated in the presence of a catalyst to give *methyl ethyl ketone** (MEK) ($CH_3-CO-CH_2-CH_3$).

(b) *From reaction with chlorine.* The two isomers of normal butylene react with chlorine to give 2–3 dichlorobutane (DCB), which, on heating evolves hydrochloric acid and leaves 1–3 *butadiene* ($CH_2=CH-CH=CH_2$). This hydrocarbon is the basis of the synthetic rubber industry. Practically all the synthetic rubber made in the United States during recent years was produced by polymerizing butadiene mixed with other chemicals.

Iso-butylene Derivatives

(a) *From reaction with sulphuric acid.* Iso-butylene, unlike the normal butylenes, is readily soluble in 65% sulphuric acid, which fact is used to remove this hydrocarbon from feedstocks which require pure n-butylene. The fat acid is stripped with steam, which removes *tertiary butyl alcohol* (TBA).

(b) *From reaction with chlorine.* Chlorine reacts with iso-butylene to give *methallyl chloride* ($CH_2=C(CH_3)-CH_2Cl$) and hydrochloric acid. By treatment with soda, the chlorine in methallyl chloride is replaced by hydroxyl (OH), giving *methallyl alcohol* (CH_2=$C(CH_3)$—CH_2OH).

TOLUENE

Wartime demands for toluene, an intermediate in the synthesis of T.N.T. (tri-nitro-toluene), caused the petroleum industry to undertake the large-scale production of aromatics. Toluene occurs naturally in petroleum, and methods were developed for its extraction. In addition to the hydroforming process (*vide* chapter XVI), toluene is also synthesized from dimethyl-cyclopentane and methyl-cyclohexane, two naphthenic hydrocarbons found in straight-run gasolines.

In the toluene process, the principal reaction is the dehydrogenation of the methyl cyclohexane. However, since the supply of naturally occurring methyl cyclohexane is limited, the Shell Group developed methods of increasing its availability by isomerizing dimethyl cyclopentane. The overall reaction may be represented as follows :—

dimethyl cyclopentane   methyl cyclohexane   toluene

HELIUM

The remarkable rare gas helium is obtained from certain natural gases, in which it is present in very small quantities. So far it has only been found in quantities up to 2% to 3% in some natural gases in the United States (Kansas, Texas and Arizona) and Canada. Helium is a very light, inert gas which is noninflammable and, therefore, specially suitable for airships. Its

Fig. 3.   Butadiene Plant nearing Completion.

lifting power for this purpose is 92% that of hydrogen ; on the other hand, it diffuses 30% less through the material in the gas bags into the atmosphere, and this property gives it an added importance for use in airships.   Helium is also used in the atmosphere of special chambers for divers recovering from high-pressure conditions.   It is possible to allow divers to return to normal atmospheric pressures in a much shorter time when helium is mixed with the air breathed during the depressuring period.

Helium was discovered in 1868, not on the earth, but by means of the spectroscope, as one of the elements present in the sun.   In 1895, it was found to exist on the earth, too, as one of the gases of the atmosphere, though in extremely small quantities—that is, only about 0·0005%.   The boiling point of liquid helium is minus 270° C. (minus 454° F.)—that is, very near to the absolute zero.

It can be separated from natural gas by liquefying, step by step, all the other components present, such as propane, methane, nitrogen and hydrogen.

A VERSATILE RAW MATERIAL

During the past fifteen years a whole new chemical industry has been built on petroleum, and today, out of every hundred barrels of petroleum processed, 1·6 barrels are used as the raw material for chemical synthesis.   One of the properties of petroleum molecules that makes them valuable in chemical synthesis is the ease with which they can be re-arranged and combined.   For example, it is this property that makes them ideally suited for the synthesis of long chain compounds that make up synthetic resins and fibres.

Acetic anhydride, carbon bisulphide, thiophene and vinyl chloride are but a few of the many new and varied additions to the list of chemicals available from petroleum.   While for some time to come we can expect petroleum to be a source of potential energy and a lubricant for our cars, ships and aeroplanes, we shall, nevertheless, become more and more conscious of its role as a vast storehouse of chemicals that is virtually unlimited in its versatility.

XIX

TRUNK PIPELINES

CRUDE oil starts its life above ground in a small storage tank on the producing field, whence, after treatment for the separation of water, it is pumped through the collecting-line system into one of the steel storage tanks in the field tank farm. This tank farm may be situated on the coast, if the field is not far distant, as at Ras Gharib, in Egypt, or far inland, as is more usual. In the former case, the crude oil is then transported to the refinery by tank steamers, as, for example, in Venezuela ; in the latter case, by pipelines.

TRUNK PIPELINES

The possibilities of trunk pipelines have long been realized. One of the earliest was that constructed in 1897 between Baku and Batum, on the Black Sea, for the bulk transportation of kerosine. Another well-known set of lines is that between the refinery centre in Roumania (Ploesti) and the shipping port of Constanza, on the Black Sea. Many thousands of such lines have been laid, particularly in the United States, the great majority of which have been constructed for the transport of crude oil from the main field to the refineries, often at great distances. The Shell Petroleum Corporation constructed such a line, 1,400 miles long, to carry crude oil from Texas to the refinery at Wood River (Illinois).

During World War II several such schemes were undertaken, some to set free tankers which were in desperately short supply, and others, notably those in the United Kingdom, partly for strategic reasons and partly to relieve the load on the railways, which were hard put to it to cope with the vast volume of additional traffic necessitated by wartime requirements. Outstanding amongst these wartime projects were the so-called Big Inch and Little Inch lines in the U.S.A., the former being 24 inches diameter and over 1,300 miles long, for the transport of crude oil from Longview, in Texas, to Bayway, New Jersey, and the latter 20 inches diameter and over 1,500 miles long, for the conveyance of refined products from Baytown, Texas, to Bayway. The throughput capacity of the Big Inch was no less than 40,000 tons per day, there being twenty-six main line pumping stations throughout its length, each requiring about 4,500 horse-power at full load. It is interesting to note that merely to fill the line in the first instance requires nearly 485,000 tons of crude oil ! In the case of the Little Inch, the throughput capacity depends of course on the product being handled, the maximum being about 25,000 tons per day, with twenty-seven main line pumping stations, each requiring 3,750 horse-power at full load. An interesting feature about this line is that a number of different products are handled, comprising several different grades of gasoline, kerosine, and a light gas oil. No attempt is made to separate the products—they are simply pumped consecutively into the line at Baytown, in quantities to suit the requirements at the points of delivery, and, provided that the linear speed of the products passing through the line is kept above a pre-determined minimum, the degree of contamination between consecutive products is surprisingly small and only persists over a few hundred feet of the pipeline. This ''contaminated plug'', as it is called, is simply degraded to one or the other of the products handled. It will be appreciated that, with the enormous volume of individual products handled, the actual contamination amounts to only a very small fraction of 1 %, and is quite negligible from the practical point of view. In a line of this length, frequently four or five different products are in different parts of the line at the same time, for delivery either to the receiving terminal or to intermediate points tapped off along the route of the line.

Mention should also be made of the trunk pipelines laid in the U.K. during the war, which, whilst not on the ambitious scale of those laid in the U.S.A., being in general only 8 inches and 10 inches in diameter, nevertheless made a marked contribution to the successful prosecution of the war. They enabled all tankers to discharge on the west coast and thus avoid the hazardous journey through the English Channel or round the north of Scotland, and they transported the oil to the principal centres of consumption.   In particular, the aviation gasoline circuit, with branches to the principal bomber aerodromes, so that the aviation spirit was literally ''on tap'', contributed largely to the sustained bomber offensive during the latter part of the war. In the aggregate, these pipelines totalled over 1,000 miles in length.   Branches were extended to strategic points on the south coast, to feed the PLUTO (Pipe Lines Under the Ocean) system of cross-Channel lines that were laid to maintain supplies of gasoline to the Allies at the time of the invasion of Hitler's Europe.   These cross-Channel lines were of 3 inches diameter steel pipe, lengths of pipe being welded together to give one continuous length sufficient for the Channel crossing.   For laying, the lines were wound on to huge floating drums, shaped somewhat like a cotton reel, the drums being 40 feet in diameter and 60 feet long.   Each drum was towed across the channel by a tug, the drum actually rolling on the water as it were, and paying out the pipeline as it progressed.   A number of these lines were laid, and thousands of tons were pumped through them to the Allied troops in Normandy until such time as it was possible to send tankers direct to discharge on that coast.

The tremendous increase in trunk pipelines for the transport of petroleum products during World War II should not lead to too much emphasis being given to this method of distribution.   The fact that the great majority of such lines, laid at very considerable expense, have since the war ceased to be used, should in itself sound a note of warning.   This is not to say that ''pipeline consciousness'' should be discouraged—far from it, as naturally lines laid to meet strategic and military needs are not necessarily suitably situated to meet commercial requirements.   On the other hand, the cost of such projects is necessarily considerable, and can generally only be justified financially if the required throughput is sufficient to keep the line fully employed, pumping twenty-four hours per day.   The fact that for smaller quantities a smaller diameter line can be used does not result in a proportional decrease in capital charges, as in the case of buried lines the cost of trenching, testing and back-filling*, which together account for a large proportion of the total cost of the pipeline proper, differs very little whether the pipe itself is 4 inches, 6 inches or 8 inches diameter. For this reason, the recent tendency in many countries to adopt above-ground trunk pipelines will greatly increase their possibilities, as capital costs are greatly reduced, inspection and maintenance are greatly simplified, and corrosion troubles, whether due to soil corrosion or electrolytic effects, are practically eliminated.

Naturally, distribution by pipeline is not so flexible as other methods of distribution, and is therefore limited to deliveries to large centres of consumption, the route, where circumstances permit, being arranged to pass through minor centres where intermediate offtake points can be provided. Alternatively, the main pipeline may be routed directly between terminals, and branches or spurs connected to intermediate offtake points.

CONSTRUCTION OF PIPELINES

The general route of the line is first laid down on a map, either a direct line between terminals or a series of straight lines through intermediate offtake points, and by simply studying the map the more obviously necessary deviations, to avoid built-up areas and physical obstructions, may be set down. Subsequently, every yard of the route must be surveyed. Rivers, canals, railways and roads do not as a rule present serious obstacles, but often the route of the line has to be switched somewhat to find convenient crossing places. If possible, lines should be more or less parallel to roads, as this simplifies distribution of materials, mechanical trenching equipment, etc. In agricultural land, the line should be laid with a minimum of 2 feet cover, so that agriculture may continue over the pipe after it has been laid, tested and back-filled. Particular care must be taken to make good any drains damaged during pipelaying, as otherwise heavy claims for compensation are almost inevitable sooner or later.

The protection of buried pipelines against corrosion is of the utmost importance, and generally comprises at least a coating of bitumen, a wrapping of asbestos felt, and a final application of bitumen. This protection is often applied at the maker's works, but pipe joints, generally welded, must be protected in the field, and any damage to the coating during transit or laying of the pipe must likewise be made good. Machines are now available for coating and protecting the line on site after it has been welded up and prior to lowering into the trench.

The field organization involves the division of the line into a number of sections, each staffed and worked as a self-contained unit, central control being exercised in the supply of materials to ensure that all sections finish more or less simultaneously. The number of sections and the number of points at which work can be carried on in each section depends entirely on the rate of supply of pipe and the amount of labour available. For pipe up to 4 inches diameter, screwed or welded joints are employed ; above 4 inches, welding is normally employed.

Sectioning valves are provided in the pipeline so that in the event of trouble a comparatively short section can be isolated. The length of sections depends on the type of country traversed, being up to five or six miles in open uninhabited country, and much less in built-up areas. At major river and rail crossings, and in some cases at main roads, valves should be provided on each side of the crossing. When laying the line, tees should be introduced at any points where there is a likelihood in the future of a branch line being required. If the line is to handle a large proportion of gasoline, provision must be made for periodic internal scraping, and insertion and withdrawal chambers must be provided at suitable intervals so that scrapers can be introduced and removed from the line without interrupting pumping. Normally these chambers are located at pumping stations.

An inhibitor is nowadays normally introduced into the pipeline to retard the formation of rust. This inhibitor is introduced in the form of an aqueous solution in small daily doses, and not only assists materially in loosening any scale or rust that may have already formed, but produces a film on the inner surface of the pipe which retards further rust formation. Scraping and inhibiting should be practised from the outset where gasoline is the major product handled, as otherwise rust formation will result in a rapid falling off in the efficiency of the line.

OPERATION OF PIPELINES

Pumps. For low viscosity products such as those referred to above, the pumps used are almost invariably of the centrifugal type, which permit of very great flexibility in throughput. If electricity supplies are available, electric motors will normally be used to drive the pumps, but more often than not external power supplies are not obtainable, and oil or petrol engines with suitable gearing are employed. For the more viscous products, such as the heavier fuel oils, centrifugal pumps are unsuitable, and reciprocating pumps, driven by oil engines, are employed. Pipelines for such products present very serious problems, due to the wide variation in viscosity resulting from comparatively small changes in temperature, and may call for heat exchangers at intervals along the whole length of the line to keep the viscosity low enough to maintain the desired throughput during the cold season. Unfortunately, it is very often the case—and naturally so—that during the cold season the demands for such fuels are heaviest, and costly heating equipment and large diameter lines must be provided, both of which are unnecessary during the greater part of the year.

Instruments. Prompt communication throughout the system is of the utmost importance, and a private telephone line, giving immediate connection, should be installed, connecting all pump stations and terminal points. In addition, each pump station should be provided with a recording flow-meter, together with pressure recorders for both the suction and delivery sides of the pump, making it possible to see at a glance whether everything is functioning normally. As an additional safeguard, high and low pressure alarms, capable of being set to suit the particular pumping conditions pertaining at the time, and operating either visual or aural alarms or both, should be provided. The above can be regarded as the minimum requirements in the way of instruments, and just how far to go beyond this is dependent on local conditions, labour costs, and other factors. In some cases pressure-operated switches and relays are provided on the suction and delivery sides of the pumps so that the station is automatically brought into operation or shut down. Such refinements are sometimes installed where labour costs are high, but such devices must in turn be provided with safeguards against breakdown, and if carried too far necessitate the employment of a staff of skilled mechanics continually touring the pump stations to maintain the equipment.

XX

SEA TRANSPORT

HISTORICAL

THE first cargo of petroleum to be transported across the Atlantic ocean was carried in wooden barrels stowed in the single hold of the brig "Elizabeth Watts" in the year 1861. This method was employed for some years afterwards, and the price of petroleum to the consumer in the United Kingdom included the cost of filling and emptying the barrels, returning the empties and loss of freight due to the circular shape of the barrels requiring large space in proportion to the amount of oil carried.

Ships of that period were mostly made of wood, and the first attempt to reduce the price of petroleum sold in the United Kingdom took the form of fitting iron tanks of comparatively large capacity into the cargo holds, and subsequently the wooden hulls were lined with felt on cement. In this way, the idea of transporting oil in bulk progressed.

The "Shell" fleet of tankers was inaugurated in the year 1892 by the steam engine propelled tanker "Murex" of 5,010 tons carrying capacity. This pioneer tanker, built at West Hartlepool, would not compare favourably with modern ships of this class, but at the time she represented the last word and in many respects was a great advancement upon the 60 to 70 tankers then sailing under British, American and Russian flags. The "Murex" was the first ship to carry oil in bulk through the Suez Canal. This chapter in history was written during the latter part of 1892.

TANKER CONSTRUCTION AND EQUIPMENT

Arrangement of Cargo Tanks. Because of the fluid nature of oil cargoes and the liability of ships to pitch and roll in adverse weather, the cargo space of the earliest bulk oil carriers was divided into two symmetrical parts by providing a centre-line bulkhead extending fore and aft for the whole length of the space, which has the effect of controlling the position of the centre of gravity of the cargo and preventing the stability of the ship being adversely affected. The length of the cargo space was divided into a number of compartments by the provision of athwartship* bulkheads, which prevented surging of the cargo in heavy weather and damage to the ship. These bulkheads also give added strength to the ship and enable different grades of cargo to be carried at the same time. A typical cross-section of such a tanker is shown in fig. 1.

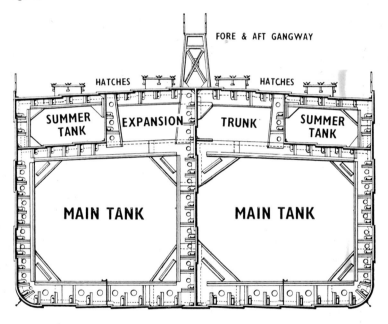

Fig. 1. Cross Section of Summer Tank Tanker.

The summer tanks on each side of fig. 1 run longitudinally between the main and upper decks and extend from the ship's side to what is called the expansion trunk of the main tanks. The object of this form of construction is to reduce to within narrow limits the free surface of the liquid in the main tanks. The free surface could of course be eliminated if the tanks were completely

filled, but this is impracticable as oils have a relatively high coefficient of expansion and space must be provided to allow for
increase in volume, which may amount to 2% under certain
conditions.

The summer tanks are filled only when cargoes of very low
specific gravity are carried, and although this form of construction
is now obsolete the principle is applied to certain classes of

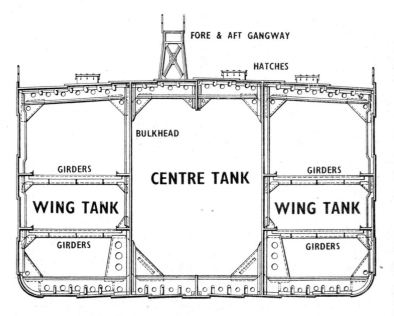

Fig. 2.   Cross Section of Modern Tanker.

tankers, chiefly small coasters.   In such ships the summer tanks
are eliminated, the expansion trunk protruding above the upper
deck.

After the 1914/18 war the form of construction of tankers was
changed, and in this new development the Group's marine technicians again played a leading part.   The new form comprised two
longitudinal bulkheads and no summer tanks.   This resulted in

greatly increased strength for the same weight of steel used and more flexibility in the carriage of cargoes, as the centre tanks only required to be loaded to 98% capacity ; the wing tanks could be loaded similarly to any desired ullage* without adversely affecting the stability of the ship in bad weather. The arrangement of the bulkheads in a modern tanker is shown in figs. 2 and 3.

Cofferdams. The transverse and longitudinal bulkheads are made oil-tight and form a sufficiently safe division between different grades of oil in adjacent tanks. In time, however, ships which must of necessity be flexible to a certain degree in order to reduce intensity of stress, during periods of unequal weight distribution or bad weather, become strained and the divisions become less reliable. Also, with certain grades of cargo the slightest admixture would be disastrous, and to ensure absolute separation under all conditions of weather cofferdams are provided. Cofferdams comprise a space between two cargo tanks enclosed by the transverse bulkheads of adjacent tanks. In other words, the adjacent tanks are separated by two oil-tight transverse bulkheads instead of one.

Cofferdams are always provided at each end of the cargo space. In some cases the after cofferdam is made large enough to accommodate the cargo pumps, but generally the cargo pumps are installed in cofferdams situated in the cargo space and are called pumprooms. When there are two pumprooms, as in fig. 3, the cargo space is divided into three completely isolated portions, and three different grades of cargo could be carried without the least possibility of admixture and, as such tankers are provided with at least three cargo pumps, the three grades can be loaded or discharged simultaneously through separate pipelines.

Forward of the fore cofferdam is a deep tank for a portion of the ship's bunkers, with a hold above for the carriage of dry cargo and stores. The bulkhead dividing the deep tank and the fore peak, in which is usually carried domestic water, is termed the collision bulkhead. Storerooms are situated over the fore peak, as is the anchor chain locker.

Cargo Heating System. As some oil cargoes require to be heated whilst in the ship to ensure a reasonably high discharge rate, steam-heating pipes in the form of grids are arranged over

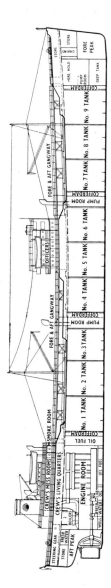

Fig. 3. Longitudinal Section of Modern Diesel Engined Tanker.

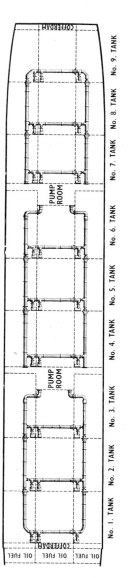

Fig. 4. Plan of Cargo Suction Pipeline in Modern Tanker.

the bottom of each tank or compartment. The capacity of this heating system is sufficient to raise the temperature of the oil to 140° F. For specially heavy petroleum products, such as bitumen, the heating system must be of even greater capacity.

Location of Machinery. The propelling machinery of tankers is generally placed at the after end in order to avoid having to provide a long oil-tight shaft tunnel through the cargo tanks situated between the engine room and the after cofferdam, were the machinery placed amidships. From a safety point of view also it is an advantage to have the engine room clear of the cargo space. The space under the machinery is divided up to form tanks which contain fuel, lubricating oil and fresh water necessary for the operation of the machinery.

Freeboard of Tankers. Tankers are permitted by the Classification Societies to load more deeply than dry cargo ships. The reasons are that the cargo tank hatches are small and strongly constructed, there are no large ventilators opening into the cargo spaces through which seas could enter and cause flooding, and, moreover, if every cargo compartment of a tanker became filled with sea water the ship would still be buoyant. Because tankers are loaded so deeply it is necessary to have a fore-and-aft gangway between the three islands—namely forecastle, bridge and poop— to enable the personnel to pass from one island to another in safety during heavy weather when the decks are awash. This fore-and-aft gangway forms a suitable structure to which are secured the various pipelines, such as steam to windlass, steam-smothering line, wash-deck line, cargo-tank venting pipes, fresh-water line to amidship accommodation, electric cables, engine-room telegraph leads, etc., etc.

Aids to Navigation. A large proportion of the Group's fleet of tankers is equipped with up-to-date main and emergency wireless sets, gyro compasses, direction finders, depth sounders, electric engine-room telegraphs, telephone system, electric speed and helm indicators, etc. The officers are accommodated amidships and the crew live aft. Spacious and comfortably furnished smoke and recreation rooms are provided for both officers and crew. The temperature of the living accommodation is controlled by circulated air which is heated in cold climates.

Ventilation of Cargo Tanks.   As oil enters the cargo tanks at a
rate up to 2,000 tons per hour an equal volume of air is displaced,
and as this air becomes mixed with petroleum vapours and forms
an explosive mixture it must be conducted away to a point where
it is not likely to become ignited.   This is accomplished by providing a pipe leading from the hatch coaming* of each tank
through a pressure-vacuum valve and into a much larger pipe
running fore and aft, the ends of which terminate about 12 feet
above the headlights on each mast.

The pressure-vacuum valves are set to act automatically when
the pressure in a tank exceeds 3 lb. per square inch, and explosive
gases are expelled into the atmosphere at a point where they can
do little harm.   Conversely, if during discharge a partial vacuum
is created in the tanks, these valves operate and allow air to be
drawn into the tanks through a double-gauze safety screen.   It
will thus be seen that the expansion of the cargo due to a rising
temperature and contraction consequent upon a falling temperature is taken care of by these pressure-vacuum valves, and the ship
is safeguarded against damage from internal or external pressure
during a voyage from a cold to a hot climate, or vice versa.

Cargo Pipelines.   The cargo pipeline system in a modern tanker
is a simple but ingenious affair which enables liquid to be drawn
from any compartment and pumped into any other compartment.
Also it is possible to draw from any compartment and pump to
the sea or draw from the sea and discharge to any compartment
without passing through the discharge line on deck.   From fig. 4
it will be seen that the main lines are led forward and aft from the
pump-rooms through the side tanks, the port and starboard lines
being joined in each tank by crossover lines, from which a suction
pipe with valve is fitted in each compartment, the open end of the
suction pipe terminating within half-an-inch of the bottom of the
tank.   A master valve is provided at each athwartship and longitudinal bulkhead which enables sections of the pipeline to be
isolated as desired.

Gas Freeing.   Cargo tanks require to be entered during ballast
voyages in order to attend to valves and expansion joints in the
pipelines, as well as to remove scale when light oils are carried,
and sediment when the cargoes are black oils.   It is necessary,

therefore, to expel the petroleum vapours left after the cargo has been discharged in order to avoid the possibility of explosion. The Group's marine technicians have given the gas-freeing operation considerable thought and have evolved a procedure which enables all traces of gas to be removed in about four hours without opening the tank hatches. Moreover, all Group tankers are provided with a sensitive recording instrument which registers at a glance the condition of the atmosphere in the tanks.

Fire-fighting Appliances. Good provision is made for fighting fires should they occur. The cargo compartments are provided with a steam-smothering system comprising a steam supply pipe running the whole length of the ship, with a branch to each compartment. The supply of steam is remotely controlled and can be instantly operated when the alarm is given. Although much attention has been given to facilities for extinguishing fires, the Group's policy is to do everything possible to prevent fires occurring. Much in this direction can be and has been done in the construction of tankers and the enforcement of rigid rules and regulations relating to the handling of cargoes and the operation of boilers and galley stoves where naked lights must be employed.

The nature of the cargo is generally noticeable when a tanker is loading and, but to a much lesser extent, when discharging, owing to small openings in the tops of the tanks having to be uncovered to enable samples to be obtained and ullages ascertained, but when Group tankers are at sea, even when there is "hardly a breath of air", the presence of thousands of tons of highly volatile petroleum spirit beneath one's feet is not in the least discernible.

Galleys. The galley stoves are oil fired, but when it would be dangerous to have such fires in operation, owing to the presence of explosive gas, steam cookers, which can be operated by ship's steam or steam from the shore, are provided. These cookers are capable of providing a three-course meal for the whole of the personnel for an indefinite period. The galleys are also provided with various labour-saving devices, while particular attention is given to the design and location of cupboards and the like so as to avoid accumulation of dirt and homes for insects. Forced ventilation is employed, so that even in the hottest climate the galleys are reasonably cool.

Life-saving Appliances. Life-saving appliances on tankers receive very special consideration. Lifeboats are made of steel. There are usually four such boats in a deep-sea tanker, two of which are engine-propelled. The usual practice is to locate two boats amidships, one hand-propelled and one engine-propelled, and the remainder aft, the engine-propelled boat aft being on the opposite side of the ship to its counterpart amidships. There is sufficient accommodation for the whole of the personnel in the boats on either side of the ship, so that in the event of fire occurring at one side of the ship as the result of collision with another ship the personnel can escape in the boats on the opposite side. Lifeboats are provided with skates or skids which enable them to be launched satisfactorily even when a ship is heeled over to 30°, and mechanical lowering gear is provided which ensures the boats being lowered on an even keel. In the past, many seamen have lost their lives due to lifeboats up-ending when lowered by hand. The lifeboats are provided with battery-operated wireless sets with a range up to 500 miles during the hours of darkness, and equipment which will protect the occupants from exposure.

Trimming. Locating the engines aft in a tanker makes trimming difficult, as in ballast condition the weight of the machinery gives the ship a pronounced trim by the stern, while the ship must, of course, be on an even keel when loaded. This calls for very careful consideration of the loading arrangements when part cargoes have to be discharged at different ports. Another trimming problem results from the consumption of bunker fuel on a voyage, amounting to from 300 to 1,000 tons, depending upon the size of ship and type of machinery. This difficulty is overcome by splitting the bunkers and storing them at both ends of the ship. As the fuel from the aft bunker is used that contained in the forward deep tank is transferred aft and the ship maintained on an even keel. In dry cargo ships the bunker fuel is kept in the double-bottom tanks extending practically the whole length of the ship, and the maintenance of an even keel is a comparatively simple matter.

Fuel Consumption and Speed. The great bulk of the Group's products is transported in tankers of 12,000 tons deadweight*, which have a speed of 12 knots. These ships are propelled by oil engines of 3,600 b.h.p., and the fuel consumption is 12 tons per day. Carrying 12,000 tons at 12 knots on a fuel consumption of 12 tons daily, the great economy of these ships is best illustrated by simply calculating the expenditure of fuel to transport 12,000 tons of cargo one mile : and the amount is 8 lb., or less than 1 gallon. This reflects credit upon these Group-designed ships as well as on the thermal efficiency of the oil engines employed.

The conditions governing the operation and the maintenance of tanker machinery differ widely from those ruling in dry cargo ships. Normally, tankers load or discharge a full cargo and discharge or take on ballast in 48 hours. In normal times a tanker spends roughly 320 days at sea every year, which is about 50% more actual steaming time than dry cargo ships. Moreover, owing to the nature of certain cargoes carried by tankers, it is not permissible to do running repairs concurrently with loading or discharging cargo, owing to the presence of explosive gases. All running repairs, overhauls, examinations and adjustments must therefore be in strict accordance with a carefully thought out schedule and, if breakdowns at sea are to be avoided, examination of every part of the machinery has to be carried out as a matter of regular routine, all data relative to these examinations being recorded and analysed by the Group's marine technical staff.

The propelling engines most employed are of the four-stroke cycle single-acting supercharged type having eight cylinders. The length of such an engine is about 45 feet, and the weight in the region of 300 tons. The weight/power ratio of marine engines is high because the revolutions rarely exceed 120 per minute, the usual rate being 110 per minute. Higher rotational speeds result in a rapid falling off in the propeller efficiency and are only employed in special cases, such as when the type of ship allows only limited space for machinery. The latest practice is to cool the cylinders and pistons by means of fresh water, the fresh water amounting to about 100 tons being cooled by sea water and used over and over again. Pistons are sometimes cooled by lubricating oil, which is very effective and has advantages over water as a cooling medium. After the exhaust gases leave the engine they are directed through a boiler in which steam is generated and used to operate the steering gear and other auxiliary machinery.

Fig. 5.   Photograph of Modern Tanker.

Although the modern tanker is a highly compact and efficient carrier of bulk oil and capable of transporting dangerous cargoes with a remarkable degree of safety, research and investigation continue energetically, and, as a result, improvements in ship form, machinery and equipment are constantly being introduced, while Group tankers continue to take the lead in providing for the comfort and convenience of those who go down to the sea in ships.

FAST TANKERS

During the recent war the tendency was to build fast tankers, the purpose being to enable such ships to operate independently of the convoy system, which restricted the average speed of the vast majority of ships.

The Marine Technical Division of the "Shell" Group prepared designs for such tankers, and ultimately ordered two of 18,100 tons deadweight, a speed of $17\frac{1}{2}$ knots and 90% welded construction. These vessels, "HELICINA" and "HYALINA", are propelled by turbo-electric machinery of 13,000 S.H.P., steam being supplied by Babcock and Wilcox water tube boilers at a pressure of 425 lb. per square inch and a temperature of 750° F., the over-all fuel consumption being 85 tons a day.

The British Admiralty also built a number of what could be considered fast tankers. These ships, of 12,000 tons deadweight, were given a speed of 15 knots by geared turbines of 6,800 S.H.P., steam being supplied by Foster Wheeler water tube boilers.

A further example of fast tankers built for war purposes are the American T-2s. A large number of these all-welded vessels were constructed, the power of the turbo-electric machinery being 6,000 S.H.P., which gives the ships a speed of $14\frac{1}{2}$ knots on a fuel consumption of 50 tons a day. The deadweight of these ships is about 16,650 tons.

Since the war, the tendency has been to build larger tankers. The Shell Group has ordered three of 28,000 tons deadweight, but because of the deep draught of such ships the number of ports which they can enter when fully loaded is small.

XXI

TANK FARMS AND MAJOR INSTALLATIONS

THE term "tank farm" is generally applied to a large collection of tanks used to store huge quantities of crude oil, perhaps from several fields, and grouped at a convenient spot adjacent to the terminal of a large trunk pipeline or a refinery. The tank farm must be of sufficient capacity to take care of the ordinary fluctuations in production of a field, to allow for fluctuations due to changes in the demands of the market, and to provide emergency storage. In many cases tank farms are necessary to hold stocks sufficient to meet the demands of a market during such periods as normal transport conditions do not obtain, as, for example, when the North American Great Lakes are ice-bound, or when the water in the great Chinese rivers is too low for navigation.

The term "major installation" has a much broader meaning, being applied to a collection of tanks with the associated plant and equipment for dealing with the storage and distribution of all petroleum products, liquid and solid. Major installations are essentially a part of the complicated marketing organization, receiving their supplies of refined products in bulk by ocean tankers and distributing them either in small bulk consignments to minor installations or depots in the same area, or in bulk lorries, drums, tins or other receptacles to the dealers and consumers within the economic range of distribution.

Installations vary much both in size and scope, from minor installations embodying only two or three tanks storing perhaps only one product, a pump or pumps, the necessary pipelines and filling arrangements for rail cars, road wagons (or tank trucks) or small receptacles, to major installations embodying large numbers of tanks for different products, possibly a power station, pump|house, boilers, steam and C.I.* (diesel) engines, tin-making and case-making plant, chemical laboratory, workshop, storage buildings, residences, staff quarters, etc.

Naturally the responsibilities of installation managers vary accordingly. In the first case, they are limited, broadly speaking, to balancing stocks against incomings and outgoings and keeping the tanks, pipelines and plant generally in good condition. In the second case, in addition to the maintenance of far more complicated plant and machinery, the actual installation duties may be of a far more responsible type, including blending of different grades of oil to produce a certain product, verifying that stocks are up to specification, and keeping in close personal contact with the local harbour, medical, sanitary and Customs authorities.

INSTALLATION PIPELINES

Pipelines are almost invariably made up of lengths of steel pipe, the joints being either screwed, flanged, welded, or one of the patented type of pipeline couplings. The last mentioned possess a certain degree of flexibility, and a number of such joints at short intervals is frequently used for the final connection of a pipeline to a tank, thus allowing for relative movement due either to expansion of the line from temperature changes, or to the slight rise and fall of the tank on poor ground due to the varying load between an empty and a full tank.

In the case of an installation handling a number of different products, it is, of course, necessary to provide different lines for the different products. As far as tanker discharge lines are concerned, it is clearly necessary to keep the black oil and white oil lines separate. In the case of different white oils—for example, gasoline and kerosine—it is generally possible to use the same main discharge line for both, the line being cleared of the product last received by pumping water through it. In the case of so-called black oils, which range from opaque black fuel oils to transparent pale gas oils, it is not advisable to clear the lines with water. If separate lines are not available, then, to avoid contamination of one product with the other, on receipt of a new cargo, sufficient of the product from the tanker must be pumped through the discharging line into the settling tank to wash out the line and to ensure that contamination is negligible, before the steamer discharge line is connected to the main storage tank. Separate lines are, however, desirable.

Heating of Pipelines. For certain products, e.g. asphaltic bitumen and very heavy fuel oils, it is necessary to heat the pipe-lines, for it is only at fairly high temperatures that such materials will flow freely. This heating may be effected either by a small steam pipe running alongside the oil line, the two lines being strapped together and afterwards covered by suitable heat-insu-lating and weather-resisting material, or by enclosing the oil line in one of larger diameter carrying steam connections, so that the space between the pipes may be supplied with steam, this being necessary in the case of asphaltic bitumen.

Valve Manifold and Hose Exchange. Pipelines may account for a considerable proportion of the total cost of an installation, so that economy in their layout and use is essential. There must necessarily be at least one pipeline to each tank, but this line may be used for delivering to or drawing from its particular tank. This double purpose may be achieved by using a valve manifold, a hose exchange or a combination of both. In the case of the valve manifold all the incoming lines from the individual tanks, filling points, etc., are arranged to run to a position generally adjacent to the pump house and to lie parallel to each other at this point. The suction and delivery lines from all the pumps are carried at right-angles across these lines, either above or below them, and connected to them by tee-pieces with a valve between. It is thus possible, by opening appropriate valves, for any pump to suck from any one line and to deliver to any other line. Where black oil and white oil pumps are housed in the same pump house, it is customary to connect the black oil pumps to the lines serving black oil tanks and filling points only, and similarly, to isolate the white oil equipment. Even so, emergency connections are fre-quently provided in the form of tee-pieces with blanked-off out-lets, to enable black oil pumps to be used for pumping white oil products, and vice versa, in the event of serious damage to part of the pumping equipment.

An alternative to the valve manifold is the hose exchange, which is a centre to which the various lines from the pumps, tanks and loading points converge. Connections from any pump to any desired lines are made, as required, by means of flexible hoses. The choice between a valve manifold, a hose exchange or a com-bination of both, depends on a number of factors, such as the amount of pumping to be done, frequency of change-overs, size of lines, risk of contamination, and even the type of labour available, each system having its own advantages and disadvantages. As a general rule, it will be found that manifolds are preferable for black oils.

TANKS

Oil is normally stored in the familiar steel vertical, cylindrical tank. This is built of mild steel plates, riveted or welded together in horizontal courses*. The cost of unit capacity of these storage tanks, within limits, decreases fairly rapidly as the total capacity increases, so that the tendency has been to increase the size of the standard tank.

Storage tanks of this type may vary in size from about 10,000 gallons (say, 50 tons of water) to 110,000 barrels (say, 17,000 tons of water). The maximum size of the Group's standard tanks is at present roughly 118 feet diameter, 43 feet high, with a capacity of 13,000 tons (approx. 3,000,000 Imperial gallons) of water. Bolted tanks were used in large numbers during the late war, but they are of very light construction and, whilst excellent for purely temporary storage, are not recommended for permanent installation work.

Foundation and Design. In normal circumstances, all that is necessary in the way of foundation for a tank is a built-up earth or chalk bed with a layer of sand on top, the whole then being surfaced over with a 2-inch layer of sand-bitumen mixture, the top surface of this foundation varying from just above ground level to approximately 2 feet 6 inches above the surface of the ground. This sand bed is made higher at the centre than at the circumference, so that when the tank is being emptied the contents may be drained off as far as possible by the drainage connection provided at the side of the tank, close to the bottom. On ground which is marshy or has poor supporting qualities, special precautions may have to be taken with the foundations—for example, by piling—before the sand bed is laid in position. Alternatively, shallow tanks of larger diameter may be employed. The conical-shaped roof is relatively light and not very strongly attached to the sides. This is arranged deliberately, as, in the event of an explosion, with

U

which a tank fire almost invariably commences, the roof acts as a sort of safety valve and it is blown right off the tank. Once the roof is blown off the fire burns more or less steadily until the oil has been consumed, during which process the sides of the tank gradually curl over and fall inwards. The fire may thus be restricted to one tank.

FITTINGS AND ACCESSORIES

(*a*) **Dip Holes and Pressure-vacuum Valves.** The fittings of a storage tank vary according to the products to be stored in it. Where products of high flash point, such as fuel oil and lubricating oil, are to be stored, the roof fittings are very simple and normally comprise a number of dip-holes and vents and one or two man-holes, the number and size of vents being decided by the rate of pumping and range of temperature that may be expected. The dip-holes are used for measuring the height of liquid, the manholes mainly for ventilating the tank prior to cleaning or repairing operations, the covers being normally kept closed.

The fittings of the roof of a gasoline tank are somewhat more complicated, the dip-holes being made gas-tight and supplemented by some form of pressure and vacuum-relief valve. These valves take various forms, but in all cases embody two valves in one fitting, one of which operates to allow vapour to escape when the pressure reaches a predetermined limit, and the other operates to let air into the tank when the vacuum reaches a pre-determined figure. These valves may be adjusted to conform to the pressure and vacuum for which the tank roof has been designed. The Group's standard tank roof is designed to withstand 8-inch water-gauge* pressure and $2\frac{1}{2}$-inch water-gauge vacuum, although, still further to combat evaporation losses, it is probable that new designs for higher pressures may be adopted in the near future.

Certain petroleum products, such as propane and butane, having high vapour pressures, cannot be stored in ordinary tanks. For such products a special kind of tank, known as the "Horton-spheroid", has been designed, capable of withstanding an internal pressure of 25 lb. per square inch above atmospheric pressure (fig. 1). It is constructed in the form of a slightly flattened sphere. For still higher pressures—up to 100 lb. per square inch above

Fig. 1.   Hortonspheroid.

atmospheric pressure—a truly spherical tank known as the "Hortonsphere" is employed (fig. 2).

(b) **Pipe Connections.**   It is possible to make good use of a tank equipped with one main pipeline connection (on the side) and one draining connection (near the bottom), but it will generally be found that an additional main connection on the side will justify itself, and in modern practice this is usually provided for.   With two main connections, a tank may be used for blending and mixing purposes as well as merely for storage.   Inside the tank, one of these two main connections is sometimes provided with a swing pipe, which consists merely of a pipe attached to the main connection by a swivel joint and provided with hoisting gear so that its free end may be raised or lowered to any position between the tank bottom and the top curb*.   Such a fitting is extremely useful when blending operations are carried out, as it enables the contents of the tank to be effectively circulated by drawing off from

Fig. 2.   Hortonsphere.

near the surface and pumping back through the second main connection near the bottom of the tank, or vice versa. The sizes of these main connections are determined by the sizes of the lines serving the tanks, which in turn are dependent upon the viscosity of the oil to be dealt with and the distance of the tank from the pumps or the steamer discharge berth. As a general rule they vary between 12 inches diameter and 6 inches diameter.

(c) **Steam Coils.** Heavy oil and asphaltic bitumen tanks must be provided with steam coils. These usually take the form of continuous pipes with numerous hairpin bends, supported in one horizontal plane within a few inches of the tank bottom. The heating of large fuel oil tanks calls for the use of considerable quantities of steam and may be a very expensive operation. For this reason, wherever possible exhaust steam (i.e. steam that has already done useful work in, say, operating pumps but still retains a good deal of heat) is used.

(*d*) **Compound or Fire Walls.**   The tanks on an installation are usually surrounded by what is known as a "compound wall". This may be constructed of earth, brick or concrete.   In most areas there are local regulations governing the height of these compound walls, generally based on the capacity of the tank or tanks in the compound.   For protection against ordinary commercial risks in the storage of refined oils, it is considered sufficient for a compound wall to be capable of retaining easily the contents of the largest tank in the group of tanks in the compound.

GASOLINE EVAPORATION LOSSES

"Breathing"—Fixed Roof Tanks.   With volatile liquids, such as gasoline, evaporation takes place even at atmospheric temperatures, so that the air above such liquids in a storage tank becomes readily charged with vapour from the liquid.   As the temperature rises during the day this mixture of air and vapour expands, a part of it escaping through the relief valve to the outside atmosphere, carrying some of this valuable vapour with it.   As the temperature falls at night, or owing to clouds or a shower of rain, the air-vapour mixture in the tank contracts, fresh air is drawn in from the outside.   This in turn becomes more or less saturated with vapour and is then expelled with the next rise of temperature.   The cycle is continually repeated.   On a modern standard tank the pressure-vacuum valves, already referred to, prevent (*a*), any escape of this air-vapour mixture until the pressure is 8-inch water-gauge above atmospheric, and (*b*), fresh air from being drawn in before the vacuum is $2\frac{1}{2}$-inch water-gauge below atmospheric pressure.   Thus, what is known as "breathing"* is reduced at both ends of the scale and the vapour loss resulting therefrom is appreciably diminished.

Breathing is directly proportional to (*a*), the temperature changes and (*b*), the volume of the vapour space.   The reduction of these losses can, therefore, be tackled in two directions.   In the first place, the range of temperature may be materially reduced by lagging the roof of the tank, i.e. covering it with a certain thickness of heat-insulating material to prevent changes of temperature outside the tank being communicated to the vapour space and, particularly, to prevent the sun's rays from striking directly on to the roof of the tank. Secondly, the volume of the vapour space may be kept small by keeping the tank as full as possible. In certain cases this is achieved by introducing water into the tank as the gasoline is withdrawn. This involves an additional fitting on the tank shell near the top, known as a high-level discharge. This can be used as a gravity feed to filling sheds, thus eliminating service tanks. Both lagging and so-called deep-water bottoms are being used and are proving successful ; they have materially reduced gasoline losses in different parts of the world.

Floating Roof Tanks. A further development is the floating roof, which, as its name implies, floats on the surface of the liquid. As the air space is thus eliminated, breathing losses disappear. The fire risk is also greatly reduced. Such roofs are considerably more expensive and their justification, in particular instances, depends on many factors, technical and physical ; these have to be carefully weighed when deciding whether to adopt a floating roof or a fixed roof tank. It may generally be said that where the offtake from the tank is small and the tank is therefore infrequently filled and emptied, the lagged fixed roof is suitable ; where the throughput is large and the tank has to be refilled frequently in the course of the year, the floating roof will often be found a better paying proposition. The cut-away illustration (fig. 3) shows sufficiently clearly the main details of construction of a floating-roof tank. Rain water drains off by means of pipes having hinged connections at their ends, these pipes connecting the centre of the roof to the water drain outside. Alternatively, the water on the tank roof may be allowed to overflow through a special tray into the gasoline, where it falls to the tank bottom, from which it is periodically removed via the drainage connection.

Water Spray. Gasoline storage tanks with fixed roofs are usually fitted with a means of supplying a water spray so that the roof and the sides of the tank may be sprayed with water in the event of fire occurring in an adjacent tank. This arrangement of water spray has also been used to reduce the temperature range in the vapour space of gasoline tanks in hot climates and, whilst a certain amount of success has been achieved by it, it is a practice which is not advocated owing to running costs and corrosion of tank roofs.

Fig. 3. Cutaway Section of Floating Roof Tank.

FIRE FIGHTING PLANT AND FIRE PRECAUTIONS FOR INSTALLATIONS AND DEPOTS

Light petroleum products such as gasoline, like most other inflammable liquids, do not catch fire unless definitely ignited either by a burning article or by an electric spark. The anti-fire precautions at an installation or depot are, therefore, directed towards (a) eliminating the possibility of contact with any burning body, by rigid rules regarding smoking, carrying of matches, etc. ; (b) adequate arrangements to avoid, as far as possible, any generation of static electricity* ; (c) the extinction or control of any fire should it unfortunately occur.

All oil installations and depots are, therefore, provided with means for combating fires adequate for the risk involved. Ample supplies of sand are placed at points readily accessible from any inflammable goods storage. Portable chemical extinguishers are similarly placed. Such fire-fighting facilities are usually considered sufficient for depots, but for main installations, where the quantities of inflammable products stored are very much greater, there is usually a system of water lines and feeding hydrants supplied from the public water mains, or by a special high-pressure water pump, or from a high-level reservoir. This water system is to combat fires in buildings and to keep oil storage tanks cool in the event of a fire in their vicinity.

Portable Extinguishers. The principal types of portable extinguishers used at oil installations and depots are :—

(a) *Foam Type Extinguishers.* The foam type, usually of 2 and 34 Imperial gallon sizes (the larger size mounted on wheels) extinguishes fire by forming over the burning material a blanket of foam which will not support combustion, and which prevents sufficient air obtaining access to the burning material for combustion to continue. This type is particularly effective for extinguishing burning oil. It consists of two liquids in two separate containers which, when the extinguisher is operated, mix together inside the extinguisher and generate a relatively large volume of foam containing carbon dioxide.

(b) *Soda-Acid Type Extinguishers.* The soda-acid type of extinguisher (2 Imperial gallons capacity) is more useful than the foam type for extinguishing fires such as might occur in an office or residence where burning oil is not involved. Soda-acid extinguishers, as their name implies, operate by the reaction of two chemicals (one at least of which is in liquid form) which, while normally kept separate, produce large quantities of carbon dioxide when mixed. This mixing takes place when the extinguisher is operated, and the mixture of liquid and carbon dioxide expelled by the gas pressure generated extinguishes fires principally through the carbon dioxide excluding from the burning material the air or oxygen necessary for combustion.

(c) *Carbon Dioxide Type Extinguishers.* This form of fire extinguishing equipment consists of a steel cylinder (or cylinders) containing liquefied carbon dioxide under pressure, with a hand valve and a cone-shaped discharge tube. On release, the carbon dioxide immediately vaporizes and can be directed against the fire by means of the discharge tube. This type of extinguisher is used extensively in aircraft, and in multi-engine planes it is designed to flood individual engine compartments. Portable units containing from 2 to 100 lb. of liquid carbon dioxide (the larger being mounted on wheels) are suitable for general use, and in particular around electrical installations. It is particularly advantageous in some cases, as the carbon dioxide gas will not injure any unburned material, even fine fabrics. However, the application of this type of extinguisher is limited to areas in which facilities exist within easy reach for recharging the extinguishers with carbon dioxide.

(d) *Carbon Tetrachloride Type Extinguishers.* The carbon tetrachloride type extinguisher is the most effective hand extinguisher for fires such as may occur around motor vehicle engines where foam cannot be directly applied to the seat of the fire. The carbon tetrachloride liquid pumped from the extinguisher on to the nearest access point to the fire volatilizes rapidly, providing a non-inflammable vapour round the seat of the fire, thus excluding air and, if applied before the fire has extended too far, will extinguish it. It is this type of extinguisher which is most frequently carried on ordinary motor vehicles, although oil tank lorries usually carry a 2-gallon foam type extinguisher as well as a quart size carbon tetrachloride extinguisher.

Naturally, at oil depots and installations, portable extinguishers are principally of the foam type, with only such soda-acid type extinguishers as may be considered necessary to protect offices, residences, etc. However, the carbon dioxide extinguisher is sometimes used to supplant both of the foregoing, as it is generally effective on all types of fires. The extinguishers are located at strategic points so that they can be utilized in the earliest stages of a fire, when they are most effective.

Large-scale Systems of Fire Extinguishers. The more elaborate comprehensive systems, comprising large solution tanks, pumps and pipelines to convey the solutions to different points and to form foam at those points, are really only justified for refineries where the fire risk is far greater than at the largest installations. The cost of such systems is very high and, for installations, out of all proportion to the risk of fire occurring. There are several somewhat simpler and less costly methods for providing foam in considerable quantities. The principal ones are :—

(*a*) *Generator or Hopper Systems.* The distinctive feature of these systems is that they generate foam by the action of water from a water hydrant system on a powder or powders. The water pressure must, for satisfactory working, be at least 80 lb. per square inch. The apparatus for those systems using two powders comprises a pair of hoppers, or inverted conical receptacles, for the respective powders, with open tops and with openings in the lower ends of the cones, set in two short lengths of pipe which form branches from a single water inlet. The outfit is portable and may be connected to any suitable point in the water supply. When the water is turned on, a stream of water passes under each hopper and powders from each hopper fall into their respective water streams and form the two separate solutions required for generating the foam. These two solutions are carried in two separate pipes or hoses of relatively small diameter to a point adjacent to the fire, where they may be connected to a special hose nozzle having two inlets. The two solutions thus mix together in the nozzle itself and generate the foam, which is played on to the fire. One disadvantage of this system is the possibility of one or other of the powders not feeding at the correct rate and thus not making a satisfactory solution. Some generator systems use only one powder. In these systems water is supplied from the ordinary mains to the generator itself. The distance from the generator at which the foam can be utilized is limited by the distance which the foam will travel through piping without being broken down by friction.   It is also limited by the pressure available to force the foam through the piping on to the fire.   The generator, being portable, should therefore be brought as near to the fire as possible.   The single powder for this system of generation is considerably more expensive than the equivalent quantity of powder required for a twin-powder system.

(*b*) *Air-Foam Systems*.   Several systems generate foam in which the bubbles do not contain carbon dioxide gas formed by chemical action, but contain air.   Such foam, although not quite so effective in extinguishing fires, per unit quantity of foam, as chemical foam (i.e. containing carbon dioxide), can be produced in such large quantities that it may, under some circumstances, be actually preferable to chemical foam for fire protection.   In one system, high-pressure water is delivered into an apparatus known as a foam branch pipe, where its discharge through a nozzle into a large chamber serves to draw in and mix with it both large quantities of air from the atmosphere and a very small quantity of foam, making a bulky foam similar to the lather of a soap solution. With any of the systems for making foam in large quantities, special devices can be provided for applying the foam to the inside of a tank or tanks.

In certain circumstances—for instance, where the installation is in a congested area partially surrounded by buildings or works, which in themselves constitute a fire danger—provision of a generator or hopper type of plant for making chemical foam or a plant for making air foam may sometimes be justified.

PUMPS

Pumps are used for transferring oil from tank to tank or from tank to daily service tank, for filling bulk lorries, railway tank cars, for loading and discharging steamers, and in fact for all movements of oil in bulk within the installation.   There is a wide variety of types of pump, but, unfortunately, no one type can be standardized as being suitable for all purposes, and every pumping problem has to be studied from various aspects to decide which type of pump will be the most suitable.   In general, the pumps may be divided into three main classes, i.e. reciprocating, centrifugal and rotary.

Reciprocating Pumps. Probably the type of pump most commonly used for all purposes, in refineries as well as in installations, is the reciprocating, duplex, double-acting pump—duplex indicating that there are two cylinders, and double-acting meaning that both sides of the piston are utilized, i.e. when the piston moves in one direction oil is drawn into one end of the cylinder and discharged from the other, and on the return stroke this function is reversed. These pumps may be belt-driven from shafting operated by an oil engine or other prime mover powered by electric motors, or they may be direct steam-driven, steam cylinders being mounted on the same bedplate in line with the pump cylinders. Advantages of the direct steam type of pump are : (*a*), the great speed flexibility, which is controlled by simply opening and closing the main steam valve ; (*b*), that it is nearly foolproof and may safely be put in the hands of practically unskilled labour ; and (*c*), that its maintenance is simple. Its principal drawback is its very low efficiency and, in pumps of large capacity, the excessive space occupied.

Centrifugal Pumps. The centrifugal pump consists of an impeller or a series of impellers rotating at high speed. The shape of the impellers combined with the high rotational speed imparts a high rotational velocity to the liquid inside the pump, and this velocity, which is merely a form of energy, is converted to pressure by passing the oil through suitable guide vanes or passages as it leaves the pump. Due to the high rotational speed, these pumps may be, and generally are, directly coupled to electric motors, forming a very compact unit of low first cost and occupying very little space. The principal drawback is that these pumps are not normally self-priming, that is to say, if the suction pipe is empty and the pump is started up, it will have no suction effect. Moreover, in view of the high speed of this type of pump, it is only suitable for pumping products with a viscosity below about 1,730 seconds Redwood I (approx. 45° Engler) at the temperature of pumping (*vide* chapter XXVIII).

Rotary Pumps. Unlike the centrifugal pump, in which the impeller is much smaller than the casing and thus provides ample clearance, the internal working parts of the rotary pump are almost, if not quite, in contact with the outer casing. Small foreign bodies in the oil which may pass safely through centrifugal pumps are almost certain to cause serious damage in the case of rotary pumps.

All three types of pump briefly described above have their special applications, and their adoption or rejection depends on the nature of the oil to be pumped, the suction and pressure conditions, the availability or otherwise of electric current, type of labour in charge of the equipment, etc.

INSTALLATION OPERATIONS

OIL STOCKS

(a) **Measurements.** Among the varied operations carried out as part of the daily routine in the working of an installation, one of the most important is the careful checking of the quantities and qualities of the stocks of oil in the storage tanks. The stock in every tank is measured by the methods described in the chapter on oil measurement (XXIII) before and after every transfer to or from it. Even if a particular tank is not involved in transfers during a period, the stock should still be re-determined at regular intervals of not more than one week, for it is only by such careful methods that proper control can be effected and losses minimized.

(b) **Analysis and Control.** At some of the larger installations the samples taken for purposes of stock calculation also serve, when more completely analysed, to control the quality of the stock. This quality control is exercised whenever any fresh material is pumped into a tank. Even when the contents have not been disturbed it is advisable to check the quality periodically.

(c) **Blending.** Blending operations may be carried out by transferring the different components, in succession, to one tank and afterwards pumping from one side connection and delivering back through the other, until a uniform mixture results. The swing pipe, which may be used as suction or delivery according to circumstances, is invaluable in this connection, since it can be placed in any desired position. Blending may be effected much more speedily and economically by pumping the various components simultaneously into one tank through a single delivery line. For a blend of four components at least two pumps will be used, each pump drawing from two different tanks, the valves on the pump suctions being regulated to allow the proper proportions of the components to be pumped. By this method, owing to the intimate mixing of the components in the delivery line, the blend is almost complete when the material reaches the tank, and can be rendered complete by a brief final circulation when the transfer has been effected. Another method frequently adopted is to use a so-called blending coil, which lies very near to the bottom of the tank. It consists of a straight length of pipe, 6 inches or 8 inches in diameter, extending very nearly right across the tank bottom, and is provided with a number of side branches of smaller diameter, each branch extending practically to the wall of the tank. These branches are perforated throughout their length with a number of small holes. When making a blend the heavier constituent is first pumped into the tank, the lighter constituent being then added via this blending coil, which distributes it over the whole area of the tank. As this lighter constituent rises through the heavier contents of the tank intimate mixing takes place, so that very little ultimate circulation is necessary.

More recent developments in blending operations are found in propeller type mixers and jet mixers. With the former, propellers are introduced through the bottom manholes of tanks, driven by flameproof or, if acceptable, explosion-resisting, motors outside the tanks. The propellers are set at a carefully determined angle, so as to set up a swirl in the tank, and intimate mixing of the contents is achieved. The jet mixer works on the same swirl principle, but is operated by the installation pumps. One of the pipe connections to the tank terminates inside the tank in an inclined jet or jets, the high velocity through the jets setting up a swirl in the tank. This jet mixing is particularly applicable to ethyl blending or the addition of small dosages of gum inhibitor to the contents of a tank. The concentrated mixture of gasoline and tetra-ethyl lead, for example, is pumped into the tank via these inclined nozzles, and so intimate is the mixing that by the time the complete dose has been introduced the contents of the tank are practically homogeneous, and it is only necessary to continue circulating for an hour or two.

The question of ethyl blending has come very much to the fore in recent years. This involves the introduction of a very small dosage of tetra-ethyl lead (T.E.L.) into a gasoline. The quantity is very small and may be of the order of a few millilitres per gallon of gasoline, so that even in a relatively large tank the total quantity of T.E.L. will still be very small. As pure tetra-ethyl lead is extremely poisonous, special equipment and methods have been evolved for carrying out this blending process. The whole blending plant is isolated and only specially-trained employees are permitted to operate the plant. The most stringent precautions are taken to avoid any ill effects from the T.E.L., such as limiting the number of times per month that a man may be engaged upon this work, providing complete changes of clothing every time he has anything to do with the plant, elaborate washing arrangements, gas masks, etc.

DELIVERY OPERATIONS

(*a*) **Lighters.** Delivery operations, though simple in themselves, call for careful attention. All the equipment to be employed—tanks, pumps, pipelines, connections and valves—must be verified as being in order. It is preferable to commence delivery at a slow rate, gradually increasing until the full throughput of the pumps is attained. Careful co-operation is necessary between lighter and shore staff to guard against overfilling of the vessel.

(*b*) **Rail and Road Cars.** Delivery to rail and road cars is made usually from delivery tanks raised sufficiently high to allow the liquid to flow by gravity through the delivery pipes, the alternative methods being direct from storage tank by centrifugal pump or through a high-level discharge and deep-water bottom. In these cases the small filling tank is not measured between each operation, but the quantity is ascertained by "dipping"* the road vehicle and by weighing or "dipping" the rail car.

(*c*) **Barrels and Drums.** In some installations the filling of relatively small packages forms one of the principal operations. Drums for the transport of the Group's products are generally made from plain steel sheets of various gauges. In the past galvanized drums were used for certain products, but their use is now discouraged as they are not considered satisfactory for aviation gasoline and certain gas oils and diesel fuels, and from the point of view of flexibility it is clearly preferable that all drums in an area should be equally satisfactory for all products. The Group has standardized on the 44-Imperial gallon drum, which is equivalent to 200 litres and thus suitable also for areas working in metric units.

The gauge (thickness) of the material of which the drums are made depends upon whether the drum is intended to be a returnable or a non-returnable package. Drums used for lubricating oil and, in some cases, fuel oils, are constructed of relatively light gauge black steel sheets, whilst those for asphaltic bitumens are of still lighter gauge, since the latter drums are not returnable.

Gasoline and kerosine drums are cleaned internally before refilling by rinsing them with kerosine, caustic soda, or boiling water, a machine with a rotating spray frequently being used for this purpose. Lubricating oil drums are sometimes cleaned internally by the application of a spray of thin lubricating oil applied by means of a rotating high-pressure spray nozzle. The drums are afterwards drained. The cleaning of fuel oil drums is effected by means of a gas-oil or caustic soda spray applied in a similar manner.

Asphaltic bitumen drums are coated internally with a wash, prior to filling, to prevent the contents adhering to the container. A mixture of clay and water is used for this purpose.

Drums are filled from storage tanks or, more commonly, from service tanks, either by a volumetric type of filling machine or direct on a weighing scale.

It is of the greatest importance that the bungs of drums should always be securely tightened, irrespective of whether the drum is full or empty. In the case of an empty drum, temperature changes cause air to be drawn in through a loose bung during the night and to be expelled during the day. This can be prevented in a full drum by storing the drum so that the contents cover the bung-hole. In humid climates any moisture carried into the drum with the air during the night is liable to be condensed on the interior of the drum, which will set up rusting. Drums left out in the open, in particular, should be stored on their sides for the same reason, as, especially if they have an end bung and are stored on end, water will accumulate in the head of the drum and, if the bung is at all loose, or the washer defective, will find its way into the interior and will set up rusting. Such rusting is difficult to remove and the ordinary drum washing referred to above is not likely to be effective. What are called ''drum rumbling'' machines are provided for such cases, in which the drums are rotated on a machine and turned over and over for an appreciable period with a loose chain or similar equipment inside them. This chain scrapes or knocks off the rust over the whole interior of the drum, but it is, of course, a somewhat slow process, and the drum must be thoroughly washed out afterwards to remove all the rust which has been loosened. Every precaution, therefore, has to be taken to avoid the formation of rust inside drums.

Fig. 4.   Tin Making Factory.

(*d*) **Tins.** The 4-gallon (Imp.) tin is largely used in many areas, and many installations are equipped with complete tin factories for its manufacture. The tinplate is received in the form of flat

x

sheets, slightly larger than the sizes required. In passing through the factory they are trimmed to exact size, impressed with designs both for identification and for increasing their strength, bent to the correct shape, assembled, and finally soldered. In up-to-date factories labour charges are reduced by the use of automatic machinery and conveyors as far as possible. The illustration (fig. 4) shows a portion of a tin factory, with part of an automatic soldering machine in the foreground. The tins are then transported to the filling shed, filled with the required product and capped. In some areas they are despatched in this condition, but in others they are packed in wooden cases, the manufacture of which again entails the provision of a special factory and equipment with printing machines for printing suitable designs on the sides and/or ends of the cases.

XXII

MINOR INSTALLATIONS AND DEPOTS, ROAD, RAIL AND RIVER TRANSPORT

THE main installation receives its supplies from the refineries and main distribution centres, generally by ocean-going tankers, but occasionally by long-distance pipeline. The main installation in turn becomes the source of supply to minor installations and depots, the former being normally fed by coastal tankers, whereas the latter may be water-fed, rail-fed, or supplied by road. Depots may be either "bulk" or "packed", or a combination of both. Bulk depots have relatively small tanks which are replenished from time to time from the main installation, and are, of course, complete with necessary pipelines and pumping equipment. Packed depots comprise buildings for the storage of packed products in tins, drums or other containers, which may be made, filled and despatched from the main installation, as and when required.

The size of the depot depends on various factors, being based in the first place on the demand for the various products in the locality served by the depot. If accessible all the year round, there is no need to provide for more than a few weeks' stocks ; in other cases it may be quite inaccessible during certain periods of the year, due to low water, ice or other conditions, and storage must be sufficient to tide over such periods. Again, in the case of water-fed bulk depots, the tankage may have to be governed by the carrying capacity of the coastal tanker or barge used for replenishing stocks. It is generally uneconomic to operate such craft except under "full load" conditions, so that the capacity of the depot tanks must be sufficient to accommodate such loads and, in addition, provide a few days' margin to cover possible delays.

FIRE PRECAUTIONS

The precautions taken to prevent an outbreak of fire are fundamentally the same, whether for a major installation or a small depot. These embody the provision of adequate safety distances between facilities in laying out the depot, electric wiring to approved standards, the use of flameproof equipment in dangerous areas, the prohibition of smoking and the carrying of matches, the use of naked lights, and so on. The scale on which fire-fighting facilities are provided is naturally determined by the size of the installation or depot. In the case of the small depot, a supply of dry sand and portable or hand extinguishers is always available, and the efficiency of the latter is ensured by routine testing at regular intervals. For larger installations the amount of such equipment is greatly increased, and water under pressure, either from local authorities' mains or our own pumping equipment or a combination of both, has to be made available. Fuller details of the fire-fighting plants at major installations and refineries are given in chapter XXI.

DISTRIBUTION FROM THE INSTALLATION OR DEPOT

The petroleum industry has always been quick to avail itself of any form of transport which would assist in the distribution of its products. Road, rail and water transport are all regularly employed, and in some special cases even air transport has been utilized. Generally speaking, before any particular form of transport can be adopted, it is necessary to adapt the equipment to the needs of the industry.

Coast Tankers and Barges. Coasting tankers, varying from 100 to about 3,000 tons in capacity, are used for supplying ports which are inaccessible to larger vessels. To supply minor installations, wharves and depots still smaller craft are necessary, and barges are employed which may be either self-propelled or ''dumb''. The former, varying in capacity from 50 to 1,000 tons or more, are usually constructed on the principle of the tanker, whilst the latter, of similar capacity, are generally designed upon the same lines, but in some cases they are constructed as ordinary open general cargo barges and fitted with two or more self-contained tanks seated on the frames of the barge. Many of these vessels are provided with living accommodation for the crew, as even on inland waterways the round trip may occupy several weeks.

Rail Cars. Whilst water transport is generally the cheapest method of supply, many depots and customers' works are inaccessible by water, and if there is a rail connection from the main installation, rail tank cars are employed to effect supplies. These cars consist of steel tanks, usually cylindrical and mounted on the underframes or carriages on suitable cradles. They vary from 10 to 20 tons capacity in the United Kingdom, but may be larger than this (30 to 50 tons capacity) in other countries. Their equipment varies somewhat with the product to be carried and the regulations of the country. In all cases, however, there is a central manhole to give access to the interior for cleaning and repairing, and in some cases this manhole houses the operating gear for internal valves, etc. In the case of most products, discharge is generally by gravity through a bottom outlet, which may be provided with branch pipes to both sides of the car, so that discharge can be carried out from either side as desired. As a safety device, in case of fracture of the outlet pipes or valves, these cars are fitted with an internal valve at the bottom. In some areas, bottom outlets are not permitted in the case of tank cars carrying gasoline and other volatile products, so that both filling and emptying must be effected by means of a pipe inserted in the top of the tank and extending internally practically to the bottom. Discharge in such cases involves the use of a pump.

Cars intended for the transport of heavy oils are provided, in addition, with heating coils situated as near the bottom as possible, and which terminate in valves outside the tank. This allows steam to be introduced into the coils to heat the oil, thus facilitating discharge.

Still further modifications are necessary when asphaltic bitumen is to be conveyed. In this case, the shell of the tank is covered with insulating material, and the outlet cock and pipe are steam-jacketed. In some countries, a connection is provided on the manhole dome to allow compressed air to be introduced to accelerate discharge.

Road Transport. Delivery by road is generally assuming greater importance and, with improved design of vehicles, better roads and the possibility of transporting larger loads, bulk bridging, i.e. feeding small depots from installations, is often more

Fig. 1.   2,000 Gallon Bridging Truck.

economical than rail transport.   The increasing use of the compression ignition engine for long-distance transport is due to its
economy, and with modern engines, long, trouble-free service is
assured.

With heavy loads, it has been proved that more powerful engines
working below their rated capacity give the best all-round results
in the way of lower maintenance costs, and 200-h.p. engines are
now common for road wagons carrying 10 tons or more.

With normal delivery vehicles operating on short hauls the
gasoline engine is still preferable, except in countries where the
difference in cost of diesel fuel and gasoline is very marked.   When
investigating the merits of different vehicles experience shows that
it is seldom economical to buy an expensive road wagon for
ordinary delivery work, as its possible mileage value cannot be
utilized before the truck becomes obsolete, and the modern mass-
produced article will, unless the operating conditions are exceptionally severe, give five or more years' economical service for
marketing petroleum products.   Every possible effort is made to
cut down the weight of the tank and fittings in order to increase
pay load to the maximum.

Increasing interest is now being taken in the fitting of meters on road wagons, which obviates the need for compartmented tanks, cuts down complaints of short measure and reduces losses (*vide* fig. 4). Meters are now being produced which give a high degree of accuracy if properly maintained. A modern type of bridging truck of 2,000 gallons capacity, intended for long distance haulage, is illustrated in fig. 1.

Quick loading and discharge of wagons is most important, as a few minutes' saving on each operation may enable an extra trip to be run, or save overtime, which is of increasing importance now that vehicle costs and wages are so high.

GASOLINE DISPENSING PUMPS

Hand-operated pumps can now be considered obsolete, except at isolated sales points where no electric power is available. The majority of the new dispensing pumps installed are electrically operated, some are of the clock face pattern, but the computor type is most popular both from the customers' and garagists' angle, and most of the new pumps now purchased use the computing head. This gives very little trouble in service and it is possible to vary the selling price per unit over a wide range by moving the setting pins to the appropriate position. One of the advantages of the computor is that it totals up the amount of each sale, which enables the operator to check his cash received against the recorder reading. A modern computor pump is shown in fig. 2. Electric pumps are usually provided with a hand-drive attachment to enable deliveries to be made in case of electricity failure. Fig. 3 shows the computing head.

AIRCRAFT FUELLING

The trend is for main route aircraft to become larger in order to carry more passengers and freight. As a result of the increased costs involved by the use of these large aircraft, it is necessary to cut down standing time to the minimum, and, amongst other things, fuelling must be speeded up. The rate of gasoline delivery has, therefore, increased and larger pumps and delivery hose are necessary. As a further aid to quick fuelling, aircraft tanks are sometimes manifolded together and the filling point is located below the wings.   The latest practice is to fit level cut-off valves in each tank, which allows fuel to be pumped through the fixed-point connections without danger of overfilling the tanks.   The aircraft may have one, two or more filling points, all of which can be used at once, and with four points up to 800 gallons per minute can be

Fig. 2.   Beck Computing Pump.

Fig. 3.   Computing Head.

loaded.   To enable very large quantities to be delivered use is
made of the gasoline mains installed in the loading area at the
airport with take-off points at convenient spots.   This enables the
aircraft to be filled without congesting the immediate vicinity with
a number of fuelling trucks, which is desirable when other vehicles
with food, baggage, etc., have to service the machine at the same
time.

Fig. 4.   1,200 Gallon Fuelling Truck.

Fig. 5.   Fuelling Launch for Flying Boat.

For medium-size aircraft, fuelling trucks giving a maximum delivery speed of 150 gallons per minute are suitable, but larger

Fig. 6.   Service Station—Puerto Rico.

units, carrying 2,500 gallons of gasoline and capable of delivering 200 gallons per minute through each of two pumps, i.e. 400 gallons per minute are also used. Fig. 4 shows the pumping end of a modern 1,200-gallon fuelling truck.

Flying boat fuelling calls for large deliveries of gasoline, which generally have to be made to the aircraft at its moorings. Fig. 5 illustrates a modern fuelling launch of 3,250 gallons capacity, which is really a miniature tanker, and from which lubricating oil and gasoline are delivered by pumps driven by the launch propelling engine.

SERVICE AND FILLING STATIONS

The distribution of fuel and lubricating oil is, to an increasing extent, carried out from service stations which concentrate on sales of these products because motorists generally prefer to take supplies from a station where quick service can be offered. Fig. 6 shows a standard type of double-drive station. These stations are well maintained, and it is essential that the standard of cleanliness, both of operation and buildings, is of the highest order. The paintwork on all distributing facilities must be carefully watched, as the publicity value of trucks, pumps and service stations is considerable.

XXIII

MEASUREMENT OF PETROLEUM PRODUCTS

MOST of the liquids used in everyday life are measured and sold by volume, by the pint, litre or gallon, depending on the liquid and the system of weights and measures used in the country concerned. Since most liquids are handled at ordinary temperatures and are sold in comparatively small quantities, the expansion and contraction effects resulting respectively from heating and cooling are generally ignored. A more exact method for expensive liquids is to sell them by weight, since the weight of a given quantity of liquid remains constant whether it is hot or cold. It is, however, impracticable to weigh on scales large quantities of liquid petroleum products, so that we have to choose one of three methods of purchasing and selling oil on a large scale :—

(1) The volume may be measured when the sale or purchase is made, and that figure is taken irrespective of temperature at the time of measurement.

(2) The buying or selling may be done on the basis of the volume at an agreed temperature, usually 60° F. or 15° C., these temperatures being common in temperate climates. If the oil, on measurement, is not actually at the agreed temperature, its temperature is recorded and its volume at the agreed temperature is calculated.

(3) The buying or selling may be done on a weight basis, the difficulty of direct weighing being obviated in the following manner : if the volume of the oil in a tank is measured accurately, say, in gallons, and the weight of exactly a gallon of that oil is also measured accurately, then the total weight can be calculated by multiplying the two figures together.

Three main problems thus arise :—

(a) All three of the above methods require accurate measurement of oil volumes.

(b) Method (2) requires accurate measurement of oil temperatures.

(*c*) Method (3) requires, additionally, the weight of a small but definite unit volume of the oil.

In practice, the calculations in method (2) also require at least an approximate knowledge of the specific gravity or the weight of unit volume of the oil. Method (3) can theoretically be carried out without a knowledge of the oil temperature, but this is so inconvenient that, in practice, the oil temperature is always accurately measured.

The usual method of arriving at the quantity of oil bought or sold is to take the stock in the tanks before and after the delivery operation. Difficulties are sometimes encountered when small deliveries are made from large tanks (when the oil meter may be found more practicable), but the system works well on the whole. The various steps which are involved in the measurement of a quantity of liquid petroleum are described in the sections which follow. One point is, however, worth stressing at this stage. The careful measurement of a quantity of oil serves two principal purposes. Firstly, it attempts to ensure that the purchaser receives the volume or weight of oil with which he is invoiced ; and, conversely, that the seller does not deliver more than the billed quantity. Secondly, it enables the owner of the oil to control his storage, transport and handling losses.

TANK CALIBRATION

By "calibration"* is meant the whole process of compiling the tables which tell us how much oil is in the tank.

There are three well-known methods of tank calibration, which are described briefly below.

Water-filling Method. By means of well-calibrated standard measures, or by a suitable meter, water may be measured into the tank. After each measured batch of water has been added, the resulting depth of water is noted. By continuing the process until the tank is full the required table is obtained. For accuracy, any change in temperature during the operation must be suitably allowed for. The time required for this process is long, so that it is most suitable for small tanks. It is, however, the most convenient process for tanks of irregular shape and may also be applied to calibrate the lower parts of large tanks, whose bottoms are usually rather irregular. It is also the method frequently adopted for the spheroidal-shaped tanks used for the storage of very light, volatile petroleum products.

External "Strapping" Method. In this process external circumferences of the tank are measured by passing a graduated steel tape round the tank or, in other words, by "strapping"* it. If the circumference of the tank exceeds the length of the tape, vertical lines are scribed on the tank shell and the tank is "strapped" in sections. The process is carried out at one or more positions on each tier of plates, owing to variations in the dimensions of the different tiers, and due allowance is made for differences between inner and outer tiers. The vertical height of each tier is measured, and other measurements are taken which enable allowances to be made for plate thickness, vertical overlaps, and any obstructions which may raise the tape from the tank surface. From these measurements the gross gallons per inch are calculated separately for each tier, and the tank table is built up, usually inch by inch. Further allowances are then made for the volume taken up by heating coils, internal ladders, external manholes, etc., at the vertical height at which they occur in the tank, and the finished table then gives the net capacity corresponding to each inch and fraction of an inch of height.

Internal Diameter Method. Tank calibration by measuring internal diameters is widely used in the United Kingdom as an alternative to "strapping". In this process, the tape is unsupported throughout its length, but allowance is made for sag. The tension is adjusted to 10 lb. by means of an ingenious automatic device. A large number of diameters is taken at different positions in each tier, and the gross gallons per inch are calculated from the average tier diameter so obtained. Subject to all necessary precautions being taken, the results obtained by the "strapping" and internal diameter methods should agree closely.

Methods for Miscellaneous Tanks. Horizontal cylinders are usually calibrated by taking a large number of internal diameters and lengths. Hemispherical or "bumped"* ends cause difficulty and are sometimes dealt with graphically ; the work is further complicated if the tanks are sloping. Tanks with a slope greater than 1 in 50 are more conveniently calibrated by water-filling.

Spherical and spheroidal tanks are usually calibrated either by water displacement or by "strapping".

The floating-roof type of tank is calibrated in the normal way for a vertical cylinder. Allowances are made for internal fittings depending on their location when the movable roof is resting on its supports, and for the volume displaced by the roof itself.

The calibration by measurement of the cargo tanks of ocean tankers presents various difficulties. The shape of the tanks varies

Fig. 1.   Tank Calibration—"Strapping" Method.

according to changes in the shape of the hull of the ship, and the internal fittings are considerably more complex than those in a shore tank. For these and other reasons, therefore, a high degree of accuracy in oil measurement cannot be expected with oil tankers. Ships' calibration tables are usually calculated from the builder's plans, average factors based on previous experience being commonly used to allow for the internal structure.

Fig. 2. Tank ''Dipping'' or ''Gauging''.   Fig. 3. Tank Sampling in Progress.

MEASUREMENT OF OIL DEPTHS AND VOLUMES

Dipping and Ullaging. It is not normally difficult to measure the depth of oil in any given tank. For this, a graduated steel tape with a weight attached at its end is lowered into the oil until it just touches the tank bottom. On drawing up the tape, the depth of the oil is read off by noting the height of the top edge of the wetted part of the tape. The operation requires a little skill if the result is to be accurate, and the tapes and weights used are always carefully standardized. With viscous oils, the tape must be immersed for a few seconds to allow the oil to rise to the correct level on the tape. In cases of difficulty, an oil-soluble paste may be smeared on the tape when measuring volatile liquids. A practice which aids speedy and accurate dipping is to record the approximate total height of the tank at a point near to the dipping hatch.

Ships' tanks contain various obstructions which may interfere with accurate dipping, and they are, therefore, usually measured

Y

by "ullaging", the ullage being the distance from a fixed dip-hatch on the deck down to the oil surface. For example, if a ship's tank has a total height of 38 feet to the top of the dip-hatch, an ullage of 3 feet would correspond to a depth of 35 feet of oil in the tank. Small ullages of a few feet are sometimes measured by a wooden ullage stick fitted with a cross-piece, graduations reading downwards from a zero at the cross-piece ; but for measuring larger ullages or for more accurate work, a steel tape and ullage rule are preferred. Ships' calibration tables are usually constructed so as to show volumes corresponding to ullages.

Vapour-tight Tanks. Where vapour-tight tanks are concerned, the opening of the tank to the atmosphere, when dipping, would be dangerous and would lead to the loss of valuable light gasoline fractions. In such cases the dip-weight and tape can be enclosed in a vapour-tight "look-box "* fixed to the tank top and operated through a gate-valve. It is thus possible to operate the dip-tape by an external wheel and to record the liquid level through the glass-fronted "look-box". Alternatively, vapour-tight tanks are fitted with gauge-glasses, particularly when the tanks contain even more volatile products and are under higher pressures. Such tanks are usually spherical or spheroidal in shape. In these cases, unless the temperature and the density of the oil in the gauge glass are the same as the oil in the tank, the gauge reading will not truly represent the oil level inside the tank. Gauge fittings are often provided with pipes extending about 3 feet into the body of the oil, so that the oil in the glass may be drawn from the main bulk.

Hydrostatic Gauges. Hydrostatic gauges are sometimes employed to measure containers which are inaccessible by the normal methods of measurement. The principle of the gauge is to balance the column of oil in the tank against a column of mercury in the instrument and then to calculate the oil weight from appropriate tank tables. This gauge is often used to measure the weight of oil in the bunker tanks of large ships. For a number of reasons, a high degree of accuracy is difficult to attain with these gauges.

Water and Sediment Measurement. Water at the bottom of the tanks containing oil is measured by applying a special water-finding* paste to a graduated rule. The paste is easily attacked by water but is insoluble in oil. The instrument is lowered to the bottom of the tank, and the depth of water is shown by a change in colour of the water-finding paste. In cases of difficulty, as with heavy oils, water-finding paper (paper treated with a water-soluble material) may sometimes give better results. The action of the paper is somewhat slower than that of the paste, and by suitably adjusting the time of immersion, it is sometimes possible to distinguish between free water and water present in suspension in the oil or in sediments on tank bottoms. The measurement of certain sediments or sludges which accumulate in tanks containing crude oil is difficult, since the level of the sludge or emulsion may vary in different parts of the tank, and the composition of the sludge may vary also. It may then be necessary to draw a number of samples by special means and to submit them to the laboratory for examination for water and sediment content.

Oil Meters. Although the oil meter is not suitable for measuring oil depth or oil volume in a stationary storage tank, it is becoming more widely employed in the following directions :—

(i) In oilfields, oil refineries and installations for the measurement of petroleum gases, crude oil flowing in pipelines and oils used in blending operations.

(ii) In oil installations and depots handling refined products, for measurement into drums, cans and similar packages, or for measuring deliveries into, or out of, rail and road tank cars.

For high rates of flow of liquids, batteries of large displacement meters in parallel are sometimes installed, a single large meter being capable of measuring a flow of 900 gallons per minute. For barrel and can filling, meters are sometimes provided with a temperature compensating device which can be adjusted so as to deliver a constant volume measured at a standard temperature. Air eliminators are used to prevent the meters measuring air, and strainers are installed to prevent the entry of dirt. All meters should be tested regularly to determine their accuracy and for any necessary adjustment.

SAMPLING

The primary purpose of sampling is to obtain a thoroughly representative specimen of the material, this then being used to determine the properties of the bulk quantity. In oil measurement, samples are required :—

(a) for determination of the average temperature of the contents of the vessel or other container ;

(b) for ascertaining the specific gravity or weight per unit volume ; and

(c) for determining the content of water, sediment or other extraneous material.

The whole procedure for sampling petroleum products is extensively described in the Institute of Petroleum's book "Standard Methods of Testing Petroleum and its Products", and in the publication of the American Society for Testing Materials, "A.S.T.M. Standards on Petroleum Products and Lubricants".

Careful and adequate sampling is of as great importance in quantitative measurement of bulk oil as it is for the determination of the physical and chemical properties of the product. The taking of a truly representative sample is often difficult ; for example, refineries are rarely able to make products of such complete uniformity that one cannot detect small differences in these from hour to hour. The large receiving tanks into which these products are pumped may, therefore, still show small differences in temperature and specific gravity according to the level from which the sample is taken.

Even when the tank contents are uniform to begin with, if the oil has been standing for any length of time in its tank, the warmth of the day causes layers of warmed oil to collect near the top of the oil, and the coolness at night causes layers of cooler oil to collect near the bottom of the tank. The quality of the oil is unaffected, but, from the measurement point of view, no oil can be considered as uniform unless it is at the same temperature throughout. If this is not so, then a single sample can no longer be drawn at random from any level in the tank with the certainty that it truly represents the average of the oil concerned. This difficulty presents itself more often than not. Its most obvious solution is to pump the tank contents round so rapidly that the oil becomes thoroughly mixed, but this is often impracticable.

One method of securing a fair average sample without circulation would be to take so many samples, all from different places in the tank, that no part of the oil could escape being sampled. The temperature of small samples tends to change so rapidly that one cannot just blend these samples and take the temperature of the blended sample as being the average temperature of the oil in the tank. It is much better to take the temperature of each sample separately and as promptly as possible after it has been withdrawn from the tank. The required average temperature is then obtained arithmetically. It is also better to determine the specific gravity separaely on each of the samples, but sometimes the samples are blended before this is determined ; this is, however, not desirable in the interests of accurate measurement.

The inconvenience of sampling at a large number of levels is obvious, and in practice a compromise is made, three samples only being taken. The depth of oil in the tank is measured, and a "top" sample is drawn from a level one-tenth of this depth below the oil surface. A "middle" sample is drawn from as near the mid-level as practicable, and a "bottom" sample from one-tenth of the oil depth above the tank bottom, or above the water surface, if the tank contains water (*vide infra*).

For rough daily or routine measurements one sample only is usually drawn from the tank, often from the middle of the oil. Sometimes, however, a "continuous" sample is taken. The apparatus for this consists, in its simplest form, of a vessel with so small an opening that it can only fill slowly. The vessel is dropped to the bottom of the oil and drawn up at such a rate that it is nearly but not quite full when withdrawn. Many other more accurate and more elaborate forms of continuous sampling apparatus have been devised ; their number attests to the frequency and difficulty of the problem described.

Great care must be taken when taking samples from gauge glasses, or from sampling cocks inserted in pipelines, that the sample is representative of the tank or pipeline. This can only be done by adequate flushing-through of the sampling system.

MEASUREMENT OF OIL TEMPERATURES

Accuracy in the measurement of temperature is at least as important as accuracy in dipping or in any other measuring operation, and considerable care is necessary if a reasonably accurate figure for the average temperature of oil contained in a large storage tank is to be recorded. The need for high accuracy in temperature measurement is perhaps best appreciated when it is realized that, because of the relatively high coefficient of expansion of aviation gasoline, an error of 2° F. in temperature measurement affects the resultant volume calculations by 0·13%.

If the tank is uniform in temperature throughout its depth, the normal top, middle and bottom samples (described under "Sampling") will reveal this, although even then the circumstances may indicate the necessity for drawing more than one set of top, middle and bottom samples from different hatches round the periphery of the tank. For most purposes, the usual type of "dip" or sampling can provided with a cork may be employed. The can is first flushed with oil so that its temperature is approximately that of the oil in the tank, the cork is inserted, and the can is lowered into the tank. When the desired depth below the oil surface is reached, the cork is sharply jerked out of the can, which then fills with oil from the level selected. The sample so obtained is withdrawn from the tank, a thermometer is quickly inserted into the dip-can immediately it reaches the tank top, the liquid stirred with the thermometer and the temperature noted. Sometimes the thermometer is lowered into the tank in the dip-can and left in the oil until the other measurements have been completed. If the temperature readings given by top, middle and bottom samples are not in reasonably close agreement, the drawing of additional samples at intermediate levels becomes necessary.

For highly volatile products stored in pressure containers, mercury angle-stem thermometers, which are fitted so that they extend up to 3 feet into the tank shell, are usually employed. These thermometers (at least four in number) are spaced at appropriate levels in the tank. But whatever methods and equipment are used in temperature measurement, a high standard of accuracy and regular control on the reliability of the instruments employed are important factors in the production of satisfactory results.

MEASUREMENT OF OIL GRAVITIES

Samples for specific gravity determination are usually drawn with a dip-can in the usual way ; normally the samples drawn for temperature measurement are subsequently used in the laboratory for specific gravity determination. In some circumstances, however, special methods involving the use of different types of apparatus may be required.

If the weight of a quantity of oil is to be determined, then its specific gravity, or weight of unit volume of the oil at the temperature at which the volume is measured, must first be found. The most convenient method of measuring this weight per unit of volume, and that generally adopted in the industry, is by means of the "hydrometer". The hydrometer is an instrument which consists essentially of a suitably-weighted glass bulb, with a narrow hollow stem attached to its upper end, the stem in turn containing a paper scale. The size and weight of the instrument are so chosen that it floats in the oil under test, sets of differently weighted instruments allowing choice of one suitable for any particular oil. The correct instrument will float so that the oil surface cuts the graduated stem. The level at which this happens depends on the specific gravity or the weight per unit volume of the oil being tested.

The oil surface will touch the stem of the hydrometer in an upward curve, and the instrument is calibrated to the bottom of this curve or meniscus. In reading hydrometers in white oils, therefore, the eye is held at such a level that the bottom of the meniscus is seen as a straight line. The level at which this line cuts the stem is the proper reading to take. In black oils, the opacity of the oil will mask the bottom of the meniscus and in this case the readings are taken at the top of the meniscus and a fair correction made for its height (*vide* fig. 4).

Specifications for hydrometers and the standard method for determination of specific gravity by hydrometer are given in the standard methods of testing petroleum products published by the Group, the American Society for Testing Materials, and the Institute of Petroleum. There are three main types of these instruments, depending on the system of measurement employed. These are known as "Imperial" (British), "Metric", and "A.P.I."* (American) hydrometers.

The Imperial hydrometers are marked "60° F./60° F.". The first 60° F. implies that the instrument has been made so as to be most correct when it is used in oil at 60° F. ; the second 60° F. implies that the temperature of the equal volume of pure water with which the weight of the oil is compared is also 60° F. Read-

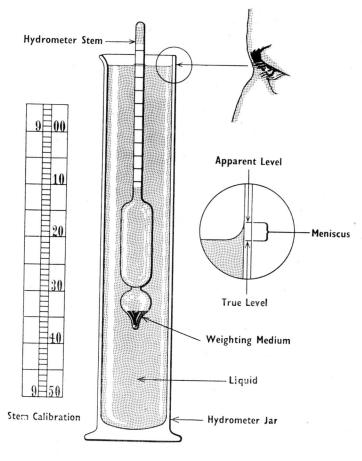

Fig. 4.   Method of Reading Hydrometer.

ings given by such hydrometers, multiplied by 10, can be taken as lb. and decimals of a lb. per Imperial gallon, e.g., a gasoline of specific gravity 0.725 will weigh 7.25 lb. per Imperial gallon.

The metric hydrometer may be marked "15° C./4° C." or, in tropical countries, "30° C./4° C.". The specific gravity reading in this case is the weight of the oil in kilograms per litre, i.e., a fuel oil of metric specific gravity 0·951 weighs 0·951 kilograms per litre.

The A.P.I. hydrometer scale is an arbitrary one, but is directly related to the Imperial (60° F./60° F.) scale according to the following formula :—

$$\text{Gravity Degrees A.P.I.} = \frac{141\cdot5}{\text{Sp. Gr. } 60° \text{ F.}/60° \text{ F.}} - 131\cdot5$$

For oil measurement, the specific gravity or the A.P.I. gravity* of a product may serve two purposes :—

(a) As stated above, it may be used to calculate the weight corresponding to a given volume of oil or to ascertain the volume of a known weight.

(b) It may be employed in the correction of a measured volume of a bulk liquid to the corresponding volume at a standard temperature, e.g. 60° F.

Where the specific gravity is used for conversion of volumes to weights, the accurate determination of the average specific gravity of the contents of an oil container is of considerable importance. An error of 0·001 in specific gravity represents more than 5 tons on a 5,000 ton quantity for a fuel oil of specific gravity 0·950. Similarly, whereas 5,000 tons of gasoline of specific gravity 0·720 occupy 1,556,000 gallons, the same 5,000 tons will correspond to 1,553,850 gallons if the specific gravity is only 0·001 higher, i.e. 0·721 ; the difference is 2,150 gallons, or 0·14%.

Accurate specific gravity determination is not of the same importance where the figure has to be used for correcting volume for temperature change. For example, all gasolines in the specific gravity range 0·726 to 0·730 have the same coefficient of expansion, i.e. 0·00064 per 1° F.

The point which requires emphasis is that, whereas highly accurate specific gravities are not nowadays of great importance in qualitative work in the oil industry, it is very necessary to have adequate sampling of containers followed by careful specific gravity measurement should this be required for computing weight quantities from volumes, or vice versa. It is for this reason that instruments with a high degree of accuracy are specified, and the procedure is carefully laid down in Group and official publications.

CALCULATION OF VOLUMES AND WEIGHT

The operation of measuring and recording a quantity of oil is not completed when the steps so far discussed have been taken. Measurements have been made of oil and water dips, average tank temperature and specific gravity. The tank capacity tables will give the volume corresponding to the depth of liquid in the tanks at the temperature recorded. It may then be necessary to calculate what the oil volume would be at a standard temperature, or the weight of oil. In the U.S.A., the American barrel at 60° F. is the volume unit, and the short ton the weight unit, most favoured ; in the United Kingdom both the Imperial gallon and the long ton are widely employed ; and in countries using the metric system, the litre, the cubic metre and the kiloton all have their supporters. As has already been shown, liquid petroleum products have first to be measured by volume before their weight can be computed.

Volume at Standard Temperature. Although the practice is not established in the United Kingdom, in the United States all relatively large quantities of liquid petroleum products are handled and sold in volumetric quantities corrected to the standard temperature of 60° F. In many areas using the metric system of weights and measures, volumes of petroleum products are adjusted to 15° C. This means that, having measured the volume of oil in a container at a certain average temperature, we have to convert or correct it to some other or standard temperature.

The tables which are widely used in the oil industry for correcting volumes to 60° F. are those contained in publications which have been issued by the U.S. Bureau of Standards and by the Institute of Petroleum. These are based on coefficients of expansion covering a wide range of petroleum products. The tables are entered against the gravity and the temperature of the products, and a factor is extracted which enables one to correct any given volume of the oil measured at the observed temperature to the corresponding volume at 60° F. Tables for this volume correction are also contained in the Group's publication, *Oil Measurement Tables*.

Weight Quantities. In the Imperial or British system, the hydrometer used for obtaining specific gravity or weight per unit volume is so scaled that, if we multiply the reading we obtain with it by 10, the result will correspond closely to the weight in lb. of a gallon of the oil. It is, therefore, quite common practice in this country to use the oil's specific gravity in this way to arrive at the weight of an oil consignment from the known gallonage. Both the oil volume and the specific gravity must, of course, be at the same temperature. Actually, results so calculated will be 0.03% too high in the case of gasolines, and 0.02% too low in the case of fuel oils. More accurate tables for conversion of volumes to weights have recently been compiled by the Group and the Institute of Petroleum. What is obviously of extreme importance in this process of conversion of volumes to weights is the accurate determination of the specific gravity of an average sample of the oil. This method, involving volumes and gravities in calculating weights of bulk quantities of petroleum products, is one which is applied whether the conversion is from Imperial gallons to long tons, American barrels to short and long tons, or litres to metric tons.

The U.S. Bureau of Standards tables (Circular C 410), the Group's tables and the Institute of Petroleum tables referred to, all give weights per unit volume as "weights in air"; in the metric system, however, the normal procedure of multiplying volumes in litres by density (metric specific gravity) results in "weights in vacuo". This subject is discussed in the two Group publications *Oil Measurement* and *Oil Measurement Tables*.

SPECIAL BULK OIL MEASUREMENT PROBLEMS

Despite care and accuracy in tank calibration, tank dipping and office calculations, discrepancies may still arise when measuring stocks, or when oil is moved from one container to another. It has already been mentioned that adequate sampling will usually take care of a tank whose contents are not homogeneous, and that in cases where a water bottom* is not carried, water calibration of irregular bottoms will suffice. Even when bottom allowances are available, however, more accurate results will usually be obtained by conducting the operations so that the tank bottom is always completely covered with oil before and after a movement. When it is suspected that the bottom plates of a tank move under varying heads of oil, or with changes in the condition of the subsoil, errors may usually be reduced by increasing the number of dip-hatches and averaging the resulting dips.

The quantities of oil contained in pipelines are a common source of discrepancies in measurement. With "internal" pipelines, difficulties may be reduced if it is possible to provide a regular and satisfactory slope when the lines are installed. Similarly, air-vents and drain-cocks installed at high and low points assist in verifying whether the line is full or empty. Where it is impracticable to pump water through a line to displace the oil, compressed air is usually employed, a common practice being to employ some standard time and procedure in order that the quantity of oil left in a given pipeline may be as near possible the same before and after an operation.

Long pipelines passing over open country give rise to problems which have not yet been completely solved, but suitably installed positive-displacement meters may reduce the difficulties, provided that air-eliminating devices are installed on the inlet side, so that air passing through the meters will not be registered as oil. For accurate work, recording thermometers should also be installed close to the meters.

INTERRELATION OF UNITS OF MEASUREMENT

Although much effort has been expended towards obtaining one system of weights and measures throughout the world, that ideal position has not yet been attained. The three principal systems in use to-day are the American, the Imperial or British, and the Metric systems. Extended work by standardizing authorities has resulted in the publishing of authoritative conversion factors by bodies such as the U.S. Bureau of Standards, the British Standards Institution, and the Institute of Petroleum. These publications have wide recognition and have assisted considerably in regularizing oil accountancy where one has to convert a quantity of oil measured in one system to its equivalent in another system. A list of conversion factors and several tables giving equivalent weights and volumes in the three principal systems will be found in the Appendix.

The importance of a high degree of accuracy in all work connected with the calculation and inter-conversion of oil volumes and weights cannot be too strongly emphasized. This importance is fully appreciated by the Shell Group, members of whose technical staffs have for many years now devoted themselves to the study of oil measurement problems. The Group publications on this subject have won wide approval.

MEASUREMENT OF SMALL QUANTITIES

Rail Cars. The usual practice is to fill the rail car to a level defined by an internal ullage plate situated just below the dome of the car. The level chosen allows the car to be filled with the maximum volume of oil that still gives safety against possible expansion of the oil after the rail car is closed. The car is always filled to this level. The number of gallons corresponding to a filling to the ullage plate is very carefully measured, since this calibration will have permanent value. The temperature of the oil is noted after loading and before discharge of the rail car. With the aid of a brief capacity table covering levels near the ullage plate, it is possible to say whether any change in gallonage is due to the observed change in temperature of the oil or whether leakage in transit has occurred.

Another method is to take the gross weight of the rail car and its contents on a weighbridge or large scales. The tare of the car having previously been determined, division of the net weight of the oil in lb. by ten times its specific gravity gives the number of gallons in the car. The tolerance in accuracy permitted by these weighbridges is laid down by law, and weights and measures inspectors control them by regular inspection.

Road or Tank Wagons. The compartments of road wagons are often calibrated by filling measured quantities of water and preparing a dip or ullage table for the container ; sometimes a special wooden dip-rod is prepared, this being graduated so that the number of gallons in the tank is directly read off. The gauge table or the graduated dip-rod facilitates the delivery of fractions of road-car compartments. In the U.S.A., volume meters are largely used for filling tank wagons, the temperature of the quantity delivered being recorded after the filling operation.

Drums and Tins. Drums or barrels may be filled by weight or volume. Automatic scales are frequently used for weight filling. The flow of oil is automatically turned off when some previously chosen definite weight of oil has been filled into the drum. Tins may also be filled by weight, but volume fillers are being increasingly used. In the weight-filling machines two adjustable counterweights are employed, one set so as to balance the empty tin, the other to give the net weight of oil it is desired to fill. The flow of oil is started by hand, but as soon as the scale tips, automatic arrangements cut it off.

Where drums and tins are filled by volume, either positive displacement meters or special volume fillers are employed. The latter are very carefully calibrated containers kept under frequent check against certified master measures. For tin filling, volume fillers are usually operated in batteries of six or more containers.

OIL MEASUREMENT STANDARDISATION

Improvements are continually being sought in procedure and apparatus used in oil measurement. Apart from the work which the oil companies themselves have carried out on this subject, the Institute of Petroleum in England, and the American Petroleum Institute, the American Society for Testing Materials, the Natural Gasoline Association of America, and the California Natural Gasoline Association, have all had committees studying oil measurement problems for many years. The trend of this satisfactory progress is reflected by the increasingly active co-operation between the various national standardizing bodies. This co-operation is much to be welcomed.

BIBLIOGRAPHY

A.P.I. *Code for Measuring, Sampling and Testing Crude Oil* (A.P.I. *Code No.* 25). (American Petroleum Institute.)

Code for Measuring, Sampling and Testing Natural Gas (A.P.I. *Code No.* 50-*A*). (American Petroleum Institute.)

Code for Measuring, Sampling and Testing Natural Gasoline (A.P.I. *Code No. 50-B*). (American Petroleum Institute.)

Oil Measurement. Peter Kerr. (The Shell Petroleum Company, Ltd.).

Standard Method for Tank Calibration. (The Shell Petroleum Company, Ltd.)

Tank Strapping. Peter Kerr. Journal of Institute of Petroleum, March, 1939.

Sampling and Measurement of Petroleum Cargoes. H. Hyams (The Shell Petroleum Company, Ltd.)

Measurement of Oil Depths. Journal of Institute of Petroleum. July, 1945.

Tables for Measurement of Oil. (Institute of Petroleum, London.)

Oil Measurement Tables. H. Hyams. (The Shell Petroleum Company, Ltd.)

A.S.T.M. *Standards on Petroleum Products and Lubricants.* (American Society for Testing Materials, Philadelphia.)

Standard Methods for Testing Petroleum and its Products. (Institute of Petroleum, London.)

National Standard Petroleum Oil Tables (Circular C 410). (U.S. National Bureau of Standards, Washington.)

XXIV

NATURAL GAS AND ITS DERIVATIVES

In chapter IX, the difference between "dry" gas, as found in strata not in contact with oil, and "wet" gas, as found in oil-bearing strata, was explained. The condensable vapours which give rise to the expression "wet" are so valuable that they are (or should be) always removed. Such naturally dry or artificially dried gases constitute the commercial product, which, therefore, consists principally of methane with some slight amounts of ethane, propane and, perhaps, butane, the amount of the latter products being dependent upon the source of the gas. It is thus produced (a) from dry gas fields under natural rock pressures from atmospheric up to 2,500 lb. per square inch ; (b) as the residual gas left after extraction of natural or casinghead gasoline from casinghead gas. This residual gas, being richer in the heavier products, such as propane and butane, is somewhat difficult to handle under high pumping pressures, because it may give trouble due to condensation. As it also has a higher heating value, it is usually mixed only in small percentages and, as nearly as possible, in a fixed ratio to the dry gas, in order to avoid fluctuations in calorific value.

The marketing of natural gas is conducted on a large scale in the United States. The total production of natural gas in the United States amounted to 5,629,811 million cubic feet in 1947. Because most of the areas in which gas is produced are remote from large centres of population, it has been necessary, in order to make gas available to those large centres, to construct an immense mileage of pipeline systems.

DISTRIBUTION

From the two sources, the gas is collected into a network of gathering lines converging to some central point in a given field. There, it is usually compressed by gas engine-driven compressors up to pressures of from 300 to 600 lb. per square inch. It ts then transported over long distances through lines which vary in size from 6 inches to 24 inches in diameter. Along these lines are located additional compressor stations, because, as the gas travels through the lines, it loses pressure due to friction, and this pressure must be restored by re-compression. Thus, it is usual to locate stations from 60 to 200 miles apart. At various points along the trunk system, gas is withdrawn through lateral lines to points of consumption, such as cities or factories. At these points pressure reducing stations are installed, where automatic equipment reduces the gas to the low pressures at which it is distributed through smaller lines to local points of consumption. At both ends of the lines the gas is metered or measured. At the gathering points it is metered by what are known as orifice meters*. From this record the amount of gas is calculated. At points of distribution it is measured again in large quantities through orifice meters or, if in small quantities, through positive displacement meters, which are simply assemblies of small bellows fitted with automatic counting mechanisms.

The handling of gas through these large trunk line systems affords an excellent example of scientific control, as gas quantities are dispatched in accordance with weather predictions as made by weather bureaux. If cold weather is predicted and increased gas consumption for heating purposes is expected, the lines are "packed" (pressures built up to higher than normal) in order to meet abnormal load conditions.

NATURAL GAS AS A FUEL

For domestic use, gas is a convenient and clean fuel, and both of these criteria also apply to its use for industrial plants. In industry it is used instead of coal, coke or fuel oil as fuel for steam plants, directly for firing of furnaces of all kinds and for many other kindred uses, or indirectly, by being converted into power by internal combustion engines. In all these cases it is cleaner burning, more easily and delicately controlled and, unless distributed at points quite remote from production areas, at least as cheap as its competitors. It is reasonable to believe that because it is so cheap and convenient its use will keep pace with its production. There are, however, several areas in the United States where the supply of natural gas far exceeds the demand for commercial use. In these areas the manufacture of carbon black flourishes (*vide* chapter XVIII).

PROPANE AND BUTANE

Propane and butane are gases at normal temperature and pressure, and they occur both in natural gas and in solution in crude oil. They are the hydrocarbons on which the "bottled gas" business is based. The physical property which makes propane and butane so well adapted for being sold in cylinders or steel bottles is that, upon compression of the gases to a higher pressure, they are easily, at ordinary temperatures and at comparatively low pressures, converted into liquids. This makes it possible to have in liquid form, in a comparatively small and light vessel, a large quantity of gas with a very high potential thermal energy. In comparison with dissolved acetylene contained in its normal cylinder, propane in its normal cylinder gives about five times as much heating value per unit of gross weight.

Certain loose terms have come into ordinary use in this connection. Propane itself is C_3H_8, the third member of the paraffin or saturated hydrocarbon series (*vide* chapter VII). In commercial usage, however, the term "propane" includes propane and propylene, propylene being C_3H_6 (the third member of the olefin or unsaturated series). Likewise, butane, as a commercial term in ordinary usage, means either butane manufactured from natural gas or gasoline or the mixture of butane and butylene manufactured from refinery gases or stabilizer tops. Both gases are frequently referred to as liquefied petroleum gas or simply as "liquid gas".

The sales of liquid gas in the U.S.A. have increased enormously in recent years. The quantity marketed in that country in 1946 amounted to 1,425 million U.S. gallons.

Propane. Propane (C_3H_8) is a gas at atmospheric pressure, its boiling point being —44° F. (—42·2° C.). It has a vapour pressure at 80° F. (26·7° C.) of 130 lb. per sq. in., and at 100° F. (37·8° C.) of 180 lb. per sq. in., so that, when confined in closed vessels as a liquid, its vapour pressure is ample to provide distribution pressure in gas systems.

This product is used for a variety of purposes. In the U.S.A. it is largely used as a very convenient domestic gas fuel. It has a high calorific value (21,500 B.Th.U.* per lb.) and yields on ideal combustion only carbon dioxide and water vapour. Its convenience gives it a great advantage, especially in areas which are not supplied with coal gas or natural gas.

Propane is used in industrial plants, in large quantities, as fuel in various types of furnaces employed for special purposes, and it is also used as a "standby" fuel. It has definite advantages over other forms of gas. As the liquid propane evaporates it gives a gas of constant composition, and, therefore, of constant calorific value per cubic foot. The amount of air required for complete combustion, therefore, remains exactly proportional to the amount of gas supplied. By altering the relative proportions of gas and air either a reducing* or an oxidizing* flame may be obtained, as required. It is, moreover, pure and contains no sulphur or other undesirable constituents. It is used for annealing*, heat treating, baking enamels and many other kindred uses.

Additional uses to which propane can be put include fuel for railroad dining cars, for railroad car refrigeration service, for trucks in cross-country hauls, for metal cutting, as enrichment for other gas fuels, and innumerable other uses ; as a refrigerant for domestic refrigerators and for trucks (in which case the product is first used as a refrigerant by boiling, the gas then being used as fuel for the truck power plant). There is also a large consumption of propane for solvent refining (*vide* chapter XII) and as a starting material for the manufacture of chemicals (*vide* chapter XVIII). The industry is still so young that it is difficult to say to what uses the product will eventually be put, but its potentialities are great. The total sales of liquefied propane in the U.S.A. in 1945 amounted to 500 million U.S. gallons, and in the last three years this quantity has substantially increased.

Butane. Butane (C_4H_{10}) is a somewhat heavier product than propane, boiling at approximately 32° F. (0° C.) at atmospheric pressure and having a vapour pressure at 100° F. (37·8° C.) of approximately 28 lb. per sq. in. The amount manufactured from natural and refinery gases, when these are treated for the extraction of natural gasoline (*vide* chapter IX), is, however, greater than that which can be blended with commercial gasoline, so that there is a surplus which is at present available for other purposes. In the U.S.A., it is used in plants commonly called "air-mix" plants. These are gas manufacturing plants which carburet air with butane to a mixture which gives a gas of approximately equivalent heating value to that of manufactured gas (approximately 600 B.Th.U. per cubic foot). The total sales of liquefied butane in the U.S.A. in 1945 amounted to 350 million U.S. gallons, but this amount was very much larger in the last three years.

The development of bottled gas sales on the continent of Europe and the Near East differs somewhat from that in the U.S.A., in that a mixture of butanes and butylenes is sold for domestic use, whereas commercial propane finds its outlets more for industrial applications. The domestic use of butane in Europe is developing at an enormous rate. In France alone, within a few years, more than half a million installations have been placed in private houses. Such an installation is simple and consists of a small bottle weighing, when empty, about 24 lb. (11 kg.) and carrying 28·6 lb. of butane gas (13 kg.) with a total net thermal output of 143,000 K. cal. (568,000 B.Th.U.) or equivalent to about 40 cubic metres (1,400 cubic feet) of coal gas. This bottle is connected to the appliance, a small hot-plate, a cooker, a geyser, or any other gas-consuming apparatus, by means of a small pressure regulator and a piece of copper tubing.

The gas is sold to customers through a network of agents, each agent having a well-defined sector in which he looks after the delivery of full bottles to clients and the taking back of empties for refilling at the filling points.

BIBLIOGRAPHY

Measurement, Compression and Transmission of Natural Gas. J. C. Lichty. (J. Wiley & Sons, New York.)

Handbook of Casinghead Gas. H. P. Westcott. (Metric Metal Works, Pennsylvania.)

Handbook of Butane-Propane Gases (and Supplement). (Western Gas, California.)

XXV

AVIATION AND MOTOR FUELS

THE term ''gasoline'' is applied to the well-defined class of volatile fuels used in normal spark-ignition engines. Petroleum is the main source of gasolines, and nearly all normal gasolines are either entirely of petroleum origin or contain at the most only a relatively small proportion of non-petroleum constituents. Certain non-petroleum constituents, such as benzole (a product of the coal carbonizing industry) and alcohols, are sometimes blended with petroleum gasoline because of certain desirable features they possess, but other undesirable features limit the proportions that may be used. In the case of alcohols, as with most other substitute fuels, their use on a relatively large scale in some countries is often dictated by political reasons and associated with a lack of indigenous supplies of petroleum. The performance of some substitute fuels, the use of which increased in some countries during the 1939–1945 period as a result of shortage of normal gasoline, is discussed later in the chapter under the heading ''Performance of Substitute Fuels''. The synthesis of gasoline from coal has been carried out in England and particularly in Germany, where this source of gasoline played such a vital part in that country's war economy.

Gasolines are complicated mixtures of hydrocarbons, and although they exhibit appreciable differences in other properties dictated by engine requirements, few have a boiling range outside the approximate limits 30° C.–200° C. A finished gasoline is the result of careful selection and blending of suitable petroleum fractions from the various refinery processes, having regard to the properties of the hydrocarbons contained in those fractions and the requirements of engines in which the gasoline is to be used. Since engines vary considerably in their fuel requirements, it is necessary to produce not one but several grades of gasoline. A single grade of gasoline suitable for all engines from the simplest single-cylinder unit to the largest multi-cylinder aero engine would obviously have an unnecessarily high anti-knock* value for the majority of engines ; what is more important, the amount that could be made available would be totally inadequate, whilst the cost would be much too high. It is always possible to produce relatively small quantities of extremely high-quality gasolines capable of giving excellent performance, whatever improvement may be made in engine design, but such superior grades are made only at great cost with an attendant reduction in the quantity of other gasolines that can be manufactured. Consequently, as the recent war period amply demonstrated, adequate supply assumes at some stage an importance comparable with that of quality and a compromise has to be made. It is, therefore, necessary to limit the number of grades ; the fuel properties must to some extent be a compromise in order to strike a balance between the number of grades of gasoline and the problems of storage and supply.

Although, in the course of time, most fuel properties have required varying degrees of modification with advancement in engine design, many have for some years reached a stage of relative stability. The outstanding exception is anti-knock value, which, particularly in the field of aviation, has increased considerably since 1918. In the earliest days of aviation, no distinct specifications, apart from volatility, were laid down for aviation purposes. After 1918 the special requirements of aviation gasoline came to be recognized, specifications were gradually established, and the production of suitable aviation grades developed as a special branch of the petroleum industry. Between 1918 and 1939 the importance of anti-knock value was recognized and this property of both aviation and motor gasoline assumed major importance. By 1939 the octane number* of most premium grade motor gasolines had reached a figure of 75 or more, whilst aviation gasoline had advanced to 87, 91, and finally 100 octane number. The last named has made possible a considerable increase in engine power output and operational efficiency. Development of aviation gasoline has naturally been spurred on by the demands brought about by recent war conditions, whilst in the same period the quality of motor gasoline fluctuated and was dictated by availability rather than engine requirements. During this period the standard motor fuel produced for military vehicles had an octane number of 80.

THE PERFORMANCE OF AVIATION AND MOTOR FUELS IN ENGINES

The engines normally used at present in aeroplanes and in cars are of the type known as spark-ignition engines : that is, a mixture of air with atomized and vaporized fuel is compressed in each cylinder successively by the motion of the piston, and is ignited by a spark at the appropriate moment, the pressure developed by the combustion of the fuel-air mixture acting as the source of power to drive the piston on the power stroke. The cycle of operations is illustrated for four- and two-stroke engines in figs. 1 and 2.

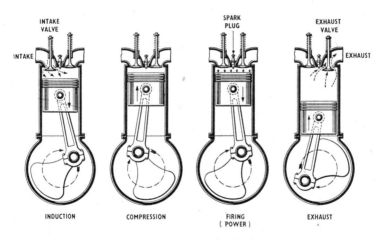

Fig. 1.   Four-stroke Cycle.

As the basic principles invol ed in aero and in car engines are similar, it is convenient to discuss aviation and motor fuels together. There are, however, certain differences in the design, and particularly in the conditions of operation, of the two types of engines, which are reflected in the different limits set in aviation and motor gasoline specifications for the properties which control the performance of these fuels. Attention will be drawn to such differences where they are important.

The requirements for gas turbine fuels are in a rather different category, and these will therefore be discussed separately at the end of this chapter.

For satisfactory performance in engines, gasolines must fulfil certain requirements, and various laboratory tests are laid down in specifications for purposes of quality control. The most important properties are volatility*, as measured by distillation characteristics and vapour pressure*, and anti-knock value, expressed as octane number or as rich-mixture rating. Other properties are, however, included, such as gum content (to avoid objectionable deposits in the intake system), sulphur content (to limit the corrosion of engine parts under certain conditions), etc.

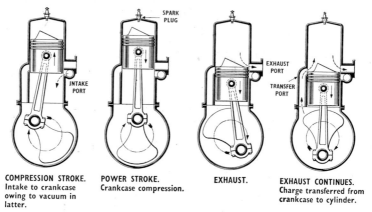

COMPRESSION STROKE. Intake to crankcase owing to vacuum in latter.

POWER STROKE. Crankcase compression.

EXHAUST.

EXHAUST CONTINUES. Charge transferred from crankcase to cylinder.

Fig. 2. Two-stroke Cycle.

The various performance factors are discussed in more detail below, but it may be helpful to list these factors, together with the relevant tests intended to control the quality of the gasoline. It should be emphasized that engine design and operating conditions, as well as the fuel, are involved ; this applies particularly to vapour lock*, detonation and mixture distribution.

Summary of Performance Factors

Performance Factor	*Fuel Test Method*
Vapour lock	Vapour pressure.
Carburettor icing ...	Distillation (sum of 10% and 50% points).
Cold starting	Distillation (10% point), vapour pressure.
Warming-up	Distillation (50% and 90% points approx.).
Detonation	Octane number, rich-mixture rating, or performance number.
Mixture distribution ...	Distillation (approx. 90% point).
Fuel consumption ...	Calorific value.
Storage stability	Potential gum.
Intake system deposits ...	Existent gum.
Weathering	Distillation (10% point), vapour pressure.
Corrosion	Sulphur content, corrosive sulphur.
Lubricating oil dilution ...	Distillation (90% point).

VOLATILITY

It will be seen from the above table that several performance factors depend on the volatility of the gasoline. Two test methods are in general use for expressing volatility, the A.S.T.M. distillation and vapour pressure tests. The former is carried out in the standard apparatus (fig. 3), and by the procedure specified by the American Society for Testing Materials (A.S.T.M.)* and by the Institute of Petroleum.

100 ml. of the gasoline are measured into flask A, which is heated by a flame or an electric heater so that distillation takes place at a specified rate. The gasoline vapour passes over a thermometer bulb, and then through a condenser C, cooled by ice and water, the condensed vapour being collected in a glass measuring cylinder D. The vapour temperature is noted at which distillation starts, at which certain fixed percentages (usually 10%, 20% . . . 90%) of condensed gasoline vapour are collected in the receiver, and at which distillation ceases. The

percentage distilled at certain temperatures (75°C., 100° C., etc.) and the undistilled residue in the flask after test are also measured. The loss, i.e. the difference between the amount of gasoline put into the flask and the sum of the residue and the total distillate collected in the receiver, is also noted, because it gives an indication of the presence of excessive quantities of very low boiling materials in the gasoline. The percentages may be reported as — % rec. (recovered), i.e. the volume actually measured in the receiver, or as — % evap. (evaporated) ; the latter is the sum of the % recovered plus the % loss.

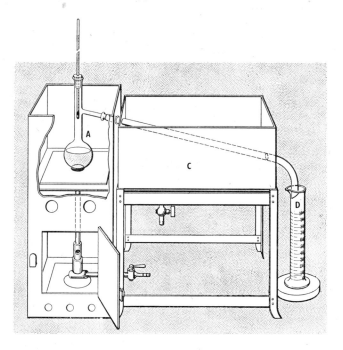

Fig. 3.   A.S.T.M. Distillation Apparatus.

The vapour pressure of a substance is a measure of its tendency to evaporate and form vapour. The sum of the vapour pressure of a liquid and the pressure due to any dissolved gases (e.g. air) is equal to the pressure on the liquid. The vapour pressure increases with rise of temperature, as illustrated in fig. 4 for a typical aviation gasoline, and at the boiling point becomes equal to the pressure on the liquid, that is, to the atmospheric pressure, unless the liquid is in a closed vessel.

Since gasolines are composed of a number of individual compounds whose boiling points cover a range of temperatures, the vapour pressure of the liquid will decrease as the lower boiling compounds evaporate.

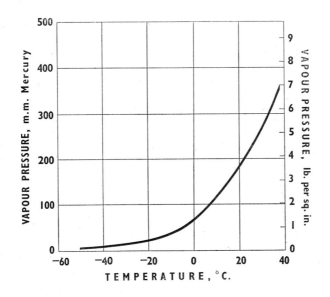

Fig. 4.   Vapour Pressure Curve of Typical Aviation Gasoline.

The vapour pressure of a gasoline depends on the volume of the space into which the gasoline is placed, i.e. on the V/L (vapour to liquid) ratio.

For practical and commercial purposes the vapour pressure of a gasoline is measured by the Reid method (fig. 5). A definite volume of the gasoline is placed in the lower part of the apparatus. The upper (air) chamber, which is provided with a pressure gauge, contains about four times as much air, by volume, as the lower (gasoline) chamber. The whole is placed in a water bath maintained at 100° F. (37·8° C.), and the increase in pressure due to the vapour pressure of the gasoline at 100° F. is measured. The

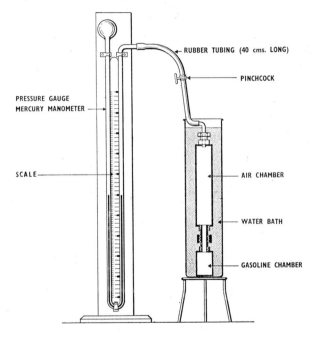

Fig. 5. Reid Vapour Pressure Apparatus

vapour pressure of gasoline is measured at 100° F., because at this temperature the vapour pressures of most gasolines are high enough to be measured easily, and also because this temperature approximates the running temperatures of carburettors in cars.

The volatility which a gasoline should have depends on several factors, some of which are mutually antagonistic, and the volatility limits included in specifications therefore represent a compromise. For example, too high a vapour pressure may cause vapour lock (*vide infra*) under certain conditions, while too low a vapour pressure may cause difficulty in starting. The vapour pressure of motor gasoline is normally adjusted to suit the climatic conditions and might be 12 lb. per square inch for cold winter conditions or 8 lb. per square inch for hot summer or tropical conditions. Aviation gasolines, on the other hand, have vapour pressures not exceeding 7 lb. per square inch, and are usually made fairly close to this limit.

VAPOUR LOCK

Gasoline normally contains about 20% to 25% of dissolved air. At high temperatures, and also at low pressures (high altitudes), bubbles of vaporized fuel and air may form in the gasoline, restricting the flow of fuel through the fuel lines, fuel pump and carburettor jets ; the engine then runs unevenly and in severe cases may stop. This phenomenon is termed vapour lock. Vapour lock is an inconvenience in motor cars, but may have disastrous results in an aeroplane. It can to a large extent be minimized by attention to fuel system design, by arranging the fuel lines so that they do not pick up heat unnecessarily from hot engine parts, by avoiding sharp bends, where pockets of vaporized fuel and air can collect, and by designing fuel pumps so that they can handle reasonable amounts of vaporized, in addition to liquid, gasoline.

In the case of motor cars, atmospheric temperature is a major factor, though vapour lock has occurred in mountainous districts, partly owing to the lower atmospheric pressure at high altitudes and partly owing to the relatively high engine, and therefore fuel system, temperatures resulting from continued low-gear operation.

Conditions in aircraft operation are somewhat different. The atmospheric pressure decreases with altitude, as shown in fig. 6. In the aero engine, vapour lock is due to evolution of dissolved air and vaporization of the lower boiling gasoline fractions due to this reduction in atmospheric pressure during climbing. The atmospheric temperature decreases at the rate of about 2° C. for each 1,000 feet of altitude, up to an altitude of about 35,000 to 40,000 feet, above which it remains constant. These lower temperatures at high altitude would tend to reduce vapour lock.

However, during a rapid climb, very little cooling of the gasoline
occurs by conduction and radiation to the surrounding air,
though, if conditions are such that the gasoline boils, the gasoline
would be cooled owing to the (latent)* heat absorbed by the
vaporization. Since vapour lock in aero engines is due to low
pressure rather than high temperature, any form of seasonal control of vapour pressure, as for motor gasolines, is obviously out
of the question, and it is for this reason that aviation gasolines are
blended to an approximately constant vapour pressure.

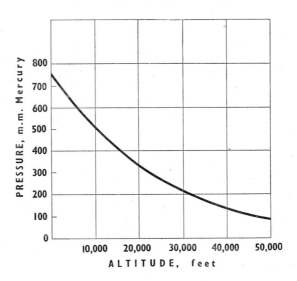

Fig. 6.   Variation of Atmospheric Pressure with Altitude.

In addition to the methods listed above in the first paragraph
of this section, vapour lock in aero engines may be reduced by
fitting booster pumps in the fuel tanks to maintain a slight
pressure in the fuel lines and thus decrease vaporization, etc., or
by installing a relief valve on the tank vent, which has a similar
effect.

CARBURETTOR ICING

In the carburettor the greater part of the fuel passing through is vaporized into the air stream to the engine. This vaporization absorbs a definite amount of heat, the latent heat of vaporization of the fuel fraction vaporized, which lowers the temperature of the air-fuel mixture. Under certain conditions of atmospheric temperature and humidity, this reduction in temperature may cause the moisture in the air to separate as ice on the carburettor venturi*, throttle, etc., thus restricting the flow, freezing the throttle, and in severe cases causing stoppage of the engine. This problem is essentially one of *aircraft* operation, in which it can be minimized by the application of heat to the carburettor by circulating warm engine oil, or by the injection of special fluids such as alcohol, to dissolve the ice. Occasionally interruption of fuel flow may occur in motor car engines due to freezing of water droplets in the carburettor jet. These droplets may be formed by condensation of moisture in the air in the fuel tank due to a decrease in atmospheric temperature.

Gasolines of the same boiling range differ only slightly in latent heat. However, since the fuel is not completely vaporized in the carburettor, the volatility of the fuel can have some effect, because a fuel of higher volatility will vaporize to a greater extent than one of lower volatility and thus give a greater cooling effect and greater tendency to ice formation. This tendency is related to the sum of the 10% and 50% distillation points, and minimum limits for this sum are often included in aviation gasoline specifications.

COLD STARTING AND WARMING-UP

Difficulty in starting at low temperatures may be due to a variety of factors, some of which are mechanical, while others are concerned with the fuel or lubricant. Among the mechanical factors are incorrect carburettor adjustment, obstruction of fuel flow due to rust, ice, etc., faults in the ignition system, and the fact that the output of any battery or accumulator falls off rapidly at very low temperatures, being only one-third of normal at —30° C.

All lubricating oils increase in viscosity as the temperature is lowered, and at low temperatures with oils of low viscosity index

(*vide* chapter XXIX) the increased engine friction due to the high
viscosity of the lubricant may make starting difficult. As the temperature is still further reduced, the effect of fuel volatility increases
relative to that of lubricating oil viscosity.

A mixture of air and vaporized fuel is only inflammable if its
composition lies within certain limits, about $1\frac{1}{2}\%$ to $6\frac{1}{2}\%$ by
volume of fuel vapour in the case of gasoline. Unless a sufficient
proportion of the fuel vaporizes to give the weakest ignitable
mixture, the engine will not fire. The ability of a gasoline to give
easy starting at low temperatures therefore depends on the more
volatile fractions it contains, and is measured by either of two
closely related properties, the vapour pressure or the temperature
at which 10% distils. As shown in fig. 4, the vapour pressure of
gasoline decreases rapidly as the temperature is reduced. The
carburettor in a car engine is usually fitted with a choke to assist
starting. This choke restricts the flow of air to the carburettor ;
the suction of the engine then reduces the pressure in the carburettor near the jet and a larger amount of fuel is thus drawn
through the jet, giving a richer fuel-air mixture. This compen-
sates for the smaller proportion of the gasoline vaporized under
cold starting conditions ; for example, if the mixture is twice as
rich, only half the percentage of fuel need be vaporized to give the
same total amount of fuel *vapour*.

The ease with which a car engine warms up depends partly on
the engine (carburettor design and adjustment, mixture heating,
etc.) and partly on the gasoline. Ease of warming-up may be
measured by the time, or the distance travelled, after starting until
the engine operates smoothly without the use of the choke.

The rich mixtures obtained by use of the choke cause wastage
of fuel, and also uneven running of the engine, due partly to poor
mixture distribution (*vide infra*) and partly to the difficulty of
correct choking by hand. For good warming-up, a gasoline
should have the correct proportion of volatile material, but the
less volatile fractions are also important, since they also influence
mixture distribution. The warming-up properties of a gasoline
have been found to be related roughly to both the 50% and 90%
points. The increasing use of automatic chokes should result in a
general improvement in the warming-up performance of car
engines.

DETONATION

Detonation, also called knocking or pinking*, is the sharp, metallic sound or "ping" emitted from the cylinders of spark-ignition engines under certain conditions. When the mixture of fuel and air, compressed by the motion of the piston, is ignited by the spark, a flame travels from the spark plug across the combustion space at a speed of the order of about 50 to 100 miles per hour. The progress of combustion causes a considerable increase in pressure, and hence the unburnt mixture beyond the flame is rapidly compressed, and therefore raised in temperature. Under certain conditions this may raise the fuel above its self-ignition temperature and cause a sudden very rapid burning (explosion) of the remaining unburnt mixture. The effect of this sudden explosion is like that of a hammer blow on the cylinder, and the resulting vibrations set up in the latter cause the familiar sound of detonation. This sequence of events has been very well demonstrated by means of high-speed photographs of detonating and non-detonating combustion in an engine fitted with a transparent quartz window in the cylinder head.

It will be evident from the preceding description that detonation increases the mechanical and heat stresses on the engine. In supercharged aero engines the pressures and temperatures in the cylinders are higher than in car engines, and detonation in the former may lead to burning and fracture of the piston and failure of the engine. Further, owing to the high noise level of aero engines, the onset of detonation is not so easily detected as in car engines.

Detonation depends partly on the design and operating conditions of the engine, partly on the fuel. The effects of the various engine factors can often be predicted from the description of detonation given above, bearing in mind that any factor which increases the pressure and temperature, and hence the tendency to self-ignition, of the last part of the fuel-air mixture to burn, will also tend to cause detonation. Such factors are increase of compression ratio (*vide* fig. 7), throttle opening, degree of supercharge, spark advance, intake air or coolant temperature. If the spark is retarded, the latter stages of combustion occur later in the power stroke, when the pressure in the cylinder is decreasing,

AA

and thus detonation is reduced ; at the same time power output and efficiency are decreased. An increase of speed generally reduces detonation to an extent depending on the fuel used, and also on engine characteristics, particularly the way in which the volume of fuel-air mixture drawn into the engine varies with speed.

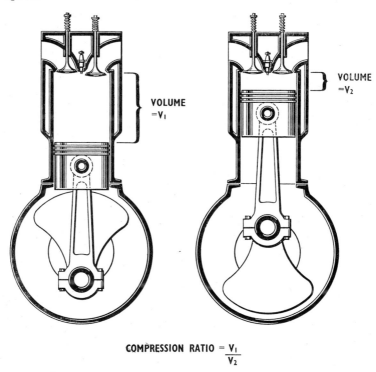

$$\text{COMPRESSION RATIO} = \frac{V_1}{V_2}$$

Fig. 7. Diagram Illustrating Compression Ratio.

The shape of the combustion chamber also has an important effect, and considerable improvement in combustion chamber design has taken place in the last twenty years or so, largely in the direction of controlling the rate of burning of the fuel-air mixture.

Our knowledge of the deton tion behaviour of gasolines in relation to power output and efficiency is derived largely from the pioneer work of Sir Harry Ricardo and his staff, in collaboration with the Asiatic (now Shell) Petroleum Co., Ltd., in 1920 to 1922. This work showed that there are marked differences in detonation tendency between different gasolines and hydrocarbons, aromatics such as benzole and toluole being particularly good.

KNOCK TEST METHODS

Chemical and physical laboratory tests do not yet indicate the anti-knock value of a gasoline with sufficient accuracy, and it is necessary to employ engine tests under carefully controlled conditions.

The Ricardo E.35 was the earliest single-cylinder engine designed specifically for this purpose. The compression ratio of this engine can be varied continuously during operation. In carrying out a test the compression ratio is increased until a definite degree of audible detonation occurs ; this compression ratio is called the "highest useful compression ratio", or, shortly, the H.U.C.R., of the fuel. With a given gasoline the power output is highest at the H.U.C.R., and decreases at higher or lower compression ratios.

H.U.C.R.s determined on the E.35 engine give a better indication of the actual anti-knock values of fuels in British cars, and also give simpler blending relationships, than do A.S.T.M. Motor Method octane numbers (*vide infra*). For these reasons the E.35 test has been widely used within the Group, in addition to the Motor Method. About 1930 the C.F.R. engine (fig. 8) was developed by the Co-operative Fuel Research Committee in the U.S.A. for testing motor gasolines. The method finally adopted by the A.S.T.M., for general routine purposes, is known as the A.S.T.M. Motor Method. A similar method, using less severe operating conditions, and called the Research Method, is used in the determination of the "sensitivity" of motor gasolines, i.e. the dependence of gasoline anti-knock value on engine conditions.

For aviation gasolines certain modifications of the engine and operating conditions are used (*vide infra*). The 1–C method was devised to indicate the anti-knock value of such fuels under cruising conditions, while the 3–C method is intended to correlate with take-off conditions ; the Motor Method is sometimes used instead of the 1–C method, because it is, in some respects, more convenient and rapid, and for normal aviation gasolines there is an approximately constant difference between the 1–C and Motor Method ratings.   These four methods, which have been generally adopted in America and in the United Kingdom, are sometimes referred to by their C.R.C. designations (C.R.C.=Co-ordinating Research Council, which includes the C.F.R. Committee) :—

$$\text{C.R.C. Method F–1} = \text{Research Method}$$

		F–2 = Motor	,,
,,	,,	F–3 = 1–C	,,
,,	,,	F–4 = 3–C	,,

Fig. 8.   C.F.R. Engine.

The C.F.R. engine, like the Ricardo E.35, is a variable compression engine. In the Research and Motor Methods the compression ratio is adjusted until a certain specified intensity of knock occurs. The compression ratio at this point, even for one and the same fuel, varies slightly from day to day, owing to slight differences in atmospheric and in engine conditions. To overcome this difficulty the test fuel is matched, at the above compression ratio, with a blend of two reference fuels, one of high, the other of low anti-knock value. The standard reference fuels are iso-octane and normal heptane. The anti-knock value of iso-octane is arbitrarily taken as 100, that of normal heptane as zero. If the matching reference fuel blend contains, say, 70% iso-octane and 30% heptane, the anti-knock value of the test fuel is said to be 70 octane number.

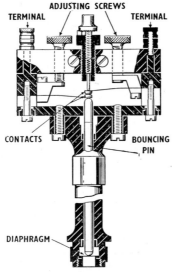

Fig. 9. Sectional View of Bouncing Pin.

In the Motor and Research Methods detonation intensity is not estimated by ear, but is measured by means of an instrument called the "bouncing pin" (fig. 9). This is screwed into a hole in the cylinder head at approximately the point where detonation occurs. There is a thin steel diaphragm at the lower end, with a light metal rod resting on it. A leaf spring presses on top of the rod, and immediately above this spring is a second leaf spring. Each spring is provided with an electrical contact, and the springs are adjusted until the contacts are 3/1000th inch apart. The two contacts form part of an electric circuit. When no detonation occurs, no current flows through this circuit. When detonation is sufficiently intense, the resulting rapid increase of pressure causes the diaphragm to throw the pin upwards, thus closing the circuit. The more intense the detonation, the longer is the time during which the circuit is closed, and the greater is the amount of current. The latter is indicated by a knock meter. This consists of a hot wire ammeter, in which the current flows through a metal wire resistance surrounding a thermocouple. The resistance is heated by the current, and the thermocouple circuit is arranged to indicate the potential produced and thus the intensity of detonation.

In the 1–C (C.R.C. F–3) method, the compression ratio is adjusted to give a specified knock intensity, and detonation intensity is indicated by a special thermocouple, called a thermal plug, which is screwed into the hole occupied by the bouncing pin in the Motor Method ; thus, this method is based on the temperature rise rather than rate of increase of pressure, due to detonation. The 1–C method also employs a higher speed, higher jacket temperature, and greater spark advance than the Motor Method. For gasolines above 100 octane number the anti-knock value is expressed as ml.* tetra-ethyl lead per U.S. gallon of gasoline, or as performance number (*vide* page 358).

Maximum power is required during the take-off of an aeroplane, and to achieve this rich fuel/air mixtures are used. The extra fuel has a certain cooling effect, and this permits an increase in boost (degree of supercharge). It was found that the octane number did not give a true indication of the relative anti-knock values of aviation gasolines under take-off conditions, and the 3–C (C.R.C. F–4) method was developed for this purpose. The following description refers to the 3–C method as used in British laboratories ; this differs from that used in the U.S.A., particularly in the method of expressing results. This method utilizes the C.F.R. engine with

certain modifications.   The engine is operated at constant compression ratio, detonation being induced by increase in boost.
Fig. 10 illustrates the principle of the 3–C method.   Each curve
shows the way in which power output, as limited by detonation,
varies with mixture strength.   Such curves are called mixture-
response curves.   The power output is plotted in terms of mean
effective pressure.   This is calculated from the power output

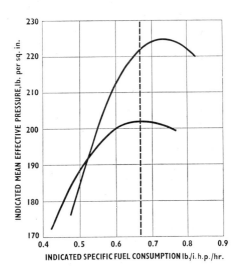

Fig. 10.   Principle of 3-c (CRC-F4) Test.

(horse-power), and represents the average pressure on the piston
which would give the observed horse-power.   It is a more convenient unit than the latter, which depends on the size and speed
of the engine, and permits results on different types of engines to
be compared directly.   The *brake* horse-power, mean effective
pressure, is that available at the engine shaft, measurable by a
dynamometer or brake, while the *indicated* horse-power, etc., is
that developed on the piston, i.e. the sum of the brake power and
the friction and pumping losses.   The mixture strength is given in

terms of specific fuel consumption, that is, pounds of fuel consumed per hour per horse-power developed.

Mixture response curves are determined either by increasing the boost at constant mixture strength, or by weakening the mixture at constant boost, until detonation occurs. (The latter method is usually more convenient in full-scale single or multi-cylinder aero engine tests.) In the 3–C method, detonation is estimated by ear. It will be noted from fig. 10 that the maxima on the two curves occur at different specific fuel consumptions. The test and reference fuels are compared at the specific fuel consumption at which the maximum occurs on the reference fuel curve. Thus, assuming a rating of 100 for the reference fuel, the rating of the test fuel in the example given would be :

$$\frac{100 \times 222}{202} = 110.$$

The reference fuel used in the 3–C test is iso-octane plus 1·28 ml. tetra-ethyl lead per U.S. gallon, and its rating is fixed by agreement at 100.

In the American method, the reference fuel is unleaded iso-octane, and the mixture response curves are plotted in terms of fuel/air ratio instead of specific fuel consumption. Results are reported as performance numbers, based on unleaded iso-octane as 100. The performance number scale relates the 3–C rating to the average i.m.e.p. obtained in full-scale engine tests. A British rich-mixture rating of 100 is equivalent to a performance number of 130. The performance number scale is also used for 1–C ratings.

RELATION BETWEEN ANTI-KNOCK VALUE AND PERFORMANCE

Detonation is the principal factor limiting engine output, and the anti-knock value is therefore an important property of the fuel. The relation between fuel anti-knock value and power output depends on the method by which the power output is increased. This can be done by increasing either the compression ratio or the degree of supercharge (boost), or by a combination of the two. Fig. 11 shows the results of tests made in a C.F.R. engine. The upper curve would correspond roughly with the case of motor-car engines, the lower curve with that of aero engines under cruising conditions. Fig. 11 indicates that increased supercharge is more effective than increased compression ratio for improving power output ; at the same time, higher supercharge means that a greater amount of fuel-air mixture is burnt, and thus the heat stresses on the engine are increased.

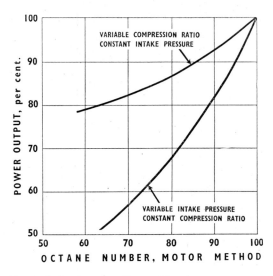

Fig. 11.   Relation between Octane Number and Power Output.

The higher the compression ratio of an engine, the higher is its thermal efficiency, i.e. the ratio of power actually obtained to the power which would be available if the fuel were completely burned, and all the heat thus evolved converted into mechanical power.   Hence increasing the octane number of the fuel permits the use of higher compression ratios, giving higher efficiency and lower fuel consumption.   This is illustrated in fig. 12.   On the other hand, an increase in degree of supercharge reduces the overall efficiency, because the supercharger is driven by the engine, and the power absorbed by it increases with the degree of supercharge.

It must be emphasized that fuels of higher anti-knock value will only permit improvements in power output and fuel consumption if the engine is designed to take advantage of the higher anti-knock value. An increase in anti-knock value beyond that required to suppress detonation confers no advantage.

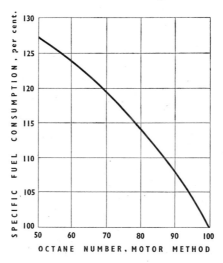

Fig. 12.   Relation between Octane Number and Specific Fuel
Consumption.

In some respects the detonation problem is more complicated in car engines than in aero engines. The former operate over a much wider range of speeds and loads and are provided with automatic spark advance mechanisms containing two types of control, one a centrifugal governor which increases the spark advance as the engine speed increases, while the other, operated by the intake manifold pressure, alters the spark advance so that the advance is less at larger throttle openings. The anti-knock value of the gasoline required by a car engine under various conditions of speed and load therefore depends to a considerable extent on the characteristics of the spark advance mechanism, which is generally adjusted by the engine manufacturer to give satisfactory performance on the gasolines normally supplied.

During the last fifteen years or so a large number of road tests have been carried out, both in America and in England, to test the validity of the Motor Method for predicting gasoline performance of cars, and also to determine the "octane requirements" of

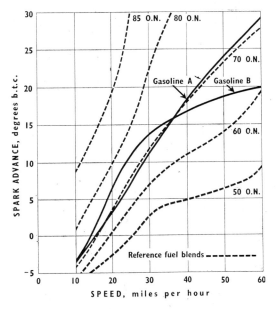

Fig. 13. Borderline Knock Curves.

various cars. Several methods have been used for determining the road ratings of motor gasolines, but all consist essentially in comparing the test fuel with reference fuels of known octane number. One widely used method is known as the "borderline knock procedure". The centrifugal and manifold vacuum spark advance mechanisms are put out of action and arrangements made to advance the spark manually. The car is allowed to accelerate at full throttle up a convenient slope, and the speed noted at which the knock dies out. This procedure is repeated at various degrees of spark advance, using (a) a series of reference fuel blends of known octane number, and (b) the test fuels. Typical curves obtained are shown in fig. 13, the reference fuel curves being shown dotted, with the curves for two different types of gasoline, A and B, superimposed. Both gasolines were of 70 Motor Method octane number. By comparing the test fuel and reference fuel

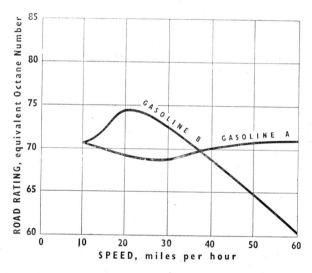

Fig. 14. Road Ratings of Two Gasolines at Various Speeds.

curves the road ratings, in equivalent octane numbers, can be obtained. Thus, gasoline B has a road rating equivalent to 74½ octane number at 20 miles per hour and to 61 octane number at 60 miles per hour. Fig. 14 shows how the road ratings of these two gasolines compare at various speeds. The rating of gasoline A varies little with speed, while that of gasoline B decreases at high speeds.

In figs. 15 and 16 the borderline knock curves of these two gasolines are compared with the actual spark advance given by the distributor mechanism ; when the actual spark advance is greater than that indicated by the borderline knock curve, detonation occurs, as shown by the shaded areas.

The road rating of a gasoline may vary considerably in different cars. In co-operative road tests of the type described, it is therefore necessary to test a considerable number of cars if the results are to be of general application. By a similar procedure, it is

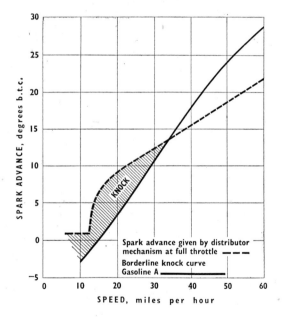

Fig. 15. Road Knock Characteristics of Gasoline A.

possible to determine the "octane requirement" of individual cars, i.e. the octane number of the reference fuel blend required to limit detonation to a specified intensity. There is a considerable variation in the octane requirements of different makes of cars, and even of different cars of the same make and model.

A series of co-operative road tests carried out in the U.S.A. in 1941 by the C.F.R. Committee showed that the Motor Method gave a reasonably good indication of the road anti-knock values of different types of actual motor gasolines, though this was not

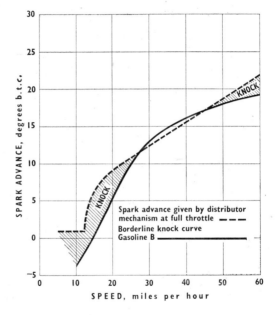

Fig. 16.   Road Knock Characteristics of Gasoline B.

true for certain experimental blends. British tests in 1937 showed that certain gasolines, particularly blends containing alcohol or fairly high percentages of aromatic hydrocarbons such as benzole, had better anti-knock performance in cars on the road than was indicated by their Motor Method octane numbers. The H.U.C.R. determined on the Ricardo E.35 engine gave better correlation than the Motor Method octane number with the results of the British car tests.

For any spark-ignition engine there is an optimum spark advance (varying with speed), at which the power output is a maximum. Automatic spark advance mechanisms are normally adjusted by the engine manufacturers to give somewhat less than the optimum spark advance partly in order to allow for an increase in the octane requirement through the formation of deposits of "carbon", etc., in the combustion chamber. Another important reason is that increasing the compression ratio and retarding the spark gives an improvement in power and fuel consumption. It is evident from the preceding discussion that detonation can be reduced or in some cases eliminated by retarding the spark. Retarding the spark, without increase of compression ratio, however, tends to reduce power output and increase fuel consumption.

Certain fuel components have Research Method octane numbers up to 10 units or more higher than their Motor Method octane numbers, and these components also show the greatest variation in anti-knock value with change in engine conditions. The relative anti-knock values of gasolines, either on the road or in aircraft engines, may therefore show considerable differences according to the engine in which they are tested. Paraffinic fuels are relatively "insensitive" to changes in engine conditions, while the "sensitive" fuels include aromatics, unsaturated hydrocarbons (present in cracked gasolines), alcohols, etc.

Motor gasolines consisting mainly of paraffinic hydrocarbons, either with or without ethyl fluid, tend to knock more at low than at high speeds in cars on the road. Cracked gasolines and those containing aromatics show the reverse behaviour, and tend to knock at high rather than low speeds. In practice, the results depend on the characteristics of the spark advance mechanism of the car engine, and it is possible with certain combinations of fuel and car to obtain knock at high and low speeds, but not at intermediate speeds (cf. fig. 16).

BLENDING VALUES

When two gasoline components of different anti-knock value are blended together, the anti-knock value of the blend is sometimes proportional to the percentages of the two components, but in other cases may be higher or lower than that calculated on the basis of simple proportion. An example is given in fig. 17 for two components, X and Y, which have octane numbers of 80 and 60 respectively. A blend of 40% X + 60% Y has an octane number of 70 instead of 68 as calculated by simple proportion. Thus, in

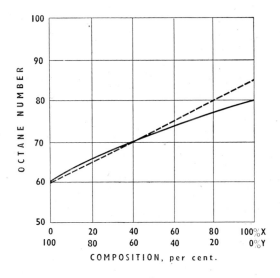

Fig. 17. Diagram Illustrating Blending Value.

the blend quoted, component X has a "blending value" in base stock Y of 85, as indicated by extrapolating the octane number of the blend to 100% X (dotted line). Such blending values vary with the percentages of the component present, and in some cases with the base stock with which the component is blended.

A knowledge of the blending values of components decreases the labour involved in deciding on the composition of blends to meet a given anti-knock specification. An important advantage of E.35 H.U.C.R.s over Motor Method octane numbers is that they give straight-line blending curves for all normal components of motor gasoline.

ANTI-KNOCK DOPES*

It has been found that the addition to gasoline of certain compounds containing lead, iron, nickel or thallium markedly increases the anti-knock value. All these compounds are poisonous. The best known and most effective is tetra-ethyl lead, $Pb (C_2H_5)_4$, which is added in proportions up to a few ml. per gallon of gasoline (1 ml. per gallon = about 0.05% by weight). It is used in the form of ethyl fluid, which contains, in addition to tetra-ethyl lead (T.E.L.), a dye (to indicate the poisonous nature) and compounds of bromine and chlorine (ethylene dibromide and dichloride). During combustion in the engine T.E.L. forms lead oxide, a solid of very high boiling point, which readily deposits on the combustion chamber surfaces, spark plugs, exhaust valves and valve seats, etc. These deposits cause spark plug failure and pitting of exhaust valves and valve seats, resulting in loss of power and in some cases stoppage of the engine. In the presence of ethylene dibromide (or dichloride) the more volatile lead bromide (or chloride) is formed in place of lead oxide and passes out through the exhaust. The amount of ethylene dibromide or dichloride in the ethyl fluid is normally that required just to remove the lead. Such an ethyl fluid is designated as a 1–T Mix (1 times theoretical). The concentration of ethyl fluid used is expressed in terms of the effective anti-knock component, i.e. as ml. T.E.L. per gallon of gasoline.

T.E.L. increases both the octane number and the rich mixture rating of gasoline. Its effectiveness decreases as its concentration is increased, and also depends on the base stock to which it is added.

FUEL INJECTION AND INTERNAL COOLANTS

In recent years a number of aero engines have been built in which the fuel is injected directly into the cylinders by a pump and injectors, similar to those used in diesel engines, instead of being vaporized and atomized in a carburettor. Direct fuel injection eliminates the possibility of carburettor icing and reduces difficulties due to uneven mixture distribution (*vide infra*). On the other hand, the pumps and injectors offer certain difficulties in manufacture, because they have to be made to very close tolerances in order to ensure accurate deliveries of small quantities of fuel to each cylinder.

A useful increase in detonation-limited power can be obtained by injecting water into the induction system. Water has a high latent heat, and its vaporization in the combustion chamber exerts a cooling effect, which permits a higher degree of supercharge before detonation is encountered. Addition of materials such as methyl alcohol, which are themselves combustible, permits a further increase in power output. In this application, materials such as water, methyl alcohol/water mixtures, etc., are termed "internal coolants".

Alcohol/water mixtures, alone or containing T.E.L., have been proposed for use in automotive engines (e.g. trucks), the idea being that a gasoline of relatively low octane number is used for normal operation, arrangements being made to inject the fluid automatically into the induction system at large throttle openings.

PRE-IGNITION

Pre-ignition is due to premature ignition of the fuel-air mixture in the cylinder by hot spark plugs, red-hot carbon deposits, etc. If the ignition is switched off while pre-ignition is occurring, the engine may continue to fire. Pre-ignition is distinguished from detonation in that it occurs before, not after, the passage of the spark. It may occur after prolonged detonation, which causes overheating. The effects of pre-ignition on the engine are similar to those of detonation, though it may be more dangerous than the latter owing to the sudden back pressure on the piston during the compression stroke causing mechanical damage to the bearings. The cure for pre-ignition usually lies in changing the spark plugs or in decarbonizing the engine.

MIXTURE DISTRIBUTION

In carburettor engines the gasoline is largely, but not completely, vaporized before it enters the cylinders. The uniform distribution of the unvaporized liquid to the various cylinders is no easy matter, particularly in ''in-line'' engines. A swirl may develop in the intake pipe leaving the carburettor, and the resulting centrifugal action tends to cause the fuel droplets to collect as a film on the walls of the pipe. Where the intake pipe divides into two branches, the fact that the liquid is travelling spirally along the inner circumference may cause most of the liquid to enter one of the branches. The air and vaporized fuel are more evenly distributed among the various cylinders. Hence those cylinders which receive an excess of liquid gasoline heavy ends will receive a richer mixture than the average ; those which receive too little, a weaker mixture. Detonation is a maximum at a mixture strength approximating the chemically correct fuel-air mixture for complete combustion, and is less at richer or weaker mixtures. Uneven distribution may therefore result in detonation in certain cylinders, causing rough running of the engine, loss of power and efficiency, and possible damage in those cylinders where detonation is greatest. So far as the fuel is concerned, distribution is related to the latter part of the distillation curve (approximately to the 90% point). However, it also depends on the design of the intake manifold and on the temperature existing in the latter ; thus, distribution will tend to become less uniform as the 90% point of the fuel increases and as the intake air temperature decreases.

The effects of maldistribution are more pronounced with leaded gasolines. T.E.L. boils at 200° C., and when a leaded gasoline is partially vaporized by the carburettor, most of the T.E.L. will tend to remain in the unvaporized liquid. The cylinders receiving the richest mixtures will therefore receive more T.E.L. than the average, and vice versa. As rich mixtures have less tendency to detonation, the effects of maldistribution of the fuel itself and of the T.E.L. act in the same direction, thus increasing the differences in intensity of detonation in different cylinders.

In aero engines, which use gasolines of relatively high T.E.L. content, it has been shown that the fuel-air ratio and T.E.L. contents of the fuel reaching individual cylinders may vary over ranges of 17% and 100% respectively of the average values for all cylinders. Samples of the unvaporized fuel flowing along the walls of the intake manifold have in some cases been found to contain as much as 90 ml. T.E.L. per gallon. Thus, even though the amount of unvaporized liquid may be small, the effects of maldistribution may be considerable. In car engines, which use gasolines of lower T.E.L. content, the maximum variation in fuel-air ratio and T.E.L. content may be 7% to 8%, and 30% respectively, of the average values.

Maldistribution has another important effect. In those cylinders which receive too high a proportion of T.E.L., difficulties due to deposits of lead compounds on spark plugs, and pitting of exhaust valves, valve seats, etc., will be accentuated. These difficulties are also increased by the fact that, while the T.E.L. tends to remain in the unvaporized liquid in the manifold, the "lead scavengers" (ethylene dibromide or dichloride) boil at 132° C. and 84° C. respectively, and are therefore largely vaporized. Thus, those cylinders which receive too high a proportion of T.E.L. receive less than the correct amount of lead scavenger.

It has been possible to reduce these difficulties in certain aero engines by fitting a longitudinal baffle in the main intake pipe from the supercharger ; this baffle has a slight twist, designed to counteract the natural swirl in the intake pipe. Charge heaters have also been used to maintain the mixture at a temperature sufficiently high to ensure reasonable distribution ; they have the disadvantage, however, of causing some loss of power. Another method used has been to run the engine for occasional short periods at high power, which raises the engine temperatures and removes the lead deposits.

FUEL CONSUMPTION

The fuel consumption of an engine may be affected by the nature of the fuel in two ways. As noted above, higher anti-knock value fuels permit the compression ratio of the engine to be increased, resulting in higher efficiency and improved fuel economy. In addition to this, however, fuels may differ in the quantity of heat developed during their combustion. If a fuel is completely burned under ideal conditions, the total amount of heat developed is called the calorific value*. The principal units in common use for expressing quantity of heat are the calorie* (cal.), kilogram calorie (kg. cal. or Cal. = 1,000 calories), and British thermal unit

(B.Th.U.). The calorie is the amount of heat required to raise the temperature of 1 gram of water through 1° C. ; the B.Th.U. is the amount required to raise 1 lb. of water through 1° F. Calorific values are commonly expressed in terms of cal. per gm. or per litre, kg. cal. per gm. mol., B.Th.U. per lb. or per gallon, etc.

Calorific value is determined in the laboratory by burning a known quantity of the fuel in a steel bomb filled with oxygen under pressure. The bomb is completely immersed in a special vessel containing a known amount of water, the rise in temperature of which, due to the combustion of the fuel, is accurately measured. From the rise in temperature of the water the calorific value can be calculated. At the end of the test the temperature of the whole apparatus is slightly above the initial temperature of the water, and the steam produced inside the bomb by combustion of the fuel is condensed to water. The calorific value thus measured is termed the *gross* calorific value. Engine exhaust temperatures are considerably above the boiling point of water and the steam produced during combustion of the fuel is not condensed. In calculations on engine fuel consumption one therefore uses the *net* calorific value, which is lower than the *gross* value by the heat of vaporization of the water formed in the combustion. The net value is difficult to determine directly and is usually obtained from the gross value from tables in the case of hydrocarbon fuels, or by calculation from the hydrogen content of the fuel.

Gasolines of low specific gravity have higher calorific values per lb., and lower calorific values per gallon, than those of high specific gravity. However, the differences in calorific value between gasolines are quite small, varying from about 20,000 to 20,400 B.Th.U. per lb. gross or 18,700 to 19,000 net. Such differences can only be detected in cars on the road by carefully controlled experiments. Fuels, such as methyl or ethyl alcohol, which contain oxygen, may have calorific values appreciably below those of purely hydrocarbon fuels.

For motor car engines the calorific value per gallon is of greater interest than the calorific value per lb., since the fuel is purchased on a gallonage basis. However, owing to the varying conditions of operation of cars, and the difficulty of making exact comparisons, calorific value is not an important property of motor gasolines. In the case of aircraft, however, operating conditions frequently conform to a fairly definite schedule. Further, every additional pound of fuel carried means 1 lb. less pay-load. High calorific value per lb. is therefore of much greater importance in aviation than in motor gasoline. With aviation gas turbine fuels the calorific value per unit volume may be important (*vide infra*).

GUM

Imperfectly refined cracked gasolines may contain a sticky substance known as "gum". If present in more than small amounts it may be deposited in induction manifolds and on inlet valve stems, causing the latter to stick in their guides and impairing the power output and efficiency of the engine.

The gum content of a gasoline is determined by evaporating a known quantity of gasoline in a shallow glass dish on a steam bath, a jet of air being directed on to the surface of the gasoline. The object of the air jet is to hasten the evaporation and thus to avoid the formation of additional gum. The gasoline boils away, and the gum, which is not volatile, remains behind on the dish and is weighed. This test measures the amount of gum actually present in the gasoline at the time of test, and is therefore known as the existent gum test. The existent gum content of aviation or motor gasoline does not normally exceed a few milligrams per 100 ml. of gasoline.

When unstable gasolines are stored for long periods, particularly if the atmospheric temperature is high, as in the tropics, the gum content may increase, and some of the gum may deposit as a brown, insoluble, sticky material ; at the same time, the gasoline usually becomes darker in colour. This gum is formed by oxidation of the gasoline. Leaded gasolines sometimes become cloudy after long storage, or deposit a white powdery material consisting of lead compounds.

The tendency of a gasoline to form gum in storage is measured by a potential gum test. In this test, a definite amount of the gasoline is placed in a steel bomb, which is then filled with oxygen under pressure and placed in a bath of boiling water. The bomb is fitted with a pressure gauge. For motor gasolines, the "induction period'' is measured. With normal gasolines of reasonable stability, the pressure in the bomb remains constant for some time, and then starts to decrease as the gasoline begins to oxidize and form gum. The time from the start of the test until the pressure falls by a definite small amount is called the induction period. In the case of aviation gasolines the test is made more severe by placing in the gasoline a strip of steel, which increases the rate of oxidation. The test is carried out for a definite period, at the end of which the bomb is taken out of the bath, cooled and opened. The gasoline is filtered, any precipitate weighed, and the gum content of the filtered gasoline determined.

The tendency of gasolines to form gum and deposit lead compounds in storage can be decreased by the addition of small quantities, of the order of 1 lb. to 4,000 to 5,000 gallons of gasoline, of certain ''inhibitors''. These delay the commencement of oxidation of the gasoline and extend the induction period. They are not substitutes for proper refining, and they are, in fact, more effective in well-refined gasolines. It is quite useless to add an inhibitor to a gasoline which has already started to form gum.

WEATHERING

This is a term applied to the loss of volatile fractions from a gasoline through slow evaporation during storage. Weathering reduces the knock rating of an unleaded gasoline, because the lower boiling fractions of a gasoline have higher knock ratings than the higher boiling fractions. Owing to the relatively high boiling point of T.E.L. (200° C.) very little of the latter evaporates during weathering, and in the case of leaded aviation gasolines the combined effect of loss of volatile high octane components and the increase in T.E.L. concentration is either no change or a slight increase in knock rating.

CORROSION

Practically all gasolines contain at least traces of sulphur. Free sulphur and chemically-combined sulphur in the form of mercaptans, which can corrode metals directly, are removed during the refining treatment. The remaining organic sulphur compounds, such as sulphides or disulphides, are not corrosive.

Three laboratory tests are in use for determining whether a gasoline contains corrosive sulphur compounds. In the copper strip test, a strip of clean polished copper is immersed in the gasoline, which is heated to 50° C. (122° F.) for three hours. The copper dish test, included in some aviation gasoline specifications, employs a hemispherical copper dish, in which the gasoline is evaporated to dryness on a steam bath. In either of these tests, there should be no grey or black discoloration of the copper after test. In the Institute of Petroleum method 65/42, the gasoline is boiled (using a condenser to prevent loss of gasoline) with copper-bronze powder for one hour, and the corrosive sulphur, which reacts with the powder to form copper sulphide, is determined chemically.

When gasoline is burnt in the cylinder of an engine, the sulphur is converted to oxides, which are not harmful provided that temperatures are such that the steam, always present in the products of combustion, is not condensed. At lower temperatures, these oxides of sulphur combine with the water to form sulphurous and sulphuric acids, which are corrosive. Under normal conditions, temperatures are sufficiently high to prevent this. However, at low atmospheric temperatures, with gasoline of high sulphur content, and under conditions of intermittent operation, condensation and corrosion may occur. This corrosion may be manifested in cars, trucks, etc., as excessive cylinder wear, and other parts which may be affected are piston pins and bushings and crankshafts. Gasolines with a sulphur content as high as 0·25% have, however, given no trouble from corrosion, even at low temperatures. The sulphur content of most motor gasolines does not exceed 0·1%, and in the case of aviation gasolines is only a fraction of this.

LUBRICATING OIL DILUTION

In normal operation of cars, a small quantity of unburnt fuel finds its way into the lubricating oil film on the cylinder walls and works down past the pistons into the crankcase ; blow-by past the piston rings may also introduce fuel vapour into the crankcase. The fuel in the crankcase oil can be separated from the latter by distillation, and is known as diluent. Starting with fresh lubricating oil the amount of diluent increases for a time and then remains approximately constant, providing the operating conditions are not changed.

The tendency of a gasoline to dilute the lubricating oil is related to its 90% distillation point. The latter is a measure of the dewpoint*, i.e. the temperature to which the vaporized fuel must be cooled to deposit liquid. (The dewpoint, of course, depends on the amount of air with which the vaporized fuel is mixed.)

Several other factors besides the fuel itself affect the extent of dilution of the lubricating oil. Dilution may be increased by rich mixtures (due to the use of too large a jet in the carburettor or excessive use of the choke), to low crankcase temperatures (due to cold weather or short runs and frequent stopping and starting of of the engine), or to excessive blow-by caused by badly worn pistons with too great a clearance, or defective piston rings. In aero engines, the operating temperatures of which are fairly high, the dilution does not normally exceed about 1%. In cars, however, the dilution may be as high as 12% in very cold weather.

FREEZING POINT

Since cars are not operated at atmospheric temperatures so low that the gasoline is likely to freeze, motor gasoline specifications do not include a limit for the freezing point. Aeroplanes, on the other hand, frequently operate at altitudes where the atmospheric temperature is extremely low. Aviation gasoline specifications therefore usually include an upper limit of $-60°$ C. for the freezing point, this being the lowest temperature likely to be encountered at the highest altitudes.

Most of the hydrocarbons which may be present in aviation gasoline have freezing points below $-60°$ C., the principal exceptions being benzene and xylenes, and the freezing-point specification therefore limits the percentages of these hydrocarbons which can be included.

WATER TOLERANCE

Aviation gasoline specifications usually include limits for water tolerance. The solubility of water in hydrocarbon fuels is quite small, normally below 0·02%. The presence of certain oxygen-containing compounds, such as alcohols, however, increases the amount of water which can be dissolved ; when the blend is cooled to low temperatures (as at high altitudes), the solubility decreases, and this water may separate as ice crystals, blocking carburettor jets, fuel filters, etc. In effect, the test limits the amounts of such components which can be blended with the gasoline. The test is carried out by shaking four volumes of gasoline with one volume of water, allowing to stand and observing any change in volume of the gasoline and water layers.

PERFORMANCE OF SUBSTITUTE FUELS

Although gasoline made from petroleum is by far the most widely used fuel in spark-ignition engines, certain other fuels have been used to a limited extent, either for special applications, or in certain countries lacking adequate indigenous supplies of petroleum.

Ethyl alcohol has been used in cars, both unmixed and also blended with gasoline. It has a high octane number, 95 O.N. Motor Method. Owing to its high latent heat, over $2\frac{1}{2}$ times that of gasoline, the vaporization of the fuel in the carburettor cools the fuel-air mixture to a lower temperature than when gasoline is used ; a greater *weight* of mixture is therefore drawn into the cylinders, giving an increase in power. The calorific value of alcohol is, however, about 35% less than that of gasoline, which results in a higher fuel consumption for the same power output. For complete combusion, the mixture strength is somewhat richer with alcohol than with gasoline, and carburettors set for use with gasoline therefore require adjustment (larger jets) when alcohol is to be used. Other disadvantages of alcohol are more difficult starting in cold weather and a greater tendency to vapour lock. Blends of about 10% to 20% in gasoline may separate into two layers through absorption of water.

Similar remarks apply to methyl alcohol, which has been used in special blends for racing cars, where power output is of prime importance and the increased fuel consumption relatively unimportant. Its latent heat is even higher than that of ethyl alcohol, while its calorific value is only about half that of gasoline.

Butane, which has an octane number of 92, is used fairly extensively in western districts of the U.S.A., particularly in refrigerated trucks, where it can conveniently be used as a refrigerant as well as fuel.

Gaseous fuels such as producer gas, town gas, and methane, have also been used. Producer gas suffers from the disadvantages that the producer, in which gas is made by passing air and steam over hot coal or charcoal, is a heavy and bulky piece of equipment, needs a certain amount of attention, and engine wear tends to be high owing to fine ash from the coal or charcoal carried along in the gas stream ; the removal of this fine ash from the gas is not an easy problem.

Town gas has been used to a limited extent, being carried in ''balloons'' on top of the vehicle. Obviously the weight of gas which can be carried in this way, and the range of operation, are limited.

Methane is the main constituent of natural gas and marsh gas, and also occurs in sewage gas. It has a very low boiling point (minus 161° C.) at atmospheric pressure. It has been employed compressed in steel cylinders, which, however, add considerably to the weight carried by the vehicle.

These three gases—producer gas, town gas, and methane—have fairly high octane numbers. Their densities in the gaseous state are considerably below that of vaporized gasoline ; furthermore, in the case of gasoline, part of the fuel enters the cylinders in the liquid state. Hence the weight of fuel drawn into each cylinder is less with these gases than with gasoline, and as a result the power developed is less.

AVIATION GAS TURBINES AND THEIR FUELS

The principles involved in jet propulsion are quite different from those involved in the combination of the conventional aero engine and propeller. Two types of motive power are used for jet propulsion in aircraft : (a) some form of rocket (with which we are not here concerned) and (b) the gas turbine, either alone or in conjunction with a propeller. The considerations involved in the choice of fuels for gas turbines differ markedly from those involved in the choice of aviation gasolines. For example, the gas turbine does not suffer from detonation, and hence the octane number of the fuel has no significance.   However, other problems peculiar to the gas turbine arise.

Basically, jet propulsion depends on Newton's Third Law of Motion, which may be expressed in two synonymous forms : (a) action and reaction are equal and opposite, and (b) momentum can neither be created nor destroyed.   This law may be illustrated by a simple analogy.   Imagine a man on a raft at rest on a motionless lake, and suppose that he has a small pile of brickbats with him on the raft.   He throws a brickbat horizontally with all his strength.   The momentum of the brickbat is the mass (m) of the brickbat multiplied by the velocity or speed (v) with which the brickbat leaves his hand, i.e. the momentum is $m \times v$.   Newton's Third Law states that the raft will move in the opposite direction to the brickbat at a velocity (V) such that $M \times V = m \times v$, where M is the combined mass of the raft, the man and the remaining brickbats.   Thus, if the man throws a 4-lb. brickbat at 20 miles per hour, and if M is 240 lb., the raft will recede at one-third mile per hour.   By continuing to throw brickbats the man can increase the speed of the raft until the thrust he produces is balanced by the resistance of the water and air to the motion of the raft.   The gas turbine jet propulsion unit substitutes a stream of air for the shower of brickbats in the analogy.

In the gas turbine (fig. 18), air is sucked into the front of the unit, compressed by some form of compressor, and delivered through one or more combustion chambers to the jet at the rear. Fuel is injected into each combustion chamber, atomized and burnt.   The expansion of the air due to the combustion causes the stream of heated air and combustion gases to be ejected through the jet at high velocity, and it is the increase in the momentum of this stream which propels the unit.   The compressor is on the same shaft as the turbine and is, in fact, driven by the latter.   The power used to drive the compressor is nearly twice the power left available as thrust in the jet.

The temperature produced in the combustion is high, and, as the mechanical properties of any metal which could be used for the turbine blades deteriorate at high temperatures, it is necessary to cool the combustion gases by addition of "secondary" air.

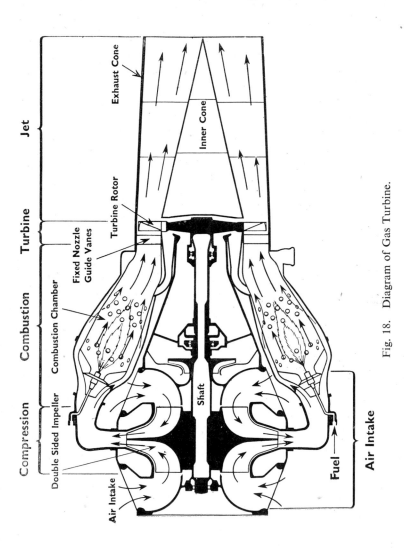

Fig. 18. Diagram of Gas Turbine.

The gas turbine therefore operates at weak mixtures, of the order of 60 to 80 : 1 air-fuel ratio.

The density of the atmosphere decreases as the altitude increases, hence an unsupercharged engine would give less power at high altitudes, and conventional aero engines are therefore fitted with superchargers to improve altitude performance, though obviously there is a limit to what can be done by supercharging. In a similar way the weight of air drawn in by the compressor of a gas turbine unit decreases with altitude. However, since the power required to drive any compressor decreases as the intake air temperature is reduced, and since the temperature of the atmosphere decreases with altitude, the overall thermal efficiency of the gas turbine unit increases with altitude.

The propulsive efficiency of a propeller reaches a maximum at about 300 miles per hour and decreases at higher speeds ; it also decreases at lower air densities, i.e. at higher altitudes. At low speeds the propulsive efficiency of the jet is low, but it increases continuously with increase of speed, and exceeds that of a propeller at speeds of 500 to 550 miles per hour, this critical speed decreasing with altitude (fig. 19).

Furthermore, the gas turbine unit is lighter and can be made of smaller frontal area than the conventional aero engine. It can therefore more easily be streamlined into the thinner wings required for good aerodynamic performance at high speeds and altitudes, and it is in this field that the gas turbine shows advantages over the conventional unit.

It is also possible to use a gas turbine in conjunction with a propeller by coupling the turbine-compressor shaft with the latter through a reduction gear to reduce the speed to that suitable for propellers. This improves the low altitude performance and rate of climb, and this type of unit appears to have possibilities for medium speeds and altitudes.

The fuel consumption of the gas turbine is high, though owing to the high speed developed the comparison with conventional units is less unfavourable in terms of miles per gallon of fuel than on a specific fuel consumption basis (fuel per hour per horsepower). Gas turbine fuels should therefore have as high a calorific value as possible. In the conventional aircraft, the weight of fuel reduces the pay-load by a corresponding amount, and the calorific value per unit weight of fuel (B.Th.U./lb.) is important ; in the gas turbine aircraft, owing to the smaller space available in the thinner wings of the aircraft (*vide supra*), and the larger amount of fuel which must be carried, B.Th.U./gallon is also

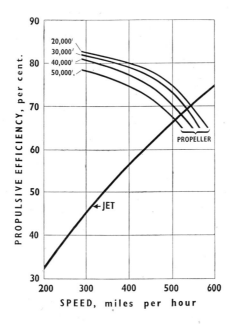

Fig. 19.   Relative Efficiencies of Propeller and Jet.

important.   In the former case, the steam produced in the combustion is not condensed, and the *net* calorific value is specified ; with the gas turbine, the steam adds slightly to the thrust deveoped by the jet, and the *gross* is found to be rather more significant than the *net* calorific value, even though the water formed by combustion is not condensed.   (So far as the combustion system and gas turbine alone, ignoring the jet, are concerned, it is of course the *net* calorific value, as with the piston engine, which is significant.)

These considerations, together with the obvious advantage of using as cheap a fuel as possible, have led to the use of kerosine-type fuels in gas turbines, though for reasons of supply leaded aviation gasolines have been used on occasion.

In addition to calorific value, certain other properties are important in gas turbine fuels. The speed of the air through the combustion chamber is high. Flame speed is therefore important, and under certain conditions the flame may "blow-out". The flame must also have the correct shape ; too long a flame may cause burning of the turbine blades. Incomplete combustion results in a loss of efficiency and may also give rise to deposits of "carbon" etc., which interfere with the proper operation of the unit.

These factors, of course, depend not only on the fuel, but on the design and operating conditions of the unit. However, they serve to indicate the types of fuel problems which are being studied in connection with gas turbine operation. Finally, the low atmospheric temperatures at high altitudes demand a fuel of low pour point and satisfactory viscosity at low temperatures ; as in the case of diesel fuels, viscosity must be controlled to ensure correct atomization in the burners.

INFLUENCE OF HYDROCARBON TYPES ON FUEL CHARACTERISTICS

Gasoline derived from petroleum is composed almost wholly of hydrocarbons (*vide* chapter VII). Until quite recent times, gasolines were largely mixtures of hydrocarbons from one or more of the straight distillation or cracking processes, but modern developments show an increasing tendency to incorporate, particularly in aviation gasoline, more and more pure hydrocarbons which are extracted or synthesized because of the desirable properties they possess (*vide* chapter XVI).

Gasoline specifications, particularly those for aviation grades, are very severe, and, since the fuel is composed essentially of mixtures of hydrocarbons, only those which will ensure that the specification is met can be utilized. The following are among the important characteristics of a fuel and its components that have to be considered :—

(a) Anti-knock value
(b) Calorific value (i.e. heat given out by combustion)
(c) Stability
(d) Volatility (i.e. boiling point and vapour pressure).

(a) **Anti-knock Value.** In anti-knock value the hydrocarbons may be placed in the following approximate order of merit :—

(i) Aromatics
(ii) Branched chain paraffins of the iso-octane type
(iii) Olefins
(iv) Naphthenes
(v) Straight chain paraffins.

Since the anti-knock value of the straight chain paraffins depends, to a certain extent, upon the molecular weight of the individuals, it may not be altogether correct to place these hydrocarbons at the bottom of the list. For a given molecular weight, however, the straight chain paraffins are the lowest in anti-knock values. The relative knock ratings of the various types of hydrocarbons depend, furthermore, on the engine operating conditions.

(b) **Calorific Value.** Since it is the function of the internal combustion engine to convert heat into mechanical work, the fuel which produces the greatest amount of heat during the combustion of a given quantity will be the most advantageous, provided that its other properties are also in line. Of the two hydrocarbon constituents hydrogen gives out more heat on combustion than does carbon, when the same weight is burned in each case. It therefore follows that the hydrocarbons richest in hydrogen will have the highest calorific value per unit weight. From this viewpoint the hydrocarbons fall into the following order of merit :—

(i) Paraffins (straight and branched chain)
(ii) Naphthenes and olefins
(iii) Aromatics.

As with anti-knock value, this order of merit is strictly true only when hydrocarbons containing the same number of carbon atoms are compared.

(c) **Stability.** The paraffin hydrocarbons, both straight and branched chain, are very stable and will not produce deleterious products (petroleum gum) on storage. Both the aromatic and naphthene type hydrocarbons are also satisfactory in this respect. The olefins are somewhat less stable but are important constituents of motor grade gasolines, where adequate stability may be effected by the use of "inhibitors" (*vide* chapter XI).

(d) **Volatility.** On this basis, all the hydrocarbons are satisfactory provided they boil within the approximate ranges of 30° C.–200° C. for motor gasolines and 40° C.–180° C. for aviation gasolines.

From the above brief review of the utility of the different hydrocarbons from the points of view of anti-knock value, calorific value per unit weight, stability and volatility, it will be seen that the branched chain (or iso-) paraffins rank high in order of merit on each count. The aromatics also show considerable merit, but their chief disadvantage appears to be their lower calorific value on a weight basis. In this connection, however, it must be remembered that gasoline is normally bought by volume ; hence a gallon of the material with the higher specific gravity will contain a greater weight of material, and, since the paraffins have a lower specific gravity than the aromatics with the same number of carbon atoms (e.g. n-hexane 0·66, benzene 0·88), it is possible for a highly aromatic type of gasoline to produce even more heat units than an equal volume of paraffinic fuel. Differences between the calorific values of fuels may not, therefore, be of great importance, but in the case of conventional aircraft, where loading is an important factor, it will be evident that the fuel with the highest calorific value per unit weight is the most acceptable, other things being equal.

BLENDING THE FINISHED GASOLINE

The numerous petroleum products manufactured for the preparation of aviation and motor gasolines may be divided into two broad classes :—

(a) Base stocks. (b) High anti-knock blending agents.

(a) **Base Stocks.** As the name implies, a base stock forms the basis of the finished blend, and is its main constituent. In fact, motor gasolines are frequently prepared from base stocks alone, whilst high anti-knock aviation type fuels are blended from a selected base stock (or mixture of base stocks), one or more high-octane number constituents and lead tetra-ethyl. Base stocks may be derived from two general sources :—(1) Selected crude oils and natural gasoline (straight-run gasolines and casing-head gasolines are in this category) ; and (2) The various conversion processes from which are produced typical base stocks such as catalytically cracked gasoline and hydropetrol (derived from gas oil by a hydrogenation process). When used for aviation blends, some base stocks have to be specially treated. For example, straight-run gasolines would have to be treated to an adequately low sulphur content to improve the lead susceptibility, whilst catalytically cracked gasolines would be treated for olefin removal.

(b) **High Anti-knock Blending Agents.** From a practical standpoint it may be accepted that it is impossible to produce the higher octane grades of aviation fuel by the simple expedient of adding a knock-suppressing agent such as tetra-ethyl lead to a single-base stock. Although certain of the lower octane grades may be made in this way, the amount of tetra-ethyl lead required would, in general, be in excess of specification requirements. Present-day methods of increasing the octane number of base stocks to the high level required are :—(1) The addition of high-octane hydrocarbons, such as iso-octane (and iso-octane mixtures exemplified by alkylate and hot-acid octanes) and iso-pentane ; and (2) The addition of compounds whose blending octane numbers are sufficiently high to give a relatively large increase in octane number of the blend when small percentages are added. Such compounds consist mainly of aromatic hydrocarbons, of which iso-propyl benzene (cumene) and mixed butyl benzenes are the better known, and amino-aromatics, such as certain xylidines and monomethyl aniline. Certain alcohols and ethers have been used, but they are not desirable in view of their lower calorific values or heats of combustion.

"SAFETY" OR "HIGH-FLASH" AVIATION FUELS

Several investigations have been carried out into the causes of the fires that frequently arise when an aircraft crashes. The actual cause of such a fire may be ignition of lubricating oil coming in contact with hot engine parts or flashing of the fuel as a result of similar contact. Aviation gasoline, because of its low flash point (many degrees below 32° F.) and high volatility, burns explosively, and because of this a considerable amount of attention has been paid to so-called "safety" or "high-flash" gasoline.

"Safety" fuels which have so far been considered for aviation purposes have had flashpoints of 100° F. or higher, boiling ranges of approximately 160°–205° C. and relatively high octane ratings. They are intended for use with direct injection equipment and would be quite unsuitable for carburettor engines on account of their low volatility. It would be necessary to start and warm up the engine using aviation gasoline, and it is most probable that a volatile fuel would have to be used also for restarting the engine under certain conditions of flight, e.g. after a prolonged glide.

For engines of the spark-ignition type it is essential that the "safety" fuel shall have as high an octane rating as possible. Such fuels consist of high-boiling aromatics or branched-chain paraffins, or mixtures thereof, together with tetra-ethyl lead to raise the octane number, where necessary. The principle underlying the proposal to utilize "safety" fuels is that the likelihood of ignition of the fuel by contact with hot surfaces is less than for lubricating oil, since the "spontaneous ignition temperature" is higher ; even if the fuel does catch fire, the rate of spread of the fire is less than for normal gasoline, since safety fuel is less easily vaporized than the latter. The term "safety" is, however, relative, and not absolute.

It is to be noted that the hazards involved with the type of fuel proposed are comparable with those of kerosine and high-flash white spirits, and under certain conditions of temperature and altitude an explosive mixture could be formed in the vapour space of fuel tanks, whereas normal aviation gasoline under comparable conditions would give a mixture too rich to be within the explosive range.

"Safety" fuels have been available for many years but have not achieved any great popularity for various mechanical, technical and economic reasons, apart from the questionable degree of safety attained by their use. Consequently, no specifications have been generally accepted.

DIFFERENCES BETWEEN AVIATION AND MOTOR GASOLINE

The main distinctions between aviation and motor gasolines which result from the different requirements of the respective classes of engines may be summarized as follows :—

(*a*) The use of motor gasoline in combat aircraft powered by piston engines cannot be considered because the anti-knock value is too low, although certain types of light aircraft are powered with engines which will operate on gasolines of the motor type. The anti-knock value of motor gasoline is specified by an octane number only, which is a lean mixture rating, whilst aviation gasoline is additionally described by a rich mixture rating. Motor gasolines, by virtue of the fact that the quantities of olefins and aromatics present vary over a wide range, are quite variable in rich mixture anti-knock properties.

(*b*) In general, an aviation gasoline has a narrower boiling range (40° C.–180° C.) than a motor gasoline (30° C.–200° C.) and is more volatile in respect of the temperatures at which 50% (vol.) and 90% (vol.) distil. Some motor gasolines are, however, adjusted to a high initial volatility (and high vapour pressure) to meet winter conditions.

(*c*) The Reid vapour pressure of motor gasoline is invariably higher than that of aviation gasoline. Current aviation gasoline specifications rarely allow a vapour pressure of more than 7 lb. per square inch, whilst a figure as high as 12 lb. per square inch may be encountered with motor gasoline intended for use during very cold weather.

(*d*) Aviation and motor gasolines differ appreciably in chemical composition. Almost all motor gasolines contain some olefins, and the amount is often appreciable. Aviation gasolines rarely contain even small quantities of these hydrocarbons. The aromatic content of aviation gasoline is limited by calorific value and freezing point specifications, but motor gasoline is not subject to the same limitations. In respect of sulphur content, aviation gasoline is limited to 1 part in 2,000 parts of gasoline, whilst some motor gasolines contain as much as 1 part sulphur in 500 parts gasoline.

(e) The allowable limit of tetra-ethyl lead (T.E.L.) is lower for motor than for aviation gasolines. Motor gasolines are generally not allowed to contain more than 3·6 ml. T.E.L./Imp. gallon, and usually contain considerably less, whilst aviation gasolines are now usually restricted to 4·8 ml. T.E.L./Imp. gallon, although 7·2 ml. have been used. The ethyl fluid used for aviation purposes contains ethylene dibromide (to assist evacuation of the lead compounds from the cylinder), whereas a mixture of ethylene dibromide and ethylene dichloride is used in the ethyl fluid for motor gasoline.

BIBLIOGRAPHY

Report of the Empire Motor Fuels Committee. (Institution of Automobile Engineers, London, 1924.) Description of Ricardo's work.

The Principles of Motor Fuel Preparation and Application (2 vols.) Nash and Howes. (Chapman and Hall, London, 1935.)

Fuels for Aircraft Engines. E. L. Bass. (Royal Aeronautical Society, London, Aeronautical Reprints, No. 79, 1935.)

The Science of Petroleum, Vol. IV, Parts III and IV. (Oxford University Press, London, 1938.)

The Internal Combustion Engine, Vol. I. D. R. Pye. (Oxford University Press, London, 1937.)

Aviation Gasoline Manufacture. M. van Winkle. (McGraw Hill Publishing Co., London, 1944.)

Aviation Petrol. The Aeroplane, 1944—**67**—422, 443, 471.

C.R.C. Handbook. (Co-ordinating Research Council, Inc., 30, Rockefeller Plaza, N.Y.) 1946 edition.

Fuels and Lubricants for Aero Gas Turbines. C. G. Williams. (J. Inst. Pet., 1947—**33**—267.)

XXVI

KEROSINE

HISTORY AND TREND OF DEVELOPMENT

KEROSINE distillates have formed an important class of petroleum products ever since crude oil was first produced in quantity. It was, in fact, the demand for a satisfactory illuminant that first stimulated the search for petroleum, and consequently in the original production of kerosine from crude oil, efforts were directed mainly towards producing the maximum quantity of this burning oil. The more volatile petroleum fractions (e.g. gasoline), and the fractions heavier than burning oil, were at that time relatively unimportant products. With the spread of motoring and the development of industries demanding the supply of petroleum products other than kerosine, outlets were found for the whole range of petroleum fractions. Nowadays, kerosine has lost its place as the principal product of crude petroleum, but it has become perhaps all the more interesting owing to the increasing number of applications to which it is put.

Because of the variety of names applied to the kerosine distillates, nomenclature has caused, and still causes, much confusion. The distillates are generally known by the terms Paraffin, Kerosene or Kerosine. If the distillate is required for illumination or heating purposes the product may be referred to as Paraffin, Lamp Oil, Kerosene, Kerosine or Burning Oil ; when a rather more volatile grade of distillate is required, for use as an engine fuel, it may be called Paraffin, Kerosene, Kerosine or Vaporizing Oil. Unfortunately, the old terms continue to persist and, although the spelling ''KEROSINE'' has been officially adopted by the petroleum industry on both sides of the Atlantic for many years, the word ''KEROSENE'' is still often used, even in Statutory Rules and Orders issued during the last war.

USE OF KEROSINE

Large quantities of kerosine are still used for lighting and heating, in spite of the progress made in the distribution of coal gas, "bottled" gas (butane) and electricity. The domestic type of kerosine burning appliance is usually self-contained and does not require wiring or piping. As regards efficiency, the modern type of mantle lamp compares favourably with gas appliances, and kerosine, moreover, is relatively cheap and is comparatively efficient as a fuel for heating and cooking.

Another wide use of kerosine is as a fuel for internal combustion engines, and large quantities of vaporizing oil are consumed, particularly in petrol/paraffin type tractors employed on agricultural work.

A list of the main applications of kerosine is given below :—

As a source of light   ...   (a) Domestic lamps.
(b) Railway signal lamps.
(c) Ship's lamps.
(d) Lighthouse lamps.

As a source of heat   ...   (a) Space heaters.
(b) Cookers and stoves.
(c) Incubators.
(d) Water-heating systems.
(e) Garage and car heaters.
(f) Greenhouse heaters.
(g) Heating of varnish kettles, etc.

As a source of power   ...   Fuel for internal combustion engines, particularly tractors and, more recently, "jet" engines (vide chapter XXV).

Miscellaneous   ...   ...   (a) As a degreasing agent for leather and skins.
(b) As a constituent of insecticides, anti-malarial oils, cattle and sheep dips, polishes, paints, etc.
(c) As a cut-back material in the manufacture of bituminous products for road construction.
(d) As a quenching agent, e.g. in tin foil manufacture.

GENERAL PROPERTIES

Any petroleum product with a boiling range between the approximate limits of 140° C. and 300° C. can be classed as a kerosine distillate. The properties of individual kerosine distillates vary according to their use, the requirements for a good burning oil, a good vaporizing oil, and a good solvent differing markedly.

The most important properties of the kerosine distillates are the chemical composition, volatility, flashpoint, viscosity and surface tension*, and calorific value. Colour and odour are also important from a marketing standpoint and, in addition, burning oils are required to have a good "smoke point"* and low "char value", while the application of vaporizing oils as engine fuels demands that the distillate shall have a high octane rating.

Chemical Composition. The kerosine distillates are composed essentially of hydrocarbons, but they usually contain as impurities small proportions of sulphur, nitrogen and oxygen. The sulphur content rarely exceeds 0·4% and is an undesirable impurity ; in burning oils, excessive sulphur will cause discoloration of the lamp glasses, and in vaporizing oils it may give rise to corrosion, particularly of any brass or copper parts.

The hydrocarbons of the kerosine distillates are usually classified as paraffins, naphthenes and aromatics, the last being those bodies which can be removed by 98% sulphuric acid. The proportion of each class of hydrocarbon present will depend on the source of the crude oil from which the distillate was produced, and will also vary according to the boiling range. Good burning oils are designed to contain a high proportion of the paraffin hydrocarbons, because the burning properties of these compounds are far better than those of the naphthene or aromatic bodies, which cause most lamps to smoke and give heavy deposits of "char" on wicks. On the other hand, the aromatic hydrocarbons have high anti-knock values and their inclusion in vaporizing oils is desirable. The highest grade burning oils are produced by solvent extraction refining methods, and the aromatic hydrocarbons removed by the treatment are used as a component in vaporizing oils.

Volatility. In order to safeguard the user, legislation has been introduced in most countries, fixing minimum flash point limits, to prevent the inclusion of any highly inflammable volatile fractions in kerosine distillates. These volatile fractions might be the cause of serious accidents if the kerosine containing them were used as a burning oil.

In Britain, legislation is also used as a basis for taxation, and distinguishes between those petroleum products classed as ''Motor Spirits'' and those classed as ''Heavy Hydrocarbon Oils'', users of each product paying different rates of duty.

The legal definition of a Heavy Hydrocarbon Oil as laid down in the Finance Act, 1928, demands that the product shall have the following characteristics :—

Flash Point (Abel)   ...   ...   Not less than 73° F.
Per cent. distilling to 185° C.   ...   Less than 50%.
Per cent. distilling to 240° C.   ...   Less than 95%.

In order to take advantage of the lower rate of duty payable on Heavy Hydrocarbon Oils, it is essential that kerosine distillates in the United Kingdom shall conform to these requirements. The limitations are important and greatly affect the quality of the vaporizing oil type of kerosine distillate, where it is desirable that the product shall be readily volatile, in order to form a combustible mixture with air in engine cylinders. Prior to 1928, vaporizing oils in the United Kingdom were appreciably more volatile than they are to-day.

Flashpoint. The flashpoint is a measure of the inflammability of the kerosine, and it is closely allied to the volatility. The determination is carried out in a standard apparatus, and the method consists in slowly heating a quantity of distillate until sufficient vapour is evolved that, mixed with air, it will ignite when a small flame is applied. Methods and apparatus used for the determination vary between different countries ; the standard British method is that of the Institute of Petroleum, which demands that the Abel apparatus be employed for products having flash points below 120° F., and the Pensky-Martens apparatus for oils with flash points above 120° F. In the U.S.A., the Tagliabue (Tag.) instrument is used.

Viscosity and Surface Tension. Both these properties are important, particularly for burning oils, as they are a measure of the extent to which the kerosine will rise up a wick. The viscosity of a kerosine, as may be expected, will vary with temperature, but surface tension, on the other hand, does not vary so greatly. Viscosity is measured in terms of absolute units called ''centistokes''* by timing the flow of kerosine through a capillary* tube; for a burning oil kerosine the value should be between about 1·5 and 2·5 centistokes at the normal atmospheric temperature at which the kerosine is to be consumed.

Calorific Value. The calorific value is a measure of the heat available in the kerosine if it is burned 100% efficiently. For normal grades, the gross calorific value is about 19,900 B.Th.U. per lb. The property is particularly important in kerosine used for heating.

Smoke Point. In order to determine the tendency of a burning oil to smoke, it is burned in a standard smoke point apparatus, which consists of a special lamp with an adjustable wick. In the determination, the height of the flame is increased until smoking begins, and then the wick is lowered until the smoky tail of the flame just disappears ; the height of the flame measured in millimetres is the smoke point. The higher the flame can be raised without the appearance of smoke, the better is the kerosine for illuminating purposes.

The smoke point depends mainly upon the chemical composition of the kerosine, for, as has been mentioned already, the paraffin hydrocarbons have little tendency to smoke, while naphthenes and aromatics smoke more. Smoke point also depends on the temperature and draught conditions, and in the test determination there is a strict method of procedure to be followed to ensure repeatability.

Burning Test. To determine the qualities of a burning oil over a period of time it is usual to carry out a 24-hour test in a standard burning test lamp. The method of testing is rigidly standardized to ensure repeatability, and the results show the rate of consumption of kerosine for a standard size and type of flame, the general burning qualities of the oil, and the amount of char formed on the wick. In the case of railway signal lamp oils it is usual to carry out a seven-days burning test in an actual signal lamp.

KEROSINE AS A SOURCE OF LIGHT

It will be appreciated that the type of kerosine used as a burning oil should have, in particular, a suitable viscosity and surface tension, a good smoke point and a low char value.

The apparatus in which these kerosines are used may be classified into three main types :—

(a) Yellow flame type—wick fed.

(b) Incandescent mantle type—wick fed.

(c) Pressure vaporizer type.

The majority of lamps in use are still of the yellow flame wick-fed type, although incandescent mantle lamps are gaining ground. The efficiency of the three types varies greatly with the design, but in general it may be said that the yellow flame wick-fed types are less efficient than the incandescent mantle types, which in turn compare favourably with gas illumination.

The cause of luminosity of flames has been the subject of much investigation, and it is now generally accepted to be due to incandescent particles of solid carbon. The vaporization of kerosine at the wick surface gives rise to hydrocarbon vapours which decompose and produce carbon particles. The combustion takes place at the flame surface and the carbon particles are responsible for the luminosity of the outer envelope of flame.

Wick-fed Lamps. The ordinary wick-fed lamp consists of a reservoir containing kerosine, into which dips a wick ; one end of the wick passes upwards through a flame guide, which is usually surrounded by a draught deflector and carries a chimney. Oil flows up the wick by capillary action and is vaporized at the surface of the wick by the heat of the flame. In a properly designed lamp the flame should be approximately $\frac{1}{2}$ inch above the top of the wick once the lamp has thoroughly warmed up in operation. The quantity of oil burned in a given time depends on a number of factors, including the height of the top of the wick above the level of the oil in the reservoir, the size and nature of the wick, the size of the flame, and the viscosity and surface tension of the oil.

Wicks. Wicks are of various types. They usually consist of plaited cotton, but wicks of asbestos or of woven glass fibre are now employed. Wicks may be flat (strip), round (solid) or

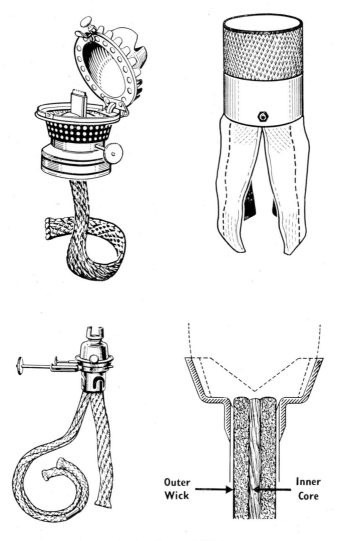

Fig. 1.   Types of Wick.

circular (hollow) in shape. The various types are shown in fig. 1. Two flat wicks are often used in the same lamp, as in Duplex Burners. Flame spreaders (an example is shown in fig. 7, page 402) are often used in connection with circular wicks.

Signal lamps often have special wicks designed to ensure a continuous even supply of oil to the flame. Such wicks may incorporate a "feeder wick" of felt in addition to the usual

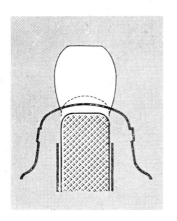 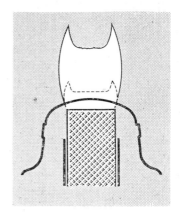

Fig. 2.   Diagram illustrating Wick Trimming.

cotton wick, or, in the case of round wicks, a core of woven cotton or jute may be surrounded by a wool feeder wick or felt sheath.

The trimming of wicks for the maintenance of the correct flame shape is important. Flat wicks should not only be cut straight across, but should also have the edges taken off at the corners (*vide* fig. 2). For circular wicks a special cutter should be used to give the desired bevel to the circular edge.

Precautions should always be taken to ensure that water does not enter the reservoir of the lamp, as it may be trapped in the wick fibres and obstruct the flow of the kerosine, resulting in a drop in the flame height. In order to maintain the normal flame height when using a damp wick it is common practice to turn up the wick, but this will produce a heavy char and give results even worse than before. It is always advisable to dry wicks before fitting them to kerosine burning equipment.

Influence of the Oil Level. The influence of the oil level is important. Shallow, flat reservoirs are better than deep ones, since in the latter, as the oil level falls, the capillary action is not sufficient to raise enough oil to maintain full flame size, and a diminution in luminosity will result. It is essential to ensure that sufficient air can get to the oil reservoir to replace the kerosine as it is consumed. Reservoirs should always be provided with air holes. These are usually located in the filler caps, and care should be taken to make certain that they never become blocked.

The temperature of the room in which the lamp burns is of importance, as also is the amount of heat conducted from the flame to the oil contained in the reservoir. Flame size usually tends to increase after the lamp has been lit and the kerosine warms up. After lighting a lamp it is often necessary to readjust the flame height.

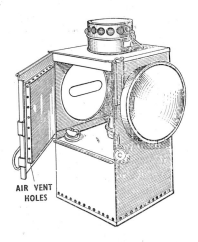

Fig. 3. Welch Signal Lamp, Showing Air Holes in Door.

Ventilation. Another vital point in lamp construction is the design of the chimney and the air holes. Central draught may be provided in the case of lamps with circular wicks, whereas with signal lamps ventilation may be arranged either through holes in the door, as in the Welch lamp (fig. 3), or air may enter through the top, as illustrated by the Adlake lamp (fig. 4).

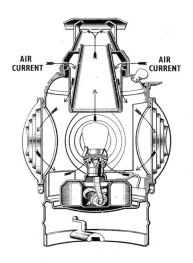

Fig. 4.   Adlake Signal Lamp.

Discoloration of Lamp Glasses. ''Bloom'', due to the formation of white or brown deposits on the lamp glass and resulting in a reduction of illumination, is formed more readily on the cooler parts of the glasses, e.g. on the wider parts of bulbous-shaped chimneys. A white bloom is caused by the deposition of sulphur compounds, while the brown colour of some blooms is attributed to the deposition of the resinous products of combustion. The cleanliness of the atmosphere affects the extent of the bloom, and fog or the presence of ammonia greatly promotes its formation. An excessive amount of bloom is usually produced when new lamp glasses are used for a burning test, and the I.P. (Institute of Petroleum). Burning Test Method specifies the treatment which new glasses must undergo before being used for test purposes.

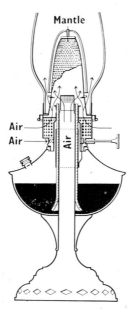

Fig. 5.   Wick Fed Incandescent Mantle Type Lamp.

Wick-fed Incandescent Mantle Type Lamp.   The principle of operation with this type of lamp involves the vaporization of kerosine at the top of a circular wick and its complete combustion on a mantle which becomes incandescent.   A typical design is shown in fig. 5.

Pressure Vaporizer Lamps.   In these lamps no wicks are used, but instead arrangements are made for the kerosine to be pre-heated and vaporized, and in this state to issue from a jet to a mantle, where it is burned.   Such lamps have the disadvantage of not being silent, but score because of their high illuminating

DD

power. It is for this reason that pressure vaporizer lamps have been used in lighthouses.

To start pressure vaporizer lamps it is usual to burn a small quantity of methylated spirits in a cup under the vaporizer. The temperature of the vaporizer is subsequently maintained by the heat of the kerosine flame, since the vaporizer is located in the

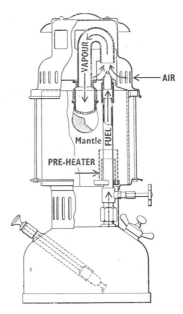

Fig. 6.   Pressure Vaporizer Lamp.

flame combustion zone. The supply of kerosine to the burner is regulated by working the pump in the reservoir, forcing the kerosine through the vaporizer tubes (*vide* fig. 6).

KEROSINE AS A SOURCE OF HEAT

When heating appliances were first developed there was a tendency to incorporate burners based on experience gained in designing

lamps, and some time elapsed before it was realized that the design of kerosine burners suitable for incorporation in other appliances presented new problems.

In the same way as with kerosine used for lamps, the efficiency of the combustion process in heaters depends mainly on the amount of air supplied to the burner and on how this air is brought in contact with the kerosine vapour. In all cases the aim is complete combustion with the correct amount of air in order to avoid unpleasant smells and smoking. With too little air, smoking will occur, and if excess air is supplied then the flame will be chilled. Thus the burner designer aims at supplying :—

    (a) The desired amount of kerosine, an amount which will determine the heat output of the apparatus.

    (b) The exact amount of air to effect clean and odourless combustion.

Yellow and Blue Flames. Although there are many types of kerosine burners used in heating appliances, they produce one of two main types of flame, either a yellow flame or a blue flame. In those burners producing a yellow flame, the air supply is so adjusted that microscopic solid particles of incandescent unburnt carbon appear in the flame and cause it to be luminous. The particles are completely burned in the upper part of the flame and complete combustion of the kerosine is ultimately effected.

In the blue flame burners, the air supply is so controlled in regard to volume, direction and velocity, that the kerosine is completely burned without the appearance of any incandescent carbon particles.

Yellow Flame Heaters. These may have long, flat wicks, often of the duplex type, or circular wicks. They are more sensitive to draughts than the blue flame types, but have a psychological advantage in that the luminosity of the yellow flame is more attractive, especially if shown through a red window (fig. 7a).

Blue Flame Heaters. Blue flame heaters have circular wicks and operate with a central draught travelling up the centre of the wick. The air supply is arranged so that the primary air is warmed and mixes with the vaporized kerosine at the surface of the wick, and the mixture burns with the secondary air at the base of the chimney, giving practically complete combustion and a blue flame.

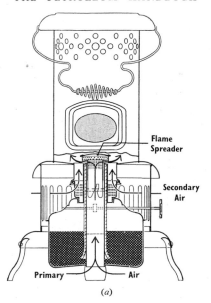

(a)

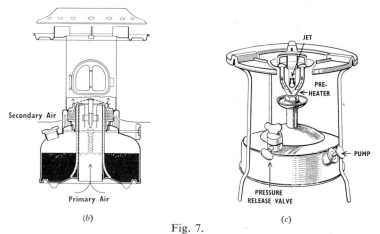

(b)   (c)

Fig. 7.

(a) Yellow Flame Heater.   (b) Blue Flame Heater (Bluet Boiler).
         (c) Pressure Type Heater (Primus Stove).

The main advantage of the blue flame heater is that with the better combustion there is less likelihood of smoke developing if the air is in any way restricted or accidentally reduced. The combustion also takes place with less smell than in yellow flame heaters.

In the Bluet Boiler (fig. 7b), fuel is fed by a multi-feed wick to a trough, where it is vaporized between two perforated metal shells. The equipment operates as a blue flame heater, the fuel, supplied with secondary air, burning between the outer and inner shells as innumerable pin-points of blue flame. The heat of the flame vaporizes more kerosine from the surfaces of the wicks.

Pressure Type Heaters. With pressure type appliances combustion takes place with a blue flame. The best known is the Primus Stove (fig. 7c.), which relies for its operation on the air drawn into the combustion zone by a fast-moving stream of kerosine vapour. The fuel is forced to the combustion zone by air pressure from a small hand-operated air pump fitted to the oil reservoir. Between the reservoir and the combustion zone there is a vaporizing coil, where the kerosine is pre-heated and vaporized. The vaporized liquid is ignited and burns on issuing from a jet, thus heating the fuel line coming from the reservoir. This heating of the fuel line will ensure the regular vaporization of the kerosine so long as the pressure which forces the fuel out of the reservoir is maintained.

All pressure type heaters have to be started, in the same way as pressure lamps, by means of methylated spirit ignited in a small cup under the vaporizing coils. In some types kerosine can be used in place of methylated spirit, and this eliminates the necessity for stocking an additional grade of fuel.

Cooking Appliances. Some of the heating appliances already mentioned, e.g. the Bluet Boiler and the Primus Stove, are used principally for cooking, but with these the contents of only one pot or pan can be cooked at a time. In the larger cooking appliances there are usually three or four separate burners fitted in a range or stove. These burners may be of the yellow or blue flame types already described, or else of the creeping flame type.

The creeping flame type of burner (fig. 8) operates in a similar way to the Bluet Boiler mentioned earlier. The fuel, fed to a trough containing a circular kindler of glass or asbestos, is vapor-

ized and burns between two perforated shells, the heat from the burning fuel serving to vaporize more kerosine.

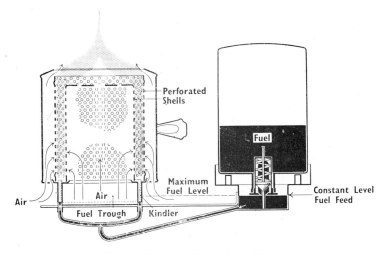

Fig. 8.   Creeping Flame Type Heater.

Maintenance.   The most common complaint with oil-burning equipment is one of smell, nearly always due to careless maintenance.   To ensure trouble-free operation the first essential is cleanliness ; particles of char, fluff, etc., not only obstruct the air flow but absorb the fuel, so that when the burner warms up the kerosine will vaporize and smell.   Overfilling gives a similar result, and incorrectly fitting wicks or the fitting of damp wicks, with the consequent restriction of oil flow, should always be avoided.

In all pressure-fed burners it is necessary to ensure that the fine jet remains clear.   If it is obstructed by foreign matter it can be cleaned when the apparatus is working without any interruption of operation, by using a pricker for the jet.

KEROSINE AS A SOURCE OF POWER

Kerosines are used for power purposes in two main types of

engine, i.e. hot-bulb engines and relatively low-compression spark-ignition engines.

Hot-bulb Engines. The hot-bulb engines, by far the older type, are of comparatively low speed internal combustion design. Ignition is ensured by means of a hot bulb, attached to the cylinder head, into which kerosine is sprayed at the correct period of the engine cycle. The bulb is heated initially with a blow-lamp for starting purposes, and subsequently maintains its temperature by the combustion of the fuel. On the suction stroke of the engine, fuel vaporized at the hot bulb, together with air, is drawn into the cylinder and compressed on the return stroke of the piston. The temperature rise in the air/fuel mixture caused by the compression and the heat derived from the hot bulb are sufficient to cause the mixture to ignite, and to release the energy necessary for the power stroke. It will be appreciated that there are no electrical ignition arrangements in hot-bulb engines.

The fuel used and the design of head must be carefully chosen, so that the head maintains the correct temperature for operation and neither overheats nor cools below the temperature necessary for ignition. A paraffinic type of fuel is normally used, of reasonably good volatility, giving say, 30% minimum distilling to 200° C. Since, in these engines, the kerosine is ignited by the heat of compression and by surface burning on the red-hot bulb approximately at top dead centre* of the engine, the fuel used, in addition to having a good volatility, must have a low self-ignition temperature and no tendency to crack or to form gummy or tarry deposits.

Spark-ignition Engines. The main use of kerosine for power purposes is in low-compression spark-ignition engines such as are used in farm tractors. The principle and operation of a tractor power unit resembles that of the modern car engine with a carburettor and spark ignition from plugs ; most tractor power units operate on a four-stroke cycle. The compression ratio of engines using power kerosine or vaporizing oil is of the order of $4\frac{1}{2}$: 1. For starting purposes, gasoline supplied from a subsidiary tank is used, and the switch over to vaporizing oil is made as soon as the engine has warmed up sufficiently. On account of the lower volatility of the vaporizing oil as compared with that of gasoline, it is

necessary to have some means of vaporizing the heavier fuel. This is done by means of a "vaporizer", a device fitted between the carburettor and the induction manifold.

It is essential to ensure that the change-over from gasoline to vaporizing oil is not made too soon, and before the vaporizer has warmed sufficiently. A temperature of 180° F. for the cooling system is considered the minimum that should be maintained under all working conditions.

Vaporizing oils generally have a much higher aromatic content than burning oils and their lower smoke point makes them unsuitable for use in lamps and heaters. Similarly, the low octane number and low volatility of burning oils makes them unsuitable for spark-ignition engines. Properties such as gum stability and freedom from corrosive properties are as necessary in a vaporizing oil as in a gasoline.

MISCELLANEOUS USES

Vehicle for Insecticide. Most domestic insecticides contain a proportion of a kerosine distillate, the main characteristic of which is freedom from odour. This property is obtained by heavy chemical treatment or solvent extraction to remove the aromatic hydrocarbons. The kerosine should also have a high flashpoint in order to reduce the fire risk, and a relatively low final boiling point in order that it should evaporate readily.

Degreasing Agent. In certain leather processes it is necessary to remove all grease from the leather or skin, and for this purpose kerosine distillates are often used. Vaporizing oil is preferred to burning oil kerosine because the solvent power of vaporizing oil for grease is better.

The degreasing process usually consists of rotating the batch of leather or skins in a tumbler with solvent, at a temperature of 85° F. to 95° F. After the treatment, the solvent is run off into a settling tank, and is usually recovered by steam distillation. For normal sheepskins the recommended quantity of kerosine to be used is 1–1½ gallons for every dozen skins.

The grease in sheepskins may vary between 10% and 50%, calculated on the weight of the air-dried salt-free skin, and unless removed, it is liable to cause greasiness both in chrome-tanned

and vegetable-tanned skins. The greasiness makes itself apparent after the skin has been dyed, when white patches or "spue" appear on the surface.

Bitumen Products for Road Construction. One of the most important applications of kerosine is in the manufacture of cut-back asphaltic bitumens for the treatment of roads. The main requirement of the kerosine in this application is to make the bitumen sufficiently fluid so that it can be spread easily and uniformly on the road surface ; the kerosine must then evaporate, leaving the bitumen surface in a satisfactory condition. It is necessary, therefore, that the kerosine used to make cut-backs shall be as volatile as possible, consistent with any limitations which may be imposed by legislation.

BIBLIOGRAPHY

The Science of Petroleum, Vol. IV, Part III. (Oxford University Press, London.)

The Scientific Principles of Petroleum Technology. Gurwitsch and Moore. (Chapman & Hall, London.)

Proceedings of the 1st World Petroleum Congress, London, 1933, Vol. II (pp. 693–749). (Institution of Petroleum Technologists, London.)

XXVII

DIESEL FUELS

GENERAL PRINCIPLE OF THE DIESEL ENGINE

IN mechanical principle diesel engines are, in many respects, similar to gasoline engines, but there are fundamental differences in the methods of mixing the fuel with air for combustion in each type. This, together with the method of ignition used, calls for a less volatile fuel for the diesel engine.

As is well known, the gasoline engine piston draws into the cylinder a mixture of air and gasoline vapour prepared outside the cylinder by the carburettor. After compression, the mixture is ignited by a timed electric spark. The resultant burning and pressure rise on the piston provide the power stroke. The compression ratio of modern non-supercharged automotive gasoline engines is in the region of 6 : 1 to 7 : 1, whereas diesel engines employ compression ratios of 13 : 1 to 17 : 1.

The diesel engine draws in air only direct from the atmosphere (possibly through an air filter) and compresses it to a much higher degree than in the gasoline engine, consequently producing a higher temperature and pressure. Just before the piston has completed this compression stroke, a spray of fuel is admitted through the injector (otherwise called sprayer, atomizer or nozzle) into the highly compressed air, which is sufficiently hot to initiate combustion without the aid of an electric spark. The resultant burning and further pressure rise on the piston provide the power stroke. It will be appreciated that a diesel engine has no carburettor or electric ignition system, but instead has an injector and a fuel injection pump driven by the engine as an auxiliary.

Fig. 1 shows indicator diagrams of a gasoline engine and a diesel engine from which it will be clear that for the same power output the diesel compression and combustion pressures are much higher. For the same power output, therefore, the diesel unit must be more robustly constructed, and in consequence is somewhat heavier than a gasoline engine designed for a similar duty.

In the same way that there are both four- and two-stroke cycle gasoline engines there are also four- and two-stroke diesel engines. There are, however, further varieties of compression ignition engines known as double-acting and opposed-piston types. The former have been made in two- and four-stroke versions, whilst the latter is confined to the two-stroke system.

It may be convenient here to clear up the respective meanings of the terms "diesel engine" and "compression ignition engine".

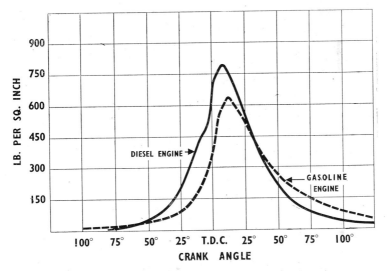

Fig. 1.   Indicator Diagram of Gasoline and Diesel Engines.

The "diesel" is a particular type of compression ignition engine, but, as Dr. Rudolph Diesel was among the first successful experimenters, his name now tends to be applied to all types of compression ignition engine. The engine developed by Dr. Diesel, and widely used in the larger-sized stationary installations, was also called the "blast injection" engine, as the fuel was injected together with a small amount of high-pressure air to assist atomization and ready admixture with the compressed air in the cylinder. This system has now fallen into disuse, although existing engines of this type are still met. The type of engine in which the fuel is injected without air blast is referred to as the "solid injection" engine. Obviously, as the term "blast injection" is rarely used, its complement, "solid injection", is redundant, although practically all modern diesel or compression ignition engines are, in fact, solid injection units.

It is of purely historical interest to note that Dr. Diesel's early endeavours were to make his engine function on pulverized coal and that he turned to liquid fuel only as an afterthought.

THE COMBUSTION PROCESS

The combustion process may be conveniently considered as taking place in three definite phases :—

(1) The initial period, during which fuel is admitted but no burning occurs.

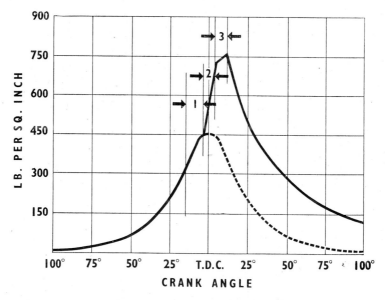

Fig. 2. Indicator Diagram Showing Three Phases of Fuel Injection.

(2) A period of rapid combustion due to flame spread, which results in rapid pressure rise.

(3) Burning of the remaining portion of charge *as it enters* the combustion chamber, which maintains or increases the pressure.

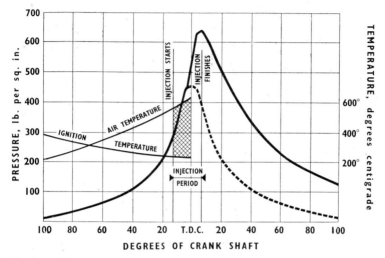

Fig. 3.   Diagram Showing Pressures and Temperatures Likely to Obtain in Four-stroke Engine.

Fig. 2 is an indicator diagram illustrating these three phases, and fig. 3 shows the pressures and temperatures likely to obtain in a conventional four-stroke engine.

The first stage of the combustion process is of particular importance, as its duration is related to the engine design and operating conditions, and also to the properties of the fuel as mentioned under the section "Ignition Quality". It should be appreciated that the shorter the "delay period", or "ignition lag", the smaller will be the accumulation of fuel at the commencement of combustion and, therefore, the smoother will be the pressure rise.   Conversely, if the delay period is long, a large proportion of the charge will be waiting to burn and, further, the time available for burning, i.e. stages (2) and (3), will be shortened ; therefore, the rate of pressure rise must be increased.   The rapid pressure rise associated with long delay period manifests itself in the well-known "diesel knock".

TYPES OF DIESEL ENGINES

Diesel engines are made in a wide variety of speeds and power outputs, and the following arbitrary classification has some relation to the type of fuel employed :—

(1) High-speed engines running above about 800 revolutions per minute. This includes automotive types and many rail traction and industrial engines, the maximum speeds of some of which may be as high as 3,000 r.p.m.

(2) Medium-speed engines of between 300 and 800 r.p.m., in which group are included most of the larger stationary and auxiliary marine engines.

(3) Slow-speed engines of below 300 r.p.m. This includes marine main propulsion engines and many of the largest stationary installations.

Broadly speaking, the high-speed class requires gas oil as fuel although certain mixtures containing a proportion of residual fuel may be satisfactory. Fuels for the medium and slow-speed engines may be gas oils, mixtures of gas oil and residual, or

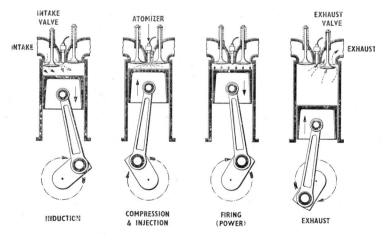

Fig. 4.   Four-stroke Cycle of Operations.

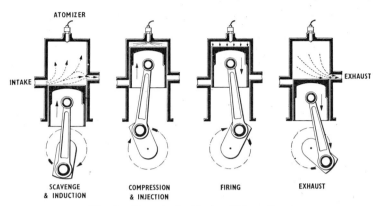

ATOMIZER

INTAKE

EXHAUST

SCAVENGE
& INDUCTION

COMPRESSION
& INJECTION

FIRING

EXHAUST

Fig. 5.   Two-stroke Cycle of Operations.

residual oils alone.   Slow-speed engines frequently employ residual fuels of high viscosity, but, for purely mechanical reasons of pumpability and filtration, arrangements are necessary to preheat the fuel to lower its viscosity before it reaches the injector pump.   For this reason the viscosity of industrial diesel fuels does not usually exceed 100 seconds Redwood 1 at 100° F. (*vide infra*). More detailed information in this connection will be found in the section on Properties and Testing.

Four-stroke Engines.   In each complete cycle of operations in the four-stroke engine the crankshaft turns through two revolutions and the piston completes four strokes, two upward, two downward, as illustrated in fig. 4.   During the one power stroke some of the energy is stored in the flywheel, which energy is returned to the crankshaft and piston to provide momentum to maintain the cycle during the three idle strokes.

The valves illustrated in fig. 4 are of the conventional poppet type and are mechanically operated by a timed mechanism driven from the engine crankshaft.   Other types of valve, including sleeve and rotary forms, have been employed, but the principles outlined remain the same.

Two-stroke Engines.   In engines employing the two-stroke cycle, which is illustrated in fig. 5, the process involved in the

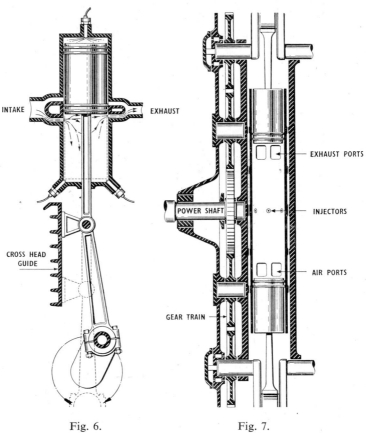

INTAKE

EXHAUST

CROSS HEAD
GUIDE

EXHAUST PORTS

POWER SHAFT

INJECTORS

AIR PORTS

GEAR TRAIN

Fig. 6.
Two-stroke Cycle
Double-acting Engine.

Fig. 7.
Two-stroke Cycle
Opposed Piston Engine.

four-stroke cycle is compressed into two strokes, which occur
during one revolution of the crankshaft, thus giving one power
stroke for each revolution of the engine and only one idle stroke.
This contributes to the smoothness of the engine and enables
more power to be developed than is the case with a four-stroke
engine of the same size and weight.

Two-stroke engines have been used almost as long as the four-stroke type, but their development has been hampered by major difficulties arising from the shorter time available to exhaust or scavenge the burnt gases from the cylinder.

Double-acting Engines. Such engines are designed to obtain increased power outputs without corresponding increase in size. Combustion takes place not only above the piston but also below, which means that the bottom of the cylinder must also be closed to provide a second combustion chamber. As will be seen from fig. 6, this necessitates incorporating a rigid piston rod provided with a packing gland to prevent gas leak, the piston rod being pin-jointed to a connecting rod guided by a cross-head.

Nearly all double-acting engines are of the two-stroke type and find their principal application as ships' main propulsion engines or as stationary electricity generator units.

Opposed-piston Engines. This two-stroke type, illustrated in fig. 7, presents a further method of obtaining increased power output without increase in size or number of cylinders. Each cylinder has two pistons which move inward on the compression stroke ultimately forming a combustion space between their crowns. After injection of the fuel the two pistons move outward, and by means of rods or gears their power is transmitted to a common output shaft.

FUEL INJECTION

The difference in magnitude of the spray issuing from an injector nozzle in air at atmospheric pressure compared with the same injector functioning in highly compressed air is not always appreciated. The spray in atmospheric air is projected as much as a few feet from the injector nozzle, whereas in air at 500 lb. per square inch the distance will be reduced to a few inches or less. The ultimate aim is to burn the atomized fuel in ''mid air'' and not to allow any part of the fuel charge to impinge on the combustion chamber walls or piston crown. On the other hand, it is essential to distribute the fuel charge more or less evenly throughout the combustion air to ensure that each fuel droplet comes into intimate contact with the required amount of air to obtain complete combustion. In view of the short time available for

EE

injection and the many conditions to be satisfied, it will be appreciated that the design of fuel injection equipment is a complex matter which has resulted in many different approaches to the ideal.

Solid Injection. There are a great many different systems of solid injection, but they all tend to fall into one of two main divisions commonly referred to as the ''common rail'' and ''jerk injection'' systems.

In the first method, all the injectors are connected to a common pipe in which fuel is constantly maintained at high pressure by suitable pumps. The injector release valves are mechanically or electro-magnetically opened to admit fuel to the various cylinders as required by the engine cycle. This system is fairly widely used on the medium and large-sized stationary and marine engines.

The second system is the commonest and consists of a separate plunger pump connected by a fuel pipe to each injector. The time of injection is not mechanically controlled, but relies on the pre-set spring-loaded injector needle valve being lifted from its seat when the pressure in the fuel line rises above the opening pressure. For convenience of construction, the separate plunger pumps may be incorporated in a common body unit and actuated by a common camshaft, or they may be located individually and operated by special cams on the engine camshaft.

Atomizers. The solid injection type of atomizer, illustrated in fig. 8, may employ one or a variety of holes through which the fuel finally passes to the combustion chamber. The type of nozzle employed is largely dictated by the combustion chamber form. Air swirl chamber engines (*vide infra*) can successfully employ the pintle type nozzle (fig. 9a), which gives a coarse compact spray, even distribution of which is assisted by the high rate of air turbulence* inherent with this type of engine. The advantages of this system include comparatively low injection pressures of about 1,500 lb. per square inch and the self-cleaning tendency of the nozzle due to the pintle or projecting portion of the needle valve.

Direct injection engines normally require a multi-hole type of nozzle, of which one of the numerous forms is shown in fig. 9b. Due to the relatively low air turbulence usually associated with this type of engine, fuel distribution is achieved by higher injection

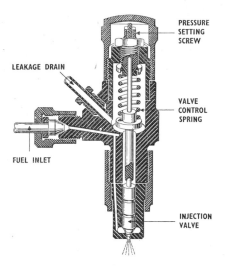

Fig. 8.   C.A.V. Jerk Type Atomizer.

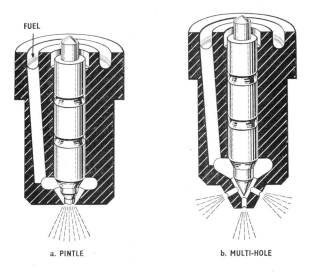

a. PINTLE

b. MULTI-HOLE

Fig. 9.   Types of Solid Injection Nozzles.

pressures, frequently of the order of 3,000 lb. per square inch, and by the highly penetrative effect of the hole-type sprays. The higher injection pressures tend to throw greater loads on the whole injection equipment, and the multi-hole nozzles require more frequent maintenance than the pintle type.

COMBUSTION CHAMBERS

One of the most important single factors governing engine performance is the shape of the combustion chamber so that it is not surprising to find a great variety of these in existence. One of the fundamental aims of diesel engine design is to attain satisfactory mixing of air and fuel in the combustion chamber. This mixing is achieved in part by the fuel injection arrangements, but the combustion chamber design, including valve arrangement, is of outstanding importance. Both the injection system and combustion chamber arrangement have a marked influence on the fuel quality requirements of engines.

Other factors governed by combustion chamber design include economy, flexibility, smoothness and colour of the exhaust. The first of these is of great importance in nearly all applications, whereas the second, third and fourth apply in certain applications only, and the order of their importance varies. For instance, a high standard of all four factors is essential for automotive applications, whereas in the case of electricity generation at more or less constant speed and load, flexibility is of minor importance. Unfortunately, the conditions necessary to obtain one or two of these criteria may be directly opposed to those likely to achieve the remainder. This accounts for the numerous types of combustion chamber and the considerable overlapping of particular claims of one against another.

A common broad classification is "open chamber" and "separate chamber" types. As will be seen, however, there are several sub-divisions to be considered, particularly in the case of the "separate chamber" forms.

It has already been stated that combustion chamber design contributes greatly to intimate fuel-air mixing, and this is achieved by providing means to impart vigorous movement to the air charge. This movement may be described as "swirl" or

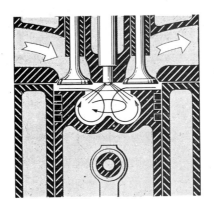

ATOMIZER

EXHAUST
POPPET VALVE

MASKED
INTAKE VALVE

(a) Gardner

(b) A.E.C. (Toroidal)

Fig. 10.   Types of Direct Injection Combustion.

"squish" ; the first involves a rotary air movement in the combustion chamber, and the second a lateral movement resulting from the air being squeezed between the piston top and cylinder head surfaces. A further, less ordered, air movement is frequently termed "indiscriminate turbulence".

Some of the more typical combustion head designs are briefly described in the following pages, but it should be realized that only a representative selection of the many types has been made.

Direct Injection or Open Chamber. In open chamber engines it is usual to achieve the desired air movement during the induction stroke. This movement, known as induced swirl, persists during the compression stroke and may be supplemented by "squish". The rotational movement is obtained by suitably disposed air ports or by means of such devices as masked inlet valves (*vide* figs. 10a, 10b).

The unavoidable disadvantage of air swirl is that, due to intimate contact with the relatively cool metal surfaces, heat is more rapidly dissipated. As, in this type, swirl is induced during the induction stroke when temperatures are low, heat losses are proportionately less. This contributes to the low fuel consumption and good cold starting qualities usually associated with open-chamber engines. On the other hand, the compact form of the open combustion chamber presents a relatively small hot surface to assist in raising the compression temperature. This tends to result in rough running and fuel sensitivity. In view of the comparatively low turbulence of these engines, it should be remembered that it is usual to employ hole-type atomizers and high injection pressures.

Separate Chamber Types. It is convenient to divide these into three sub-types :—

(1) *Pre-Combustion Chamber.* This system (fig. 11) was among those early developed and was widely used on the continent of Europe. It tended to include some of the advantages of the air or blast injection engines without their attendant weaknesses. It will be seen that fuel is injected into a small chamber which contains insufficient air for complete combustion. Commencement of burning causes a rich air/fuel mixture to be forced rapidly through small holes into the main combustion chamber. These

holes, or in some types a single passage, are designed to ensure the best possible mixing of the fuel and air throughout the main combustion chamber. Such engines usually employ pintle nozzles and are comparatively non-selective in their fuel requirements. On the other hand, due to high heat losses they tend toward poor fuel economy.

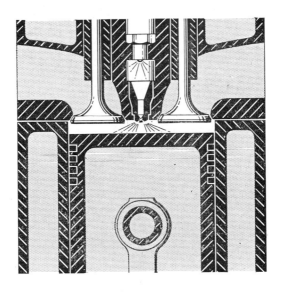

Benz

Fig. 11. Pre-combustion Chamber.

(2) *Air Swirl Chamber.* At first sight fig. 12a may not indicate any clear line of demarcation between this and the pre-combustion types ; there are, however, two essential differences. Firstly, the air swirl chamber is larger relative to the main combustion space above the piston crown and may represent as much as 50% of the total clearance volume. Secondly, the connecting passage between the two chambers is arranged so that the air is given a

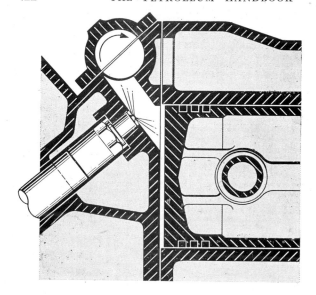

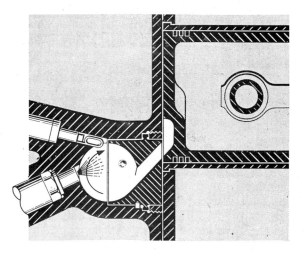

(a) **Ricardo
Mark III**

(b) **Perkins**

Fig. 12.   Air Swirl Chamber Types.

high degree of swirl during the compression stroke. The fuel is injected across and down the air stream and, instead of the "fuel finding the air" as in the direct-injection engine, "the air finds the fuel". This allows of the employment of pintle nozzles and lower injection pressures, with their attendant advantages of relatively infrequent injector and fuel pump maintenance. In addition, they are less susceptible to nozzle deterioration.

Some engines of this type employ a heat-insulated member as part of the swirl chamber. This is clearly visible in fig. 12b and is incorporated to conserve heat from one cycle to raise the air temperature of the next charge to a higher degree than would be achieved by heat of compression alone.

Although fuel consumption may be slightly higher than in direct-injection engines, air swirl types are capable of digesting a wider range of fuels of lower ignition quality (*vide infra*) and are less prone to diesel knock. Further, owing to the excellent fuel/ air mixing capabilities and the adequate space available for inclusion of large diameter valves, relatively higher "smoke free" power outputs are obtained than with comparable engines employing other combustion chamber arrangements.

(3) *Air Cell Chamber*. To some degree this system may be viewed as a reversal of the pre-combustion chamber type. Two chambers are employed, but the fuel is injected, not directly into the one remote from the main combustion chamber, but across and through the main chamber towards the restricted throat communicating with the air cell. The combustion initiated in the air cell forces air and some fuel back into the main chamber, where it meets the remainder of the fuel charge still issuing from the injector nozzle. This combustion swirl achieves good mixing, wherein some fuel finds the air and some air the fuel.

The most widely met modern application of this class is the Lanova system (fig. 13), produced in the United States and on the European continent. The main combustion chamber is so shaped that the swirl takes the form of two circular air movements in opposite directions. This tends towards a more controlled and orderly movement than with the earlier pre-combustion chamber system shown in fig. 11. Comparatively low compression ratios can be employed with consequently low maximum pressures, but fuel consumption is fairly high and the engines are very sensitive to fuel quality.

SEMI-DIESEL AND SPARK-IGNITED OIL ENGINES

Semi-diesel or hot-bulb engines are now obsolescent, although many old examples will still be found working small machinery plants, fishing boats and barges. The fuel employed is either

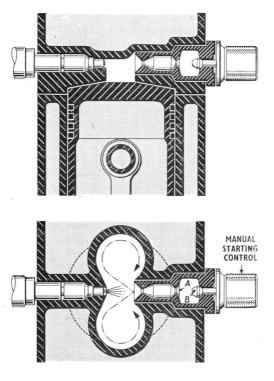

MANUAL
STARTING
CONTROL

*NOTE Throat (A) is closed manually by valve (B)
to give higher compression for starting.*

Fig. 13.   Lanova Air Cell Chambers.

kerosine (*vide* chapter XXVI) or gas oil of high volatility and high cetane number (*vide infra*).

Compression pressures are much lower than in C.I. engines, and ignition is accomplished by an uncooled heat-retaining member in the combustion space. Variations of speed and load tend to alter the temperature of the hot bulb, causing incomplete combustion or overheating. Starting is normally accomplished by heating the exterior surface of the hot bulb with a blow-lamp or similar device. Due to the low compression pressures, thermal efficiency is low and fuel consumption high compared with C.I. engines.

The Hesselman engine was developed as an attempt to combine the desirable characteristics of both diesel and gasoline engines. Compression pressures are low, giving smoothness, and an electric spark provides ignition. Fuel is injected as in a C.I. engine and the combustion chamber is a direct injection induced-swirl arrangement. In Hesselman engines, gasoline can be employed or gas oil of high volatility and high cetane number.

PROPERTIES AND METHODS OF TESTING

Diesel fuel, often but less correctly termed diesel oil, is in its most literal sense any suitable grade of fuel which can be burned in compression-ignition engines, and since the latter vary considerably in size and speed, it is not surprising that the fuels which can be successfully utilized cover a wide range of properties.

Specific Gravity. In itself the specific gravity (*vide* chapter XXIII) has no technical significance, and the employment of this property to deduce other properties may be very misleading. It is true that fuels derived from the same source may exhibit an increase in viscosity with increase in specific gravity, but it would be quite wrong to assume that fuels of similar viscosity have identical specific gravities. The specific gravity is, however, used for converting volume to weight (and *vice versa*), such as in calculating the fuel consumption of an engine in terms of weight from the actual volumetric measurement of the fuel used.

Flashpoint. As an indication of fuel performance the flashpoint (*vide* chapter XXVIII) has no significance, since there is no direct relationship between this property and other characteristics, such as viscosity and ignition quality (the term used to indicate the readiness with which a fuel will ignite in a compression ignition engine).

In most countries there is a legal requirement that the flashpoint of oil fuels shall be not less than 150° F. (140° F. and even 130° F. in some places in the U.S.A.) as a precautionary measure against fire risks. This requirement is virtually the only reason why the flashpoint test is carried out.

Viscosity.   The viscosity (*vide* chapter XXIX) of a diesel fuel is of considerable importance, particularly when the requirements of the high-speed engines are considered. Although pumps and injectors of good design are capable of handling fuels having a wide range of viscosity and, in general, limits are not specified for minimum viscosities, consideration has to be given to this point. Too low a viscosity may cause fuel leakage from high-pressure pumps and injector needle valves and poor penetration of the fuel into the combustion chamber as a result of too high a degree of atomization. A very low viscosity may also mean that the fuel lacks sufficient lubricating properties which it should possess to deal with the fuel pump plungers, and these parts may suffer from a high rate of wear. This cannot be generally applied, however, since kerosine and gasoline, both having viscosities lower than most normal diesel fuels, are handled by some engine fuel pumps without undue trouble occurring.

In the high-speed diesel engine the pumps and injectors operate rapidly and could not handle, in the short periods available, a fuel of high viscosity. This operating condition in the high-speed engine therefore imposes an upper viscosity limit which is usually set at about 100 seconds Redwood 1 at 100° F. For other than high-speed engines an upper viscosity limit is imposed by considerations of handling the fuel without pre-heating. Clearly the viscosity must be sufficiently low at the working temperature to allow flow of fuel to the pump, good atomization and correct penetration in solid injection engines. Even with air injection engines poor delivery may result from too high a viscosity. If the diesel fuel can be pre-heated and the engine is designed to consume high-viscosity oils, then theoretically there is no upper limit to the fuel viscosity. Without pre-heating, the fuel viscosity can be as high as 100 seconds Redwood 1 at 100° F., assuming that such fuels are satisfactory in other respects. However, most diesel fuel specifications stipulate lower viscosity limits than this to allow a safety margin and because high viscosity is wrongly assumed to infer combustion difficulties.

Distillation Range. The test procedure for determining this property of diesel fuels is similar to that applied to gasolines (*vide* chapter XXV). Apart from a few light diesel fuels it is not possible to determine the full distillation range of most fuels with this test, since at about 350° C. cracking of the fuel commences. It is usual to record the percentage of distillate at particular temperatures (e.g. 300° C., 325° C. or 350° C.) or the temperature at which a definite percentage distils over ; the information is of some value in assessing fuel performance. Since diminishing volatility is in general an indication of increasing viscosity, the latter test together with the carbon residue value (described later) is a better criterion of the suitability of a fuel for an engine of established requirements.

Sulphur. Traces of sulphur are sometimes present in diesel fuel, and when the fuel burns, any sulphur present is converted into gaseous oxides of sulphur. These, as such, are not harmful, but in the presence of water they form acids which may cause corrosion of metal parts under certain conditions, such as very cold jacket temperatures. Corrosion of the exhaust system may therefore be an indirect result of a high sulphur content, but wear of cylinder liners and exhaust valves may be due to other causes, since many engines operate satisfactorily with a fuel having a sulphur content of approximately 2% by weight. Most diesel fuel specifications include a limit for total sulphur. These limits are frequently lower than is necessary, and although, broadly speaking, sulphur may be an undesirable constituent of diesel fuels, conflicting data exist and it is not possible to be dogmatic on the subject. Fuels of the gas oil type, such as are employed in the small high-speed automotive diesel, are usually specified to have not more than 1·5% by weight of sulphur (1·0% in the U.S.A.).

The "corrosion" so far described has been considered as an effect of sulphur oxides which will be derived from the "total" sulphur present in the oil, irrespective of the form, free or combined, in which the sulphur exists. There are also sulphur compounds which are harmful as such in that they do not require to be burnt to oxides and form acids in order to attack metal. Such compounds (e.g. free sulphur and mercaptans) may be detected by a copper strip corrosion test similar to that applied to gasolines (*vide* chapter XXV under the heading Corrosion), and their presence is indicated by severe discoloration or pitting of the copper strip. Normally, finished diesel fuel gives a negative copper strip test, showing that harmful sulphur compounds have been removed.

Conradson Carbon. The Conradson Carbon test is an empirical method of assessing the coke-forming tendency of a fuel. In this test the fuel is distilled and burned off under controlled conditions of air supply and temperature, and the residual carbon or coke is weighed. The carbon so determined should not be confused with the total carbon content of the fuel (which is approximately 86% for practically all fuels—*vide infra*, Elementary Analysis), whereas the Conradson Carbon of the heaviest grade of diesel fuel rarely exceeds 2·5%. The Conradson test gives a reasonable indication of the tendency of a fuel to form carbonaceous deposits on the atomizer nozzle, but it is to be noted that such deposits may well be due to insufficient cooling of the nozzle. Gas oils usually have a Conradson value of 0·05% or less, and, for high-speed diesel engines, distillate fuels having a Conradson value of this order are usually desirable. Slower speed units can, however, accommodate fuels of higher coking values which are associated with fuels containing proportions of residual fuel. A Conradson value of 2% is about the limiting value for a satisfactory diesel fuel. (Recently some fuels with a value in excess of 10% have been used in slow-speed units with reasonable success.)

Asphaltenes. The "asphaltene" material in a fuel is precipitated when a non-aromatic solvent such as petroleum ether is added to the fuel, and the amount present is determined by carrying out this procedure under carefully controlled conditions. Generally speaking, the asphaltene value and carbon residue of a series of fuels move in parallel, but the relationship of these values will vary considerably according to the source and nature of the fuels. Further, the asphaltenes can be removed from a heavy fuel by a suitable process without much reduction in the Conradson value. The asphaltene figure is, therefore, less informative than the Conradson value and cannot be said to correlate closely with coking tendencies in practice.

Ash Content. The ash content of a fuel is the residue remaining after all combustible matter has been completely burnt away and denotes the quantity of mineral matter, such as rust or sand, present. An ash content of approximately 0·01 % is the usual figure for distillate fuels and diesel fuels generally, particularly those consumed by high-speed engines, but heavy residual fuels may have an ash content of 0·1 % or more. It is important to realize that the actual ash content value may not always indicate the true abrasive potentialities of the fuel since a small amount of ''hard'' sand may cause more wear of engine parts than a larger amount of ''soft'' contaminant such as alumina. Mineral contamination is, in the main, removable by mechanical means, such as filtration and centrifuging or merely by settling.

Pour and Cloud Points. The pour point of a fuel is determined in the laboratory by slowly cooling a small volume of the sample under carefully specified conditions until it only just flows under its own weight. The temperature at this stage is the pour point (*vide* chapter XXIX). Owing to the vast differences which exist between the test conditions and practical storage, pour point temperatures may be of little value. For example, the test does not reproduce those practical conditions in which the fuel is under a considerable head, and it will certainly flow or be capable of being pumped at a lower temperature than the pour point suggests. Also, whereas bulk setting of the small quantity of fuel involved in the test can readily be realized at a specific temperature, only the outer skin of the contents of a large storage tank may set at the same temperature.

The cloud point is the temperature at which, under test conditions similar to those of the pour point determination, the sample first exhibits a haziness or cloud due to the separation of minute wax crystals. This temperature will be higher than that of the pour point since the fuel does not fail to pour until some of the wax crystals have coalesced. There are some indications that filter troubles due to blockage may occur at temperatures approximating to the cloud point, but no clear-cut relationship is yet available.

Calorific Value. The meaning and determination of calorific value have already been described in chapter XXV under the heading "Fuel Consumption", and apply equally to diesel fuels. It is of interest to note that the calorific values of various petroleum fuels show little variation by comparison with solid fuels. Coals, for example, may vary in calorific value from about 10,000 to 15,000 B.Th.U. per lb., whilst few petroleum fuel oils are outside the range 18,000 to 19,500 B.Th.U. per lb.

Sediment and Water. Both sediment and water are undesirable contaminants of oil fuels. Sediment is classified as all material not soluble in the fuel (excluding water) which can be removed by filtration. In the laboratory, the material removed by the filter is freed from fuel by washing it with a special solvent and is then dried and weighed.

After contact with water the normal diesel fuel retains only a relatively small amount in suspension and in solution and is generally specified by a maximum of 0·25 or 0·5%. In general, the heavier grades of fuel are capable of holding more water in suspension than the lighter grades. To determine the water content of a fuel the latter is mixed with a petroleum solvent having an initial boiling point slightly lower than the boiling point of water. When this mixture is boiled the solvent and water distil over together and, since these are not miscible, the volume of water can be directly determined.

Colour. In general, colour will become darker with increase in the amount of residual fuel present. Distillate oils such as gas oils are frequently pale straw in colour, whereas most residual fuels are black. Colour has little significance although preference is usually, often without justification, given to the pale product. As a means of indicating contamination, other methods, such as the distillation or Conradson carbon tests, are more reliable.

Stability. Occasionally fuels are required for special purposes which require that the fuel shall not form deposits under specific heat treatment. For such purposes, various tests have been devised for assessing the stability of fuels under special conditions.

Elementary Analysis. For certain combustion problems it is necessary to know the composition of a fuel in terms of its constituent elements, which are essentially carbon and hydrogen, together with traces of sulphur, oxygen, etc. Diesel fuels vary little in their carbon and hydrogen contents. The hydrogen figure is normally within the range of 11% to 13·5% by weight, whilst the percentage of carbon varies from 85·5% to 87·0%.

TESTS FOR IGNITION QUALITY

Efforts to evolve a simple laboratory test method, as opposed to an actual engine test, for determining the ease of combustion of fuel in a diesel engine have met with limited success. Flashpoint and distillation range are without significance for this purpose. Whilst an engine test, therefore, remains as the only reliable method, its application is not always possible or convenient and the aniline point, or diesel index, is resorted to for an approximate indication of ignition quality.

(1) **Aniline Point.** Below a certain temperature equal volumes of aniline and diesel fuel will not mix. Above this temperature the two components become miscible and form a clear homogeneous solution. The temperature at which this transition occurs is the "aniline point" and varies according to the hydrocarbon composition of the fuel. Aromatic hydrocarbons are miscible with aniline at low temperatures, whereas paraffin hydrocarbons require much higher temperatures. Since the paraffin hydrocarbons have higher ignition qualities in a diesel engine, a high aniline point indicates a better fuel from this viewpoint. A normal aniline point for high-speed diesel fuels is approximately 70° C. Whilst useful, this test sometimes gives anomalous results and is not applicable to doped fuels, shale oils or fuels not of mineral origin.

(2) **Diesel Index.** The diesel index (D.I.) of a fuel is calculated from the following formula :—

$$\text{D.I.} = \frac{\text{Aniline point in } °\text{F.} \times \text{A.P.I. gravity}}{100}$$

The diesel index is a better guide to fuel ignition quality than

FF

the straight aniline point, but even so it does not always correlate accurately with the ignition quality determined by engine test and, being derived from the aniline point, is subject to the same limitations such as doped fuels, etc. A minimum diesel index of 45 is usually required for a suitable high-speed diesel fuel.

(3) **Cetane Number.** It is convenient to emphasize at this stage that ignition quality is only one property of the fuel and does not express "fuel quality". In order to have a good over-all quality the fuel must satisfy other requirements apart from ignition quality, however important this may be for certain high-speed engines.

The ignition quality of a fuel as determined in an engine is expressed in terms of the cetane number. Cetane is a straight-chain paraffin hydrocarbon ($C_{16}H_{34}$) of high ignition quality and is assessed on an arbitrary scale as having a cetane number of 100. At the other end of the scale, an aromatic type hydrocarbon known as alpha-methyl-naphthalene ($C_{11}H_{10}$), having an ignition quality lower than that of any known petroleum fuel, is used as the zero cetane number reference fuel. The cetane number of a fuel is, numerically, the percentage by volume of cetane in a mixture with alpha-methyl-naphthalene, which is equivalent in ignition quality to that of the fuel undergoing test.

The object of a cetane number test is to determine the ignition delay. As already explained, between the start of the injection of the fuel into the combustion chamber and the moment when it begins to burn there is an interval known as the delay period, which for a given engine and injection timing is approximately constant for a given fuel when measured in degrees of crank angle. Ignition delay is influenced by the hydrocarbon composition of the fuel and by engine design. The more paraffin hydrocarbons present the shorter the ignition delay, whilst aromatic type hydrocarbons increase the delay.

For the determination of cetane number the following procedures are used :—

(a) *Measurement of Delay Angle.* This method, employed in the C.F.R. Diesel Engine Test, measures the delay period in crankshaft degrees. To do this it is necessary to have an instrument which will instantaneously record both the pressure variations in the cylinder and the exact point at which fuel injection begins. The cathode ray indicator is frequently employed for this function, and by a thermionic valve device, which integrates the pressure and rotation (time) functions, the combustion process can be seen in the form of a graph upon a fluorescent screen. The delay angle can thus be measured, and by repeating the test with reference fuels and plotting the relationship (*vide* Throttling Method) the equivalent cetane number can be deduced.

(b) *Throttling Method.* This is a simpler method which may be carried out on any four-stroke C.I. engine. With the engine running at normal speed and light load, the air supply to the engine is reduced, by means of a throttle valve, until misfiring occurs, as indicated by a puff of white smoke in the exhaust outlet. The air pressure in the throttling valve chamber at the point of misfire is then noted. The test is then repeated for reference blends of higher and lower cetane number than the sample under test. By plotting the throttle valve air pressure at misfire for the reference fuels of known cetane number it is then possible to read off the cetane number of the test sample.

Significance of Ignition Quality. Whilst the cetane number of diesel fuels and the octane number of gasolines may appear on first sight to be analogous, the readings on the two scales are not comparable and the limitations imposed by fuel quality are quite different in the compression ignition and spark ignition engines. The maximum power output of the spark ignition engine is limited by the knock rating of the gasoline in use and cannot be raised by increasing compression ratio or degree of supercharge, either of which would increase engine knock. On the other hand, in the C.I. engine, ignition delay is most pronounced at low loads, whilst an increase in compression ratio or intake air pressure reduces the knock. Similarly, an increase of engine output and temperature decreases roughness due to the shorter delay period. Since a reduction in intake air pressure increases "diesel knock" it follows that, other things being equal, a diesel engine requires a fuel of higher ignition quality at high altitudes than at sea level.

It is worthy of note that the requisite power output of a high-speed diesel engine is not necessarily a function of the ignition quality of the fuel, since with too high a cetane number ignition may take place too rapidly. Thus it is quite unnecessary to "dope" a fuel which already satisfies the cetane number requirement of the engine, since any increase could lead to increased fuel consumption.

THE INTERNAL COMBUSTION TURBINE

The internal combustion turbine has been the dream of many an engineer on account of its potentially simple means of translating

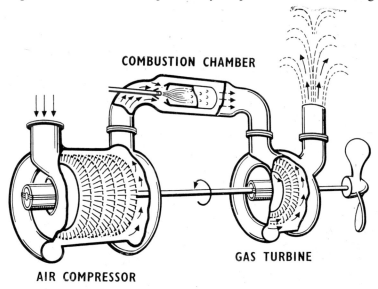

COMBUSTION CHAMBER

GAS TURBINE

AIR COMPRESSOR

Fig. 14.   Simple Gas Turbine Cycle.

the energy of fuel into rotary power without cumbersome intermediate equipment such as boilers, cranks and reciprocating machinery. The simple conception of the unit (*vide* fig. 14) comprises an air compressor, a combustion chamber in which the energy of fuel is liberated in the form of hot gases at pressure which may be passed through the blades or vanes of the turbine, causing it to rotate and thus provide available rotary power, some of this power, however, being employed to drive the air compressor.

This is no new idea, as it was employed in primitive form many centuries ago, but without the success enjoyed by its related power producers, the water wheel and the windmill. Within the last century many attempts have been made and patents filed, but, until recently, no successful commercial machine has been made which would develop net power, let alone compete with the piston engine, whether steam or the internal combustion type.

The reasons for early failure to produce a useful plant were mainly inability of turbine blade materials to withstand high gas temperatures and the lack of a suitably efficient air compressor that would provide the air for combustion without absorbing all the power generated by the turbine. Recently, however, metal alloys have been produced which will withstand high temperatures, and air compressors have been designed which will enable a unit to be operated with positive net power.

The Simple Internal Combustion Turbine. Fig. 15 illustrates, diagrammatically, the main components of a simple internal combustion turbine for developing 1,000 net h.p. It will be noted that in order to provide this power the turbine has also to drive an air compressor which absorbs an additional 2,060 h.p. The temperature and pressure of the air or gas at various locations of the plant are also indicated.

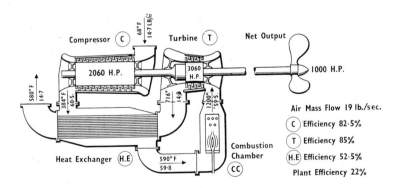

Fig. 15. 1,000 h.p. Single Shaft I.C.T. with Heat Exchanger.

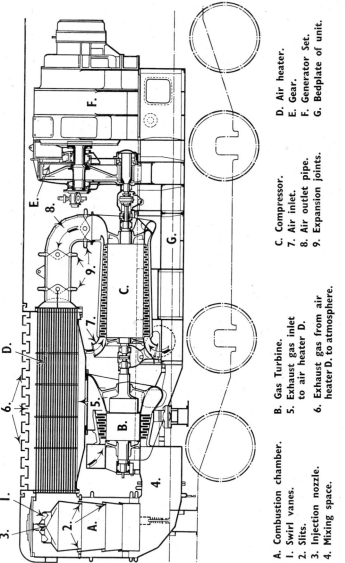

Fig. 16. 2,200 h.p. Gas Turbine for Locomotive.

A. Combustion chamber.
1. Swirl vanes.
2. Slits.
3. Injection nozzle.
4. Mixing space.

B. Gas Turbine.
5. Exhaust gas inlet to air heater D.
6. Exhaust gas from air heater D. to atmosphere.

C. Compressor.
7. Air inlet.
8. Air outlet pipe.
9. Expansion joints.

D. Air heater.
E. Gear.
F. Generator Set.
G. Bedplate of unit.

The cycle of operations of this unit is that air is drawn into the compressor, which forces it through a heat exchanger in which it takes up heat from exhaust gases, then through a combustion chamber in which it is heated by burning oil ; the hot gases (air and products of combustion) are expanded through a turbine, causing it to develop the total power of 3,060 h.p. The gases are then not much above atmospheric pressure, but are still hot and are passed through the air heater, referred to previously, to atmosphere. The unit has to be started by external means, usually by electric motor.

A unit of this type, but delivering 2,200 h.p., has been built into a locomotive by the Brown Boveri Company of Switzerland, the external view and diagram of the unit (without heat lagging) being shown in figs. 16 and 17.

Efficiency of the Internal Combustion Turbine. If this form of engine is to be developed, it will have to compete with other

Fig. 17. 2,200 h.p. Gas Turbine for Locomotive.

modern units, such as the internal combustion reciprocating engine or the high-pressure superheated steam engine, on one or more scores, such as fuel economy, specific weight or volume, ability to operate without water and to consume certain cheap grades of fuel. Development work of the internal combustion turbine is made fascinating by the almost unlimited manner in which its component parts may be arranged. A few arrangements or cycles are illustrated in figs. 15 to 21. The results which may be expected from any cycle lend themselves to resolution by calculation, and this involves the use of a wide range of knowledge of physics, chemistry, mathematics and engineering as well as the use of numerous assumptions, many of which are determinable only as a result of practical laboratory tests.

It will be realized that some of the variables upon which economy or high specific power depend are either very difficult to improve upon or may even be considered as having reached their optimum. Also that the efficiency of the whole plant depends on the efficiency of each of its component parts. The present efficiency of a turbine unit is around 87%, and it is felt that this should be capable of improvement.

The air compressor can take one of three general forms—axial flow (like a turbine in reverse), centrifugal or positive displacement. None of these can be considered as developed to the same extent as the turbine, and their efficiencies, which range up to about 85%, will probably be raised as research proceeds.

The artifices which lend themselves more to attainment of higher overall efficiency are the use of new and improved types of heat exchangers in the form of inter-coolers in the compressor plant, which enable more air to be compressed for a given power and size of compressor, and regenerators or recuperators in the exhaust system, which save heat from going to waste in the exhaust and impart it to the compressed air. There is room for inventive genius on the design of such units to give high rates of heat exchange with a minimum of pressure loss. Lastly, and by no means the least, the improvement in material for manufacture of turbine blades or in methods of cooling them which will enable high temperatures to be used. In the present stage of the art it is necessary to cool the gases of combustion so drastically before impinging them on the turbine blades that it is necessary to compress between four and seven times as much air as is required for complete combustion of the fuel. It is true that most of the extra power required to compress this vast quantity of air is recovered by re-expansion in the turbine, but the plant has to be of much greater capacity than would be the case if less dilution air were required. As an example, in the case of a 1,000 h.p. net output plant (*vide* fig. 15) the quantity of air required for combustion and cooling purposes is about 19 lb. (or 247 cu. ft.) of air per second. Of this only 2·5 lb. (or 33 cu. ft.) is required for complete combustion of the fuel.

Some Other Cycles. As mentioned previously, many cycles may be considered for various applications, but some cycles lend

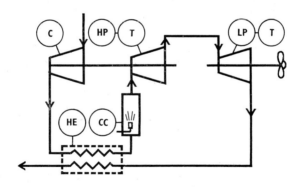

Fig. 18. Two Shaft I.C.T. with Heat Exchanger.

themselves to particular duties. For instance, where simplicity and low first cost are of more importance than overall economy, a simple single shaft unit with no heat exchangers may be used. For naval ship propulsion, where full load is required very seldom, the general duty being for ''cruising'' purposes, it is essential on the score of economy to employ a two-shaft unit (fig. 18) in order that the compressor may be operated at an efficient speed regardless of the speed of the propulsion turbine. In cases where operational economy is of more importance than first cost, as in a power station, a high degree of heat recovery may be catered for by means of a large heat exchanger which might effect a heat exchange from the exhaust gases to the compressed air of as much as 90%; or where the maximum power is required from a plant of smallest possible size, the compressor may be divided into two

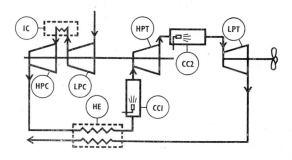

Fig. 19.   Two Shaft I.C.T. with Intercooler Heat Exchanger and Reheater.

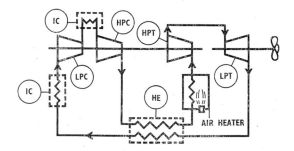

Fig. 20.   Closed Cycle Two Shaft I.C.T. with Intercooler and Heat Exchanger.

or more stages with inter-coolers between them, the effect being that the air, which rises in temperature on compression in the first stage, is cooled to reduce its volume so that the second and subsequent stage compressors can be of smaller capacity for the same duty. A complementary artifice is the dividing of the turbine into stages with re-heat between the stages by means of extra combustion chambers (*vide* fig. 19 (C.C.2)).

The Closed Cycle. There are also the advocates of the "closed" cycle, in which the working gas re-circulates in the system (fig. 20), being alternately compressed, heated by means of a heat exchanger and then by an air heater or "air boiler", expanded through the turbine, cooled and then re-compressed, and so on. There are several advantages in this system, such as a high overall efficiency, no fouling of the turbine and heat exchanger, the possibility of employing gases of high specific heat and the use of a high overall pressure permitting better transfer of heat with smaller units. The main disadvantage is the size of the "air boiler" and the difficulty of operating it at sufficiently high temperature without burning out the "boiler" tubes.

Another type of cycle is that in which the main volume of gas is re-cycled but sufficient fresh air is introduced at high pressure

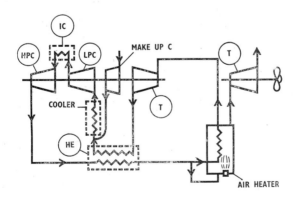

Fig. 21. Semi-closed Cycle Two Shaft I.C.T. with Intercooler and Heat Exchanger.

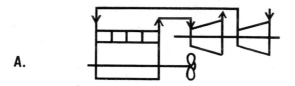

A.

I.C.T. AND COMPRESSOR AS OIL ENGINE SUPERCHARGER

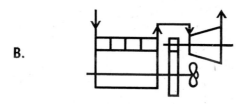

B.

PISTON SUPERCHARGED OIL ENGINE
WITH I.C.T. GEARED TO POWER SHAFT.

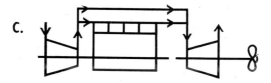

C.

COMPRESSOR SUPERCHARGED OIL ENGINE
WITH I.C.T. AS POWER UNIT.

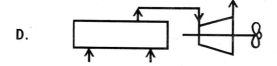

D.

FREE PISTON ENGINE WITH I.C.T. AS POWER UNIT.

Fig. 22.   Mixed Cycles—I.C.T.

to enable combustion to take place within the cycle instead of external to it. A corresponding volume of mixed gases is exhausted via one of the two turbines (fig. 21).

Mixed Cycles. Considerable thought is being given at the present time to "mixed cycle" units. These generally consist of a turbine unit in conjunction with a reciprocating engine. Such arrangements are illustrated diagrammatically in fig. 22, in which (*a*) represents a turbo-supercharged reciprocating engine in which the gas turbine-compressor unit serves the purpose only of enabling the reciprocating engine to deliver more power, while in arrangement (*b*) the gas turbine expands the engine exhaust gases and adds its power to that of the reciprocating engine. (*c*) represents a two-stroke engine driving a compressor, some of the air from the latter being used to supercharge the engine, the rest to dilute the gases which are exhausted early in the engine cycle and thus render them of suitable temperature for driving the gas turbine. In this case, all the net work is taken out of the turbine. (*d*) is a similar system, except that a "free piston" air compressor plant is used instead of the engine and compressor units.

Systems (*b*), (*c*) and (*d*) are particularly attractive, as the high temperature combustion and initial expansion occur in the combustion chamber of the reciprocating engine with the pumping of a minimum of cooling air, and expansion is continued right down to atmospheric pressure in the turbine. The disadvantage is, of course, the introduction of reciprocating machinery, although in much smaller sizes than if no turbine were used.

Gas Turbine Units in Operation. Probably the first gas turbine units to be employed regularly in commercial service were of Brown Boveri design installed in the catalytic cracking plants of several United States refineries (fig. 23). These comprise mainly axial flow compressors, for supply of large volumes of air to the refinery plant, driven by gas turbine. Normally the combustion takes place within the refinery plant, but combustion chambers are provided for starting up and boosting purposes.

Other units, apart from jet propulsion engines, comprise a 6,000 h.p. standby electric generating set in an underground power station at Neuchatel and the locomotive, both by Brown Boveri. Other Swiss firms have developed the closed, semi-closed

Fig. 23.   1,600 kw. Net Output Gas Turbine in an American Oil Refinery.

and open cycles respectively, but, so far, in experimental plant only.

The first marine unit to be operated afloat has been installed in a British naval motor gunboat. Other plant is under construction in both the United States of America and the United Kingdom. An interesting project is the order by the Anglo-Saxon Petroleum Co. of a 1,100 h.p. marine gas turbine unit from the British Thomson-Houston Co. for replacing one of four oil engines in an otherwise diesel-electric propelled tanker. This proposed unit will undoubtedly be watched with great interest. It is being designed rather from the point of view of reliability than economy, as it is essentially required to gain experience from which more efficient marine units may be developed.

Fuel for the Internal Combustion Turbine. At first it was thought that the fuel requirements of this type of engine would be easy to meet, and many statements have been published to the effect that Bunker "C" grade boiler fuel is suitable. The fact is, however, that nothing heavier than the lighter residual blends has been employed, and even then difficulties have been encountered from time to time due to deposits formed from the ash in the fuel.

As mentioned earlier, it is essential that the gas turbine uses a cheap and readily available fuel. It is therefore no use being satisfied with operation on any distillate grade. From our knowledge of burning fuels under boilers it is not considered that viscosity as such will cause any difficulty at the fuel injector, provided that there is an adequate system for fuel heating.

The carbon-forming tendency of the fuel and the asphaltene content may be important and will have to be watched in conjunction with combustion chamber design, as building up of carbon on the walls cannot be tolerated. If carbon commences to form, it will heat insulate the part concerned, causing distortion and possibly eventual burning out of the flame tube ; also, if the carbon builds up to any extent it may break away in lumps and block or damage the turbine blading.

The chemical composition of the ash in residual blends and its effects in gas turbines are likely to be important lines of research. Ash may be present in a normal bunker "C" grade fuel up to

0.2% by weight, and the chemical composition will vary according to the well from which it was produced, but it may contain silica, vanadium, iron, copper, magnesium, sodium, potassium and traces of the rare metals.

The salts in the ash may be in solid, liquid or gaseous form in the flame zone of the combustion chamber, but on passing through the gas turbine unit they will be cooled, and some of the liquids and gases will become solid, possibly passing through a plastic range. Thus, deposits may build up and become trapped in the system, the location of which will depend on the nature of the ash, the temperature and the configuration of the passages. Some ash deposits are soft or flaky, some are glass-hard. Some are soluble in water and may be flushed out, others are not. This position may become serious if deposits accumulate on the turbine blades, heat exchanger surfaces or in other narrow passages.

The best solution to these difficulties would, of course, be the elimination of the ash content of the fuel. But, unless some very inexpensive treatment can be devised, such fuels would no longer be placed in the lower-priced range. Other lines of attack on this problem might be the elimination of any undesirable elements or treatment causing the ash to form salts which may have melting points above or below that which causes difficulties in the engine.

Lubrication. The lubricating oil has an easier life in the internal combustion turbine than the internal combustion reciprocating engine, as in the latter it is exposed to the combustion chamber. The heavy gas turbines will have plain journal bearings which may be oil cooled. The designer will have to avoid running such bearings hotter than necessary, and there is no indication at the moment that special high-temperature lubricating oils will be required.

The Future. The future of the internal combustion turbine is thought to be assured and much intensive work has been done on paper, but so far little has emerged on a practical scale on account of war-time restrictions. The probability is, however, that progress will proceed rapidly, so that these notes will soon become out-dated.

XXVIII

FUEL OIL AND GAS OIL

TERMINOLOGY

THERE is no clearly defined line of demarcation between the classes of product generally known as gas oil, diesel fuel and fuel oil. It is, of course, possible to make an arbitrary division, and in commercial practice this is usually done. Each product as thus defined has its special applications in industry, but there is very considerable overlapping in the way in which these terms are used and, in fact, both gas oil and diesel fuel are frequently marketed under the generic title of "fuel oil".

Since each of these three terms will be used later on in this chapter with a specific meaning, it is as well, first of all, to try to obtain a fairly close idea of what is meant commercially when we speak of "gas oil", "diesel fuel" and "fuel oil".

By "gas oil" we mean a distillate, intermediate in character between kerosine and the light lubricating oils. Most of its special applications arise from the fact that gas oil is a distilled product ; it is, therefore, practically free from residual components and its hard asphalt content is practically nil.

It is perhaps desirable to mention that there is no uniformity of nomenclature even in English-speaking countries. In the United States, where a distillate similar to gas oil is very largely sold for domestic heating and allied purposes, it is usually described as "furnace oil", "stove oil" or even "fuel oil".

Gas oil (*vide infra*) is widely used in the gas industry as a basic material for cracking processes, as a heating oil (i.e. as a fuel oil), and for numerous other purposes, one of the most important of which is as a fuel for compression ignition engines. Diesel fuel and gas oil, however, are not synonymous terms, since only certain types of diesel engine, notably those used for automotive purposes, are sufficiently fuel selective to require a high quality distillate fuel. Diesel fuels may, in fact, be either distillates or light residual fuel oils, or carefully prepared blends of both (*vide* chapter XXVII). Even certain natural crudes may be sold as diesel fuel or as fuel oil, but not as gas oil.

Just as diesel fuels are normally rather heavier and more viscous than gas oil, so the general conception of a fuel oil is something more viscous than either. Modern commercial fuel oils may, in fact, vary in viscosity from the low figures of the gas oil range— say, 35 seconds Redwood I at 100° F. (about 1·25° Engler at 50° C.)—up to the so-called bunker "C" grade limit, which is of the order of nearly 7,000 seconds Redwood I at 100° F. (approximately 85° Engler at 50° C.). Fuel oil is no simple product, but an ill-defined range with innumerable possible combinations of viscosity, pour point, specific gravity, sulphur, asphaltenes etc., according to the origin and composition of the crude oil and the manner in which the crude oil has been worked up for the preparation of, say, gasoline, kerosine, lubricating oils or other products.

TESTS AND THEIR SIGNIFICANCE

Specific Gravity. Contrary to the belief widely held at one time, the specific gravity (*vide* chapter XXIII) in itself has no technical significance from the point of view of quality. It is still, however, sometimes used as an indication of the "heaviness" of a fuel oil, but its employment in this connection may be extremely misleading. With two fuel oils of the same origin, it is true that an increase in specific gravity usually indicates an increase in the viscosity. This simple maxim may, however, prove incorrect if one fuel is straight-run and the other is cracked, and it is very much safer not to use the specific gravity as a basis for estimating other characteristics.

The normal practical application of the specific gravity is to enable one to calculate the weight of oil sold from a knowledge of the volume involved (*vide* chapter XXIII). Generally, the specific gravity of fuel oil is below that of water, but it is possible for it to exceed 1·000, in which case precautions must be taken to avoid contamination with water.

Flashpoint. When an oil fuel is heated in a closed vessel with an air space above the liquid, vapours are continuously evolved, and at a certain temperature the mixture of vapour with air will be sufficiently "rich" to ignite on the application of a flame. This temperature is what is known as the closed cup flashpoint. Like so many of the tests carried out on petroleum products, it is a purely empirical determination and the results will vary according to the instrument which is used. Exact standardization of dimensions of the apparatus and of the method of conducting the test is essential. The instrument very largely used for determining the closed flashpoint of oil fuels is the Pensky-Martens closed cup tester. In many countries there is a legal minimum of 150° F. (65·5° C.) imposed on the flashpoint of all oil fuels, and the same figure is generally specified for commercial bunker fuels. This is in order to provide a sufficient margin of safety from fire risk during storage, handling and transportation.

It should especially be noted that the flashpoint is merely an indication of the presence of a certain proportion of ignitable vapours in a specified set of circumstances. It is not an indication of the general volatility or viscosity of a fuel.

Viscosity. Viscosity may conveniently be regarded as the converse of fluidity. It is a measure of an oil's resistance to flow and can be reported in a variety of ways (*vide* chapter XXIX).

It will be realized that with very thick (or "heavy") fuel oils the time of outflow through a Redwood No. 1 or Saybolt Universal viscometer may be quite lengthy, and it becomes impracticable to hold the oil at the correct temperature in the viscometer for so long a period. To deal with this situation, alternative versions of each instrument are in existence and are used for the more viscous oils. These are known as the Redwood No. 2 and the Saybolt Furol (an abbreviation of "fuel and road oil") viscometers, and the diameter of the jet through which the oil leaves the instrument is so constructed that the time of outflow is approximately one-tenth of that when using the Redwood No. 1 or Saybolt Universal viscometer respectively. It is, therefore, not uncommon to make the actual determination for a viscous oil on the Redwood No. 2 instrument, obtaining the Redwood No. 1 equivalent by calculation. Since Saybolt Furol viscosities of fuel oils are normally reported at 122° F. and Redwood determinations at 100° F., care must be taken whenever it is desired to convert readings from one instrument to those on another, since, of

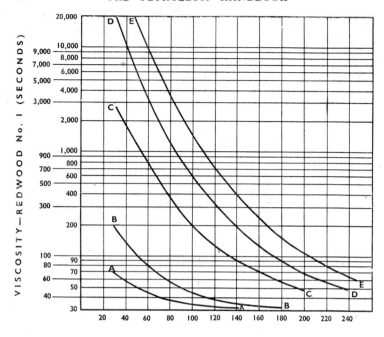

VISCOSITY—REDWOOD No. I (SECONDS)

TEMPERATURE—DEGREES FAHRENHEIT

A = Gas Oil
B = Light Diesel Fuel or Domestic Fuel Oil
C = Light Fuel Oil (200 seconds Red. I at 100°F.)
D = Fuel Oil (600 seconds Red. at 100°F.)
E = Fuel Oil (1,500 „   „   „   )

Fig. 1. Viscosity/Temperature Curves of Typical Fuel Oils.

course, direct conversion can be made only between readings at the same temperature.

Between the distillate fuel oils of low viscosity and the bunker "C" type of heavy residuum can be found infinite combinations of viscosity, pour point and other characteristics. All petroleum fuel oils, however, show one feature in common—a rapid fall of viscosity on heating. This is illustrated in fig. 1, in which viscosity is plotted against temperature in the form of a curve.

In the case of industrial and marine fuel oils, which are often of comparatively high viscosity, this increase in fluidity is very marked. Such a curve may be used to determine in advance the optimum temperature of atomization of an oil at the burner nozzle, providing the operator knows the most suitable viscosity at which he should aim. It must, however, be realized that, while fig. 1 gives a general indication of how viscosity alters with change of temperature, the actual direction of slope of the curve—i.e. the rate at which the viscosity changes—varies slightly with fuel oils of different origin.

Distillation Range. There is no method in general use for determining the volatility of fuel oils which can be considered altogether satisfactory. Distillation tests such as that of the A.S.T.M. (*vide* chapter XXV) become unreliable when the temperature approaches 350° C., because there is a tendency for uncontrollable cracking to commence. As a rule, therefore, the percentage of volatile fractions, as ascertained from the distillation test, is used as a criterion in the case of distillate fuel oils only.

Sulphur. Quite commonly the limit for total sulphur content is included in specifications for fuel oils. Sometimes this is the result of prejudice, or perhaps just merely caution, owing to the generally accepted belief that a high sulphur content is detrimental. Generally speaking, however, the sulphur content is of less interest in the case of fuel oils than in that of diesel fuels. There are instances where light fuel oils are employed for certain special industrial processes where a high sulphur content would be detrimental to the quality of the goods produced, owing to the effects of the sulphurous gases evolved during the combustion process, but in the majority of cases the sulphur content is practically without effect, and fuels of over 4 per cent. sulphur content can be burnt under suitable conditions without any deleterious results.

Coking Tests. With gas oils and diesel fuels certain empirical carbonizing tests, such as the Conradson or Ramsbottom tests, are used to estimate the coke-forming tendency. Very much the same object lies behind the test for asphaltenes, or hard asphalt, in which, under certain strictly controlled conditions of test, an "asphaltic" material is precipitated by the addition of a more volatile substance. Occasionally these tests are encountered in fuel oil specifications, but their usefulness in any grade heavier than a diesel fuel is highly questionable.

Ash Content. The ash content, which is the residue remaining after all consumable portions of the oil have been completely burnt away, may be regarded as illustrating the percentage of mineral contamination, for example, rust or sand, in a fuel. Compared with solid forms of fuel, the ash content of petroleum fuel oil is extremely low—most commercial grades being of the order of 0·1% or even less. A point which does not receive as much consideration as it should is the nature of the material which forms the ash. Insoluble mineral contaminants such as sand or clay are, in the main, removable by mechanical means (filtration, centrifuging or merely settling), but ash is sometimes derived from soluble metallic compounds in solution in the oil, and these are not mechanically removable. In this connection, it is interesting to note that the ash of some petroleum fuel oils contains vanadium ; in such cases it is worth while collecting the "soot" to recover this important metal.

Pour Point. The pour point of an oil is the temperature at which, under defined conditions of test, the oil will just flow under its own weight (*vide* chapter XXIX). The test has, however, many practical objections, since, in view of the small quantity on which the test must necessarily be conducted and the artificial conditions thereby introduced, the result may have little bearing upon practical operations. For example, the test does not indicate what happens when an oil has a considerable head of pressure behind it, such as when gravitating from a receptacle or being pumped along a line. Moreover, it does not reproduce static conditions of storage, and the fact that a quantity of about 30 ml. solidifies in a small bottle, where a considerable portion of the oil is in contact with the surface, does not mean that the same oil in bulk in a large storage tank will solidify at the same temperature, since the insulating effect of the wax skin which is formed may actually keep the core comparatively warm and still fluid.

The previous treatment of an oil has a very important bearing upon the pour point. If the oil has been heated shortly before the test is carried out, the result may be very different from what it would have been had no such treatment taken place. With fuel oil such heat treatment is quite commonplace and particular precautions usually have to be taken to ensure that the pour point determination is not affected thereby.

Since for reasons such as these many fuel oils can be pumped at temperatures well below their pour point, attempts are continually being made to devise some practical test which will reproduce the conditions of "pumpability", or in some other way correlate the laboratory pour point of the fuel with its behaviour in bulk at low temperatures.

Calorific Value. Almost all petroleum fuel oils have a gross calorific value (*vide* chapter XXV) between 18,000 and 19,000 B.Th.U. per lb. (10,000 to 10,550 calories per gram), and even the lightest gas oils do not greatly exceed 19,500 B.Th.U. per lb. (10,830 calories per gram).

The calorific value is determined by actually burning a small quantity of oil in oxygen and by accurately calculating the amount of heat units produced, applying suitable corrections for loss of heat by radiation.

It is also possible to effect a calculation of the calorific value from the ultimate (or elementary) analysis of the fuel, that is to say, the actual proportions of carbon, hydrogen, sulphur etc., since it is known what quantity of heat is liberated when unit quantities of each of these elements are completely burnt. However, the determination of the percentage composition in terms of the elements present is much more difficult than ascertaining the calorific value experimentally by means of the bomb calorimeter, and may be much less accurate.

Variation in the molecular weight of oils of differing specific gravity due to changes in the relative proportions of the carbon and hydrogen present, results in oils of high specific gravity having a lower calorific value than those of lower specific gravity when calculated on a weight basis. On a volume basis, however, the calorific value rises on increase of specific gravity, so that the buyer of a high specific gravity fuel oil will usually receive more

B.Th.U. per gallon than the purchaser of a fuel oil of low specific gravity.

Sediment and Water. These are, of course, undesirable contaminants but, fortunately, even with the heavier grades of fuel oil, the amounts held in suspension are not great. Generally a limit of 1 % is specified, though sometimes as much as 2 % sediment and water is accepted, in which case it is customary to make a proportionate allowance to the buyer when the actual water content of any delivery exceeds 1 %.

The sediment content is generally determined separately as being the quantity of insoluble material which can be filtered off when the oil is washed with certain solvents. Sometimes the total sediment and water are determined together by a centrifuge test, but this method has limitations and the results are not strictly accurate.

Stability. When a fuel oil is required for some specific purpose, certain conditions may be imposed which are not insisted upon in ordinary commercial practice. In such a category come tests for stability, which may be required on a fuel oil for naval use. This means that, when subjected to certain heat treatment, the fuel oil will not throw down a deposit which will clog strainers, preheaters or burners. Various "heater tests" are in existence which give a visual or gravimetric means of distinguishing between the relative stability of fuels, either alone or in mixtures.

It will be seen from the foregoing that, providing a buyer is given assurances in regard to contamination—i.e. that the flashpoint, water and sediment are satisfactory—the quality of a fuel oil can be almost entirely defined by its viscosity and, in certain cases, the pour point. Where special industrial uses are concerned, it may be necessary to specify a low ash or sulphur content, but on the whole these cases are comparatively rare.

STRAIGHTRUN AND CRACKED FUEL OILS

Where a fuel oil is produced as the result of "straight" distillation of a crude oil, it is referred to as a "straightrun residue". Commercial fuel oils, however, usually contain appreciable proportions of residue resulting from cracking processes. These differ slightly from straightrun fuels in certain physical characteristics—e.g. they are rather higher in specific gravity and lower in pour point. There is, however, no justification for regarding cracked fuel oils as inferior to straightrun residues. Complete combustion can as readily be obtained, and it is, in fact, rarely that the buyer is in any way conscious of whether he is using a straightrun or a cracked product or, more generally, a mixture of both.

STORAGE AND HANDLING OF FUEL OIL

One of the most important advantages of fuel oil is the ease with which it can be stored and handled, particularly where conditions for solid fuel would be impossible—such as the double bottom* of a ship.

It must, nevertheless, be realized that, however simple or elaborate a customer's fuel oil tankage may be, certain precautions must be observed if satisfaction is to be assured. A storage tank should be constructed so that it is absolutely oil-tight, and have ample strength to withstand any pressure to which it may be subjected in normal operations.

Tanks made from mild steel plate are almost invariably used ; the tanks should not be galvanized internally. For indoor use, welded tanks are preferred to those jointed or riveted, as oil is extremely searching and poor riveting results in annoying leaks which it is almost impossible to make good. (Lloyd's rules for ships' oil tanks insist that riveting shall be double, although the modern tendency is for welded tanks.) Concrete tanks are occasionally used on shore, but, since by itself it is porous to oil, it is essential that the concrete be coated or mixed with a suitable oil-resisting compound. In any case, great care must be exercised to avoid cracks, which are more likely with heated oil.

In the main we are dealing with products which are extremely safe from the point of view of fire hazard—much safer than most people realize—and even the lightest type of gas oil has, in most countries, a closed flashpoint well above 150° F. (65·6° C.). In the United States, however, the light and medium fuel oils are specified to have minimum flashpoints varying from 100° F. to 130° F. (37·8° C. to 54·4° C.). As a consequence, particularly in New York City, there are fairly stringent storage rules, but some of the so-called "fuel oils" or "furnace oils" are, in fact, kerosines or light gas oils.

It is very important that the tank should be in a position where it is readily accessible for inspection, cleaning and maintenance. There are some installations where there is no alternative but to place the tank below ground level. In order to avoid troubles associated with buried tanks due to the difficulty of cleaning and possible corrosion from the soil, an underground tank should be placed in a specially constructed brick chamber big enough to give free access around and below the tank.

Storage tanks may be situated above the burner equipment, but it is not recommended that unrestricted gravity flow to the burners be used. Additional safeguards are often employed in the form of catch pits around tanks and anti-fire valves which shut off the oil supply on the melting of a fusible link. Each storage tank should have a vent pipe large enough to prevent the tank being subjected to pressure during the filling operation. The exit from the vent pipe should be protected by a wire cage to prevent the accidental intrusion of matter likely to choke the vent, and the end should be designed to prevent the ingress of rain water.

Tanks in exposed positions should have main valves of cast steel, preferably lagged, while bends, valves or similar fittings which are likely to be exposed to sharp frosts should be of wrought iron or cast steel, not cast iron, which is apt to be brittle at low temperatures. The fuel draw-off pipe from a tank is usually some distance from the bottom so as to leave a sludge space, and a sludge cock is fitted at the lowest point of the tank to facilitate periodical removal of accumulated water and sludge. Gauge glasses should not be used on storage tanks.

Where viscous fuel oils or those of high pour point are used, it is advisable, as in the case of the refinery tanks, to fit heating coils, the use of which will not only reduce the viscosity of the oil for pumping purposes, but will also assist in cleaning the oil by facilitating the removal of dirt and water by settling. It is quite common to install two or more special coiled settling tanks* in addition to coiling the main storage tank, where heavy fuels are concerned. Such settling tanks can be maintained at a constant temperature for some time before the oil is used, and a drain valve at the bottom facilitates the removal of water and sediment. A further necessity is an efficient strainer to filter the oil as it leaves the storage tank, and another before it is fed to the burner equipment. The lighter grades, such as gas oil, do not require to be heated to ensure easy handling and pumping.

OIL BURNING EQUIPMENT

It is very difficult to ignite fuel oil as stored in bulk or to set fire to a stream of oil issuing from a nozzle. To achieve a stable and efficient flame it is necessary to prepare the oil for burning in such a way that the whole of it will find adequate air for combustion. This is the function of the oil-burning equipment, which first ''atomizes'' the oil, that is, divides it up into a very large number of small particles and introduces an adequate quantity of air to burn the oil. The transformation of the oil stream into a cloud of small particles not only ensures even distribution of air and oil, but presents a far bigger surface of oil to the air. The process of atomization probably increases this surface 600 or 700 times. In the design of good oil-burning equipment as much attention has been paid to the means of introducing the air as to the method of atomizing the oil.

TYPES OF OIL BURNERS

Oil burners can be roughly divided into three classes :—
  1. Blast burners.
  2. Pressure jet burners.
  3. Vaporizing burners.

  1. **Blast Burners.** This type of burner functions by directing a fast-moving blast of air or steam to impinge on a film of oil, which it tears first into filaments and then into droplets. The ordinary scent spray type of atomizer shown in fig. 2 is a typical but crude example of a blast atomizer. Blast burners can be designed as external mixers in which the atomizing medium only meets the oil at the mouth of the burner ; internal mixers, in which the atomizing medium mixes with the oil spray within the burner, and multi-stage atomizers, which may involve both internal and external mixing.

This type of burner can be sub-divided into four categories according to the pressure of the atomizing medium employed. This medium can be either air or steam, although the latter is not usually employed at pressures less than, say, 15 lb. per square inch. The four categories are :—

(*a*) Low-pressure air burners ...   ...   9 to 30 inches W.G.
(*b*) Low-pressure air rotary burners ...   4 to 15 inches W.G.
(*c*) Medium-pressure air burners   ...   2½ to 10 lb./sq. in.
(*d*) High-pressure air or steam burners   10 to 50 lb./sq. in.

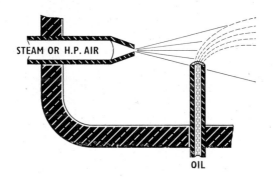

Fig. 2.   "Scent-spray" Type of Burner.

(*a*) *Low-pressure Air Burners.*   A typical low-pressure atomizer is shown in fig. 3.   For low-pressure air burners usually 25% to 40% of the air for combustion is passed through the burner at a pressure of, say, 12 inches W.G. (1 lb. per square inch = 27·7 inches W.G.).   Where such burners are well designed, care is taken to ensure that the oil is evenly divided over the air system. All the air must be arranged to hit the issuing oil at a high relative velocity, but the velocity of the oil and air mixture issuing from the nose must not be so high as to cause the flame to leave the burner nose.

(*b*) *Low-pressure Air Rotary Burners.*   For an example of this see fig. 4. which shows an " air spun " rotary burner.   The essential feature of all rotary burners is that the oil is led on to the inner surface of a cup rapidly rotating about a horizontal axis.

The cup can be spun either by a small air turbine as in the illustration or mechanically by an electric motor. The oil leaves the edge of the cup in a uniform film and so is deposited across the low-pressure air stream in an already partially atomized state. This enables this type of burner to work with a smaller quantity of air and at a lower pressure. It is quite usual to find mechanically-

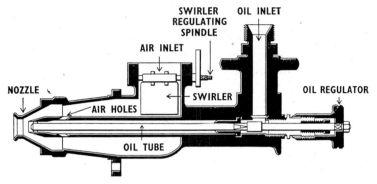

Fig. 3.   Low-Pressure Air Atomizing Burner.

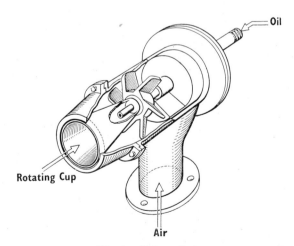

Fig. 4.   Rotary Burner.

spun rotary burners in which the atomization is completed by, say, 20% of the total air for combustion at 4 inches W.G. It should not be overlooked that, although the higher the speed of the cup the finer the atomization, this type of burner is still a low-pressure blast burner and depends upon air to complete atomization and to stabilize the flame.

(c) *Medium-pressure Air Burners.* This type of burner can be divided into internal and external mixers. Fig. 5 shows an internal mixing medium-pressure air burner, while fig. 6 shows an external mixer. The air is usually supplied by an electrically or belt-driven blower of the eccentric and radial blades type. Only a small percentage of the total air for combustion is needed

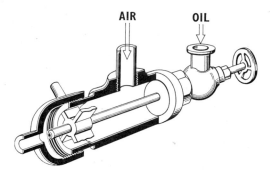

Fig. 5.   Internal Mixing Medium-Pressure Air Burner.

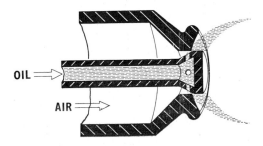

Fig. 6.   External Mixing Medium-Pressure Air Burner.

for atomization, usually about 5%, or approximately 10 cubic feet of air (free) per lb. of oil.

(*d*) *High-pressure Air or Steam Jet Burners.* Where a factory has an ample supply of compressed air it is sometimes convenient to use a high-pressure air burner or, if an adequate steam supply is available, the same type of burner can be used with steam as the atomizing medium. Such a burner is shown in fig. 7. Although the original steam supply may be at 100 or 150 lb. per square inch, it is usual to utilize for atomizing purposes the steam at a somewhat lower pressure, the reduction being effected by an ordinary hand valve or a spring-loaded reducing valve. The

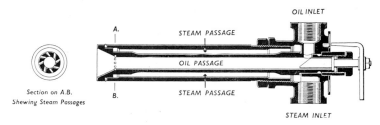

Fig. 7. High-Pressure Steam Jet Burner.

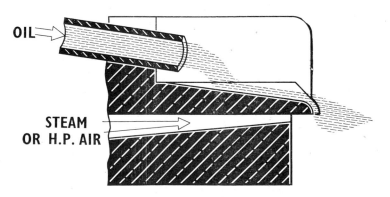

Fig. 8. "Mexican Trough" Type Steam Jet Burner.

steam pressure may be anywhere from 10 to 50 lb. per square inch. It is very important that burners of this type should not use too much steam, and on a good design the consumption should be somewhere between $\frac{1}{3}$ and $\frac{1}{2}$ lb. of steam per lb. of oil. Thus, the steam consumption for atomization should not be more than 5% of the total steam generated in an oil-fired boiler.

Fig. 8 shows another type of steam jet burner, usually known as the "Mexican trough" or "shovel" type. Here the oil is arranged to fall over a wide weir and is caught from below and

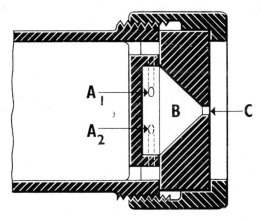

Fig. 9.   Typical Pressure Jet Nozzle.

atomized by a jet of steam issuing from a long thin slot parallel to and below the oil weir. Burners of this type have been used for many years for firing locomotive boilers.

2. **Pressure Jet Burners.**   For this type of burner no atomizing medium is employed. The breaking up of the oil into a cloud of fine particles is achieved by converting the pressure energy of the oil into velocity energy and utilizing this energy to disrupt the oil film as it issues from the nozzle. Fig. 9 shows a typical pressure-jet atomizer.   Oil flows into the swirling chamber (B) through two tangential ducts, A1 and A2.   The oil may issue from these

ducts at a velocity of, say, 30 feet per second, but in proceeding towards the exit the rotational velocity is greatly increased until the oil leaves the final orifice (C) in the form of a rapidly rotating hollow column. The oil film spreads as it leaves the orifice and breaks into small droplets, and thus atomization is obtained merely by pumping to this type of nozzle oil at a pressure of 70 to 200 lb. per square inch. All the air for combustion must be supplied through a properly designed air director through the centre of which the nozzle is mounted. There are two important characteristics of the pressure jet burner :—

(*a*) It will only function successfully when the viscosity of the oil is reduced to between 70 and 100 seconds Redwood 1. This is in contrast to the powers of the blast burner, which can usually atomize oil when it has a viscosity as high as 200 seconds Redwood 1.

(*b*) The output of the nozzle varies as the square root of the applied oil pressure, so that at oil pressures between 70 and 200 lb. per square inch we can only get a range of oil output of 1 to 1·7. This contrasts unfavourably with most blast burners, where it is quite usual to find that for low-pressure atomization the maximum oil throughput is three or four times the minimum oil throughput at which stable flame can be obtained, while with medium-pressure air burners a range of 10 : 1 or more is feasible.

Wide-range Pressure Jet Burners. The last ten years have seen the development of many types of pressure jet burners with which it is possible to get a range of oil throughputs of as high as 1 to 10. These wide-range pressure jets maintain good atomization at the lower ranges of oil consumption by spilling a controlled proportion of the oil passed from the tangential ducts into the swirl chamber back to pump suction. An alternative method is to alter the ratio of swirling grooves to final orifice by increasing the effective area of discharge of the swirling grooves in proportion to the atomizing pressure or by bringing more swirling grooves into play as the pressure rises.

3. **Vaporizing Burners.** Fig. 10 shows a natural draught vaporizing burner of the carburettor type. The oil is dripped into the base of the pot, where it lies in a pool. This pool is kept by the radiation from the flame at a temperature high enough to vaporize

the oil steadily, but not high enough to decompose the oil by cracking. The air is admitted progressively to the vaporizing pot or carburettor so that there is an insufficient quantity near the surface of the pool to permit flame to take place in that zone. Although the small radial blue flames can be seen at the points where the air enters the pot and is burning in an atmosphere of oil vapour, the main luminous flame occurs near the mouth of the pot, where the bulk of the air is supplied. This type of burner

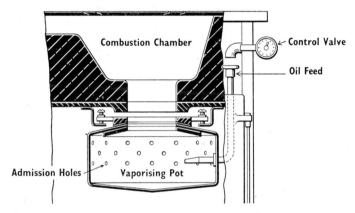

Fig. 10.   Vaporizing Burner—Carburettor Type.

can be lit with a gas flame or by lighting a few pieces of paper in the base of the pot and then turning on the oil drip. When used for domestic purposes it should be fitted with safety devices to ensure that the oil supply will be turned off should the pot become inadvertently flooded. The natural draught burner has two main requirements :—

    (*a*) A steady draught of the required order, and hence an automatic draught regulator is essential.

    (*b*) The right grade of oil.

The chief features in this respect are the distillation range and the Conradson value. If an attempt is made to burn an oil with too high a Conradson value, frequent cleaning of the pot will be necessary. Kerosine, range oil or stove oil is used for this type of burner.

Forced Draught Vaporizers. Fig. 11 shows a forced draught vaporizing pot. Here air is supplied in a casing around the pot at a pressure of 2 or 3 inches W.G. The high-velocity air jets, blowing across the oil lying in a pool on the base of the pot, not only carry away the vapour as it is formed, but probably whip up the surface and promote the process of vaporization. There is

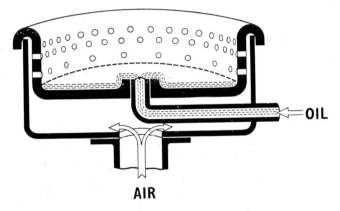

OIL

AIR

Fig. 11. Vaporizing Burner—Forced Draught Type.

evidence that the forced draught vaporizing pot is rather less selective regarding its fuel than the natural draught pot.

Air Control. Any type of burner is sensitive with respect to the means used to introduce air for combustion. If insufficient air is introduced or the air is led into the combustion chamber at a point too far from the atomizing nozzle, an unstable flame may be obtained. This may be accompanied by incomplete combustion. Fig. 12 shows simple "hit and miss" air directors with the burner mounted in the centre. In most blast burners the atomizing medium itself exerts a formative and stabilizing effect on the flame, and hence air directors of this simple design are often sufficient for blast burners. Fig. 13 shows another simple way of introducing the air for combustion for a burner of the medium-pressure air type.

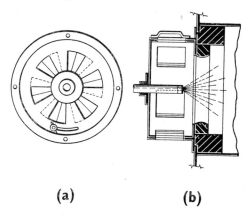

(a)   **(b)**

Fig. 12.   ''Hit and Miss'' Air Directors.

In the case of pressure jet burners the design of the air control apparatus or air director, as it is usually known, is far more important.   The oil spray given out by a pressure jet burner is not very stable, and good combustion with a satisfactory shaped flame can only be obtained by admitting the air to the pressure jet spray in the right proportions and in the correct zones relative to the flame formation.   Fig. 14 shows a typical pressure jet natural-draught air director.   The air is divided into two parts, the smaller portion is led in around the burner, while the major outer portion is given a tangential motion by means of guide vanes.   This tangential motion promotes a good relative velocity between air and oil particles without setting up too high a longitudinal velocity which might tend to blow the flame from the burner nose.

In the case of pressure jet burners the velocity of the air through the air director is of such importance that most burner manufacturers stipulate that they require, say, $\frac{3}{8}$ inch or $\frac{1}{2}$ inch W.G. depression in the furnace at the air director to ensure satisfactory operation of the burner.   If the design of the boiler or furnace and chimney is such as not to ensure an adequate draught, it is then advisable to add to the natural draught of the chimney by installing an induced draught fan. Alternatively, a forced

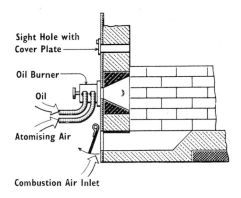

Sight Hole with Cover Plate

Oil Burner

Oil

Atomising Air

Combustion Air Inlet

Fig. 13. Medium-Pressure Burner with Air Inlet below.

draught fan can be used which will supply all the air for combustion through a trunk to an air casing around a special forced-draught air director.

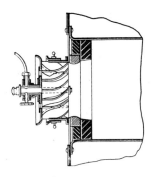

Fig. 14. Air Director for Pressure Jet Burner.

The Installation. Although the atomizer and means of air supply are the most important components, an oil-burning installation includes many other parts, such as are listed below :—

Storage tank.

Accessories—Filling pipe.

Vent pipe.

Contents indicator.

Heating coil or electric immersion heater.

Drain cock.

Outlet control valve.

Outlet filter.

Manhole to facilitate cleaning.

In storage, a ton of fuel oil occupies approximately 40 cubic feet, which compares very favourably with the space taken up by solid fuel, which may vary from 45 cubic feet to the ton for anthracite to 90 cubic feet to the ton for coke.

The storage tank is preferably of welded steel construction, thus eliminating the risk of leaks from joints, and must be adequately vented to prevent an undue pressure being set up in the tank when the fuel oil is pumped into it. Where a heavy grade of oil is used it is advisable to preheat it in the storage tank so that its viscosity will not exceed 3,000 seconds Redwood 1, when it should be sufficiently fluid to flow to the oil pump. The outlet filter from the tank need only be of a coarse type to prevent any adventitious matter that may have got into the oil from damaging the pump.

Pumping and Heating. Although there are many oil-fired installations embodying a gravity feed from tank to burner, it is generally recognized to-day that for accurate control of the oil burners it is better to deliver the oil to the burner by means of a pump at a steady pressure. In the case of blast burners of the low-pressure air and medium-pressure air type an electric motor is usually provided to drive the fan or the compressor, and the additional load due to driving a pump from the same shaft is not appreciable. In order to reduce the viscosity of the oil to a suitable figure at which it may be atomized, say, 150 seconds for blast burners and 70 seconds for pressure jets, the oil is brought up to the atomizing temperature by means of line heaters. For small installations these line heaters usually consist of a small cylindrical vessel in which is mounted an electrical immersion heater and a thermostat, which controls the heater so as to maintain a reasonably constant temperature on the oil flowing to the burner. Larger installations, where steam is available, employ steam coils or pass the oil through a nest of tubes surrounded by steam. It is important that the oil passages in all heaters should be readily accessible for cleaning.

Filters. It is very difficult to filter heavy oil in a cold condition without rapidly choking the filter. Nevertheless, the pumps should be protected by a coarse strainer and fine filtration reserved until after the oil has been heated to the burning temperature. At this stage it is necessary to pass the oil through a filter unit having sufficiently small orifices to eliminate any foreign matter, which may cause either choking up of the burner control valves or the passages of the atomizer itself. Filters should be either of a type which can be mechanically cleaned without dismantling or else mounted in duplicate, so that one filter can be dismantled and cleaned while the other is in operation so as not to interfere with the working of the plant.

Although in the pressure jet burner, given a steady temperature and pressure of the oil, the output of the atomizer will be constant, with blast burners some kind of control valve is necessary, and in order to get a steady flame condition it is essential that the oil should arrive at the control valve—

    (*a*) at a constant pressure,

    (*b*) at a constant temperature, and

    (*c*) after adequate filtration.

The provision of a constant pressure is not easy where several burners are fed from one oil line since the lighting or shutting off of one burner tends to disturb conditions on adjacent burners. This can be avoided by feeding all the burners from what is known as a ring main, around which is pumped a quantity of oil considerably in excess of the total amount likely to be handled by all the burners. At the far end of the ring main is a pressure-regulating valve which should ensure a constant pressure at all the burner control valves irrespective of how many burners are in action. The surplus oil is returned either to the pump suction or to a service tank by way of the pressure-regulating valve.

EFFICIENCY OF COMBUSTION

When a pound of oil is burned the products of combustion will contain some $3\frac{1}{8}$ lb. of carbon dioxide and $1\frac{1}{8}$ lb. of steam. The air for combustion contains about 11 lb. of nitrogen, which will be found unaltered in the flue gases. It is very difficult to burn any fuel with just the chemically theoretical amount of air, and in actual practice some 20% to 30% excess air is usually needed. If greater quantities of unnecessary air are fed into the flame it has a doubly wasteful effect because—

(a) the temperature of the flame will be considerably reduced, and hence the amount of heat which can be given up by the flame in its early stages will be less,

(b) the weight of gases leaving the chimney will be increased, and hence the flue gas or waste loss will be greater.

In order to obtain good combustion efficiency excess air must, therefore, be kept to a minimum. An indication of the amount of excess air can be obtained by measuring the proportion of carbon dioxide (CO_2) in the flue gases. Although the actual weight of CO_2 remains unaltered as excess air is added to the combustion chamber, the proportion of CO_2 present becomes less. Thus, for a typical fuel oil with 30% excess air the CO_2 content of the dry flue gases may be 12%, while with 100% excess air the CO_2 content will only appear as 7·8%. There are many types of CO_2 meters available, and by installing a CO_2 meter and keeping a careful watch on the excess air considerable savings in fuel can be obtained.

AUTOMATIC CONTROL

There are two main methods of automatic burner control. The fundamental object of each is to ensure that the oil will be burnt at a rate which will match the fuel input with the demand for heat.

(a) **Intermittent Flame or On/Off Burner.** For most central heating work and a great many industrial applications to-day, the fully automatic intermittently operating burner is used. The fuel consumption is varied, not by altering the size of the flame but by arranging so that the thermostat or heat-sensitive device regulates the ''on'' and ''off'' periods of the burner to suit the load to be carried.

(*b*) **High-Low Flame.** It is possible to arrange for a thermostat to control the size of flame between two defined limits. As the demand for heat increases so the size of flame increases. With proper controls the size of flame should match the load demand, but with a simpler type of control the burner may be set to operate either at a maximum or a minimum rating with no intermediate stages.

A similar system can be operated with two burners, one of which is constantly alight and provides the minimum heat input, while the other lights intermittently, thus providing the maximum heat input as required.

It is impossible to lay down hard and fast rules as to the type of automatic control required. A great deal depends upon the type of combustion chamber and process involved. A brickwork combustion chamber may not be able to resist the sudden build up of pressure which may occur when a large intermittent burner suddenly lights. There are to-day burners which represent a compromise between the two systems because they light and shut down automatically and, while operating, graduate the size of flame to the load demand.

APPLICATIONS OF FUEL OIL

There are innumerable applications of fuel oil for industrial and other purposes. Broadly speaking, they may be classified under the headings of Steam Raising, Domestic Uses, Industrial Furnaces and General Applications.

Steam Raising

About 50% of the fuel oil burnt is used for the generation of steam in boilers, in oil-fired locomotives and in steamships. In such cases the facility for preheating fuel oil generally exists and, as a consequence, the heaviest grades of fuel may be used for these purposes. The so-called bunker ''C'' grade specification, which permits the delivery of fuel oil with a viscosity up to 300 seconds Saybolt Furol at 122° F. (corresponding with a viscosity of approximately 6,500 seconds Redwood I at 100° F.), is regarded as the normal limiting standard for such supplies.

In the section devoted to the bunkering of ships will be found some of the advantages which oil fuel possesses over coal for marine use. In industrial boiler plants, many of the special conditions which make oil fuel so superior at sea are absent, and in countries where coal is obtained comparatively cheaply the use of oil is generally limited to cases where oil fuel possesses some special advantage, such as cleanliness, exact control, saving of labour or of space, which outweigh a possible increase in fuel costs as compared with solid fuel. Even where the relative prices make oil firing uneconomical as the main fuel, employment can often be found for oil as an auxiliary to coal or other fuel. Instances where this is the case are standby boilers in power stations, where the fact that the plant can be started up at a moment's notice is of paramount importance, and the ignition of large pulverized coal burners by means of oil burners.

Domestic Uses

Central Heating. Oil fuel is used extensively for central heating in offices, factories, churches, hospitals, cinemas and many other types of building, including private dwelling-houses. The tendency nowadays is towards the use of an automatic type of burner operating under thermostatic control. Generally speaking, these burners require a light grade of fuel oil, usually of the gas oil type. The fully automatic burner combines in one unit the burner itself, motor, fan and pump, and provides for a thermostat or pressure sensitive device for automatically starting the motor and lighting the burner when heat is required, and also for shutting down the burner when a given temperature or pressure is reached. Linked with these units is an electric control system providing safety devices against all contingencies, including failure to ignite, loss of flame, failure of electric supply, and so on.

Oil fuel can be regarded as an almost ideal fuel for central heating, advantages being cleanliness and silence, fully automatic operation, saving in space and ease of fuel storage and handling. Although the fuel used for central heating purposes is in the majority of cases a distillate falling in the gas oil or diesel fuel category, the improvement of burners, and particularly their automatic controls, has produced fully automatic burners for central heating capable of using fuel oils with viscosities up to about 200 seconds Redwood I at 100° F. (approximately 228 seconds Saybolt Universal at 100° F. or 4° Engler at 50° C.).

Domestic Hot Water. Burners similar in type to those used for central heating are also employed for domestic hot-water boilers. In the case of private residences considerable headway has been made with a system where one water boiler, with its fully automatic oil burner, is used for providing both central heating and domestic hot water. The automatic burner is of particular value in cases where domestic servants are either unskilled or unobtainable.

Cooking. Ships, hotels and similar large establishments frequently have their cooking ranges fitted with oil-burning equipment, on the larger types of which atomizing oil burners have been very successfully installed. Small portable cooking ranges with vaporizing burners of the carburettor type are gaining in popularity.

Industrial Furnaces

Oil fuel is eminently satisfactory for a large number of industrial heating operations on account of the following important advantages :—

(*a*) Accurate temperature control.

(*b*) Control of the furnace atmosphere—oxidizing, neutral or reducing, as desired.

(*c*) The products of combustion are free from matter harmful to the material being heated.

(*d*) Almost entire absence of ash.

With oil fuel it is possible to obtain flames with high temperature and emissivity* values, and, therefore, it can be used for all high-temperature furnace work. Further, owing to the ease with which temperature and atmosphere can be controlled, oil fuel is also widely used for ''low temperature'' applications.

In applying oil firing to furnaces there are a number of fundamental considerations, such as :—

(*a*) A suitable appliance for burning the oil.

(*b*) A combustion chamber of the right shape and dimensions, which for high-temperature work should be built with the best grade of refractory brick.

(*c*) Correctly designed furnaces or heat-transferring appliances, taking into account the working temperature and the quantity of heat required.

Oil is used successfully in the following applications :—

Metallurgical Furnaces. Under this heading we can include, amongst others :—

> Smelting of ores.
> Metal melting in the open hearth, rotary or semi-rotary furnaces and the crucible pot furnace.
> Welding, forging and bending of bars.
> Heat treatment of materials in a direct-fired muffle, semi-muffle type furnace or salt bath.
> Heating of galvanizing or tinning baths.
> Lead melting and cable manufacture.

Pottery and Brick Kilns. Oil fuel is used with success in all types of pottery kiln. In brick-making, oil-fired kilns give very satisfactory results. Direct oil heaters can also be used in drying sheds where a mixture of air and gaseous products of combustion dries the bricks.

Rotary and Vertical Kilns. Large oil-fired rotary cement and lime kilns, rotary sand drying kilns and vertical kilns are used in the manufacture of cement, lime and hard plaster.

Glass Manufacture. For the production of standard-shaped articles, such as bottles, jars etc., large oil-fired tank furnaces are employed for melting the glass.

Special glass, such as that required for optical work, is melted in oil-fired pot furnaces. As first made, a glass article is very brittle ; it must, therefore, be subsequently re-heated and very slowly cooled. This process is known as annealing, and the furnaces in which it is done are known as lehrs.

Enamelling and Stoving. Oil-fired furnaces are used in the application of vitreous enamelling to cast-iron baths, gas stoves, weighing machines and similar ware.

Furnaces for stoving low-temperature enamelled articles and drying ovens for painted articles are also oil fired.

Pot Furnaces for making Paint and Varnish. Temperature control is essential with this class of work, since if the charge is overheated it is liable to catch fire.

General Applications

Road Making. There are many types of plant used in the preparation of road material. The advantages of oil fuel for this class of work lie in the fact that preparation of the surface materials can be effected as and when required. The main applications include stone drying, bitumen kettles and road-surfacing plant.

Orchard and Glasshouse Heating. Oil fuel burned in simple heaters is used to save fruit during frosty weather. In England, the lighting of 70 oil heaters per acre on two or three nights in the year may preserve a valuable crop. For indoor crops under glass, accurate temperature control can be ensured by the use of automatic oil burners which, by clock and thermostat control, can anticipate and avoid sunset and other temperature changes.

Food Production. Oil is a suitable fuel for all types of bakers' oven, from the small direct-fired brick chamber to the large continuous or travelling oven. Ovens used for baking special biscuits and certain classes of cereal food are also oil fired. There are many other products which are dried or roasted by hot air supplied by oil-fired air heaters or, in many cases, by the diluted products of combustion. We may take as examples the drying of tea, hops, grain and grass, and the roasting of coffee, malt and nuts.

Boiling pots, such as those employed in jam making, sugar boiling, brewers' kettles, and for similar purposes in which temperature control is of the utmost importance, can be oil fired and, due to the ease with which the heat input can be regulated, the charge can be brought to the correct temperature without risk of overheating.

Other Uses. The examples quoted above are not by any means exhaustive. Oil is used extensively in crematoria furnaces, numerous types of air heaters, lighting-up gear for large power-station boilers fired by other fuels, pig singeing, weed burning, locust destruction, cloth singeing, and numerous cases where cleanliness and exact temperature control are important factors.

BUNKERING OF SHIPS

Fuel oil is, of course, very extensively used for bunkering purposes. When a vessel has suitable facilities for heating viscous grades, fuels of viscosity up to the bunker "C" grade limit are supplied. Bunkers are loaded in bulk direct from the wharf in a fashion very similar to that in which they are loaded as cargoes into tankers, but, normally, in considerably smaller quantities at a time. These bunker supplies are frequently made in between or during the loading of other cargo, the average rate at which merchant vessels are able to take bunkers being in the neighbourhood of 250 to 350 tons an hour. Certain of the giant liners and battleships, however, require very large quantities of bunkers, in some cases even as much as a small cargo, and such vessels are so equipped that they are able to load the oil at rates up to 1,000 tons an hour, and in these cases direct supply from tanker to vessel is frequently arranged.

At a number of ports the commercial wharves are so situated in the harbour that it would necessitate ships being moved to the oil wharf in order to take their bunkers direct from the pipeline, and in such cases, where the bunker demand warrants it, the oil suppliers provide lighterage facilities. These lighters are loaded at the installation wharf and go alongside the merchant ships, which are thus able, if desired, to continue loading ordinary cargo whilst taking in oil bunkers.

SOME ADVANTAGES OF OIL OVER COAL

The use of oil for ships' bunkers is increasing very considerably. This is due, in the first place, to the fact that the oil has (very approximately) a 40% higher calorific value than its equal weight in coal, and, therefore, for direct-firing under boilers, it has a proportional advantage in consumption and storage space required. This latter advantage is further increased by at least 10% since a liquid fuel wastes no storage room, whereas spaces are inevitable between the lumps or particles of solid fuels. When used in vessels fitted with internal combustion engines, which in themselves have a greater efficiency than the steam engine, the oil consumption is only about one-third of that of the weight of coal required by a coal-fired steamer of similar tonnage and speed.

This, therefore, enables ships either to reduce their bunker spaces, with a corresponding increase in cargo capacity, or to obtain a greater cruising range for the same bunker space. An important factor as compared with coal is the frequent use of double-bottom space for the carrying of oil fuel bunkers. This would not be practicable with coal, due to the difficulty of conveying the coal to the stokehold, and also the need for using the double-bottom space for ballast from time to time.

For naval purposes this consumption advantage of oil over coal applies with even greater force, since it enables warships either to carry more guns and increase their fire power accordingly, or, due to the greater cruising range, to obtain enormous tactical advantages in maintaining stations for long periods.

A second important reason for bunkering ships with oil fuel is the rapidity with which steam can be raised, where the type of boiler permits. This saves time for the merchant ship, and has even more importance for naval vessels, where the utmost speed in emergencies is essential. The fact that oil fuel enables a ship to operate practically without smoke is also an asset with naval craft, as it helps to conceal the vessel from long-range observation.

The greater speed with which oil can be loaded on board a ship as compared with coal is obvious, and the saving in time so obtained enables the ship to make a quicker turn-round in port.

In addition to this speed of delivery, oil has the advantage of extreme cleanliness as compared with coal, and here again not only time but expense is saved in the cleaning up of the ship when bunkering is finished. General economies are also effected in reduced stokehold staff when oil fuel is used.

When due consideration is given to these and other advantages which oil possesses, not only over coal but over all kinds of solid fuel, it follows almost as a matter of course that practically 100% of the ocean-going passenger liner tonnage of the world uses oil fuel for bunkering purposes.

PETROLEUM COKE

Although this chapter deals with liquid fuel, it is not out of place to include in it a mention of petroleum coke, which is formed as the solid residue in the thermal cracking process (*vide* chapter X).

Viewed as a raw material for further manufacture it is regarded as the purest form of industrial carbon available in large quantities, and as such is essential to many important industries.

The aluminium industry is one of the large consumers of carbon in the form of electrodes. The consumption of petroleum coke in the electrolytic production of aluminium is said to approximate 1 ton for each ton of aluminium produced. Owing to the sensitiveness of aluminium to impurities this industry calls for a high-grade petroleum coke, low in volatile matter, sulphur, ash and soluble salts.

Among other industries calling for a high-grade coke are those concerned in the manufacture of abrasives, artificial graphite, calcium carbide, electric furnace resisters and linings and dry cells ; also in steel and cast-iron carbon enriching, and so on.

A big field for petroleum coke, however, is as a rich, clean, ashless and smokeless fuel, in domestic and industrial heating and as a fuel for ships' bunkers—for both of which the specification limits are less exacting than for the above special manufacturing processes. Here, petroleum coke has proved to be much superior to other forms of solid fuel. It is easy to handle and, with the infrequent cleaning of fires, steady maximum boiler pressures can easily be maintained. It should be noted, however, that, owing to the small ash content of petroleum coke as compared with coal, it is necessary to protect boiler furnace fire-bars from the intense local heat by a layer of broken fire bricks.

Petroleum coke in its raw state is usually friable, with a tendency to disintegrate, and as such is unsuitable as a "foundry coke", since it is physically unable to withstand the weight of metal to be melted.

For many of the outlets already mentioned, petroleum coke has to be calcined (i.e. heated) to reduce volatile matter to a minimum. The resultant product is higher in carbon ; it is also much harder and therefore less liable to disintegrate in storage or in transit.

THE USE OF PETROLEUM OIL FOR GAS MAKING

The gas industry is quite a large consumer of petroleum oils, the quantity used for gas making in the U.S.A. being nearly $2\frac{1}{2}$ million tons in 1942. In Great Britain, the consumption of gas oil for carburetted water gas manufacture in 1947 was over 600,000 tons, nearly three times that in 1938, and this increased use of oil has been an important factor in the maintenance of town gas supplies during wartime difficulties and the continuing coal shortage.

Gas oil, in fact, owes its name to this use, but during the last twenty years rival demands for this product have developed enormously. Cracking plants use it as a raw material for making gasoline ; compression ignition engines and heating plants use it as fuel. This competition has forced the gas industry, particularly in the U.S.A., to use the heavier fuel oils, with the result that to-day a variety of oils ranging from distillates to residues is employed in the manufacture of gas.

The gas maker will normally choose, out of the oils available to him, that which will give him the optimum yield of gas in his plant at the lowest price.

OIL GAS PROCESSES

The first patent on record covering the manufacture of a gas "from vegetable or animal oil, fat, bitumen or resin" was obtained by John Taylor in England in 1815, but the best known of the early processes for oil gas manufacture was that developed by Pintsch, in Germany, in 1873. This process, which was one of violent cracking by introducing gas oil into a highly heated retort, gave a gas of high calorific value, 1,000–1,500 B.Th.U. per cubic foot (9,000–13,500 K. cal. per cubic metre). Pintsch gas was at one time much used in certain countries for carriage lighting and cooking on railways and for marine illumination (lighthouses, buoys etc.), but its use has been on the wane for many years owing to its gradual replacement by more modern fuels such as "bottled gas" (*vide* chapter XXIV).

Large-scale production of oil gas is common in the Pacific Coast region of the U.S.A., where petroleum oils are locally produced and coal is only available at high freight costs. The same oil is normally used both for heating the plant and for gas making, and is generally of the heavy residual type. In Great Britain there are a few oil gas plants of the "Jones" type operating on fuel oil or pitch ; considerable quantities of "carbon" are formed as a by-product in this process.

II

The simplest type of plant used—the single-shell machine—consists of a single brick-lined, cylindrical steel shell partially filled with checker brickwork, which is built over arches which form a combustion chamber at the base of the shell. The heating oil burners, air blast and gas offtake are situated in the bottom of the shell, the gas-making oil and steam sprays, together with the stack valve, at the top.

The process, like that of carburetted water gas manufacture, is intermittent, consisting of alternate heating and gas-making periods. First, the generator is heated to a temperature of 870° C.–990° C. (approximately 1,600° F.–1,800° F.) by means of the oil burners at the bottom of the shell. Steam and gas-making oil are then introduced. The oil vapour cracks as it passes through the hot checker brickwork, thus forming oil gas and free carbon or lampblack ; a portion of the latter reacts with the steam to form carbon monoxide and hydrogen, i.e. water gas. As a final step in the process, air is blown through the apparatus in order to burn off carbon deposited on the checker brickwork during the gas-making period. The product resulting from this process consists of a mixture of oil gas and water gas, having a calorific value of about 550 B.Th.U. per cubic foot (4,950 K. cal. per cubic metre). The overall yield of gas is about 0·8 therm* (80,000 B.Th.U.) per Imperial gallon.

CARBURETTED WATER GAS

Water gas, a gaseous fuel produced by the action of steam on red-hot coal or coke, is largely employed by the gas industry to supplement its production of ordinary coal gas. It is a mixture of hydrogen and carbon monoxide, and has a calorific value of about 300 B.Th.U. per cubic foot. (2,700 K. cal. per cubic metre), which is too low for general utility. The object of carburetting, i.e. enriching with oil gas, is to raise the calorific value to the required figure—generally 400–560 B.Th.U. per cubic foot (3,600–5,040 K. cal. per cubic metre).

The modern carburetted water gas plant consists essentially of three parts—a generator, a carburettor and a superheater, plus the usual condensers, scrubbers and purifying apparatus. The generator contains the fuel (coke or coal), while the carburettor and the superheater are filled with fire brick, arranged checker-wise.

The process is an intermittent one, consisting of two operations, the "blow" and the "run", carried out alternately. During the "blow" the coke is raised to incandescence by blowing a limited supply of air through it, thus producing carbon monoxide, which is burnt with further air admitted into the carburettor and super-heater in order to heat the checker brickwork to red heat. This being achieved, the air supply is shut off and steam is admitted to the generator for the gas-making "run". The water gas so pro-duced passes into the carburettor, where sufficient gas oil is sprayed in to effect the desired degree of enrichment ; the oil is vaporized and partly cracked, and the mixture of water gas, oil gas and vapour then passes to the superheater, where the cracking process is completed.

As the reaction between the steam and coke absorbs heat, the generator, carburettor and superheater become cool during the run, so that after a few minutes it is necessary to revert to air blowing in order to heat them up again. In practice, the run generally lasts for five or six minutes, and the blow for three or four.

Under proper conditions, 1 Imperial gallon of good gas oil will yield about 1·25 therms (i.e. 125,000 B.Th.U. = 31,500 K. calories) of gas, and for every gallon of oil used per 1,000 cubic feet of gas the calorific value of the latter will be increased by about 100 B.Th.U. per cubic foot (900 K. calories per cubic metre). In addition to gas, tar is produced equivalent to about 15% (volume) of the oil used.

In the U.S.A., heavy fuel oils are also used to a certain extent for carburetting water gas. The process is less efficient than with gas oil, the average yield in therms per gallon being about 20% lower. There is a slight saving in the coke used in the generator of some 3–4 lb. per 1,000 cubic feet of gas, but the plant requires more supervision than with gas oil and more frequent idle periods are necessary for maintenance purposes.

If carburetted water gas plant designed for gas oil is required to run on heavy fuel oil, modifications are necessary. For ex-ample, practically all checker brickwork may be removed from the carburettor, the oil being then injected into the carburettor as with gas oil, or the oil may be injected into the top of the generator instead of into the carburettor. Alternatively, a combination of these two methods may be adopted.

In addition to modifications to the actual plant, arrangements would have to be made for the storage and handling of heavy fuel oil as described in the section on the Storage and Handling of Fuel Oil.

OTHER USES OF GAS OIL

By an absorption process similar in principle to that used for recovering natural gasoline from natural gas (*vide* chapter IX), gas oil is used by many gas works and coke ovens as a solvent for extracting the benzol which is contained in coal gas.

Gas oil is also widely used in gas works for removing naphthalene from the gas prior to its distribution, this being a constituent which, by condensing and forming solid deposits, causes blockages in mains and service pipes. The gas immediately before it passes to the gas holders is washed with oil (generally in a scrubber of the horizontal rotary type) at a rate of about 20 Imperial gallons of oil per million cubic feet of gas.

BIBLIOGRAPHY

Oil Fuel. Fuel Oil General Department, The Shell Petroleum Co., Ltd., London.

Oil Burning. H. A. Romp. (Martinus Nijhoff, The Hague.)

Oil Burners. Kalmar Steiner, Ch.E. (McGraw Hill Publishing Co., London.)

Le Chauffage par les Combustibles Liquides. A. Guillermic. (Libraries Polytechnique, Ch. Beranger, Paris and Liège.)

Guide du Chauffage aux Huiles Lourdes. Editions O. Lesourd, Paris.

The Oil Heating Handbook. 3rd edition. H. A. Kunitz. (Constable Ltd., London.)

A Textbook of American Gas Practice. Morgan. (J. J. Morgan, New Jersey.)

The Manufacture of Coal Gas from Fuel Oil. G. M. Gill and Leon B. Jones. (Journal of the Institute of Fuel, Vol. 11, 1938.)

XXIX

LUBRICATING OILS, SPECIAL OILS
AND GREASES

LUBRICATING oils represent on an average about 4% to 5% of all the petroleum products produced from crude oils. They are fractions of suitable viscosity, which are capable of reducing the friction between moving surfaces and thus preventing the generation of excessive heat. Without adequate lubrication high temperatures would be developed with consequent damage, and ultimately destruction of the surfaces engaged. Besides suitable viscosity, lubricating oils must possess a number of other properties, chief of which is chemical stability, i.e. resistance to excessive change during use. Deterioration of lubricants in service can lead to many difficulties, some of which will be described later.

Practically all crude oils contain fractions with viscosities within the lubricating oil range, but not all hydrocarbons of suitable viscosity possess the other properties required for good lubrication. Few crude oils contain high proportions of the desirable lubricating oil hydrocarbons, and there is a wide variation in the types of crude oils and in their content of lubricating fractions (*vide* chapter VII).

TYPES OF LUBRICATING OILS

Lubricating oils may be divided into two categories—those produced as distillates and those produced as residues.

Distillates are produced by distillation—usually under reduced pressure—of a suitable fraction of the crude oil (*vide* chapter XIII). They are then refined either by solvent extraction, which yields a raffinate and an extract, or else by conventional acid treatment, yielding an acid refined distillate and an acid sludge.

The refined bulk distillate may then be redistilled into a number of fractions of different viscosities. Alternatively, the unrefined bulk distillate may itself be redistilled into the requisite fractions, each of which is separately refined.

Should the crude oil from which the distillate is made be paraffinous in type a certain amount of wax may be present in the distilled oil. This must be removed during subsequent refining so that the oil may remain liquid at low temperatures.

Finished distillate fractions may vary in viscosity from spindle oils, with a viscosity of 40 to 60 sec. Redwood I at 140° F., to heavy machine oils of about 300 sec. viscosity, or even higher. They are often classified according to their viscosity, as, for instance "500 Red", which indicates a red-coloured distillate of viscosity 500 sec. Saybolt at 100° F. Classification by Saybolt viscosity is general in the U.S.A. and is recognized in many other countries. Outside the U.S.A., however, classification is also made in terms of other viscometers which are in common use, e.g. Redwood I at 140° F. and Engler at 50° C.

Considering residual oils, crude oils of the paraffinous (Penna) type contain so little asphaltic matter that the residual oil remaining after distilling off the lighter lubricating portions may be used as a lubricant for certain purposes without any special refining. Such oils are known as "steam refined" or S.R. cylinder oils, and may be used for the manufacture of filtered cylinder stocks and bright stocks.

A filtered cylinder stock is simply a steam-refined type residue after it has been filtered by percolation through a special refining earth. This treatment removes traces of asphaltic matter and dark coloured constituents and leaves the oil with a strong green fluorescence or "bloom". The oil, however, will still have a high pour point owing to the presence of wax. Removal of this wax (by the dewaxing process described in chapter XV) converts the filtered stock into a bright stock. The waxy constituents which are removed are worked up into petroleum jelly or petrolatum*.

Bright stocks can also be made from the paraffinous crude oils, which contain some asphaltic matter, but in this case some refining with acid and earth may be necessary. Solvent extraction has also been applied to the production of bright stocks, and satisfactory products can now be made from a wider variety of crude oils.

Residual oils are therefore classified as dark (or steam refined) cylinder oils, filtered stocks and bright stocks. S.R. cylinder oils are further subdivided according to their flash point or fire test (*vide* infra), while filtered and bright stocks are normally classified by viscosity, colour and pour point.

BLENDING AND COMPOUNDING

Refineries generally produce a small number of basic oils, i.e. fractions or cuts which are made to a fairly close specification. For marketing purposes these may be blended together to produce a variety of oils for the many requirements of modern machinery. Blends may be made entirely from distillate oils or from distillates and residual oils, depending upon the particular requirements.

The blending operation is usually carried out in steam-heated vessels and the oils are agitated by a stirrer, or more frequently by air blowing. The process is performed at the lowest temperature possible consistent with complete mixing of the ingredients— usually about 60° C.

In addition to the preparation of mineral oil blends from basic oils, lubricants may be made by blending or compounding fatty oils* with petroleum oils. This is done to confer some special property on the finished blend. Thus, it is desirable that oils used for lubricating marine engine bearings should emulsify easily, and this is assured by incorporating a proportion of blown fish or blown rape oil. Similarly, fatty oils are incorporated in blends when increased oiliness* is required.

A more or less recent development in the production of lubricants is the addition of dopes or additives to certain grades. It has been found possible to confer special properties on oil blends by the addition of small quantities of dopes which are organic compounds, often metallic derivatives. These dopes are usually supplied as concentrates in mineral oil and can be incorporated during the normal blending process.

PROPERTIES AND METHODS OF TESTING

Many tests, mainly of a physical nature, have been developed for lubricating oils to assess those properties which are of importance in practice.

Viscosity. The most important property of lubricating oil is its viscosity, since this determines the rate at which it flows, and to a large extent the uses to which it can be put. The viscosity of a fluid is that property to which is due the resistance to shear (or flow) ; it is defined, fundamentally, as the force required to shear a layer of a unit thickness at a velocity equal to unity. If expressed in centimetre-gram-second units the unit of " dynamic " viscosity is the " poise ".

Accurate measurements of the viscosity of an oil are usually made by timing the flow of the oil under its own weight through a calibrated capillary tube. In this case, the force acting on unit volume of the oil will vary with the density of the oil, and this factor has to be allowed for in determining the dynamic viscosity. It is convenient for most purposes, however, to ignore this factor and, by multiplying the time taken for a given volume to flow from a given height through the capillary tube by a constant, determined for the apparatus, to obtain a figure which is known

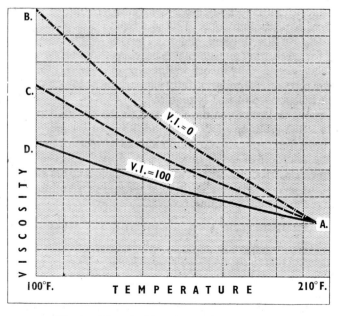

Fig. 1.   Viscosity/Temperature Relationship.

as the "kinematic" viscosity. The dynamic viscosity may be obtained from the kinematic viscosity by multiplying the latter by the density of the oil. The unit of kinematic viscosity in the C.G.S. system is the " stokes ". Except for very viscous liquids, it is more convenient to use smaller units and the centipoise and the centistokes are used, each being equal to one hundredth of the larger unit. At room temperature the viscosity of castor oil is about 20 stokes, while that of water is about 1 centistokes.

When the viscosity of an oil is required accurately it is determined as above, but for commercial purposes a number of simpler instruments are employed which give results approximately proportional to the true viscosities. These instruments determine the rate of flow of the oil through a hole of standard size. In England the Redwood instrument is used, in America the Saybolt, and on the European continent the Engler, the results being expressed as the time in seconds taken for a given volume of oil to flow through the hole. The Engler viscosity is more usually expressed as a ratio of this time to the time taken by water at 20° C., the ratio being known as "degrees" Engler.

Not only are different instruments used in different countries, but different standard temperatures are used for the determination as shown below :—

	Viscometer	Usual Viscosity Temperatures		
U.S.A. ...	Saybolt Universal	100° F.	130° F.	210° F.
U.K.	Redwood ...	70° F.	140° F.	200° F.
The European Continent ...	Engler	20° C.	50° C.	100° C.

Viscosity Index. The viscosity-temperature characteristics of a mineral lubricating oil vary according to the crude oil from which it is derived and the methods by which it is refined. The viscosity index was devised as an arbitrary measure of these characteristics. Lubricating oil distillates from Pennsylvanian crude oils possessed the best, i.e. the flattest, viscosity-temperature curves of the oils known at the time, and were therefore assigned a viscosity index of 100. Similarly, distillates from the Gulf crude oils, which possess steep viscosity-temperature curves, were given a viscosity index of 0. The viscosity-temperature curve of an oil is then compared with these curves of the standard oils as shown in fig. 1, and the viscosity index determined as follows :—

The viscosity of the oil is determined at 210° F. (A) and at 100° F. (C). Two distillates, one of 100 V.I. and the other of 0 V.I., both having the same viscosity at 210° F. as the oil under consideration, are taken and their viscosities determined at 100° F. These are represented by points D and B respectively in fig. 1. In this figure, AB represents the steep curve of the 0 V.I. oil, AD the flat curve of the 100 V.I. oil, and AC the curve of the oil under consideration. The viscosity index of the latter oil is given by the proportion $\frac{BC}{BD} \times 100$, so that if, for example, its viscosity at 100° F. falls midway between those of the two reference oils, its viscosity index will be 50. In practice, it is necessary only to determine the viscosity of the oil under consideration at 100° F. and 210° F., the viscosity at 100° F. of the standard oils having the same viscosity at 210° F. being determined from tables.

Flashpoint. The flashpoint of an oil is the minimum temperature at which it gives off inflammable vapours under specified conditions. As with viscosities, different instruments are used to determine the flashpoint in different countries. Thus, in the United Kingdom the Pensky-Martens apparatus is used (*vide* chapter XXVIII), in America the Cleveland, in France the Luchaire, and in Germany the Marcusson instrument.

The flashpoint of an oil is influenced to a large extent by its most volatile constituents. Thus, a very small amount of kerosine will reduce the flashpoint of a lubricating oil nearly to that of kerosine. The flashpoint, therefore, gives no indication of the volatility of the oil as a whole. Except as a measure of inflammability, the flashpoint is of little practical significance, although it is often supposed to be a criterion by which the suitability of an oil for an engine can be judged. This is erroneous, since the temperatures of the surfaces which an oil has to lubricate in, say, a motor car, are usually about 100° F. below the flashpoint of the oil, while in the combustion space in internal combustion engines the oil will be burnt anyhow irrespective of its flashpoint.

The flashpoint as normally measured in the Pensky-Martens

apparatus is referred to as the "closed flashpoint", as the determination is carried out while the oil cup is covered with a lid. After observation of the closed flashpoint, the lid of the oil cup is removed and the temperature is raised further until a flash due to ignition of the oil vapour is obtained, when the pilot flame is brought near to the surface of the oil. The temperature at which this occurs, which is usually 20° F. to 40° F. (11° C. to 22° C.) higher than the closed flashpoint, is known as the "open flashpoint". The "fire test" is measured by continuing the heating of the oil until the lowest temperature is reached at which it will continue to burn when a flame is brought into contact with its surface. The fire test is generally from 30° F. to 60° F. (17° C. to 33° C.) higher than the open flashpoint.

Pour Point. The pour point of an oil refers to the lowest temperature at which the oil will flow under specified conditions. The test is carried out by putting a small quantity of oil into a bottle of standard size, which is then placed in a freezing mixture. A thermometer is fixed in the oil, and, as the temperature falls, the bottle is removed from the cooling bath at every 5° F. fall in temperature and tilted to see whether the oil will flow. The lowest temperature at which the oil still remains liquid is known as the "pour point".

There are two factors which limit the practical significance of the pour point ; it indicates that at a certain temperature a waxy structure develops in the oil and interferes with its flow, but it gives no indication of the flow characteristics of the oil on agitation or if a considerable force were exerted on it at or below that temperature.

Colour. The colour of an oil by transmitted light, and the presence or absence of a "bloom" in reflected light, give no indication whatever of the behaviour of the oil in practice. The colour of an oil is determined by comparing a layer of the oil in a standard glass cell with a number of standard coloured slides. Tests for colour are only useful in connection with refining practice. Colour is of no value as a method of comparing lubricating qualities of oil, although, if oils from a given source are being compared, it may be said that, in general, the oil of the paler colour is the more stable. Very pale colour is sometimes required in technical applications when the oil comes in contact with materials on which it must show no stain, or where it is required for toilet or medicinal preparations.

The apparatus most commonly used is the A.S.T.M. Union colorimeter, in which the colour of an oil is matched against those of a series of standard colour glasses. The colour of the oil is expressed as that of the nearest glass which it resembles. The glasses are given letters or numbers indicating their colour. Thus, the glass known as G or no. 1 is pale yellow, and that described as R or no. 8 is deep red in colour.

Carbon Residue. A number of tests have been devised with the idea of giving some information on the amount of carbon which would be formed from an oil used in an internal combustion engine. All these tests involve heating the oil strongly out of contact with the air and weighing the residue of carbonaceous material. The best known of these tests are the Conradson and the Ramsbottom tests. While these tests give some general indication of the carbon forming tendencies of an oil, the figures are apt to be rather misleading, since the conditions to which the oil is subjected in an engine are entirely different from those obtaining in these tests.

Oxidation Stability. Many tests have also been proposed for assessing the stability of oils towards oxidation under conditions they would experience in practice. None of these laboratory tests has yet been entirely satisfactory in predicting the behaviour of the oils in use.

For engine oils the best known of these tests is probably the British Air Ministry Oxidation Test, in which air is blown through a tube of the oil at 200° C. under specified conditions and the increase in viscosity and in carbon residue determined after the test. This test, while giving some indication of the stability of an oil towards oxidation, has now been dropped from the Air Ministry specification since it did not correlate with engine tests.

More promising results have been obtained in tests in which oxygen is circulated through the hot oil in the presence of iron and copper catalysts, and it is possible that some test will ultimately be developed on these lines which will give satisfactory correlation with engine tests.

A number of oxidation tests have been developed for examining other types of oil, such as turbine oils and electrical oils, and these, where necessary, are described under the products concerned.

THE THEORY OF LUBRICATION

There are two types of lubrication : hydrodynamic or fluid lubrication*, and boundary lubrication*.

Fluid lubrication occurs when there is a copious supply of lubricant between two surfaces which are moving relative to one another at moderately high speeds. The film between the surfaces is maintained by the lubricant being dragged in between the surfaces due to the movement between them, and depends solely on the viscosity of the lubricant and the relative speed of the surfaces ; it is independent of the nature of the lubricant. Thus, it is possible to lubricate high-speed spindles by means of air or any other gas at high pressure. Similarly, water or any other liquid would be a satisfactory lubricant under certain conditions. A mineral oil, however, has a number of advantages over most other fluids, e.g. high viscosity and relatively high resistance to chemical change. An example of fluid lubrication is in a journal bearing where the rotation of the journal drags the oil between it and the bearing, so that the journal is separated from the bearing by a film of oil. The thickness of the film varies with operating conditions of the bearing, but it will be very thin by ordinary standards—probably something of the order of a thousandth of an inch. This is very thick, however, compared with the dimensions of the molecules of which the oil is composed. About 100,000 or more of these molecules, placed end to end, would be required to form the thickness of this film.

Under these conditions of fluid lubrication the friction between the journal and the bearing will be low and will depend on the viscosity of the lubricant, the speed of rotation and the pressure exerted on the journal.

We have seen above that the conditions of fluid lubrication are maintained by the speed of rotation of the journal, which drags the lubricant between it and the bearing. Now, when the journal is stationary it will sink through the lubricant. The majority of the lubricant will be squeezed out from between the surfaces, and direct contact may occur between irregularities of the surfaces of the journal and the bearing. The area over which contact occurs will depend on the load. If the journal carries an appreciable load and rotates very slowly it will not drag in sufficient oil to give a continuous film. Under these conditions, where the speed is low and the load high, fluid lubrication cannot be maintained and the lubrication is of the boundary type. The friction is some thirty times as great as in the case of fluid lubrication ; it is independent of the viscosity of the lubricant and depends only on the load carried by the surface and the so-called "oiliness" of the lubricant. This oiliness is due to the power certain molecules have of attaching themselves to the metal surfaces so as to provide a thin film on each surface, probably not more than one molecule thick. These films reduce the direct metal-to-metal contact between the surfaces and so reduce the friction. Molecules which attach themselves to the surfaces in this way contain active (polar) groups. Thus, fatty acids*, which consist of a hydrocarbon chain with a carboxyl (COOH) group at the end, are active in reducing the friction under conditions of boundary lubrication because they are anchored to the metal surface by this carboxyl group, and so are not squeezed out by the pressure on the surfaces. But even the most effective materials only reduce the friction under boundary conditions to about one-third of that obtained with a straight mineral oil.

Modern refining methods, which are designed to produce an oil stable towards oxidation and possessing good viscosity-temperature characteristics, remove many of the polar bodies which would assist lubrication under boundary conditions. Small amounts of fatty acids, fatty oils or special "oiliness" additives are, therefore, sometimes incorporated in oils when good lubricating properties under boundary conditions are desirable. It should be emphasized, however, that these conditions of boundary lubrication cannot be tolerated to any extent in practice owing to the large amount of energy which would be lost as a result of the high friction, and which would appear as heat, with disastrous results to the bearing surfaces. Consequently, machines are so designed that the lubrication occurs as far as possible under fluid conditions.

The most carefully finished metal surface is not truly flat, but is covered with minute projections and depressions. It has been shown that if contact occurs between these minute projections, due to the absence of a sufficiently thick film of oil between the moving surfaces, very high temperatures can be produced at these points. These local temperatures are often sufficiently high to cause melting of the metal, with consequent damage to the surfaces. For this reason it is normal to use a low melting point metal, e.g. white metal, for bearings, so that if the lubrication breaks down the bearing and not the journal is damaged. It is desirable, therefore, to use different metals for the rubbing surfaces whenever possible. In certain cases, such as in gears, for example, like metals or two metals with high melting points are used and a high load is carried over a small area. The development of local high temperatures at the high spots is unavoidable. In this case special compounds known as E.P. (extreme pressure) additives are incorporated in the oil. These additives are capable of attacking the metal surfaces at the "hot spots" and forming a protective film which prevents seizure and consequent damage to the surface. This point will be dealt with more fully later in this chapter.

LUBRICATION SYSTEMS

Lubrication systems may be divided into three broad categories :—

    (1) Total Loss Systems (non-circulating).
    (2) Circulating Systems.
    (3) Bath and Splash Systems.

(1) **Total Loss Systems.** With this method a comparatively small quantity of oil is delivered either intermittently or continuously, to the bearing surfaces. The used oil from these working surfaces runs to waste and is not re-circulated. The fresh oil may be applied in a number of ways, using methods ranging from hand oiling to complicated centralized pressure systems. Typical examples of methods in common use are as follows :—

(*a*) *Drip-feed Lubricators.* A lubricator of this type consists of an oil cup with an adjustable outlet, from which the oil falls drop by drop on to the bearing. A window is provided so that the oil

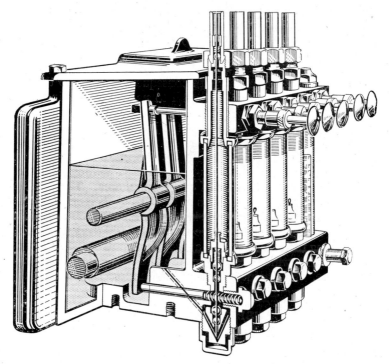

Fig. 2.   Sectional Illustration of a Forced Feed Group Lubricator.

drops can be seen and the flow can be regulated to a given number of drops per minute.   A disadvantage with this type of lubricator is that it must be turned on and off by hand each time the machine is started and stopped.

(*b*) *Mechanical Lubricators*.   The advantage with this method of lubrication is that the supply of oil starts and stops automatically, and the quantity delivered varies according to the speed of the engine or machine.   The engine or machine normally operates a number of pumps, each of which delivers a given amount of oil through a series of pipes to the various lubricating points.   On its way the lubricant passes upwards in the form of droplets through a sight glass filled with water so that the rate of flow can be seen and controlled. This method is widely used in group lubrication systems, e.g. large diesel engine cylinders, air compressors, steam engines etc., the number of pumps per unit varying between one and sixteen. Fig. 2 illustrates a conventional lubricator combining pumping elements and sight glasses. This type may be operated by either a rotary or ratchet drive.

(2) **Circulating Systems.** In this case, a relatively large supply of oil is kept in circulation and is delivered under pressure to the bearings. From a reservoir, oil is fed by pump or gravity through pipes or passages to the working surfaces. Excess lubricant may be returned to the reservoir by gravity or by means of a scavenge pump. Typical examples of such systems are to be found in the case of automotive engines, aero engines and steam turbines.

In addition to lubricating the moving parts the oil also functions as a coolant, and for this reason an oil cooler is very often included in a system so as to dissipate the heat which the oil removes from the working surfaces. A filter can also be incorporated on the delivery side of the pump to ensure that only clean oil is supplied.

(3) **Bath and Splash Systems.** A typical example is the ordinary gear box, where the pinions dip into the oil and splash it freely around all bearings and moving parts. Variations of this method are ring or chain oilers, where a ring or endless chain rotating loosely on the journal or shaft dips into a bath of oil and carries the oil up to the bearing surfaces. In other cases, a shaft or spindle may rub against a felt pad impregnated with oil, or oil may be syphoned from a bath to the bearing above, by means of wicks, as in the lubrication of certain types of railway axle bearings.

TYPES OF BEARINGS

A bearing is a support provided to hold a moving member of a machine in its correct position. There are many types of bearings in use, and they may be divided into two broad categories: (1) plain bearings, (2) anti-friction bearings.

(1) **Plain Bearings.** In its simplest form this type of bearing consists of a hollow cylinder in which a shaft revolves, that portion of the shaft within the bearing being termed the journal, and

the support a journal bearing. If the revolving shaft is subjected to an end load, a thrust bearing must be provided, and this may consist of a collar on the shaft rotating against a flange on the support.

Another form of plain bearing is that designed to support a shaft or spindle which does not revolve, but moves backwards and forwards in the direction of its longitudinal axis. This is termed a guide bearing. To reduce frictional losses and to protect the moving shaft, it is usual in all these combinations to have a lining of relatively soft metal attached to one of the bearing surfaces.

Lubrication of plain bearings is usually effected by oil of suitable viscosity, although in special cases grease may be used.

''Self-oiling'' bearings represent a type of bearing material which, it is claimed, will give lengthy service without the supply of any external lubricant. These bearings, which are suitable for light duty applications, are made of sintered powdered metal—normally bronze—and have a highly porous structure. They are impregnated with oil during manufacture and may contain as much as 30% by volume of the lubricant.

(2) **Anti-friction Bearings.** In this type of bearing the sliding motion which exists in the case of the plain bearing is replaced by rolling motion. This is done by inserting a row of steel balls or rollers between races, which are hardened steel rings attached to the moving and stationary parts. A cage or separator is normally used to ensure that the rolling elements are correctly spaced and to prevent them from rubbing one against the other.

(a) *Ball Bearings.* Such bearings may consist of a single or double row of balls designed to cater for either radial or combined radial and thrust loading. These bearings are widely used in electric motors, high-speed machine tools etc.

(b) *Roller Bearings.* These are normally designed to carry heavier loads than ball bearings, and are therefore used where conditions of operation are more severe. The rollers may be straight, tapered, barrelled or concave, depending on the application in question. Thus, straight rollers are generally employed for radial loads, whereas tapered rollers can support both radial and end thrust loadings. Barrel or concave rollers ensure self-alignment.

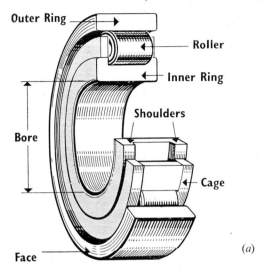

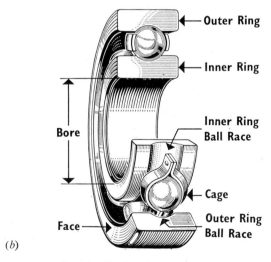

Fig. 3. Ball and Roller Bearings.

A special type is the needle roller bearing, in which the rollers may be assembled direct on to a hardened shaft without either inner or outer races or separators. Owing to the length of the rollers relative to their diameter, they tend to skew. However, they are generally used for oscillating movements where reversal of movement corrects this tendency. Fig. 3 illustrates typical ball and roller bearings. Theoretically, rolling contact does not require a lubricant, but in operation a small amount of sliding can take place due to the distortion of the balls or rollers in contact with the races when under load. In addition, sliding occurs between the rolling elements and the cage or separator. It is necessary, therefore, to provide effective lubrication to reduce friction and wear to a minimum.

Where possible oil is used as the lubricant, but in many cases grease lubrication is desirable. Grease does not leak out of bearings to the same extent as oil, and, moreover, will form a protective seal against the entry of dirt and moisture, which are the greatest enemies of anti-friction bearings.

The grade of oil or grease used depends on many factors. Oils can vary from spindle grades for small high-speed bearings to high-viscosity stocks for slow-speed, heavily loaded bearings. Similarly, in selecting a suitable grease the viscosity of the oil base and the nature of the soap are important factors.

LUBRICATION OF INTERNAL COMBUSTION ENGINES

Aircraft Engines.

Most aircraft engines are lubricated on the dry sump principle, i.e., the oil is stored in a tank separate from the engine and pumped under pressure, through pipes and oilways drilled in the shafts, to the big-end and main crankshaft bearings, camshafts, rockers and other parts requiring a copious supply of lubricant. The oil escaping from the big end is flung up on to the cylinder walls, providing a supply of lubricant for the pistons and filling the crankcase with a mist of finely dispersed droplets of oil, which settle on the exposed surfaces and drain into the sump. A scavenge pump having a pumping capacity about 30% to 50% greater than the pressure pump returns the oil from the sump to the tank.

The scheme of lubrication of a liquid-cooled aero engine is shown in fig. 4. In this diagram the engine is represented by E, and the oil reservoir by R. Oil from R is pumped through the cock G and oil filter F by the pressure pump P, which delivers the oil to a triple-pressure relief valve unit V. This unit has three spring-loaded non-return valves, the loading on each valve being adjusted so as to provide oil at three different pressures through

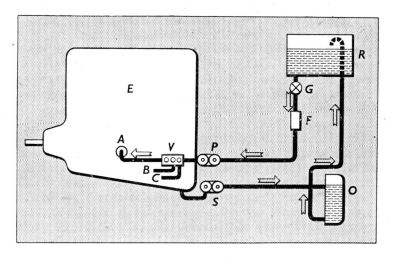

Fig. 4.   Lubrication System of Liquid-cooled Aero Engine.

the outlets A, B and C. The high-pressure supply is used for operating the hydraulically controlled variable-pitch airscrew ; the intermediate pressure for the crankshaft bearings and the low-pressure supply for the camshaft, gears, rockers and other highly-loaded working parts. The oil draining to the bottom of the crankcase is returned by the scavenge pump S through an oil cooler O to the reservoir R.

The advantages of the dry sump over the wet sump system used on automobiles is that it enables the engine to be made more compact and allows a much larger volume of oil to be in circulation.

This facilitates the cooling of the oil and consequently renders it less liable to deterioration.

As a result of service requirements the power output of aero engines has increased considerably during the last few years. This increase in performance has led to the oil being subjected to higher temperatures and more severe conditions generally than in the pre-war engines. Consequently, improvements in the oil have had to keep pace with developments in engine design. Owing to the high temperatures encountered in aero engines more viscous oils are required than is usual for other internal combustion (I.C.) engines. For example, the viscosity at 140° F. of Aeroshell 100 is almost double that of Double Shell motor oil.

As we have seen above, the oil in the crankcase of an aero engine is dispersed as fine droplets and settles as a thin film on hot parts of the engine, such as the underside of the pistons and the cylinder walls. These conditions facilitate the oxidation of the oil by the oxygen of the air in the crankcase. Oxidation of a lubricating oil gives rise to products which are more unstable than the oil itself and which polymerize to more complex resinous compounds. These adhere to metal surfaces, giving a varnish-like film which is known as "lacquer", and in the combustion chamber carbonize more easily than the original oil, giving rise to carbonaceous deposits which interfere with the transfer of heat and promote detonation and pre-ignition. The oxidation products also give rise to deposits in the piston-ring grooves which may eventually cause the rings to stick. When this occurs the rings no longer effectively seal the combustion chamber, and the hot gases "blow-by" the piston and escape into the crankcase. This blow-by will accelerate the sticking of the rings remaining free ; it may damage the piston and eventually lead to engine failure. Acidic substances are also formed by oxidation of mineral oils, and these acids cause trouble by corrosion, particularly of certain types of bearing metal. Stability towards oxidation is, therefore, a very important criterion of an aircraft oil, and for this reason aero engine oils are blended from highly refined solvent-extracted stocks. The best straight mineral oil obtainable will not, however, give sufficient protection against ring-sticking in some air-cooled engines.

The ring-sticking tendencies of oils are investigated on single-cylinder test engines. For the sake of simplicity and economy these are usually air-cooled motor cycle engines, although sometimes single-cylinder units from actual aero engines are employed in the final tests. The test engines are run under very carefully controlled conditions, ring-sticking tendencies being determined either by taking the time for a certain degree of ring-sticking to occur under standard conditions, or by measuring the cylinder temperature at which a certain degree of sticking occurs at the end of a given time. Various complex organic compounds, derived from phenol or salicylic acid, containing such metals as zinc, calcium or barium, have been developed to combat ring-sticking. These additives function on account of their anti-oxidant and detergent properties and under standard test conditions will, at concentrations of the order of 1%, raise the ring-sticking temperature by some 50° C. They also have the advantage of reducing the formation of deposits in the engine so that it is possible to run for greater periods between overhauls.

The formation of sludge by deterioration of an aero engine oil is also very undesirable, since sludges are separated in parts of the engine such as crankpin oilways and supercharger clutches, where they are subjected to centrifugal force. Troubles due to deposits of sludge in these regions are, however, often connected with the high lead tetraethyl content of the fuel, and consist of lead compounds such as sulphate, chloride and bromide, which find their way from the combustion chamber past the piston into the lubricating oil.

So far, we have considered only the properties of the lubricating oil at the operating temperatures in the engines, but aircraft often encounter very low temperatures at high altitudes and when standing in the open in cold climates. It is essential, therefore, that an aircraft oil has a low pour point and a high viscosity index, so that it can circulate freely to the vital points which it has to lubricate, and also so that it does not cause too high a drag, which would prevent easy starting. To improve ease of starting of aero engines at low atmospheric temperatures the Worth oil dilution system is sometimes used. In this system the oil tank is separated into two parts by a baffle reaching nearly to the bottom of the tank.   Just before shutting down the engine, the oil in the smaller part of the tank is diluted with gasoline.   On starting up the engine again oil is circulated from this portion of the tank.   The gasoline cuts down the viscosity of the oil, and therefore makes starting easier.   As the engine warms up, the gasoline in the oil boils off and the oil returns to its normal viscosity.   At excessively low temperatures it may be necessary, in addition, to inject special volatile fuels into the fuel intake manifold, in order to make a start possible.

Another difficulty that may arise in the operation of aero engines is due to the frothing of the lubricating oil in service.   As mentioned above, aero engines are lubricated on the dry sump system, and to ensure complete draining of oil the scavenge pump is given a capacity in excess of that of the feed pump.   The result of this is that a large volume of air is sucked in with the oil at the scavenge pump inlet.   This air becomes dispersed in the oil, and in those parts of the oil system where the oil is under high pressure it will dissolve only to be released in regions of lower pressure. Thus, an intimate mixture of oil and air may be delivered to the oil tank.   Much of the air will separate and escape, but the smaller bubbles will be carried through with the oil by the delivery pump. Aerated oil will thus be passed into the engine and find its way into the sump, where it may become further aerated as it is picked up by the scavenge pump and returned to the tank.   Many tanks are vented to the sump, and with excessive production of foam in the tank the foam level may reach the vent pipe and pass into the sump.   The scavenge pump may be incapable of handling the large volume of foam, and the sump may fill with foam, leading to loss of oil from the breathers.   The presence of air in the suction line of the delivery pump reduces the volume of oil supplied to the engine owing to the displacement of oil by air, and the efficiency of the pump is adversely affected by the expansion and contraction of the air.   Loss in oil flow through this cause may lead to engine failure through lack of lubricant.

The addition of anti-ring-sticking and detergent additives often increases the stability of the foam.   Fortunately it is possible to overcome this difficulty by the addition of a minute quantity of a complex compound of silicon, hydrogen, carbon and oxygen, known as a silicone, which is extremely effective in breaking the foam. Improvement in the design of oil tanks, pump and pipelines has also largely overcome the troubles experienced at one time due to excessive foaming.

The requirements for gas turbine lubricants are somewhat different from those for piston engines. Aero gas turbines are best fitted for aeroplanes operating at high altitudes, where atmospheric temperatures are low. Hence, lubricating oils for such engines must flow readily at low temperatures, and oils with viscosities of the order of 40 to 50 seconds Redwood I at 210° F. have been used ; a high viscosity index and good oxidation stability are also desirable. In some cases a spray of oil and air has been used for lubricating ball bearings in such engines, and in this case the oil should have rust-preventive properties. For turbine/airscrew combinations the oil probably should have some extreme pressure properties to give satisfactory lubrication of the reduction gearing.

Automobile Engines.

In most automobile engines the lubricating oil is contained in a sump placed at the base of the engine, and containing between one and two gallons of oil, according to the size of the engine. In general, all modern high output automobile engines are lubricated by the force-feed system. A pump driven by the engine picks up oil from the sump and circulates it under pressure through pipes, or oilways drilled in the cylinder block, to the main bearings, camshaft, timing gears, etc., and through oilways drilled in the crankshaft to the big end bearings. The oil escaping *via* the clearances of the big ends is flung on to the cylinder walls, and the crankcase is filled with a mist of small droplets of oil which settle on all the exposed surfaces, covering them with a film of oil. The lubrication system of a typical automobile engine is shown in fig. 5.

Although operating conditions in an automobile engine are not usually as severe as those in an aircraft engine, troubles may result from the deterioration of the lubricating oil. Thus, as mentioned above, some of the warm oil is flung off from the big ends on to hot metal surfaces, such as the underside of the piston and the cylinder walls, and the crankcase is filled with a mist of small droplets of warm oil. These conditions—contact with hot metal surfaces and the exposure of a large surface area of the oil to the oxygen of the air—facilitate oxidation of the oil. When a lubricating oil is

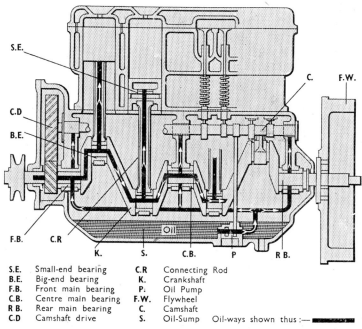

S.E.	Small-end bearing	C.R	Connecting Rod
B.E.	Big-end bearing	K.	Crankshaft
F.B.	Front main bearing	P.	Oil Pump
C.B.	Centre main bearing	F.W.	Flywheel
R B.	Rear main bearing	C.	Camshaft
C.D	Camshaft drive	S.	Oil-Sump Oil-ways shown thus :—

Fig. 5.   Lubrication System of Automobile Engine.

oxidized it increases in viscosity, forms acidic substances which may corrode certain bearing metals, such as copper-lead alloys, and gives rise to gummy resinous deposits, known as "lacquer", on the pistons and other hot metal parts. Deterioration products of the oil will also clog the piston ring grooves and hinder the functioning of the piston rings, although actual sticking of rings followed by blow-by and the subsequent troubles which are sometimes experienced on aircraft engines do not occur as often under the milder operating conditions of automobile engines. Severe oxidation will also give rise to sludges which may settle out in various parts of the engine and choke oilways screen and filters. It is obvious, therefore, that the most important requirements of a lubricating oil for automobile engines must be its stability towards oxidation, freedom from deposit-forming tendencies and its anti-wear characteristics.

Furthermore, an oil of high viscosity index is required, so that it will be of sufficiently low viscosity to be circulated freely to all the moving parts when the engine is cold and yet not be of too low a viscosity when the engine is hot. The use of an oil of high viscosity index also has the advantage that it decreases the viscous drag of the lubricant before the engine has warmed up, and so facilitates starting from cold. The pour point of an automobile engine oil must be below the lowest temperature to which the engine is likely to be subjected (e.g. when standing in the open on a frosty night) so that the pump is able to circulate the oil when the engine is started.

All these requirements are met by oils produced by the modern solvent refining processes, and high-grade automobile engine lubricants are invariably blended from such oils.

Although these solvent refined high viscosity index oils do not deteriorate in use nearly as rapidly as the older distillate type of oils, they can be still further improved by the incorporation of various additives. A considerable amount of research work is continuously going on to improve automobile engine lubricants, and oils containing additives which give improved performance are being marketed. These oils are known as ''Premium'' motor oils to distinguish them from the undoped or ''Regular'' lubricating oils ; they have greater oxidation stability and are less liable than straight mineral oils to form acids which corrode bearing metals. Premium oils may also possess some degree of detergency, which helps to prevent the formation of deposits on the pistons, rings etc. In the section on '' Heavy Duty Oils '' detergent action is more fully discussed.

A number of laboratory tests have been developed to give some indication of the behaviour of oils in service with regard to oxidation, bearing corrosion, sludging, lacquer formation and ring sticking. Although these tests may give useful information of the behaviour of oils under carefully controlled standard conditions, none of these is entirely satisfactory in predicting the behaviour of the oil in an engine. The reason for this is that there are so many different factors operating in an engine, and, although these may be controlled to a large extent in one particular engine, they vary from one type of engine to another. This results in different engines assessing the oils differently.

In the development of automobile engine lubricants tests are first carried out on single-cylinder engines, as in the case of aviation oils, for reasons of simplicity and economy. The final bench tests are made on standard production types of multi-cylinder engines. Since an oil in practice has to operate satisfactorily under a variety of conditions, each of which may lead to some trouble fostered by that condition, bench tests are run to simulate various conditions on the road. For example, the American Co-ordinating Research Council devised the C.R.C. L-4 test to study oxidation, lacquer formation and bearing corrosion under severe operating conditions. This test employs a standard six-cylinder Chevrolet engine ($3\frac{1}{2}$ inches bore $\times$ $3\frac{3}{4}$ inches stroke), which is run for 36 hours at 3,150 r.p.m. when developing 30 b.h.p. under carefully controlled conditions. Performance of the oil is judged by examination of the pistons, rings, bearings etc., for varnish and sludge deposits, ascertaining the loss in weight of the test bearings, and by examination of the analytical data obtained on the used oil. Under these test conditions the oil rarely forms the sticky black sludge which normally arises from the emulsification of carbonaceous particles in the used oil and water condensed from the products of combustion present in the crankcase. This emulsion is formed when the engine operates for repeated short periods under cold conditions. These conditions also result in excessive cylinder and ring wear due to corrosion. To study the behaviour of the oil under such conditions some form of " cycling " test is usually employed, in which the engine is run as cold as possible for a repeated series of short periods under different conditions.

Other test conditions are devised to investigate piston cleanliness, cylinder wear and the behaviour of engine filters.

Finally, as all these bench tests are necessarily carried out under accelerated conditions, before a new motor oil is put on the market it must be extensively tested in as many vehicles as possible on the road, and these tests may take as many weeks as the bench tests take hours to give the required information.

Owing to the confusion which arose in the past due to the arbitrary use of the terms "Light", "Medium", "Heavy" etc., in branding motor oils, the Society of Automotive Engineers in America instituted a system of numbering in which they standardized the grades in terms of the Saybolt viscosities as follows :—

				Viscosity Range (*Saybolt Universal*)	
S.A.E. No.				*at* 130° *F.*	*at* 210° *F.*
10	...	...	...	90–120	—
20	...	...	...	120–185	—
30	...	...	...	185–255	—
40	...	...	...	255 minimum	80 maximum
50	...	...	...	—	80–105
60	...	...	...	—	105–125
70	...	...	...	—	125–150

The general trend is towards the use of oils of lower viscosity in modern high-speed automobile engines, an oil with a high viscosity index and a viscosity of about 150 seconds Redwood I at 140° F. being very suitable. The advantages of using such an oil are : ease of starting from cold, small power loss when cold due to viscous drag, adequate lubrication during the warming-up period and a copious supply to all vital bearings, which assists in dissipation of heat.

Lubrication Troubles.

A minute proportion only of the mechanical failures on automobile engines are directly due to the lubricating oil. The deterioration of an engine oil in service is not in general due to any depreciation of its lubricating qualities. When such an oil becomes unfit for further use this is due to its becoming contaminated with impurities such as abrasive particles of road dirt, carbonaceous particles from the combustion chamber, diluent from the heavy ends of the fuel, lead compounds from a leaded fuel and water from leakages in the cooling system or condensation of the products of combustion. The majority of bearing and piston failures result from the lack of an adequate supply of lubricant, which may be caused by blockage of the oil system by sludge.

If an engine is continually operating under cold conditions, some of the heavy ends of the fuel which escape combustion and settle on the cylinder walls may find their way into the sump, particularly if the cylinders are worn. This gives rise to dilution of the oil and lowering of its viscosity. This trouble can become particularly serious on engines such as those of agricultural tractors, which run on a less volatile fuel such as kerosine. In cases of excessive dilution, the lubricating properties of the oil may be impaired to such an extent as to give rise to excessive wear or even engine failure.

A serious trouble on automobile engines, which is not directly due to failure of the lubrication, is excessive cylinder wear. This occurs particularly in the case of engines operating for short periods, i.e. under cold conditions, e.g. in the case of a doctor's car, certain delivery trucks etc. It is due to condensation on the cold cylinder walls of the water formed in the combustion chamber. This water will be acid due to the presence of carbon dioxide, traces of sulphur dioxide or trioxide from the small amount of sulphur present in the fuel and lubricant, and oxides of nitrogen, and will corrode the cylinder walls. The desirability of an oil possessing the property of protecting the cylinder wall from this corrosion is borne in mind in the development of new motor oils. It is obviously desirable, however, to warm the engine up as rapidly as possible and to operate continuously with a cylinder block cooling water outlet at a temperature of not less than about 70° C.

The thick black sludge which forms in the crankcase and in the cooler parts of the engine consists of droplets of water associated with carbonaceous particles and dispersed in the oil as a stable "mayonnaise" type of emulsion. This water may come from the cooling system *via* a leaking gasket, but, as previously mentioned, it is usually derived from the products of combustion containing water vapour, which "blowby" the piston rings and find their way into the crankcase, where the water vapour condenses. This will naturally occur to a greater extent in the case of worn engines, and is best eliminated by the use of an efficient "breather" for the crankcase.

Diesel Engines.

Diesel engines may conveniently be classified as high-speed and low-speed engines, the limit for low-speed engines being placed at 300 r.p.m. High-speed engines have trunk pistons, that is to say, the piston is connected directly to the crank by means of a connecting rod. Low-speed engines sometimes have trunk pistons, but more usually, they have pistons of the cross-head type. In the cross-head type of engine the piston is rigidly fixed to a piston rod at the end of which is the connecting rod. The side thrust due to the varying inclination of the connecting rod is, in this type, taken up by a cross-head which slides in the same plane as the piston. These two types are shown in figs. 6 and 7.

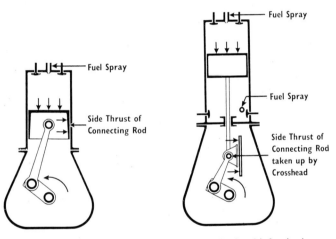

Single Acting 4 Stroke with Trunk Piston   Double Acting 4 Stroke with Crosshead

Fig. 6.   Trunk Type Piston.   Fig. 7.   Crosshead Type Piston.

Modern high-speed engines are lubricated by a force feed system in the same way as an automotive type gasoline engine, but in general their operating conditions—particularly in the case of high-output two-stroke diesel engines—are somewhat more severe.

Owing to the large bore diameters and reduced oil throw from the big ends obtaining on low-speed engines, with consequent difficulties in maintaining a film lubricant on the cylinder walls, it is customary to arrange a separate oil feed to the cylinders. This is also necessary on cross-head engines where the design is such that no communication exists between the crankcase and cylinder bores. In such an engine it is usual to employ a more viscous oil for the cylinder than for the bearings.

The conditions to which the oil is subjected in a high-speed diesel engine, such as that used for automotive work, are very severe, and consequently an oil which is more stable towards oxidation is required. It is customary, therefore, to use a solvent-extracted oil for these engines, and such an oil has a high viscosity index, which is an advantage when the engine has to start at low temperature. The development of high-speed two-stroke diesel engines led to the oil being subjected to still higher temperatures, since in any given number of revolutions there are twice as many combustions, and trouble arose due to ring-sticking, piston lacquering and carbon formation on the piston lands, with consequent scuffing and scoring. Similar troubles also occurred with four-stroke engines when their output was increased. After a considerable amount of intensive research it was found that these troubles could be largely overcome by the addition of small quantities of certain organic compounds of metals, such as calcium, barium and zinc, to the oil. These additives became known as "detergents" because, after running on oils containing them, the pistons of the engine were very much cleaner than when the engine had been operated on a straight mineral oil. The term "detergent" is not, however, a very satisfactory one for describing the functions of these additives, since one understands by detergents something like soap, which cleans away dirt. Although there is some evidence that these additives may loosen and remove some deposits in engines, their real function is to prevent the formation of deposits by keeping the decomposition products of the oil in suspension and so preventing their flocculation and deposition. Some detergent additives promote the oxidation of the oil and the consequent development of acidic products which lead to corrosion of certain bearing metals. It is usual to employ an anti-oxidant in conjunction with these additives. The effect of a suitable additive-type oil possessing good detergent and anti-oxidant properties on the condition of an engine is very striking. It is possible to run for a much longer period between overhauls, and troubles due to ring-sticking, ring packing and the clogging of the ring oil holes and screens by decomposition products of the oil are practically eliminated. In fact, some engines are only able to function satisfactorily for long periods when lubricated with an oil containing suitable additives.

Numerous attempts have been made to devise laboratory tests for additive-type diesel oils, which would correlate with results on full-scale engines, but these have met with only limited success, as in the case of automobile and aircraft oils. In developing additives for diesel oils, tests are first carried out on small single-cylinder engines modified to examine various aspects, such as oil stability, ring-sticking and piston cleanliness at high cylinder wall temperatures, so as to simulate conditions in practice. If the additive shows promise it is next examined on single-cylinder diesel engines. The Co-ordinating Research Council of the United States have specified a number of engine tests for assessing "HD" or heavy duty oils for use in high-speed diesel engines. Various laboratories in the United Kingdom are collaborating with the Institute of Petroleum in developing a standard test procedure, and possibly a standard test engine, for assessing HD oils.

In general, large slow-speed diesel engines do not develop such high piston temperatures as the smaller high-speed engines, and the use of an additive type oil is not essential. These types have, in fact, been lubricated for a number of years with straight solvent extracted oils, which are stable towards oxidation and inherently able to keep in solution resins and asphaltenes produced by oxidation. Furthermore, slow-speed engines do not usually operate over such a wide range of temperature as the high-speed engines, e.g. in road vehicles, so a high viscosity index is not so necessary. Some of these large diesel engines produce very finely divided "soot" in the combustion chamber, and part of this finds its way into the crankcase oil. The presence of this soot in the oil leads to an increase in viscosity, and it is customary on large engines to

LL

keep the quantity of soot at a low level by the use of an efficient filter fitted in a by-pass in the oil circuit. In this way the engine is able to operate for long periods between oil changes, and it is necessary only to top up the sump at intervals. The difficulty in extending the use of HD oils to those engines which are prone to contaminate the oil with combustion soot lies in the fact that in the presence of detergent additives, filters, which are efficient with straight oils, rapidly clog, and the less efficient filters fail to remove the soot. If it were not for this drawback HD oils could be used with advantage in slow-speed engines which suffer from sooting.

LUBRICATION OF STEAM ENGINES

The method of lubrication and the choice of lubricant varies with the type of engine, and a rough classification of engine types is therefore included here :—

(1) **Horizontal**. This is a slow-speed engine (up to 150 r.p.m.) with an open or exposed crankshaft. This type is not used for marine propulsion, but is common on land.

(2) **Vertical**. (*a*) *Open Type*. This is the normal marine engine open crankcase, and runs at any speed between 80 and 300 r.p.m. (*b*) *Closed Type*. Used mainly for high-speed (up to 1,200 r.p.m.) small sets, its lubrication system is similar to that of a large internal combustion engine. The crankcase is totally enclosed and normally forced-feed lubrication is employed.

The terms ''horizontal'' and ''vertical'' refer to the movement of the piston.

In all steam engines the cylinder lubricant is different from the bearing lubricant.

Cylinder Lubrication.

The normal method with all types is to introduce the oil into the steam supply pipe, where it is atomized. The oil mist is then carried by the steam to all working parts in the valve chest and cylinders. This method may be supplemented by direct injection at certain points.

Generally, straight mineral oils are employed. With wet steam, however, compounded oils may be desirable, since they atomize more readily and spread more easily over wet metallic surfaces.

If steam with a high degree of superheat is used, compounded oils are not suitable owing to the fact that fatty oils are not stable at the high temperatures of operation. The extremes which must be avoided are the use of an oil of low viscosity and high volatility which, while atomizing easily, may evaporate and endanger lubrication, and a high viscosity oil which will not atomize well and may thus settle on the cylinder walls and bake into hard deposits. Except for relatively mild operating conditions, paraffinic base residual oils are used.

Bearing Lubrication.

(1) **Horizontal Type.** A refined naphthenic-type distillate of medium viscosity is generally used, and is applied by drip feed or mechanical lubricator.

(2) **Vertical Type.** (*a*) *Open.* The oiling system is of the "total loss" type, and the oil in the bearing must be capable of absorbing any water which finds its way down the piston rod. Compounded oils of viscosity 175/300 seconds Redwood I at 140° F. and containing blown rape, fish oil or other emulsifying agents are used. (*b*) *Closed.* As a circulating system is employed here, the oil used must separate easily from mixtures with water. A high quality oil of the turbine oil type is usually employed.

LUBRICATION OF STEAM TURBINES

In the operation of a steam turbine, high-pressure steam impinges on blades which are set around the circumference of a revolving drum or rotor, causing it to rotate at high speeds. The majority of turbines carry several rows of moving blades on the rotor alternating with rows of fixed plates on the casing, which direct the steam on to the successive rows of rotor blades.

The essentials of the lubricating system of a turbine are shown in fig. 8. Lubricating oil is circulated to the bearings on which the rotor revolves, and this oil operates the governor control and lubricates the governor mechanism and the reduction gears. Modern turbines revolve at very high speed with rotors often weighing several tons, and thus efficient lubrication is vital. Besides acting as a lubricant, the oil must function as a cooling medium by carrying away heat from the working parts of the turbine. This function has increased in importance in recent years, since designs have become more compact and higher steam temperatures and rotor speeds have become common.

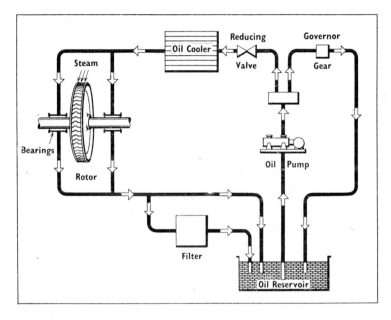

Fig. 8.   Lubrication System of Steam Turbine.

Turbine oils are expected to remain in use for periods measured in years without replacement, except for small additions of fresh oil added from time to time to make up for consumption losses.   Thus they must be very resistant to the oxidation   effects   of   high   temperatures   and   hot   air. Oxidation increases with temperature, and for this reason oil temperatures are kept as low as possible by the use of an oil cooler in the circulating system.   Hot steam under pressure tends to blow past the glands on the turbine casing and leak into the bearings, where it condenses and the water formed mixes with the oil. It is essential that the oil and water should separate quickly and cleanly so that the oil can be returned to the lubrication system. These conditions therefore make it necessary that turbine oils should be of the highly refined type to resist oxidation and with good demulsification properties.

In addition to the effects of oxidation, temperature, condensed steam and dirt in promoting breakdown of the oil, the metals with which the oil comes into contact in service may play a large part. Copper is particularly bad in causing deterioration of oils, and its use in lubricating systems should be restricted as much as possible. Bronze and brass are less active in this respect, while iron, steel and tin are relatively harmless.

It is important to give turbine oils frequent and regular cleaning in use by drawing water and sludge from the bottom of the oil reservoir and by purifying the oils periodically by filtration and centrifugal treatment. Thorough flushing of the oil system of a turbine when the oil is changed is also an important precaution to ensure the long life of the lubricant.

Turbine oils were formerly made from high grade Pennsylvanian and Russian oils. A light refining treatment sufficed to produce from these crudes, oils of good demulsification properties and moderate resistance to oxidation. Solvent extraction, which removes the less stable components from an oil, now enables us to produce turbine oils from a wide variety of crudes, and these oils are for the most part superior to the older types. The solvent-refined oils are capable of still further improvement by the addition of inhibitors. Thus, the oxidation resistance of modern turbine oils is considerably increased by incorporating in the lubricant small proportions (up to 0·5%) of oxidation inhibitors which increase service life considerably beyond that of the older types. Recently, anti-rusting dopes have also been incorporated in turbine oils to confer protection against rust formation.

Rust-inhibited oils were first produced by the Shell Company at the request of the United States Navy, following serious rusting of gears. The rust formed was black magnetic iron oxide, which also caused trouble through abrasion and choking of ports in governors of land units. Rust inhibitors must be selected so that they do not adversely affect the oxidation stability or the demulsibility of the oil.

The lubrication of the reduction gears in a turbine is generally carried out by the same oil which serves the rest of the system. These oils are of low viscosity, but at the moment are able to lubricate the gearing satisfactorily. Any increase in the loading of the gears, however, would necessitate an increase in the load-carrying capacity of the oils, and developments in this direction may be expected in the near future.

Apart from the usual laboratory inspection tests there are few special tests for turbine oils which have gained general acceptance. Demulsibility is an all-important property, and such a test is always included in any examination of a turbine oil. The most generally accepted test is the A.S.T.M. Steam Emulsion Test. In this, steam is passed into 20 ml. of the oil in a measuring cylinder until the total volume of oil and condensed water is 40 ml. The measuring cylinder is then transferred to a hot-water bath and the time taken for the 20 ml. of oil to separate out is measured, the result being expressed in seconds. Thus, if 20 ml. separates out in two minutes the oil is said to have an S.E. (Steam Emulsion) number of 120.

There are a number of tests available for examining the oxidation resistance of these oils, involving the maintenance of the oil at a temperature around 100° C. in the presence of metals, water, air or oxygen. In latter years, rusting tests have also been developed, and these indicate the protective properties of turbine oils to metals exposed to fresh or salt water.

LUBRICATION OF GEARS

Gears are employed to increase or decrease the speed of shafts, etc., and also to change the direction of the drive. Spur gearing is employed for speed variation only, while worm gears and bevel gears change the direction of drive as well. Some typical gears are shown in fig. 9. Where speeds and loads are high, straight-toothed spur gears are somewhat noisy, and helical gears are therefore frequently used in their place. They provide a smoother transfer of load from one tooth to the next, and consequently are quieter in operation.

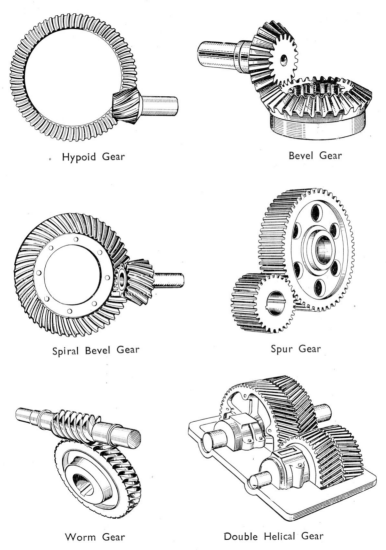

Hypoid Gear

Bevel Gear

Spiral Bevel Gear

Spur Gear

Worm Gear

Double Helical Gear

Fig. 9. Typical Gears.

Gears are normally splash lubricated by the bath system, but for high-speed conditions, such as exist in turbine gearing, lubrication is often effected by jets of oil directed on to the teeth. For open gears a non-throwing oil or grease is desirable, and blends of oil and bitumen are often used.

In theory, the mating teeth of spur gears should roll on each other without sliding, but in practice such conditions exist only when the middle of the tooth faces are in contact. Above and below this point the teeth slide over each other, and thus a film of oil must be maintained between these rubbing faces. With worm gears the movement between the teeth is mainly one of sliding, and such gears normally operate immersed in a bath of oil. Common examples of this type of gearing are the steering boxes in motor vehicles and the back axles of many heavy lorries.

One form of bevel gear—the hypoid*—which is used in the back axle of certain modern cars, has high tooth loading combined with very high sliding velocity. The employment of these gears has only been possible through the development of special oils known as "extreme pressure" (E.P.) lubricants. Certain compounds— often containing sulphur—when added to a mineral oil greatly increase the load-carrying capacity of the base oil. This action is probably due to chemical interaction between the additive and the metal surface of the gear tooth forming a protective film which prevents metal-to-metal contact. Such interaction occurs, in the main, when the temperatures and pressures between the rubbing faces become high.

A number of methods and a variety of pieces of apparatus have been developed to assess the load-carrying properties of the "E.P." oils. One of these—the Four-Ball machine—has been developed by the Shell Group, and has achieved considerable popularity. In this apparatus a $\frac{1}{2}''$ dia. ball held in a clamp revolves in contact with three similar stationary balls immersed in oil and locked in contact with each other in a metal cup. Increasing loads are applied, and wear scars are measured after one-minute runs. In addition, coefficient of friction is plotted against time for the various loads. The highest load which can be applied without welding is also measured.

The Timken machine is another apparatus for measuring E.P.

properties. In this case, a narrow steel cylinder is rotated in contact with one surface of a rectangular block of the metal and a jet of oil is directed on to the rubbing faces. Loading is increased until the smooth scar formed under low loads changes to a ribbed scar indicative of local welding or pick-up. The highest load which can be carried without the formation of a ribbed scar is an indication of the load-carrying capacity of the lubricant.

Agreement between the various test methods for measuring some E.P. property of the oil is not, however, particularly good.

SPECIAL OILS

A number of oils are marketed for special purposes, often not directly connected with lubrication, and some examples of these are given below.

Metal Working Oils.

(1) **Cutting Oils.** When steel or other metals are being turned, drilled or given any other type of machining operation, a fluid medium is usually required to carry away the heat generated by friction and to lubricate the surface of the tool as the metal cuttings pass over it. Such media are called cutting fluids. They may be divided into two classes :—

(*a*) *Soluble cutting oils.* In many cutting operations the most important requirement of the cutting fluid is as a coolant. Water is a much better cooling medium than oil, and at one time water or aqueous soap solution was often used for light operations. However, such liquids possess poor lubricating properties and, moreover, are liable to cause rusting if used with ferrous metals. Consequently, soluble cutting oils are now used for this kind of work. They consist of mixtures of mineral oils and emulsifiers, which can be diluted with water to form stable emulsions over a wide range of concentrations. For some classes of work, emulsions containing only 1% oil are used, but concentrations in general use range up to 10%. These dilute emulsions are circulated over the site of the cutting operation and, besides causing effective cooling, carry away the metal particles formed. Chief amongst the emulsifiers used for this type of oil are naphtha sulphonates (by-products of the acid refining of certain oils) and sulphonated fatty oils.

(*b*) *Straight cutting oils.*   These are used when conditions of cutting are more severe, making lubrication more important than cooling.   Such conditions are encountered when cutting speeds are relatively low and pressures high.   Mineral oils alone are not very satisfactory cutting fluids, since they do not reduce the friction sufficiently and their wetting properties are not very good. Fatty oils are an improvement on straight mineral oils in both these respects.   They will stand higher loads and possess greater oiliness, which tend to give improved lubrication.   Such oils, however, are generally not stable to oxidation, and consequently they become rancid, develop acidity and in some circumstances form objectionable gummy residues.

Blends of fatty and mineral oils have been used for a number of years, and until comparatively recently represented the standard type of cutting fluid.   However, as conditions have become more stringent, oils with better performance characteristics have been developed.   Elementary sulphur dissolved in oil is known to facilitate cutting operations when conditions are difficult, and is quite extensively used for this purpose, but such solutions are apt to be unstable, and, moreover, cause blackening of yellow metals. Sulphurized fatty oils, however, formed by heating together sulphur and fatty oils under certain conditions, will give the excellent effects of free sulphur without its disadvantages, and these oils are to-day used as constituents of many straight cutting oils.   Chlorinated compounds have also been used with good effect, but in general are not as popular as the sulphurized products.   Oils in which both sulphurized and chlorinated additives are present are also finding increased use.

The performance of cutting oils cannot be easily assessed by laboratory tests, and practical cutting tests are sometimes the only answer.   The extreme pressure properties of such oils can be determined in the laboratory test machine, but correlation of the results obtained with practice is not always good because of other factors.

(2) **Rolling Oils.**   In the manufacture of metal sheets and plates, billets of the metal are passed through a succession of rolls

to reduce the thickness to the required dimensions. It is necessary to lubricate the metal during its passage through the rolls, and the oil used depends to some extent on the metal being processed and the particular operation in hand. Spindle oils containing about 3 % olein* are commonly used. White oils containing 1 % olein are recommended when bright annealing is being carried out. In this case, annealing is effected in an inert atmosphere to maintain a bright surface, and the lubricant used in the rolling must be such that no deposits or lacquers are formed on the metal during the subsequent annealing process.

(3). **Drawing Oils.** For the manufacture of many metal articles, metal sheets are pressed into the required shape in suitable dies. Wires, rods and tubes, on the other hand, are produced by drawing, again through special dies. These processes, which often need to be carried out in several stages, must have adequate lubrication so as to reduce friction, prevent wear of the formers or dies, and assist in the production of good surface finish. A variety of oils is used for these operations, ranging from heavy mineral oils and compounded oils to aqueous emulsions of partly saponified fats, with or without mineral oil. A non-petroleum lubricant is dry powdered soap, which is particularly effective for steel wire. Oils, or aqueous emulsions, are preferred, however, for non-ferrous wire-drawing and many ferrous wire-drawing operations are similarly done with emulsions.

Heat Treatment Oils.

These oils are used in the manufacture of steel parts for imparting certain qualities to the finished product. They may be divided into two classes :—

(a) *Quenching oils.* When high carbon steels are heated to a high temperature and cooled slowly they remain soft, but if cooled quickly they harden, and this hardening effect is of great importance in extending the range of usefulness of such materials. The rapid cooling is effected by plunging the heated steel (at a suitable temperature in the range 760° C. to 950° C.) into a bath of cold water or oil, depending upon the type of steel being treated. Water quenching gives faster cooling and is used for hardening plain carbon steels, while oil quenching, which is a slower process,

is used for alloy steels.   The oil used should be of a low viscosity
to facilitate heat transfer and should naturally have as low a
volatility as possible.   In practice, specially refined high-flash
spindle oils are used, and these have almost completely replaced
the rape and whale oils formerly used for this purpose.

(b) *Tempering oils.*   During the quenching of steel, dangerous
stresses are set up, and the metal also sometimes becomes harder
than is desirable for certain applications.   The tempering process
is designed to soften and toughen the steel, and also to remove the
stresses.   In this process, the steel is reheated to a temperature
within the range 180° C. to 650° C., the actual tempering temperature depending upon the type of steel and the degree of softening
required.   Suitably heated oil baths can be used for tempering in
the lower part of the range, from 180° C. to 320° C., and for this
purpose heavy, non-volatile oils of the steam cylinder type are
chosen.   Such oils must have a high flashpoint, and should also
have high oxidation stability, so that sludging and thickening in
use are retarded as much as possible.   In carrying out the tempering operation the oil is simply heated to the required temperature,
and the steel work piece is then immersed for a suitable length of
time, after which it is cooled in air.   Oils cannot be used above
320° C., because of inflammability, and other methods must therefore be used for tempering temperatures higher than this.

Heat Transmission Oils.

Oil is often used as a medium for supplying heat for industrial
processes, and for this purpose is generally circulated from a
heater or furnace through pipes to the required sites and back to
the heater again.   It is, of course, essential that the oils selected for
this application should be stable to heat so that deposits are not
formed in the feed lines or furnace tubes.   They should also have
as low a viscosity as is compatible with low volatility, so that there
is no difficulty in pumping around the circuit when the plant is
started up from cold.   Heat circulating oils are used in the plastics
industry to soften mouldings and for heating the autoclaves at
the Barton (near Manchester) grease plant, to give but two examples from the multitude of industries where such oils render excellent service.   Viscosities vary according to the conditions which

are operative in the circulating systems, and range from medium viscosity distillates to heavy cylinder oils.

Electrical Oils.

(1) **Transformer Oils.** When an electrical transformer is in operation, heat is developed in the core and windings and must be effectively dissipated. In large transformers adequate cooling cannot economically be maintained by air currents, and the windings and core are placed in a bath of oil which serves the double purpose of electrical insulation and of cooling by the convection currents set up in the oil. In some of the largest transformers the oil is circulated through external coolers by means of a pump.

Transformer oil must possess (i) high electrical resistance, since it must effectively insulate the windings ; (ii) low viscosity, so as to flow readily and remove heat efficiently ; (iii) great stability, so that it is substantially unaffected by heat and atmospheric oxidation, which by causing deterioration of the oil with formation of acids and deposits would interfere with insulation and the flow of oil. To meet these requirements transformer oils are made from low-viscosity distillates and are given a special refining treatment to remove those constituents likely to affect stability adversely. These oils are thus very pale or even colourless. Additives are sometimes incorporated to improve stability still further.

Special tests have been devised to examine this type of oil. Thus, resistance to electrical breakdown is measured by immersing in a bath of oil a pair of electrodes of specified shape and dimensions, separated by a standard gap and increasing the voltage between them until arcing occurs. There are a number of tests of this kind, of which the British (B.S.I.) test may be quoted as an example. To pass this test an oil must prevent arcing at a voltage of 30,000 volts across a gap of 4 mm. for a period of one minute. Similarly, artificially accelerated ageing tests are used to give an indication of stability in service. These consist generally in heating the oil in contact with air or oxygen, usually in the presence of metals such as copper, for a given period of time under carefully prescribed conditions. On completion of the test the oil is examined for changes which have taken place, the criteria most commonly adopted being the amounts of sludge and acidity which have formed.

(2) **Switch Oils.** Oil-filled switch gear is widely used, particularly for high voltages. The function of the oil is to quench the arc formed between the contacts when the switch is operated, and to prevent the tendency of the arc to persist or re-strike. The oil should possess good mobility and high dielectric properties*. Transformer oils fulfil these requirements, and this type of oil is generally used.

(3) **Cable Oils.** The insulation of solid cables is commonly effected by winding them with paper impregnated with material of high electrical resistance. One of the most frequently used impregnants is a petroleum oil of the naphthenic type, with a viscosity about 400 seconds Redwood I at 140° F., containing 25% to 35% rosin. Cables of the ''oil-filled'' type contain one or more internal ducts, which are kept full of low-viscosity mineral oil by means of gravity supply tanks situated at points along the run of the cable. The insulating material is thus kept saturated with oil. An important consideration is that the cable compound or oil should be stable under high electrical stress.

(4) **Capacitor Oils.** A capacitor (less correctly called a condenser) stores electrical energy as stress in insulating material located between conducting surfaces. In one common type of capacitor the conducting surfaces are formed by metallic foil, and the insulation by paper impregnated with mineral oil or petroleum jelly. Normally, oxidizing influences in capacitors are very small because of the low operating temperatures and the almost complete exclusion of air. Consequently, stability towards oxidation is of less importance than it is in the case of a transformer oil. The chief long-term factor to consider is the effect of the high electrical stress on the impregnant ; for example, there is a tendency for gas to be formed (''gassing'') under these conditions, and this may lead to failure of the capacitor. This is the principal reason why transformer oils are not entirely suitable for use in capacitors and why it has been necessary to develop special grades.

Vacuum Pump Oils.

The lubrication of rotary vacuum pumps and blowers involves

the lubrication of the rotor shaft bearings and the provision of an oil film between the casing and the rotating vanes. The function of this film is twofold : to reduce friction between the vanes and the casing and to form a seal to prevent leakage of gas back past the vanes. A highly refined oil of medium viscosity is normally used, although when temperatures are unusually high (above about 180° C.) it may be desirable to use refined cylinder stock for this latter purpose.

When high vacua of the order of 10^{-5}mm. or less are required oil-immersed multi-stage pumps are used. Stable oils having low vapour pressure and of medium to light viscosity are most suitable for this purpose, and they are generally selected from solvent refined lubricating oils.

To obtain even higher vacua, diffusion pumps are used in conjunction with rotary backing pumps. These diffusion pumps originally operated with mercury as the working fluid. Some years ago, however, it was found possible to substitute for mercury specially prepared hydrocarbon oils made by a very high vacuum process. These oils, marketed as "Apiezon" products, lie within the lubricating oil range. They possess extremely low vapour pressures.

Corrosion Preventives.

The prevention of rusting and corrosion of metal surfaces is of vital importance to industry, since losses through these causes can be considerable. Permanent protection is usually afforded by painting or lacquering. There are occasions, however, when temporary protection only is required, as, for example, the protection of metal surfaces between various processing stages. In this field, the petroleum industry has made a notable contribution.

For many years temporary protection was afforded by covering surfaces with mineral oil, petrolatum or by solutions of tallow or lanolin in volatile solvents, and for some cases these materials are still quite effective. Before such protectives can be applied, however, the surfaces must be completely dry, otherwise they will not form a continuous coating.

During the 1939–45 war it was often necessary to protect surfaces which were already wet and could not be easily dried, and for this purpose a series of water-displacing rust preventives has been developed. These all contain in a solvent medium a surface-active component and a spreading agent, which together displace the water from the wet surfaces. They also contain a protective medium, which forms a film over the surface after displacement of the water, and thus prevents attack by exposure to the atmosphere during storage. The film formed by these fluids must be relatively easily removable, and this differentiates this class of corrosion preventives from paints and lacquers.

As an example of the application of such protectives, their use during the heat treatment of duralumin sheets may be quoted. In the heat treatment process, the sheets are first of all quenched from molten salt baths into water and are then washed to remove adhering salt. Unless the water left on the sheets is completely removed at this stage, it will cause staining during their subsequent processing. By treating them with a water-displacing protective, however, this trouble is completely avoided.

In the case of highly finished machine parts the corrosive effects of even fingerprints received in the course of normal handling may be very harmful, and here again de-watering protectives play an important role.

The corrosion of the cylinder bores of engines, particularly aero engines running on leaded fuels, has been encountered for many years and has been attributed to acid formed during the combustion of the leaded fuel. This trouble was originally, and to some extent still is, treated by spraying a corrosion-inhibited oil into the cylinder *via* the spark-plug holes immediately the engine is shut down.

A new method of treatment was developed during the 1939-45 war, when aeroplanes made in various parts of the United States were flown to the eastern seaboard and transhipped to Britain. These engines suffered severe corrosion during transport and often arrived badly damaged. This trouble was overcome by employing a protective aero-oil which contained an acid-neutralizing component as well as a medium capable of forming a protective film. Such an oil was not suitable as a lubricant under normal operating conditions, since it tended to form deleterious deposits. It was, however, satisfactory for flights at cruising speed from factory to port, and the engine during shipment was protected by the special lubricant which had been circulated to all working parts. These oils, known as "fly-away" oils, could be diluted with gasoline and sprayed into engine cylinders if required.

Protective instrument oils have also been developed during recent years. These products give satisfactory protection from atmospheric corrosion and are entirely non-corrosive themselves. They are prepared by incorporating a corrosion inhibitor in a highly refined low viscosity mineral oil.

Textile Oils.

The modern high-speed oil-bath spindle used in spinning operations rotates at speeds varying between 4,500 r.p.m. and 14,000 r.p.m. and may run for periods up to 4,000 hours on the initial charge of oil. Highly refined straight mineral oils, of low viscosity and possessing marked resistance to oxidation and thickening in service, are normally used for applications of this nature.

For the general lubrication of textile machinery it is an advantage to use high-quality oils and greases which can be applied sparingly, thereby reducing any tendency towards splashing, a condition which may lead to the staining of the yarn or fabric.

Moving parts which require particular care in the selection of the lubricant from the point of view of oil staining are the drafting rollers, which are used to stretch or draw out the yarn, and ring travellers (a small loop-shaped piece of metal which moves freely round the flange of a steel ring in ring spinning and directs the thread on to the bobbin which is being wound), because of the close proximity of the yarn to the points of lubrication. The overhead mechanism fitted to certain types of looms in weaving, where the short jerky motions of the overhead movement tend to throw off the lubricant on to the fabric below, also calls for special attention. The lubricants used for such applications are usually compounded so that in the event of the yarn or fabric being stained the contaminant can be removed during a subsequent scouring operation. In addition to possessing good scouring properties, a lubricant for the overhead movements of looms may also possess non-throwing characteristics which will effectively resist the jerky motions referred to above.

MM

The choice of lubricant is also very important in the case of knitting or stitching machines, as it is called upon to protect the highly polished surfaces of the steel needles against corrosion in humid atmospheres in addition to performing its normal function as a lubricant. At the same time, since the lubricant comes into contact with the material, it is essential that it should possess good scouring characteristics.

The effective removal of oil from all yarns or fabrics during scouring is of primary importance, as such stains, if allowed to remain, may give rise to uneven dyeing during subsequent operations. Where it is not possible to scour the material, a highly refined colourless oil, which will not discolour on exposure to air, is very often used.

Oils are also used for lubricating textile fibres, particularly wool, during the manufacturing processes, and such oils must be easily removed in the subsequent scouring processes. Scourable lubricants based on mineral oils have been developed and are being used in place of normal fatty oils. In the production of rayon goods the main function of the lubricant is to prevent the breaking of the fine filaments during the processing operations. Emulsifiable oils based on low viscosity technical white or pale oils are normally used.

Medicinal Oils.

These consist of mineral oils drastically refined so that all unsaturated constituents, and those which impart colour to the oil, have been removed. Usually such oils are solvent extracted and then repeatedly treated with strong sulphuric acid and alkalis. Various grades of medicinal oil are manufactured to meet the specifications drawn up by the Pharmacopœia authorities in different countries. These specifications differ in detail ; for instance, the British Pharmacopœia specification for Liquid Paraffin demands an oil with a minimum viscosity of 260 seconds Redwood I at 100° F., while the corresponding minimum viscosity in the United States Pharmacopœia specification is 156 seconds. The main requirement of such specification, however, is that the oil shall be free from all harmful components.

White Oils and Half-White Oils.

These oils are made from spindle oils by a less drastic refining treatment than is used for medicinal oils. Their main use lies in the manufacture of hair oils and cosmetics, but they find application in a number of other directions. These include their use in horticultural spray oils, for egg preserving as a substitute for water glass and for imparting a polished appearance to currants and raisins. Such oils are also used for the lubrication of machinery handling food, e.g. bacon shears and machinery making food containers.

Dust Allaying Oils.

Oil is frequently used for spraying the floors of large buildings in order to absorb the dust and allow it to be removed without spreading into the atmosphere. Thin spindle oil is generally used for this purpose.

A recent development is the use of emulsified white oils for treating bed-linen and blankets in hospitals to prevent the dissemination of fluff and so reduce the risk of air-borne infections.

Refrigerator Oils.

The most commonly used refrigerating media fall into two classes : those which are not miscible with lubricating oil and those which are miscible.

The first class, which include ammonia, carbon dioxide and sulphur dioxide, necessitate the use of an oil of low pour point which will not solidify and be deposited in the colder parts of the system. In the case of ammonia and sulphur dioxide it is also important to use highly refined oils, as these gases will react with chemically unstable elements present in mineral oil and cause the formation of deposits.

The second class, of which methyl chloride and certain of the "Freon" series of refrigerants are common examples (sometimes called halogen refrigerants), mix freely in all proportions with mineral oil, and consequently a mixture of oil and refrigerant is always present in the system. The effects of this are two-fold : the refrigerant dilutes the oil and reduces its viscosity so that thicker oil must be used than would be required with a non-miscible refrigerant, and it bestows on the mixture a low pour point so that it is not so necessary for the oil itself to possess this property.

Solvent extracted naphthenic type oils have been found extremely satisfactory for use in refrigerator systems, and an oil with viscosity around 80 seconds Redwood I at 140° F. is commonly used.

LUBRICATING GREASES

Greases are semi-solid lubricants consisting essentially of mixtures of soaps and oils. Although as a rule they are somewhat inferior to oil as a lubricating medium, there are a number of applications where conditions render grease lubrication more suitable than oil. Such applications vary from lightly loaded ball bearings on small electric motors and fans to heavy-duty plain and anti-friction bearings on the largest of steel mill rolling equipment. Greases are also used where the bearings to be lubricated are difficult of access or where the sealing arrangements, particularly in the case of ball or roller bearings, are inadequate, in which case advantage is taken of the self-sealing properties of the grease to prevent the ingress of moisture and foreign matter from the surrounding atmosphere.

The bulk of greases used in industry are lime or soda base products, i.e. mixtures of mineral oil with either a calcium or sodium soap.

The lime base greases can be considered as general purpose lubricants and can be relied upon to give good service in bearings operating at moderate temperatures. They are of a buttery texture with melting points around 100° C. Melting points of greases do not always indicate maximum usable temperatures of these products, however, and, in general, lime base greases are not recommended for temperatures above 50 ° C. These lubricants are unaffected by water.

Soda base greases, on the other hand, have higher melting points than lime base greases, extending up to 200° C., and are somewhat more fibrous in texture, although the modern tendency is to produce a product with as smooth a texture as possible. For plain bearings, certain grades of these greases can be applied up to temperatures of the order of 150° C. Such grades, however, would be unsuitable for ball and roller bearings because of their hard consistency, and special grades are therefore produced which offer a minimum of resistance to the movement of the rotating elements. These are not normally required for use above 100° C. In general, soda base greases tend to emulsify in the presence of water and are not usually applied in the presence of excess moisture.

Aluminium greases have a smooth texture and good water resistance. They possess good adhesiveness and hence are used as chassis lubricants and for application to chains, cams and oscillating surfaces.

Lithium greases were developed during the 1939–45 war, mainly for aviation purposes. They combine high melting points (up to 200° C.) with excellent low-temperature properties and are also highly resistant to water.

Barium greases have also been produced in the last few years. They are capable of use at elevated temperatures and have resistance to water equal to the best calcium greases. Their texture varies from fibrous to fairly smooth. At present they have not been used to any extent outside the United States but their applications may very well increase.

Laboratory tests on grease always include a determination of the drop point (or melting point) and the penetration.

The drop point measures the temperature at which the grease is sufficiently fluid to drip from the bottom of a small cup. The penetration test measures the consistency of a grease and is determined by measuring the depth of penetration of a metal cone into a sample of the product. Since greases in use in bearings suffer considerable agitation and churning they are normally "worked" in a standard form of "worker" before the penetration is measured.

BIBLIOGRAPHY

The Principles and Practice of Lubrication. Nash and Bowen. (Chapman and Hall, 1937.)

General Discussion on Lubrication. Institution of Mechanical Engineers, 1937.

Modern Petrol Engines. Judge. (Chapman and Hall, 1946.)

The Internal Combustion Engine, Vol. II.　Pye.　(Clarendon Press, Oxford, 1943.)

The High Speed I.C. Engine.　Ricardo and Glyde.　(Blackie, 1941.)

Roller Bearings.　Allen.　(Pitman, 1946.)

Gears.　Merritt.　(Pitman, 1946.)

Insulating Oils.　Institution of Electrical Engineers Symposium, May, 1942.

XXX

PETROLEUM WAXES

FREQUENT reference has been made to the solid material—known collectively as ''wax''—which is met in crude oil during production and refining. From its very nature, wax is most undesirable in liquid petroleum products, and where lubricating oil is concerned, its effects are so detrimental that its actual removal must be undertaken.

After separation from oil, however, wax constitutes a valuable and interesting product in its own right, with special qualifications for a number of important uses.

In common with other petroleum derivatives, wax is essentially a mixture of hydrocarbons, but is unusual in that these hydrocarbons belong mostly to one family—the paraffin series. The simplest member of this series is, indeed, a gas (methane), but the more complicated members are successively liquids and then solids as the carbon and hydrogen atoms per molecule progressively increase in number.

Petroleum wax, then, is principally a mixture of the solid paraffins, the number and nature of which have a considerable effect upon the properties of the mixture. For a given composition, a number of different paraffin hydrocarbons exists, depending on the manner in which the component atoms of carbon and hydrogen are linked together. These ''isomers'', as they are termed, fall into two broad classes—normal and iso-paraffins respectively. In the first, the carbon atoms are joined together in one continuous chain, and in the second type some carbon atoms are attached branchwise to others in the main chain (*vide* chapter VII).

Various kinds of wax are obtainable from crude oil, differing markedly in their physical properties and commercial applications, and it is believed that the relative proportion of normal and iso-paraffin hydrocarbons is an important factor contributing to these differences.

GENERAL PROPERTIES

Two main classes of petroleum wax are commonly recognized—
distillate waxes, such as distil over from the crude oil with lubricating oil fractions and eventually yield ''paraffin wax'', and the
less volatile waxes, which remain behind in distillation residues.
The latter type of wax is usually made up of much smaller crystals,
and is considered to contain a larger proportion of iso-paraffins
than the more common paraffin wax.   In association with oil,
these ''micro-crystalline waxes'', as they are called generally, form
petrolatums of various consistencies.

Slack wax removed from lubricating oil by solvent de-waxing
processes is probably intermediate between the two general classes
of wax just described, depending, of course, on the character of
the parent de-waxing stock.   This slack wax is becoming an important source of finished commercial waxes through the provision of a solvent de-oiling step for the wax immediately following its removal in the solvent dewaxing plant.   Both crystalline
and micro-crystalline waxes are being produced commercially
from their respective slack waxes by this means.

Wax, being a solid, has certain properties which do not have to
be considered in other petroleum products.   Perhaps the most
characteristic of any solid substance is its melting point, or the
temperature at which it becomes liquid.   In the case of a single
substance, such as any one of the solid paraffin hydrocarbons,
melting occurs suddenly on gradual heating.   Wax, on the other
hand, as it is a mixture of such individual hydrocarbons, becomes
softer and more plastic without actually liquefying until heating
has been continued to a higher temperature.   It is impossible,
therefore, to find a true melting point for wax in this way.   It
happens, however, that the reverse process—solidification of
melted wax—begins at a temperature which can be easily
measured.

This ''setting point'' is found by allowing a small quantity of
the melted wax to cool undisturbed.   A thermometer shows that,
at first, the temperature of the liquid wax falls continuously but
remains steady for several minutes when setting begins.   For commercial purposes, the temperature found in this way is adopted as

the melting point. In this sense the term ''melting point'' is used throughout this chapter.

All petroleum waxes are crystalline in some degree, and reference has already been made to the obvious difference in this respect between paraffin wax, which consists of large visible crystals, and the residue waxes, in which the crystals are of microscopic size. The crystal size of paraffin wax may be greatly reduced by a mixture of certain other substances. As a pertinent example micro-crystalline petroleum waxes induce a very small crystal size when blended with ordinary paraffin wax in a proportion of 1 % or less. In this connection it may be mentioned that a pronounced crystalline texture is disadvantageous for most uses of wax, although necessary to wax manufacture, in which well-developed crystals facilitate pressing and sweating.

PARAFFIN WAX

Crude paraffin wax is obtained in large quantities during the manufacture of lubricating oils, but at present only a part is further refined for its own sake. This is the material separated from lubricating oil distillates by chilling and pressing. The crude wax is subjected to sweating, as described in chapter XV, or to solvent refining methods, with the dual object of removing oil and separating the wax into several fractions of different melting points.

If sweating is stopped when only a small proportion of oil remains, scale wax is produced. This is frequently sold as such for uses which do not demand a higher degree of refining. Scale wax is of relatively wide cut, i.e. it contains a large number of solid hydrocarbons of widely differing melting points ; but, by further sweating, which at this stage is really fractional melting, it can be divided into narrower cuts of various melting points. In this way, several grades of wax can be produced from one crude oil. It should be noted that, for marketing purposes, ''grade'' denotes melting point, and does not refer to quality of the wax.

Paraffin waxes having melting points of 100° F. to 155° F. (37·8° C. to 68·3° C.) are available commercially, the higher grades, of melting point 135° F. (57·2° C.) upwards, being especially plentiful in the crude oils from British India and the Netherlands East Indies. Waxes melting above about 120° F. (48·9° C.) may be made practically free from oil and are then semi-transparent, colourless and odourless. At ordinary temperatures, waxes of this quality (fully refined grades) are hard and frequently brittle, but on warming they become progressively softer and more plastic, finally melting to a thin, clear liquid. The presence of small proportions of oil, due to insufficient refining, greatly affects certain properties ; such wax easily discolours when exposed to light and, with as little as 0.5% oil, is much reduced in mechanical strength, becoming mealy or easily crushed to a fine powder.

The lower melting grades ($100°$ F. to $120°$ F. = $37.8°$ C. to $48.9°$ C.) usually contain oil and are more or less yellow. Wax of this kind is soft and plastic at ordinary temperatures.

APPLICATIONS OF PARAFFIN WAX

As a Combustible. When paraffin wax burns it gives a clear, luminous flame, and very large quantities of refined grades are consumed annually in this way in the form of candles and night-lights. Current statistics cannot be quoted, but it is probable that at least half the world production of refined paraffin wax is used for this purpose.

A candle is made by casting paraffin wax in a cylindrical metal mould, the bottom of which is closed by a piston of such a cross-section that it forms the tip of the candle. The mould can be heated or cooled at will by water of suitable temperature. The first step is to pass the wick through a hole in the piston and then centrally up the mould. The mould is then warmed and melted wax poured in around the wick. The wax is caused to set and harden quickly by turning on the cold water ; on raising the piston the candle is pushed out of the mould, pulling up a further length of wick into position for the next candle. After the latter has been moulded and set, the wick is cut to release the first candle.

Fully refined grades of paraffin wax, of melting point $122°$ F. ($50°$ C.) upwards, are normally used for candle-making, although for the cheaper article scale wax is frequently employed. The latter type, however, is rather fragile, mottled and quickly discoloured due to the oil present in the scale wax. Owing to the composite nature of paraffin wax, candles made therefrom, particularly those of the lower melting grades, tend to soften and bend easily in warm weather. This is corrected by adding to the wax a small proportion of a stiffening agent, usually stearine (obtained from fats). The higher melting paraffin waxes need less stiffener for adequate stability to warmth.

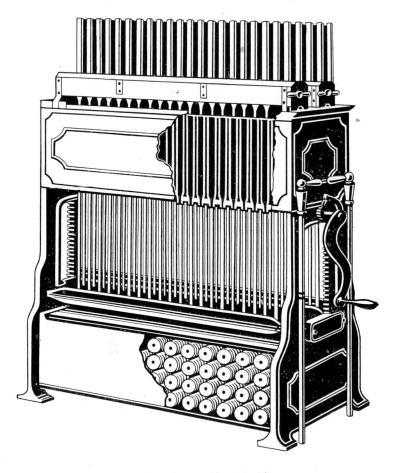

Fig. 1.   Candle-making Machine.

The composition of the wax, i.e. the range and proportion of its constituent hydrocarbons, is held to affect the suitability of the material for candle-making in a manner which cannot be foretold from the melting point, which is really an average value. A paraffin wax of relatively wide cut is more likely to bend or soften in warm conditions and to stick in the mould during candle manufacture than one of similar melting point in which the range of hydrocarbons is shorter. A frequent cause of candles sticking in the moulds, however, is the use of cooling water at a temperature insufficiently below the melting point of the wax or, alternatively, the use of wax of too low melting point.

Nightlights are also made by casting in moulds and usually consist entirely of paraffin wax, their wicks being inserted after moulding. Wooden matches are impregnated with low-melting paraffin wax for at least part of their length before the heads are put on. The function of the wax is to make the wood take fire easily when the match is struck.

Many types of fire-lighter contain low quality or damaged wax as the chief combustible constituent.

Waterproofing. One of the most characteristic properties of solid paraffin wax is its chemical inertness or resistance to attack by powerful reagents (strong acids and alkalis, air or oxygen etc.). Furthermore, in common with other petroleum products, it is insoluble in water and, in the form of a thin continuous film, it is practically impervious to air and moisture. Combined with its cheapness, these qualities help to make the wax a valuable proofing agent, especially for purposes in which an attractive appearance and cleanliness are assets. Since it is quite innocuous and tasteless as well as odourless, it is particularly well qualified for proofing wrappers and containers for foodstuffs. Nowadays, when the sale of food and other perishables in ready-wrapped, non-returnable packages is much favoured, there is a large demand for waxed paper and cardboard. This use of paraffin wax ranks next to candle-making and may be expected at least to compensate for an inevitable, though slow, decrease in candle consumption.

Waxed paper, as used for bread wrappers, biscuit packages etc., is made by passing a continuous sheet of thin paper between heated rollers, at least one of which carries melted wax picked up from a heated trough, or by direct immersion in melted wax. Excess wax on the surface is squeezed off by rollers and the paper travels over a water-cooled drum, or through a bath of cold water, in order to harden the wax as quickly as possible, ready for re-reeling. The extent to which the wax impregnates the body of the paper or is left as a surface coating, depends greatly upon the speed of the paper sheet through the machine. If the liquid wax has time to penetrate into the paper in the interval between waxing and chilling—and this period may be deliberately prolonged by interposing heated rollers—impregnation, rather than surface waxing, is achieved. Paper may be waxed on one side only, the wax being applied by means of a roller. This type is in demand for certain purposes where direct contact between wax and the wrapped

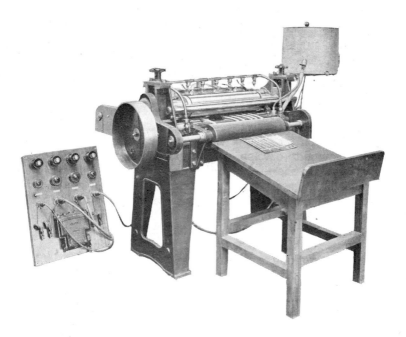

Fig. 2.   Carton Waxing in a High-speed Roller Machine.

commodity is undesirable, e.g. in wrapping sweets while still hot.

The roller-waxing method enables flat cardboard blanks to be rapidly treated before they are formed into cartons etc., and at the high speed at which such machines usually run the wax film sets by its rapid movement in air, without special cooling. Fig. 2 illustrates a waxing machine of this kind.

Waxed cartons made from thin paper or cardboard are being widely used, in place of metal or glass containers, for packing materials such as milk, sugar, confectionery and biscuits. Pre-shaped containers of this type are generally waxed by immersion in melted wax for a few seconds and, after draining, may be cooled in a current of cold air, but are frequently allowed to set without specially arranged sudden cooling. The extra opportunity thus given for the still liquid wax to impregnate the paper thoroughly is a definite advantage in many cases.

In certain special types of machine, cartons are proofed by spraying melted wax over the inside surface.

In general, only the fully refined grades of paraffin wax, containing as little oil as possible, are acceptable to makers of waxed paper articles. The effect of oil is to hasten discoloration of the wax, particularly on exposure to light, to cause odour and to weaken the wax film. The question of odour is one concerning which food packers are very critical, and it must be mentioned in this connection that a wax which is satisfactory when supplied is often caused to develop odour through lack of care in service. Experience has shown the need for stressing this point both to users and designers of paper-waxing equipment. As already stated, paraffin wax in the solid state is unaffected by air, but when melted and kept in an open trough or bath at high temperature for prolonged periods, slight oxidation may occur, producing a small quantity of odorous material. This risk is minimized by keeping the working temperature of the wax below about 190° F. (87·8° C.), which is best achieved by using low-pressure steam as the means of heating.

Large wax-melting baths should be avoided in order that the ''make-up'', or rate of replacement of fresh wax, shall be reasonably rapid. A further precaution, which is again a question of design, is to ensure that the surface of melted wax exposed to the air is kept as small as is practicable. A safeguard which can be practised by the user is frequent and thorough cleaning of all baths or troughs used for hot wax.

Paraffin wax, either alone or in admixture, is used for waterproofing many materials besides paper. Its application to sole leather, canvas, timber and concrete exemplifies the scope of this field.

In certain cases, the wax may be applied directly to foodstuffs without the intervention of paper. Oranges, lemons, cheeses and eggs may be kept in condition by the application of a very thin layer of paraffin wax. In these instances, the object of the treatment is to prevent access of air or to inhibit loss of moisture from the food.

For many years paraffin wax has been valued by the electrical industries, not only for its waterproofing qualities, but also for the extremely high resistance which it offers to an electric current. Its use as an insulating and dielectric material has greatly increased with the growth of the radio, motor car and electrical distributive industries. It is chiefly used in small components and for impregnating the coverings of cables.

PARAFFIN WAX SOLUTIONS AND EMULSIONS

In all the uses described up to this point, the paraffin wax has been applied in the melted state. Reference will now be made to a few applications in which it is convenient to use the wax in conjunction with a liquid medium. There are three ways in which paraffin wax is used in this manner :—

(a) As a clear solution in a suitable solvent.

(b) As a wax paste, i.e. a solvent containing more than enough wax for saturation, the excess wax separating as a uniformly distributed solid.

(c) As an emulsion, or suspension, in water.

At moderate temperatures (60° F. = 15·6° C.), the refined grades of paraffin wax (melting points above 120° F. = 48·9° C.) dissolve only to the extent of a few parts per cent., even in the best solvents. Waxes of lower melting point are more readily soluble but, in either case, the solubility rapidly increases when the temperature of the solvent is raised. The most effective solvents for paraffin wax are light petroleum distillates, coal-tar benzole, and the non-inflammable chlorinated solvents, such as carbon tetrachloride.

Solutions. Solutions of paraffin wax in a volatile solvent, which is subsequently evaporated off, are particularly useful when a very sparing application of wax is required, e.g., in shower-proofing clothing, or when the temperature of melted wax would be a drawback.

Pastes. The most important use of paraffin wax in paste form is the manufacture of polishes for footwear, furniture and floors. Polishes of this class are essentially mixtures of waxes of several kinds with a solvent, usually white spirit or turpentine. The wax mixture commonly consists of paraffin wax with natural waxes such as carnauba*, candelilla* or beeswax*.

The solvent is blended with the melted wax mixture and, after some cooling, the wax in excess of that required to saturate the solvent separates, causing the whole mass to form a soft paste which is filled off into tins and left to cool to air temperature.

Without admixture with other waxes, paraffin wax has little polishing value. It yields a dull, easily smeared film, and the paste which it forms with solvents is very crystalline, readily allowing solvent to separate as a free liquid. Its recognized value in polish-making is not solely as a cheapener, enabling the more expensive glossing waxes to go further, but as a modifier. In particular, it plays an important part in building up the desired consistency of the polish paste and also has a controlling effect on the rate at which solvent is lost by evaporation from the tin. Paraffin wax serves to soften the other component waxes, which, in general, are rather hard and difficult to gloss by rubbing.

Emulsions. As an alternative to a solution, an emulsion of paraffin wax can sometimes be used when a light wax treatment is wanted. An emulsion consists of very small particles of wax (0.0004 inch or less in diameter) suspended in water ; a third substance, e.g. soap, is present in the water and functions as an emulsifying and stabilizing agent, preventing the wax particles from clotting together. Emulsions containing up to about 50% (wt.) of paraffin wax can be made and, since they can be highly diluted, they afford a convenient means of mixing wax uniformly with materials already containing much water. The water-resistance of paper, for example, can be improved by adding wax emulsion to the pulp before it is converted into a web of paper.

SPECIAL USES AS A PLASTIC SOLID

A large number of uses take special advantage of the solid nature of paraffin wax, and especially of its plasticity when warm. It is an important constituent of many types of modelling wax, including the dental waxes used in the preliminary stages of making and fitting dentures.

Solid paraffin wax is a poor conductor of heat and, when a mass of the wax begins to set, the solid crust retains heat in the centre for a very long time. This affords a convenient means of applying heat to the body in the treatment of rheumatic complaints. In therapeutics, a hot wax treatment is frequently given as a preliminary to massage in order to relax the affected tissues.

MICRO-CRYSTALLINE WAXES

The natural tendency of paraffin wax to form large crystals is, in many applications, a definite disadvantage. So long as the wax film remains intact and free from flaws, its merits as a proofing agent are undisputed. Under mechanical stress, however, cracks easily develop between the crystals, especially at the lower temperatures of use and cause loss of proofing efficiency or even active dislodgment of the wax.

In general, this limitation is not serious enough to outweigh the economic advantages of cheapness and ready availability, but in some applications it raises real technical difficulties. In electrical work, for example, where paraffin wax is used as a condenser dielectric or as an insulator, serious fluctuations in the electrical properties can occur in apparatus which is expected to function steadily over a wide range of temperature, humidity, etc., and are attributable to the relatively open, crystalline texture of the wax, which either allows air and moisture to enter or leads to cracking at the lower temperatures.

The petroleum residue waxes, already referred to as a distinct class (*vide* chapter XV), have considerable scope in uses where the marked crystallinity of ordinary paraffin wax is a drawback. In comparison with paraffin wax they have been made in small

NN

quantity and at high cost. It seems likely, however, that improved methods of production, particularly from the slack wax removed from residual lubricating oil by solvent dewaxing, may enable residue waxes to replace paraffin wax economically and with greater effect in some of its current uses.

Residue wax products of this nature have been available for many years under a variety of names (high melting point petrolatum, mineral beeswax, petroleum ceresin, etc.) and embrace a wide range of properties, depending on the method of extraction from oil, nature of base stock, and on the amount of high melting wax of paraffin wax type co-existing in the residue oil and simultaneously removed. All are similar, however, in that they consist of crystals which are of microscopic size. It is customary, therefore, to refer in a general way to waxes of this nature as ''microcrystalline''. These waxes all possess, in some degree, the ability to absorb or mix uniformly with large proportions of oil. With increasing oil content, products varying in consistency from a tough wax to soft petrolatum can be obtained. It is, in fact, difficult to make a sharp division between petrolatums and microcrystalline waxes, except rather arbitrarily on the basis of consistency. The difference between these two classes may be mainly a question of oil content.

Micro-crystalline waxes, sometimes containing appreciable amounts of oil, are marketed with melting points ranging approximately from 140° F. (60° C.) to 190° F. (87·8° C.). It will be recalled that the highest melting point for commercial paraffin wax is about 155° F. (68·3° C.), and this is by no means common. The micro-crystalline waxes differ importantly from paraffin wax in being ductile, or extensible, plastic even at low temperature, and in being more or less adhesive. These features give microcrystalline waxes an obvious advantage over paraffin wax in uses which require a high melting point and the ability to take up stress, due to temperature changes, without cracking. They are favoured, for example, in the manufacture of electrical components as potting compounds and as impregnants for the paper/metal foil condensers familiar in radio work. Their special properties are aptly employed in the linings of beer cans, which, after filling, are subjected to raised temperature during pasteurization, and to low temperature in storage.

When, from the circumstances of manufacture, residue wax contains a large proportion of high melting paraffin wax, the material is still composed of very small crystals but tends to be granular and more brittle than the micro-crystalline waxes just described. The so-called " petroleum ceresins " are believed to be of this type and are specially valued for their high melting point, which may exceed 200° F. (93·3° C.). Many blends of waxes or other materials, devised for specific purposes, include petroleum ceresin as a constituent in order to attain a high melting point.

The addition of a small proportion (0·2% to 0·5%) of petroleum ceresin to ordinary paraffin wax causes the latter to develop very small crystals. Other micro-crystalline waxes act more or less similarly. Paraffin wax doped in this way forms a smooth paste when deposited from solvents, and is found to have a useful modifying effect on the texture of certain qualities of polish.

BIBLIOGRAPHY

Candles and Candle-making. D. Allan. (Journal of Institution of Petroleum and Technologists, 1933, p. 155.)

Properties and Utilization of Petroleum Waxes. C. G. Gray. (Journal of Institute of Petroleum, 1944, p. 57.)

Commercial Waxes. H. Bennett. (Chemical Publishing Co. N.Y., 1944.)

XXXI

ASPHALTIC BITUMEN

IT IS not always realized that 3,000 years B.C. there was a well-established bitumen* industry in Mesopotamia. This industry was so highly developed that it is astonishing that the knowledge of bitumen and its uses should have been completely lost for more than 2,000 years as far as Western civilizations are concerned. Natural pools and seepages of bitumen occurred near Hit, on the Euphrates, from which the Sumerians were able to secure ample supplies of bitumen.   This was refined at least to the extent of removing water and other extraneous matter.   Such bitumen would still contain some fine mineral matter, such as wind-blown sand, but it was eminently suitable for use in various building operations.

Early Uses.   Recent excavations have brought to light many beautiful examples of building constructions involving the use of bitumen.   Water tanks have been found which are still effectively water-proofed with bituminous mastic.   Domestic drains and baths have been uncovered and found to be lined or coated with mastic, and it is obvious that the knowledge of the use of bituminous mastics then available made possible excellent sanitary arrangements.   Brick river embankments were constructed with bituminous mortars and further water-proofed with mastics, and parts of these constructions now in existence are still effectively water-proof.   The use of bitumen in road construction seems to have been largely confined to the provision of a water-proof jointing material.   There are many remarkable examples in which the waterproof and adhesive properties of bitumen have contributed to the preservation of these constructions through the ages.   The Processional Road at Babylon and the floor of King Nebuchadnezzar's Temple are typical examples.

With the fall of Babylon in 538 B.C. the bitumen industry seems to have been almost completely lost, and only during the last 100 years has the new bitumen industry emerged.

About the year 1850 efforts were first made to find uses for lake asphalt* from Trinidad, and patents were granted for its use for the manufacture of reservoirs and for many insulation purposes, while in 1869 rock asphalt from the Val de Travers region, near Lake Neuchatel, was first used for the construction of a compressed asphalt pavement laid in Threadneedle Street, London.

The rapid development of the motor car at the beginning of the twentieth century, however, created an acute road problem, and the British Road Board was formed in 1909, when special consideration was given to the surfacing of main roads "with granite, basalt or other suitable material treated with tar or other bituminous compounds". Thus, the bitumen industry was primarily developed in connection with the construction of more durable roads.

NATURAL SOLID BITUMENS

Lake Asphalt. The famous Trinidad Lake contains an almost inexhaustible supply of an intimate mixture of bitumen and fine mineral matter, and, as dug from the lake, this asphalt is a uniform mixture of bitumen with gas, water and mineral matter. It is refined by heat treatment and settling to remove water and other volatile matter and any extraneous solid impurities. The final product is exported as Trinidad Epuré, which has the following approximate composition :—

Trinidad Epuré.

Bitumen (soluble in carbon disulphide)	53 to 55% by weight.
Mineral matter (clay, sand, etc.) ...	36 to 37% by weight.
Organic matter and water	9 to 10% by weight.

This Trinidad asphalt lake appears to be quite motionless, and the asphalt solid. There is, however, in the centre of the lake a patch known as "The Mother of the Lake", which is soft, and there is ample evidence that the whole lake is in complicated motion. Thus, the holes resulting from the removal of asphalt are gradually filled up, and it appears that the lake is being continuously replenished from underground. Millions of tons of asphalt have now been taken from the lake without fundamentally altering its contours.

Trinidad Epuré is a non-cohering solid and, as such, too hard to be used without further treatment. It is therefore normally softened by the addition of a suitable flux, and the asphaltic cement thus formed finds applications in all forms of road construction, roofing and flooring mastics and in the manufacture of various industrial bituminous compounds.

Rock Asphalt.   Natural rock asphalts are mined or quarried in France, Switzerland, Italy and Germany, and consist of consolidated calcareous rock impregnated with bitumen. The bitumen content of such rock asphalt varies with the source of the rock, and may range up to 10% or 12% by weight. Such rock asphalts can readily be ground to fine powders which form a suitable basic material for the manufacture of mastics.

Asphaltites.   In various parts of the world there occur deposits of bituminous substances of high melting points which have undoubtedly been derived from petroleum. The most important of these are known as "asphaltites". The best known example of this class of substance is Gilsonite, which is found chiefly in large veins in Utah (U.S.A.). This has a high melting point, varying from 120° C. to 180° C. (248° F. to 356° F.), is hard, glossy and rather brittle, and gives a brown streak when rubbed on paper—a simple test which distinguishes it from most manufactured asphaltic bitumen, which gives a near-black streak. It is used industrially in the manufacture of certain enamels and other compositions.

ASPHALTIC BITUMEN

The great developments in the methods of road construction following the introduction of the motor car created great demands for bituminous road binders of all kinds, and it soon became obvious that petroleum was a natural source of suitable materials. Thus, the asphaltic crude oils occurring in Mexico, Venezuela, California, etc., and mixed base crudes such as those occurring in Egypt, provided base materials for the manufacture of large quantities of a wide range of grades of bitumen suitable for use as road binders, and as waterproofing and insulating agents for many industrial purposes.

In this connection it should be emphasized that the crude oils used for bitumen manufacture are specially selected in view of their high content of asphaltic bitumen, which, in the case of certain Mexican and Venezuelan crude oils, is the major constituent.

A wide range of grades was soon available and, since the manufacturing process is quite flexible, the production of intermediate grades or softer grades would present no special difficulties. The storage and handling of such additional grades does, however, present very real practical difficulties, since all medium and soft grades must obviously be stored in separate specially heated and insulated tanks. These arrangements are such that any unnecessary multiplication of grades must be regarded with disfavour.

The hard grades, which cannot conveniently be stored in the liquid state, are run into specially constructed bays or moulds, where they are allowed to solidify. They are subsequently broken up and delivered naked and in bulk. Softer grades are delivered hot in bulk in insulated road or rail tank cars, or packed in drums or barrels.

NOMENCLATURE

A highly specialized industry has thus developed rapidly in many directions and in many countries simultaneously, and the terminology has inevitably become confused. In spite of efforts made by various national and international bodies, fundamental differences still exist between the terms in common use in the United Kingdom and in the United States.

The major confusion arises in connection with the terms "bitumen" and "asphalt". In British literature the product manufactured from asphaltic crude oil is officially referred to as " asphaltic bitumen" or, more briefly, merely as " bitumen". This same product in American literature is referred to as "asphalt". The position is still further confused by the fact that in the United Kingdom the term "asphalt" is reserved for natural or mechanical mixtures in which asphaltic bitumen (that is, bitumen) is associated with inert mineral matter. Thus, in the United Kingdom "asphalt" is the mixture of bitumen and stone on the road surface, or mixtures of bitumen and mineral matter, such as lake asphalt or rock asphalt.

Asphaltic bitumens manufactured by the distillation process

(*vide* chapter XIV) are often referred to as "straight" grades or "steam refined" bitumens. The term "straight" indicates that the bitumen is a direct product consisting of the unchanged asphaltic material of high boiling point, originally present in the crude oil, since the distillation process is designed to remove the volatile fractions without altering in any way the properties of the asphaltic bitumen. The term "steam refined" arose from the fact that the bitumen had been refined or manufactured by distillation in the presence of steam.

These terms are frequently used to distinguish the normal grades from the blown grades, which are produced by blowing "straight" bitumen with air under suitable temperature conditions. This fact has led to these blown grades being occasionally referred to as "oxidized" bitumen. While the use of this term "oxidized" is fundamentally correct, it may be misleading, since the term "oxidized" normally indicates a product which contains a substantial amount of oxygen. This is definitely not the case with "blown" bitumen, since this particular oxidation process results in the removal of hydrogen and not in the addition of oxygen.

PROPERTIES OF ASPHALTIC BITUMENS

Asphaltic bitumen is graded in terms of either its penetration or its softening point. The softer products are graded in terms of penetration, and the following are typical soft and medium grades : 180/200 pen., 60/70 pen. and 20/30 pen.

The harder materials are usually graded in terms of their Ring and Ball softening points, and we find such grades as 80°/90° C. and 110°/120° C. Blown grades are frequently graded according to trade names, but a more desirable system is based upon a combination of the softening point and the penetration. Thus 85/40 grade would indicate that the mean softening point would be 85° C. and the mean penetration 40. The penetration and the softening point tests are therefore of universal interest.

Penetration. The penetration test determines the distance, in tenths of a millimetre, the specified penetration needle, when loaded to a total weight of 100 gr., will penetrate into the bitumen under test in five seconds at 25° C. A typical apparatus for carrying out the penetration test is shown in fig. 1, from which it will be seen that the bitumen under test is contained in a small penetration tin which is placed in a transfer dish containing water at 25° C. (77° F.). The point of the needle is brought carefully into accurate contact with the surface of the submerged bitumen, and the dial is set by bringing the plunger in contact with the head of the needle assembly. The needle is then released and allowed to penetrate for five seconds. It is then clamped, the plunger brought again in contact with the assembly, when the distance to which the needle has penetrated can be read on the dial.

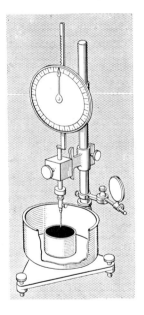

Fig. 1. Penetrometer.

Softening Point. The softening point test consists essentially in determining the temperature at which a specified steel ball will fall through a ring mould of bitumen, drawing the bitumen down through a distance of 1 inch. The apparatus used is shown in fig. 2, from which it will be appreciated that the distance between the bottom of the ring mould and the bottom brass plate is one inch. The water in the bath is stirred mechanically and heated at a specific rate, thus ensuring a uniform temperature throughout the water bath and a uniform rate of temperature rise.

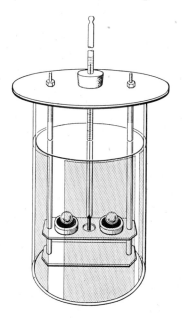

Fig. 2. Softening Point (Ring and Ball Method).

The term ''softening point'' is used rather than the term ''melting point'', since bitumen, being a mixture of many hydrocarbons, cannot be said to have a precise melting point in the strict sense of the term. Bitumen does, in fact, soften quite gradually with rise in temperature, and the best that can be done in the circumstances is to standardize very closely a set of purely arbitrary conditions and agree that the result obtained by following this standard procedure shall be accepted as the "softening point" of the bitumen.

Penetration Index. The softening point and the penetration tests may each be regarded as viscosity determinations carried out under specialized conditions, and it follows that there must be some relationship between the softening point and the penetration. It has, in fact, been stated that the softening point of any bitumen is the temperature at which that bitumen will have a penetration of about 800.

Thus, the penetration and softening point may be regarded as giving two points on a curve showing the change of viscosity with temperature for a given bitumen as measured by means of the penetration test. If, therefore, two bitumens of equal penetration at 25° C. are compared, it follows that the one with the higher softening point must, on this basis, be the less susceptible to change of temperature, since a greater rise in temperature is required to increase its penetration to approximately 800 (the penetration value at the softening point).

The accompanying table lists two such bitumens, and it is obvious that the "Oxidized S" grade is less susceptible to temperature change than is the 15/25 pen. grade, in the sense that it will withstand a higher temperature before it begins to flow, in spite of the fact that both grades have the same consistency (penetration) at 25° C.

TEMPERATURE SUSCEPTIBILITY

Grade	Penetration at 25° C.	Softening Point
15/25 (Straight)	25	140° F.
"Oxidized S" (Blown)	25	176° F.

It has generally been considered that the behaviour of asphaltic bitumen in many of its applications depends largely upon the rate at which its consistency will change with change of temperature, i.e. on its temperature susceptibility, and the "penetration index" scale derived from the softening point and the penetration at 25° C. has provided an arbitrary measure of this temperature susceptibility.

The penetration index (P.I.) provides a useful, if rather approximate, method of characterizing the general types of bitumen. Thus "straight bitumens" show penetration indices between −2 and +2, while blown products have higher indices, i.e. greater than +2. At the other end of the scale we find bitumens of an interesting type which have indices below −2.

Some of these bitumens of low P.I. are manufactured for special industrial purposes from crude oils which yield bitumens rich in resinous constituents, and containing little or no asphaltenes (*vide infra*). Such bitumens are relatively light in colour and are sometimes referred to as "Albino bitumens". These find special applications in which the black colour of ordinary bitumens would be undesirable.

Another type of bitumen with a negative penetration index can be manufactured from products resulting from certain cracking operations. These bitumens show high temperature susceptibility, but in this case the products are usually not light coloured. Because of their high temperature susceptibility this class of bitumen, with P.I. below −2, are frequently described as "pitch" type bitumens. They resemble coal-tar pitch in that they soften rapidly with rise of temperature and melt to comparatively mobile liquids at relatively low temperatures. Unlike coal-tar pitch, however, they are free from insoluble carbonaceous matter, which is present in considerable quantity in the case of coal-tar pitch. Such pitch type bitumens find special industrial applications.

The table on page 555 gives a few examples of each of these types of bitumen.

Ductility. A most striking property of many types of bitumen is their remarkable ductility. The precise significance of this property cannot easily be defined, but it is obviously associated with the adhesive, plastic nature of bitumen. This property of ductility is strongly characteristic of soft and medium grades of

Type	Penetration at 25° C.	Softening Point Ring and Ball	Penetration Index
Straight	200 65 20	40° C. 49·5° C. 66·5° C.	0 —0·7 +0·3
Blown	26 10	86·5° C. 136·5° C.	+3·6 +6·2
"Pitch"	36 26	54° C. 47° C.	—5·3 —3·2

bitumen, and no doubt accounts for the resilient nature of such structures as bituminous road surfaces.

It is difficult, however, if not impossible, to decide what measure of ductility must be possessed by any grade of bitumen in order that it may give the best results, say, in road construction. Nevertheless, it is regarded as an important factor, and the determination of the ductility has become a standard test used in the examination of bitumen. In carrying out this test a special block of bitumen is prepared in a mould of specified dimensions.

The type of mould used is shown in fig. 3. The required quantity of bitumen is poured into the mould, cut level with a hot knife and brought to a temperature of 25° C. in a specified manner. The side plates are then removed and the mould placed in the ductilometer, where the bitumen can be stretched under water at 25° C. The essential dimension of the bitumen mould is that the cross-section of the waist from the bitumen should be 1 cm. The general arrangement of the apparatus is shown in fig. 4. In this apparatus the bitumen is stretched at the rate of 5 cm. per minute.

All but the very hardest grades show some measure of ductility, and the soft and medium bitumens, under the conditions described, stretch out into long, even, slender threads, and in most cases the bitumen can be stretched through the full length of the bath, 100 cm., without the threads of bitumen breaking. In such

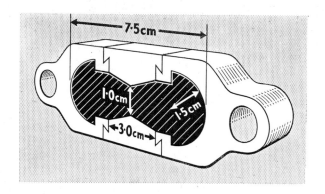

Fig. 3.   Mould for Ductility Test.

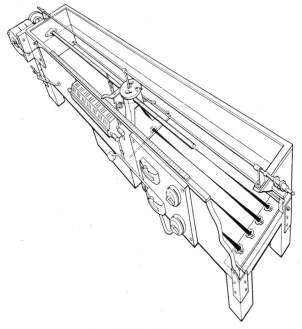

Fig. 4.   Ductilometer.

cases the result of the test is reported as ''ductility greater than 100''.

It should be emphasized that no special significance should be attached to this figure of 100. Its frequent appearance in specifications merely arises from the fact that the original ductilometers were made this length. In machines of greater length it has subsequently been shown that considerably higher ductility figures can be recorded.

The Fraass Breaking Point. It is desirable that bitumen should retain, during use, its plastic ductile properties over as wide a temperature range as possible, and, just as the softening point is designed to control its behaviour at elevated temperatures, so the Fraass breaking point method has been developed to test the behaviour of the bitumen at low temperatures. The precise object of this test is to determine the temperature at which a given bitumen will become brittle. The general arrangement of the apparatus is shown in fig. 5. A specified amount of bitumen is spread to form a film of standard thickness on a springy stainless steel plaque. This plaque is then mounted in the clips B and the whole apparatus mounted in a tube which can be cooled under controlled conditions. By operating the mechanical device C the distance between the clips can be varied in a regular manner. In this way the plaque carrying the film of bitumen can be bent at a series of descending temperatures.

The Fraass breaking point is the temperature at which cracks first appear in the film of bitumen. This test gives a useful general indication as to the temperature at which the bitumen under test may become sufficiently brittle to crack. The information so obtained, however, must be interpreted with due care. The temperature at which a film of bitumen will crack will depend upon the stress conditions, and it must be recognized that the stress conditions in practice may differ widely from those in this test. The test is, of course, of direct value for comparing the low-temperature behaviour of different types of bitumen.

Viscosity. Even the softest grades of bitumen are very viscous materials, and it is obvious that a comprehensive study of their viscosity characteristics will present many difficulties. Such a thorough study at relatively low temperatures calls for the use of

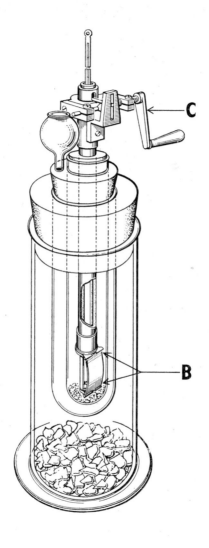

Fig. 5. Fraass Breaking Point Test.

special types of viscometers, such as the coni-cylindrical viscometer, and remains a research problem. It is, however, necessary for practical purposes for users to know the viscosity of bitumen at the working temperatures concerned. This purely practical requirement can be satisfied by viscosity determinations carried out in such conventional instruments as the Redwood II viscometer. The results obtained are usually converted and recorded in centistokes at such temperatures as 100°C., 125°C., 150°C. and 175°C.

Loss on Heating Tests. Normal grades of bitumen will not contain more than a trace of material which will be volatile at working temperatures. This point is of practical significance, since it is important that no permanent change in consistency shall occur as a result of volatile constituents being lost during the normal processing of the material. The "loss on heating" test has, therefore, been developed to give a measure of the volatility of any bituminous product when heated for five hours at 163° C.. A specially designed oven, fitted with a revolving shelf, is used and every detail of the test has been closely specified. The temperature 163° C. (325° F.) is chosen as representing the temperature to which the various bitumens may be raised in practice. Normal bitumens show very small losses as the result of such heat treatment, the actual loss being in most cases of the order of one- or two-tenths of 1%. This aspect of the test merely indicates that the product is free from contamination by volatile material. The value and significance of the test is enhanced, however, when the properties of the bitumen after this heat treatment are also determined. It is, therefore, common practice to determine the penetration of the bitumen after this heat treatment.

Solubility in Carbon Disulphide. By definition, bitumen is completely soluble in carbon disulphide, while any carbonaceous or inorganic impurities would, of course, be insoluble. Commercial grades of bitumen are normally specified as 99% soluble, but in actual fact this specification minimum is usually exceeded, figures of the order of 99·8% being quite normal.

Carbon disulphide is one of the best solvents for bitumen, but owing to its highly inflammable and toxic nature, it is objectionable in use, and efforts are being made to substitute other solvents, such as trichlorethylene. Bitumen is readily soluble in a wide range of organic solvents, such as benzol, toluol, carbon tetrachloride, methylene chloride, kerosine, white spirit, creosote etc. It is not, however, completely soluble in the lightest petroleum fractions, in which only the oily and resinous constituents dissolve readily.

Asphaltenes. In devising a method for the determination of the asphaltene content of bitumen use has been made of the fact that only the oily and resinous constituents of bitumen will dissolve readily in petroleum spirit. The petroleum spirit to be used for this purpose has been closely specified by the Institute of Petroleum, and is known as "I.P. Petroleum Spirit for Analytical Purposes". This is a volatile spirit boiling between 55° C. and 90° C., and is substantially free from aromatic hydrocarbons.

When a quantity of bitumen is brought into contact with the stipulated quantity of this spirit under standard conditions, the oily and resinous constituents are selectively dissolved and the asphaltenes are precipitated as a brownish powder. Should there be any paraffin wax present some of it may be precipitated with the asphaltenes, and special precautions may have to be taken to remove it. The asphaltenes are dried and weighed and the percentage present in the original bitumen calculated. The asphaltene content of asphaltic bitumen is defined as the percentage of wax-free material insoluble in petroleum spirit but soluble in carbon disulphide.

Composition. Little precise knowledge is available as regards the composition and structure of bitumen, but it consists entirely of complex hydrocarbons, some of which are liquid, some semi-solid, and others actually solid. The liquid hydrocarbons are oils, the semi-solid are resinous in nature, while the asphaltenes, as determined by the foregoing method, are actually solid hydrocarbons. The bitumen is considered to be a colloidal system in which the colloidal particles of solid asphaltenes are dispersed in any oily medium, the disperse phase being stabilized by the resinous bodies present. It must be appreciated, however, that this picture of the constitution of bitumen may be unduly simplified, since there can be no sharp lines of demarcation between oils, resins and asphaltenes ; oils will gradually merge into resins, and resins into asphaltenes.

GRADES OF ASPHALTIC BITUMEN

SOFT GRADES

Penetration at 25° C.			Softening Point (Ring and Ball) °C.			Ductility at 25° C.
280/320	...	...	34/38	...	...	> 100
180/200	...	...	37/43	...	...	> 100

MEDIUM GRADES

80/100	...	...	45/52	...	...	> 100
60/70	...	...	49/56	...	...	> 100
40/50	...	...	52/60	...	...	> 100
30/40	...	...	55/64	...	...	> 60
20/30	...	...	59/69	...	...	> 30
10/20	...	...	65/75	...	...	> 5

HARD GRADES

7/13	...	...	75/85	...	...	3/6
6/12	...	...	80/90	...	...	2/6
3/7	...	...	110/120	...	...	Nil
1/5	...	...	120/130	...	...	Nil

"BLOWN" GRADES

25/35	...	...	70/80	...	...	> 4
35/45	...	...	80/90	...	...	> 3
20/30	...	...	80/90	...	...	> 3
10/20	...	...	110/120	...	...	> 2
7/12	...	...	130/140	...	...	> 1

"PITCH" GRADES

Penetration at 25° C.			Softening Point (Ring and Ball) °C.
80/100	...	...	...	40/45
40/50	...	...	...	45/50
30/40	...	...	...	47/52
20/30	...	...	...	50/55
10/20	...	...	...	52/62
4/6	...	...	...	60/67
1/3	...	...	...	70/75
0/1	...	...	...	75/85

ASPHALTIC BITUMEN IN ROAD CONSTRUCTION

Steam-rolled Asphalt. Since adequate quantities of bitumen became available early in the twentieth century, rapid developments in the technique of road-making have taken place and several recognized forms of construction have been developed in which bitumen is used as a binder. Of these, the most important is "steam-rolled asphalt", a hot-mix, plant-produced asphalt. This construction normally consists of a base coat or "binder" course, consisting mainly of coarse stone aggregate with a percentage of smaller material, all coated with a medium grade of bitumen, such as 20/30 pen., 40/50 pen., or 60/80 pen., dependent somewhat upon the local climatic conditions, and a wearing course or top coat consisting mainly of sand with an appreciable quantity of filler and containing some stone, all again coated with the same grade of bitumen. Frequently, this is reduced to a single-course system resembling the wearing course from the above two-course system.

It is considered important to use a well-graded aggregate, but little precise knowledge is available as regards the technical significance of the actual grading. The nature and amount of the filler is, however, known to be a most important factor as far as the grading of the aggregate is concerned. It is customary to regard all material passing a 200-mesh sieve as filler, but in reality it is the quantity passing the 350-mesh sieve, or even finer, which is most significant. Thus, an exceedingly fine bulky powder, like hydrated lime, functions as a very satisfactory filler. The exceedingly fine particles of such fillers enter the films of bitumen surrounding the stone and sand particles and affect fundamentally the flow characteristics of the bitumen, and herein lies the real significance of the extreme fineness of the filler. The function of the bitumen binder is to coat each particle of the aggregate with an adhesive ductile film of bitumen and to cement the coated particles together. The resultant mass, when properly compacted, is of course completely waterproof, but probably the most important feature of such a structure is that it is resilient and slightly flexible. It is thus able to accommodate the shocks and stresses caused by heavy high-speed traffic.

The finished road is free from any tendency to crack and does not require the provision of expansion joints. Thus, a continuous waterproof surface eliminates entirely the danger of surface water gaining access to the foundations. The figures shown below indicate the possible composition of a two-course road using straight bitumen as a binder :—

Base Course.

Stone	Soluble Bitumen	Aggregate passing 3/16-inch mesh
65%	6%	29%

Wearing Course.

Stone	Soluble Bitumen	Aggregate passing 200-mesh Sieve	Aggregate passing 28-mesh retained 200-mesh
20%	10%	12%	58%

(All percentages by weight and approximate.)

Fig. 6 shows a photograph of a transportable, rather simple form of Hot-Mix Asphalt plant, while fig. 7 shows a simplified line diagram illustrating the construction of a plant of this type. The mixed aggregate, stone and sand, is fed to the oil-fired dryer by means of a conveyor, where it is raised to a temperature of about 350° F. and is then transferred by a second conveyor to the screens. Here the sand is separated from the stone and over-sized stones are rejected. The sand and stone fall into separate compartments in the storage bin, from which the required proportions of hot sand and stone may be drawn off into the weighing hopper.

A supply of hot bitumen is maintained at a temperature of about 350° F. (177° C.) in a storage tank, which is usually electrically

Fig. 6.   Transportable Hot-Mix Asphalt Plant.

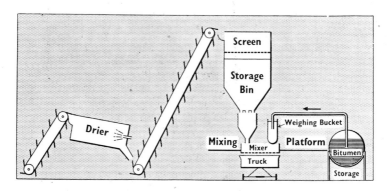

Fig. 7.   Diagram showing Construction of a Hot-Mix
Asphalt Plant.

heated and thermostatically controlled at the required temperature. The bitumen is pumped as required to the weighing bucket.
The required weighed quantities of hot sand, stone and bitumen
are tipped into the mixer, the whole mixing process being controlled by the operator from the platform. The required proportion of filler is usually not added until the coating of the aggregate
with bitumen is substantially complete. The entire process of
drying, heating, screening, measuring and mixing is completed in
a few minutes. The finished product is dropped into trucks, transported to the road and spread while still comparatively hot. This
spreading operation is of critical importance, and mechanical
"finishers" are now used to ensure an even and regular surface
of first-class "riding" quality.

It is particularly important to ensure that the correct proportion
of bitumen is used, and the total permissible variation in a given
type of carpet may only amount to 1 % of bitumen ; that is to say,
10 % may represent the lower limit, and 11 % the upper. In the
preparation of such mixtures, the bitumen is heated in order to
reduce the consistency to the point at which it will spread evenly
and thinly over the aggregate. Such mixes must be laid hot, since
they would become stiff and unworkable if allowed to cool. These
circumstances, besides necessitating the use of a fairly elaborate
plant, also limit the distance to which the hot-mix can be transported before being spread.

Mastic Asphalt. Mastic asphalt consists essentially of a high
proportion of very fine mineral matter intimately associated with
the asphaltic bitumen matrix. Both rock asphalt and lake asphalt
provide natural bituminous mixtures already containing this very
finely divided and evenly dispersed mineral matter, and it has become common commercial practice to use rock asphalt as the base
material for the manufacture of mastic asphalt, the additional
asphaltic cement required being either fluxed Trinidad lake
asphalt or a suitable grade of asphaltic bitumen, together with the
requisite amount of filler. A common process of mastic manufacture consists, therefore, of blending very thoroughly the required quantities of powdered rock asphalt and asphaltic bitumen.
The normal procedure is to melt the bitumen and gradually add
the required quantity of powdered rock asphalt, with effective

stirring. Finally, a considerable quantity of stone aggregate is added, and the hot mixture is further stirred until mixing is complete. The blended mastic asphalt is then run into moulds and cast into cakes. Mastic asphalt manufacture is a highly specialized industry, and different grades are produced which are well suited for the construction of roads, roofs and floors, and for the lining and waterproofing of water tanks and many other types of waterproofed construction.

While the traditional method of mastic asphalt manufacture is based on the use of rock and lake asphalt, these materials are not essential constituents, and large quantities of mastic asphalt are made directly from asphaltic bitumen, fine mineral matter such as limestone filler, and suitable grit. Such products are usually referred to as "synthetic" mastic asphalts, to differentiate them from those based on natural asphalts.

Providing the physical difficulty involved in the incorporation of such large proportions of very fine aggregate into bitumen is successfully overcome, there is no reason why "synthetic" mastic asphalts should not be in every way equal to those based on natural asphalts.

Cutbacks. As indicated above, the hot-mix process imposes certain practical restrictions, and it has become necessary to provide a type of bitumen binder which can be applied at lower temperatures to give a mix which can be stored until required and transported over greater distances, and finally spread cold. A range of "cutbacks", or liquid asphaltic bitumens, has been provided to meet this demand. These cutbacks are prepared by blending a medium grade of bitumen with a suitable volatile solvent or flux, which may be either white spirit, special kerosine or creosote, according to the type and grade of cutback required. Cutbacks are graded primarily on a viscosity basis, but the determination of the viscosity of these very viscous materials presents special difficulties, since the value obtained as the result of a test will depend upon the previous thermal history of the sample. Thus it is necessary before carrying out a viscosity test to maintain the sample at 60° C. for three hours in order to bring the material into a stable and standard condition. Only in this way can reliable and repeatable figures be obtained. The actual test is carried out, using the Standard Tar Viscometer, usually at 25° C. or at 40° C.

The table below gives the properties of four typical cutbacks used in the United Kingdom :—

Pool Cutback Bitumen.	No. 1	No. 1a	No. 2	No. 3*
Specific gravity at 60° F. ...	0·98–1·03	0·98–1·03	0·98–1·03	0·98–1·03
Viscosity Redwood Tar—				
At 77° F. (25° C.) ...	270–340	—	135–205	135–205
At 104° F. (40° C.) ...	—	85–105	—	—
Viscosity Hutchinson No. 2 at 77° F. (25° C.)... ...	80–100	180–220	40–60	40–60
Flux content % wt. approx.	14	11·5	17	14
Bitumen content, % wt. approx.	86	88·5	83	86
Solubility in carbon disulphide, % wt.	99 min.	99 min.	99 min.	99 min.
Mineral matter (ash), % wt.	1 max.	1 max.	1 max.	1 max.

* Special non-toxic grade.

The corresponding American specifications are drawn up along rather different lines, being largely based upon the results to be obtained in accordance with the standard distillation test (A.S.T.M. D402–36). The essential feature of this test is that the cutback is distilled to a temperature of 360° C., the distillate collected and the residue immediately poured from the flask and reserved for further examination. The temperature of 360° C. has been chosen as representing an approximation to the point at which the separation ultimately taking place on the road is effected in the distilling apparatus.

The properties of the volatile fraction so obtained will determine the type of cutback and indicate the rate at which it will "set" or "cure" on the road. The properties of the residue, on the other hand, will indicate, approximately at least, the kind of binder which will remain in or on the road when the fractions volatile under practical conditions have been lost by evaporation.

The function of the solvent is, of course, to reduce the viscosity of the resulting cutback to such an extent that it can be applied to the road surface or to road aggregates with the minimum of heating. The bulk of this solvent evaporates fairly rapidly, and the consistency of the bituminous binder left on or in the road approximates to that of the original bitumen base used. This residual material then functions normally as an effective binder.

The use of such fluid binders offers many obvious advantages, since they can be accurately and economically sprayed on to road surfaces at moderate temperatures. Their use, however, gives rise to special problems. For instance, the properties of the solvent must be such that the cutback will "set off" satisfactorily under the conditions of use. It is also important that the cutback must readily wet the road or road aggregates and not be displaced by water during subsequent early rain. In other words, it is obviously important that the cutback should wet the aggregate more readily than will water, and, once having established contact, the cutback should not be washed from the aggregate by rain water.

This danger of the binder being displaced by water only exists to any significant extent during the period in which the cutback contains most of its solvent, and is therefore quite fluid. Once the ultimate high consistency of the binder has been reached the danger of water action is normally of little practical significance. Many wetting agents have been suggested for addition to cutbacks to ensure preferential adhesion of the cutback to aggregates in the presence of water, and it is now possible to ensure that the cutback will actually displace the water film from the surface of wet aggregate. This constitutes an important development, since it may in many cases eliminate the need for drying large quantities of road aggregate, a proceeding which is both costly and relatively slow.

Bituminous Macadam*. Large quantities of cutbacks are used in the manufacture of bituminous macadam, which consists of a graded aggregate containing stone, chippings and "fines", all coated with a suitable bituminous binder (usually a cutback). The dry aggregate is heated to a temperature of about 150° F. and coated with the cutback, heated to about 250° F. This may, therefore, be regarded as a "warm" process as compared with the "hot-mix" process described above. This "warm" process has the advantage that mixing can be carried out in a centrally placed plant. The mix may be carried over considerable distances or stored until required, since, in view of the fluid nature of the binder, the mixture can be laid and compacted cold. The following shows a possible composition for bituminous macadam :—

Bituminous Macadam—2-inch Coated Work

$1\frac{1}{4}$-inch to 1-inch stone	50%
1-inch to $\frac{1}{8}$-inch chippings	40%
$\frac{1}{8}$-inch to dust	6%
Cutback	4%—5%

A mixture of this kind will provide a reasonably rough surface and will gradually consolidate to form a durable, waterproof carpet.

Surface Dressing. Cutbacks are also extensively used for the surface dressing of roads. This process consists of spraying or brushing on to the surface a coating of cutback at the rate of about 6 square yards to the gallon, followed by a liberal dressing of dry chippings. Various types of chippings have been used successfully, but probably the most satisfactory results are obtained with the larger sizes of chippings consisting of hard, tough stone approximately cubical in shape. The process is intended to be carried out with dry chippings in dry weather and, under these conditions, a firmly held, hard-wearing, rough carpet of chippings is built up to provide a safe and satisfactory surface.

Thin Carpets. In recent years a trend has developed towards the use of thin chipping carpets, using a cutback or soft grade of bitumen as the binder. The main feature aimed at in this kind of construction is to provide a non-skid surface comparable with that obtained by surface dressing, but with a useful life equivalent to three or four successive surface dressings.

At the same time, "fine aggregate" carpets have been developed and have attained a considerable measure of popularity. These fine aggregate carpets consist of quarry fines, that is, $\frac{1}{8}$-inch to dust aggregate, again bound with either a soft grade of bitumen or a cutback. This mixture is made at a medium temperature, normally laid cold, and, on compaction, presents a surface of the sandpaper type.

Mix-in-Place. It is common knowledge that a sandy or gravel soil will normally consolidate to form a serviceable road surface over a considerable range of water content ; in other words, water can function as a satisfactory binder for aggregates of this type. Unfortunately, in such cases, considerable variation in water content will naturally occur in practice. Thus, the road will disintegrate when undue evaporation of water occurs, while on the other hand the surface will lose its load-bearing capacity when the water content reaches excessive proportions. The "mix-in-place" process is based upon the assumption that such road surfaces could be maintained continuously in satisfactory condition if the water binder were replaced by the relatively non-volatile oil. The process consists, therefore, of disintegrating a suitable soil surface when in a relatively dry condition and adding sufficient oil to provide the proportion of binder required to bind the aggregate and maintain adequate stability. The incorporation of the oil is actually carried out *in situ* by means of harrows, graders, etc., the mixture being finally rolled and compacted in the usual manner. The particular value of the method is that it provides a means of laying a bituminous road surface, in suitable country, at a minimum cost, using the natural aggregate found on the site. A cutback or a suitable asphaltic residual oil may be used as binder in this type of construction.

The Wet Sand Process. This process may be regarded as a special form of plant sand-mix. An outstanding feature of this process is, however, that the work may be carried out with wet aggregates. Normally, the process is confined to the treatment of reasonably clean, naturally-occurring sands or sandy gravels. The binder consists of a special road oil which contains one of a range of known "wetting agents" which are capable, in the presence of lime, of imparting to the road oil preferential wetting properties. In applying this process 2% of lime is mixed with the wet sand, followed by 5%–6% of the special road oil heated to about 200° F. (93° C.). Under these conditions, the road oil displaces the water film and adheres firmly to the surface of the aggregate. The mixture so prepared is then spread to form a rather soft carpet. This carpet is consolidated, and during this process some of the water may be expelled from the system. Gradual hardening then takes place over a period of days, due partly to the loss of residual water and partly to the development of structure in the binder-filler mixture. During this period of curing a durable surface of adequate load-bearing capacity is developed. It is of interest to note in connection with this process that the binder so developed cannot be subsequently displaced by water action. This process has found special application in connection with the construction of aerodrome runways.

Soil Stabilization. Naturally occurring soils, particularly those containing a proportion of clay, display high load-bearing capacities over a considerable water content range, and are obviously of special interest in connection with road foundations. Normally, the main problem in connection with the successful use of such soils is to prevent excessive quantities of water gaining access to the soil, since such additional water will cause softening, and ultimately destroy the load-bearing capacity of the soil. A soil stabilization process designed to prevent these undesirable changes in water content has therefore been developed. In accordance with this process, the soil is first brought to the optimum water content (typically about 9 %) for maximum load-bearing capacity. It is then waterproofed in such a manner as will prevent any subsequent appreciable change in water content. It has been found that this can be accomplished successfully with as little as 3 % by weight of a waxy asphaltic residual oil. On mixing this quantity of oil with the moist soil, the oil rapidly spreads over the water films enveloping the particles or groups of particles of moist soil in water repellent and waterproofing oil films. The minute wax crystals present in the oil film ''leaf'' to the surface to form a somewhat rigid layer of wax crystals. This layer is highly water repellent, and thus tends to prevent further water entering the system by capillary attraction. The rigidity imparted to the oil films by the wax crystals is also sufficient to prevent the oil being displaced by any small quantity of water which may gain access to the system. The net result is that changes of water content are substantially prevented and the soil is satisfactorily stabilized. A layer of soil stabilized in such a way will form the natural foundation for roads and similar constructions. To complete the road all that is necessary is to superimpose a flexible, impervious, bituminous carpet capable of withstanding the wear and tear of traffic.

While experience in the United Kingdom with soil stabilization has been largely based on the use of a waxy residual oil, it should be mentioned that similar, and probably equally successful, work has been carried out in the United States using suitable cutbacks, preferably containing a wetting agent.

In this American process, the cutback is intended to function as a binder in addition to waterproofing the structure, and it has therefore been found necessary to use higher binder contents, of the order of 6%. This fact will constitute a disadvantage as compared with the "waxy oil" process, unless experience establishes that the "cutback" process has some compensating advantage, such as greater durability.

Road Emulsions. Although the use of cutbacks facilitated many road-making operations, there was still a demand for a "cold" process—one in which no heat was required at any stage. The production of bitumen emulsions led to the development of such a process. The essential feature of a bituminous emulsion is that it consists of, say, 55% to 65% of bitumen finely dispersed in water. Many bitumens contain natural emulsifiers, and in such cases emulsions can readily be made by adding the molten bitumen, with stirring, to a dilute solution of alkali heated to near its boiling point. In this particular process, the mechanical mixing serves primarily to bring the constituents into contact, and the dispersion of the bitumen depends mainly upon the chemical action which takes place between the alkali and the acidic bodies present in the bitumen. Various procedures and emulsifiers are used but, since a slow-speed paddle mixer is used in all cases, they are known as "mixer processes" or "chemical emulsification" processes.

The need for a continuous process was soon felt, and this led to the use of some form of colloid mill. This process has already been described (*vide* chapter XIV), and it will be appreciated that in such a colloid mill the dispersion of the bitumen is effected mechanically. Emulsions prepared by either process are normally designed in the United Kingdom to meet the requirements of British Standard Specification No. 434, 1935. This stipulates that the bitumen must have a penetration at 77° F. (25° C.) of 150 to 350, and a softening point of not higher than 120° F. (49° C.). As regards the emulsifier, the specification states that the amount of the emulsifying agent in its dry state shall not normally exceed 1% by weight on the emulsion, and must not exercise any deleterious effect upon the bitumen. The water content of the emulsion must not exceed 50% by weight, but the emulsions commercially available actually contain from 55% to 65% of bitumen according to the grade of emulsion. The average particle size of such road emulsions is of the order of 2 microns*, while few particles will exceed 10 microns.

These road emulsions are stable in storage and transport, and offer adequate resistance to frost ; also, since the specific gravity of bitumen is only slightly greater than that of the continuous phase, little sedimentation occurs. Even if slight sedimentation of the bitumen particles does occur, this bitumen can be readily redispersed by gentle agitation.

Such emulsions, whether manufactured by the mixer or the colloid mill process, are designed to break readily when applied to the road surface, and they are known as "labile" (unstable) emulsions. The breaking of the emulsion on the road is primarily due to the rapid concentration of the emulsion as water is lost by evaporation. This concentration naturally brings the bitumen particles closer and closer together until they coalesce to form a continuous film of bitumen. In practice, the process is not as simple as this, since the coagulation process is affected by other factors, such as weather conditions and the shearing action of traffic. Obviously, however, it is important that the whole process of coagulation should take place as quickly as possible, since the full binding power will only be developed when the bitumen particles have coalesced to form a continuous film of bitumen.

These labile emulsions are mainly used for surface dressing operations, and the advantages claimed include cold operation, ease of application, comparatively rapid setting under normal conditions and the complete absence of any heat treatment. The road surface is swept as free as possible from dust and dirt and the emulsion is spread and blinded immediately with fine chippings and rolled. The road can then be reopened to traffic.

Bitumen emulsions can be used in many other forms of road construction, but in each case the stability and viscosity of the emulsion must be adjusted to suit the conditions of use. Thus, if an emulsion is to be used for the pre-coating of stones, a more stable emulsion must be used to ensure that coagulation does not take place before the stone is properly covered. For this purpose it is also necessary that the viscosity of the emulsion should be sufficiently high to prevent undue drainage of the emulsion from the stone during handling operations.

Commercially these emulsions are described as ''semi-stable'', since there is also available a third class of emulsions, suitable for mixing with aggregates containing large proportions of the finer fractions. For such applications the emulsions must display exceptional mechanical and chemical stability, and they are, therefore, classed commercially as ''stable''.

Control and Research. The whole of the processes described above call for systematic laboratory control if satisfactory results are to be obtained. Many standard methods have, therefore, been developed, such as those for the determination of binder content, the recovery of bitumen from road mixes, and the various tests for the examination of emulsions. Full particulars of these tests can be found in *Standard Methods for the Testing of Petroleum and Its Products*, issued by the Institute of Petroleum, and in *A.S.T.M. Standards on Petroleum Products and Lubricants*.

All these processes have been brought to a high standard of performance by continual research, and, while the scientific principles involved are now generally appreciated, the research continues, for the problems involved are very complex, and the demands made upon the roads increase year by year as modern road traffic becomes heavier and faster. The action of water upon bituminous binders has presented a particularly difficult problem which is still under investigation. With most bituminous binders there is, with certain difficult aggregates, a danger that the bitumen may be progressively displaced by water under unfavourable conditions.

With a view to removing this slight limitation, several effective wetting-agents have been developed, but so far the wet-sand process provides the only case in which such wetting-agents have been used systematically on a commercial scale.

The use of bitumen emulsions also continues to present many interesting problems, the most urgent of which arises from the need to improve the early adhesive properties of the coagulated bitumen.

INDUSTRIAL APPLICATIONS

The industrial applications of bitumen are extensive and diverse, and only the major uses have been selected for description.

Roofing Felt. The manufacture of roofing felt and similar products may be taken to illustrate the usage of bitumen as an impregnating and coating material. The manufacturing process, though quite simple in principle, is specialized and can only be described in general terms. Paper felt is first impregnated with a soft grade of bitumen and then coated with a blown grade of higher melting point. The felt should be reasonably dry, otherwise foaming will take place when it enters the bath of hot impregnant.

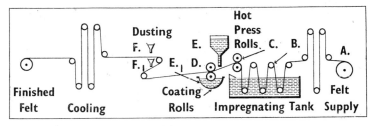

Fig. 8. Impregnating and Coating Plant.

The general arrangement of an impregnating and coating plant is shown in fig. 8. The felt leaves the roll A and is drawn through the soft molten bitumen (usually about 200 penetration) in the heated tank B, kept at about 400° F. (256° C.). The time of impregnation is controlled by varying the distance of travel by looping the felt over the desired number of rollers in the bath. The impregnated felt is then passed through the heated press rollers C, which remove excess bitumen. The amount of bitumen left in the felt is also controlled by adjusting the pressure between these rollers.

The impregnated felt is then cooled and subsequently passed to the rollers (D), which are fed with a blown grade of bitumen of higher softening point and lower penetration (E). In this way a coating of harder bitumen is usually applied to both surfaces of the impregnated felt. By various simple devices, such as varying the speed of the top roller in relation to the speed at which the felt is drawn through the plant, the finish of the coating on the top side of the felt may be varied to give a veined or crocodile finish if desired.

The coated felt is then dusted with talc or other mineral powder (F) and finally cooled and reeled for storage and transport. The talc is added to prevent the bitumen surfaces sticking together in the rolls or when the rolls are stacked for transport ; mineral granules may also be used for decorative purposes.

The precise properties of the coating material are of great importance, and it is obvious in the first place that the softening point and penetration of the bitumen used will depend upon the climatic conditions under which the roofing felt is to be used. Thus, while a blown grade of softening point 180° F. to 200° F. (82° C. to 93° C.) and a penetration of 20 to 30 at 77° F. (25° C.) may be used in the United Kingdom, a higher softening point may be required if the felt is to be used under tropical conditions. On the other hand, the coating must be sufficiently rubbery and flexible to ensure that cracking will not occur when the felt is rolled or handled prior to being transported. The coating must be continuous and free from pinholes and suchlike imperfections. This is important, since the function of the coating is not merely to resist the action of weather and to exclude water, but it must also exclude bacteria, which may attack the fibres of the felt.

Another technical consideration is the compatibility of the saturating and coating media. Should these consist of, or contain, materials which are not mutually compatible, there is a risk of undesirable separation occurring at the interface. With bitumens of the types mentioned above, this difficulty should not arise.

Floorcloth (or felt-base lino). The manufacture of floorcloth involves a similar impregnation, but the coating process is omitted. The impregnant, however, is a harder grade of bitumen than that used in the manufacture of roofing felt, since the finished floorcloth has to withstand severe local pressure, as from chair legs and heavy furniture.

The floorcloth is finished by printing an ornate pattern in oil paint on the upper surface. To obviate fluxing of the bitumen by the oils in the paint, with consequent discoloration of the pattern, it is customary to apply a sealing or isolating coat to the impregnated felt.

Waterproof Paper (Bitumenized). A wide variety of bitumenized paper products are manufactured, but those used in the packing trade are perhaps of most interest. The simplest type merely consists of paper saturated with a suitable grade of bitumen. When, however, food and delicate fabrics have to be packed, it is customary to use double kraft union or combined paper, which consists of two sheets of (brown) kraft union cemented together with a thin layer of suitable bitumen. This

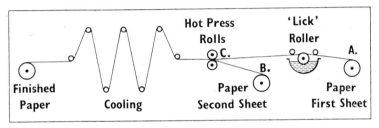

Fig. 9.   Coating Paper.

combined paper is waterproof, has considerable mechanical strength, is clean to handle, and is of pleasing appearance. The bitumen used in the manufacture must be soft enough and sufficiently ductile to ensure that there will be no risk of the bitumen film cracking in use. At the same time it must be sufficiently adhesive to hold the two sheets of paper firmly and permanently together. Since the textiles are packed under considerable pressure and the packages may be exposed to tropical temperatures, it is also essential that the bitumen shall not soften sufficiently under these conditions to stain the paper and therefore the packed goods.

The manufacturing process is quite simple, the arrangement being as indicated in a simplified form in fig. 9.

The paper is taken from the reel (A), which is supported on an unwinding roller at the front of the machine and drawn over a heated revolving drum or "lick" roller which is partially immersed in a tank of molten bitumen. This roller carries a film of bitumen on its surface and imparts a coating of bitumen to the paper. The paper then passes over a "doctor" knife, where excess bitumen is removed and returned to the tank. A paper from a second reel (B) at the back of the machine is led by the guide rollers on to the coated side of the first paper. The two papers adhere and pass to a pair of hot press rollers (C), and finally over guide rollers in festoon arrangement, where the paper is cooled before being finally wound into rolls. The finished product will normally contain about 30% of its weight of bitumen.

Modifications of this type of product include crêped papers for greater flexibility, reinforcement with fibre to increase strength, and lamination of paper with hessian, cardboard and, in special cases, metal foil. There are also bitumen-coated papers.

Bitumen Clay Emulsions and their use in manufacture of bitumenized paper. Dispersions of bitumen in aqueous clay suspensions find many applications in industry. Such dispersions are produced by mechanical means, using such materials as bentonite (clay) as the emulsifying and stabilizing agents. The resultant emulsions are pastes containing 50% to 60% of bitumen. They differ from the soap type of emulsions in some important respects, one interesting feature being that the bitumen particles are nearly all cigar-shape and not spherical.

The emulsions are extremely stable to both mechanical and chemical action, and they do not coagulate to films of bitumen until the water in the emulsion has been completely evaporated. The residual films are reinforced by the clay skeleton and are surprisingly resistant to flow under heat. Such emulsions are used in the manufacture of bituminous paper and boards.

The manufacture of paper consists essentially in the removal of water from a uniform layer of fibre deposited from a very dilute suspension of fibre in water. The preparation of the suspension involves the disintegration in a beater of the particular fibrous material used.

In view of the stability of these clay emulsions to mechanical and chemical action, it has been found possible to add them direct to the pulp in the beater and proceed to manufacture bituminous paper by the ordinary paper manufacturing process, thus eliminating the more usual separate impregnation with hot bitumen.

The emulsified bitumen is flocculated on to the fibre by the addition of coagulants, and passes through the whole process with the fibre ; the bitumen is finally remelted to form a waterproof coating on the fibres in the calendering process, which is primarily designed to give the paper the necessary glazed finish.

Stable clay emulsions are easily handled, and it is not surprising that they are used for a great variety of purposes. Large quantities are used for the manufacture of bitumenized panelboards, which find many applications in industry. The emulsion process is particularly suitable for the manufacture of the thicker bitumenized boards—e.g. panelboard—as the distribution of the bitumen throughout the whole thickness of the board is thereby more easily achieved than by hot impregnation.

An interesting although perhaps minor application of these clay emulsions is found in the manufacture of a waterproof board used for the production of certain cartons. This consists of a layer of bitumen sandwiched between two layers of white board. Here again the bitumen is incorporated during the actual manufacture of the board. Such boards are suitable for the manufacture of packages for food products which tend to absorb moisture.

Electric Cables. The cable industry also consumes large quantities of bitumen for a variety of protection and insulating purposes. It is used in many types of cables, but particularly in armoured cables, where it acts as impregnant for the jute or hessian wrappings, and also as a ''serving compound'' between the various outer wrappings. A soft bitumen is used for the impregnation of the ''cops'' of jute, and the process is usually carried out in steam-heated vessels under vacuum. The hessian fabric used as a further wrapping is usually impregnated with a harder grade of bitumen, such as 20–30 or 40–50 penetration.

Bitumen is also used in the preparation of joint box compounds, the desirable features of such compounds being good adhesion, high insulating efficiency, minimum contraction on cooling, and freedom from risk of cracking in service. The general trend is towards the use of as soft a grade as can be successfully used without danger of leakage from the box.

Trough compounds are used to fill the trough round the cable in the so-called "solid laid" systems. Straight or "filled" bitumen (containing powdered "fillers") is largely used for this purpose.

Considerable quantities of bitumen are also used as "sealing" compounds for accumulators, etc. Blown grades are preferred for this purpose on account of their good resistance to flow at elevated temperatures and their relative freedom from brittleness.

Pipeline Coating. Blown bitumens are widely used in the manufacture of compositions suitable for the lining and coating of steel pipes for protection against corrosive influences. Relatively thick applications are used, and it is obvious that such coatings must neither flow when the pipes are exposed to sun during storage nor crack at low temperatures in transport or when being laid. External coatings should also be tough enough to withstand fairly rough treatment during the "back-filling" operations (refilling trenches for buried pipelines).

The following special tests have been devised to ensure that the suggested bituminous compositions meet these requirements. These tests are known as the "flow" test and "shatter" test.

In the flow test a coat of the composition 5 mm. in thickness is applied to a flat steel plate. Horizontal white marks are then painted across the width of the coating. The assembly is placed, usually at an angle of 45 degrees, in an oven maintained at the temperature specified in accordance with the conditions under which the coating will be used. The average of the maximum displacements of the marks in millimetres after twenty hours' exposure is taken as a measure of the flow.

The shatter test consists in determining which of a series of steel balls is just capable of causing a 5 mm. thick coating of the composition to crack when the ball is dropped from a height of two metres on to a steel plate, to the underside of which the coating under test is adhering. Standard ball bearings of various sizes are used, and the weight of the ball just capable of cracking the composition is reported as the result of the test. The apparatus used in this test is shown in fig. 10, which indicates the way in which the plate is supported. It also shows the arrangement for releasing the ball electrically.

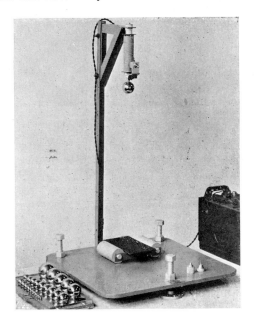

Fig. 10. Shatter Test.

Compositions complying with the following general requirements have given satisfactory results when used as inside linings :—

Softening point, Ring and Ball ... 100 to 130° C.
Penetration at 250° C. ... ... 25 to 10
Flow in 5 mm. layer at 70° C. at 45°
   inclination after 20 hours ... Less than 1 mm.
Shatter test at 15° C. ... ... 358 gr.
   ,,   ,,   0° C. ... ... 45 gr.
Maximum filler content ... ... 30% wt.

In the application of such compositions the required quantity of the hot mixture is run into the hot pipe, to which a thin priming coat has been previously applied.   The pipe is then spun at high speed and the lining evenly and smoothly spread over the inside surface of the pipe.   The whole may then be cooled by water sprays while the pipe is still being spun.

The application of thick linings naturally reduces the effective internal diameter of the pipe, and it may appear that there must be a decrease in the carrying capacity of the lined pipe.   Such is not the case, however, and it has actually been shown in practice that for diameters in excess of 20 cm., pipes with a bitumen lining 0·5 cm. in thickness will always have a greater carrying capacity than the same pipe unlined.   These observations apply to new pipes, and the advantage in favour of the bitumen-lined pipe will obviously be much greater in the case of old pipes, where corrosion products greatly increase the friction and therefore reduce the carrying capacity of the unlined pipes.

The formulation of outside coatings presents rather greater difficulties, since such coatings have to withstand the wear and tear of handling and laying.   Thick coatings based on blown bitumen are used, and special consideration should be given to the type of filler used.   Several types of filler have been used successfully, but particularly good results have been obtained with fibrous fillers such as micro-asbestos, a mixture of 70% blown bitumen and 30% of micro-asbestos being used.   In this mixture the blown bitumen is chosen, so that the composition will not flow more than 1·5 mm. at 75° C. or 40 mm. at 100° C. when tested as described above.

Before applying such coatings it is customary to apply a priming coat of a suitable bitumen solution.   The composition can then be applied by pouring on to the revolving pipe and spreading by mechanical spreaders.   If necessary, further protection may be provided by wrapping the coated pipe spirally with bitumen-impregnated hessian.   Where conditions warrant the maximum degree of protection, the pipes are first painted with red lead and primed with a bitumen solution before being coated with the composition.   Such coated pipes are finally wrapped with bitumen-impregnated coir* fabric.   This latter material is chosen as being extraordinarily resistant to the various disintegrating influences encountered in soil, including bacterial action.

Linings of Storage Tanks. Bitumen is extensively used in one form or another for the lining and waterproofing of tanks and suchlike constructions. Bitumen and bituminous compounds are strongly adhesive to concrete, brick, metal or wood ; they are sufficiently flexible to follow slight deformations and they offer good resistance to a wide variety of liquids and solutions, whether acid, alkaline or neutral in nature.

Mastic asphalt is widely used for this purpose, and particularly for the waterproofing of basements. Similarly, compounds based on blown bitumens, with or without fillers, are used for lining brick, metal or wooden tanks intended for the storage of a wide range of liquids, including such susceptible products as cider. Some preliminary treatment of the surface may be desirable to "key" the lining satisfactorily to the surface, and a simple priming with a bituminous solution will often serve this purpose. A thick coating of the hot mastic or bitumen compound is then applied, normally by trowelling. A smooth finish is obtained, and it is essential that, even on extensive vertical surfaces of considerable height, the compound should not flow at any temperature likely to be encountered in normal use.

HYDRAULIC CONSTRUCTION

Hydraulic works have provided a considerable outlet for bitumen for the protection and waterproofing of river and canal banks, dams, reservoirs, swimming pools, coast works, etc.

The use of bitumen in connection with hydraulic construction is a very large subject, and it will suffice here to consider one or two aspects in some detail.

Joint-filling Compounds. Bituminous joint-filling compounds are used in considerable quantities for a variety of purposes ; but a feature common to all applications is that the filling compound must prevent water from penetrating into the joints without the separate parts of the structure being rigidly joined. Bitumen meets these requirements very satisfactorily, since it resists even aggressive waters, whilst on account of its plastic nature it allows a certain amount of movement of the parts without damage to the joints.

The construction of a satisfactory joint is of special importance in such constructions as protective revetments* of stone or concrete on coasts, rivers, canals, reservoirs etc.   The purpose of such joints is primarily to prevent the attack of water on the underlying soil, but in the case of stone revetments their mechanical resistance is very greatly increased by the cementation of the individual stones.   It is also of great importance that such stone revetments should be able to follow slow settlements of the soil without fracture.   Bituminous jointings meet both of these requirements quite satisfactorily.

In hydraulic work the surfaces to be protected are usually sloping and the resistance to flow shown by the jointing materials becomes of outstanding importance.   It is for this reason that it is advantageous to incorporate fibrous fillers in bituminous jointing compounds to be used on slopes, even in temperate climates, and short-fibre asbestos has given very satisfactory results.   Slag wool and cotton have also been used with some success, but special care is necessary in handling and applying these materials.

Two general types of compounds have been found to give satisfactory results in practice : (1) Mixtures containing a relatively high percentage of bitumen of medium hardness, sand, and a small percentage of short-fibre asbestos.   Such mixtures can be poured at 180° C. to 200° C.   (2) Mixtures containing a relatively low percentage of soft bitumen, sand, filler and a small percentage of asbestos.   These mixtures have to be trowelled hot.

Both mixtures adhere well to stone, but type (2) mixtures are rather more ductile at lower temperatures, and in this connection it is of interest to recall that it is permissible in hydraulic work to use a harder bitumen or a higher percentage of mineral filler with a soft bitumen than would be permissible in the case of road work, which naturally calls for greater shock resistance and higher ductility.

The following major operations have been chosen as interesting examples of the use of bitumen in hydraulic construction.

The Ghrib Dam.   The upstream face of the Ghrib Dam, in Algeria, was waterproofed with adequate ''tack'' coats and 12 cm. of asphaltic concrete containing 8 % of 20/30 penetration asphaltic bitumen.   To this was added a protective and heat-insulated layer (10 cm.) of cement concrete.   This rock-filled dam was 65 metres in height, and the success of the work may be judged from the fact that percolation through the revetment under a head of 32 metres of water over an area of 8,000 square metres amounted to only 1·3 litres per minute.

Experience has shown that in the construction of bituminous revetments on steep slopes it is essential to secure a good bond between the bituminous layer and the underlying surface. Either an excess or a deficiency of tack coat will result in slipping of the bituminous layer. It is, therefore, regarded as good practice to apply the asphaltic concrete in two layers with reinforcement between the layers.

The Juliana Canal. It frequently happens that canals must pass through areas of porous soils. In such circumstances steps must be taken to waterproof the bed and sides of the canal, and flexible bituminous linings have been designed which are admirably suited for this purpose. The lining of the Juliana Canal, in Holland, provides an excellent example of this kind of work. In this case the local conditions were exceptionally difficult and it was essential that the bituminous lining should adhere satisfactorily to the underlying layer and be perfectly watertight. It was also important that the lining should be sufficiently plastic to follow any subsidence and, at the same time, possess adequate stability to resist flow on the sides of the canal.

A rich sheet asphalt consisting of sand, filler and 14% of 60/70 penetration bitumen was found to meet all these requirements when laid 5 cm. thick.

Protection of the Banks of the Mississippi. The protection of river and canal banks for generations presented serious engineering problems, and work carried out in 1934 on the Mississippi is of outstanding interest in this connection.

Asphalt mats were fabricated on the deck of a specially designed barge, with which was associated a floating asphalt plant. These mats were 2 inches thick and rather more than 200 feet wide, and were reinforced with steel mesh and steel launching cables. These cables were anchored on the bank and used to launch the mattress on to the bank. A further section of mattress was then fabricated on the deck of the barge and lowered to the bed of the river by drawing the barge further out into the river. In this way a continuous length of mattress was formed, protecting the bank and stretching out along the bed of the river. The whole operation was then repeated as often as necessary to cover the length of the bank requiring protection. The bituminous mixture used contained 23 % of loess*, 65 % of sand and 12 % of bitumen. It will be appreciated that this type of work differs from the canal lining described above in that the main object was protection against erosion, and not waterproofing.

It is probable that the use of bitumen in connection with hydraulic construction will ultimately provide one of the major outlets for bitumen.

The Shellperm Process. The Shellperm process constitutes another interesting specialized application of a bitumen emulsion in connection with hydraulic construction. In this process a very fine emulsion is pumped under moderate pressure into suitable porous sandy soils and caused to break when it has reached the desired location. The emulsion is used in a diluted form containing about 30 % of bitumen, and as used it is practically as thin as water.

As the specific gravity of the bitumen differs little from that of water, the emulsion can be made to flow without sedimentation through soil containing fine pores in the same way as does water. Under the same conditions, the emulsion moves only a little more slowly than water through sands. The emulsion can therefore be pumped through injection tubes into the sand under treatment at comparatively low pressure. Under these conditions the groundwater in the pores of the sand is replaced by the emulsion without any appreciable amount of mixing taking place. As injected, the emulsion has no particular effect upon the sand, but by the addition of suitable coagulants to the emulsion it can be made to break at the expiration of any predetermined period, which may vary from a few minutes to several days.

The coagulated particles of bitumen then clog the pores of the sand, rendering it impermeable. In this process the concentration of the emulsion injected, and thus the amount of bitumen put into the sand, is under control as well as the time of flocculation.

In applying the process, injection pipes are driven into the sand at suitable distances from each other, and to such a depth that their open or perforated ends reach the porous layer in which an impervious bitumen screen is to be formed. The required quantity of the diluted emulsion to which a suitable coagulant has been added is then poured or pumped into each of these pipes and allowed to flow into the surrounding porous sand, filling the voids of the sand until the emulsion issuing from the various pipes joins up to form a continuous impregnated layer. The essential feature of the process is that the emulsion can be caused to coagulate in accordance with the known conditions and the particular coagulant used.

In addition to rendering the sand impermeable, the deposited bitumen has a marked stabilizing effect. This process was used in connection with the extensions carried out to the Assiut barrage on the Nile. In extending the foundations of this barrage it was found that the coffer-dam within the sheet piling could not be kept dry, since water continuously seeped in from under the foundations. It was therefore necessary to render the subsoil impermeable to the normal depth of sheet piling. A suitable bitumen emulsion was injected at a low pressure to form an impermeable screen 30 metres long, 5 metres wide and 4 metres deep over the area in question. Practically complete impermeability was thus achieved.

The foregoing descriptions, while indicating the extent to which bitumen is used in industry, do not by any means exhaust even the major industrial applications. Large quantities of bitumen are used for the manufacture of brattice-cloth and bitumen-impregnated damp-coursing, while considerable quantities are used in the production of special lubricants and greases, paints, marine glues, and various ship's deck coverings. Bitumen is also used as an adhesive for cork insulation and for the preparation of moulding compounds, such as those used in the manufacture of battery boxes.

In addition to all these, there are minor applications, too numerous to mention individually.

Special Wartime Applications. Brief reference should be made to certain special wartime uses of bitumen.

The demand for bitumen in connection with its normal applications naturally continued, but, in addition to this, new applications arose from special wartime requirements. Thus, stable bitumen emulsions formed the basis of a range of camouflage paints which were required in very large quantities. Emulsions prepared from ordinary grades of bitumen, suitably pigmented, provided the darker shades, but when lighter colours were required it was necessary to use bitumens of the Albino types. Such camouflage paint could be either brushed or sprayed, and it was found that they gave very satisfactory service on very difficult surfaces, such as asbestos-cement, on which ordinary oil paints would normally fail.

Bituminized fabrics were found to be particularly valuable as wrappings to withstand tropical conditions ; the bitumen-coated packages often gave exceptionally good resistance against the activities of termites.

It was also found that suitably formulated bitumen compounds offered quite remarkable resistance to projectiles, and a type of plastic armour was developed which saved large quantities of steel and greatly facilitated the protection of vital parts of many types of craft, particularly landing craft.

Mixtures of bitumen or coal-tar pitch with stone aggregates were developed which gave protection comparable with that given by steel armour plating. The best results were obtained when the aggregate was selected in relation to the size of bullet to be stopped and the finished compound was fully compacted.

A particularly interesting development was, however, in connection with the use of hessian impregnated and coated with bitumen. This material was largely used as prefabricated surfacings for emergency landing grounds for aeroplanes. The ground was first levelled by bulldozers. Long strips of P.B.S. (Prefabricated Bituminous Surfacing) were then let down from rolls mounted on a special vehicle. As the bituminized hessian left the roll its under surface was wetted with oil by means of a "Lick" roller. A 50% overlap was allowed, thus half of the second strip adhered firmly to the first strip, while the other half established some contact with the ground. In this way a continuous bituminous surface of two layers of bituminized hessian firmly bound together was quickly built up. The effective construction of such surfaces in wet weather presented a problem. This was, however, overcome in due course, and it was ultimately possible to lay down a continuous and serviceable surface under any prevailing conditions. Such surfaces behaved well and withstood satisfactorily the stresses caused by fighter planes landing at high speeds.

This is regarded as an important technical development, and it is hoped that it will be possible to construct cheap and serviceable road surfaces along similar lines. Such bitumenized surfacings should also find applications in connection with such problems as the lining and waterproofing of irrigation canals.

Finally, the wet-sand-mix process employing S.R.O. (Special Road Oil) was a major wartime development, used successfully for many million square yards of aerodrome runways. This process has already been referred to earlier in the chapter under "Road Construction".

BIBLIOGRAPHY

Asphalts and Allied Substances. H. Abraham. (D. van Nostrand Co., Inc., 1945.)

Bituminous Substances. P. E. Spielmann. (Ernest Benn, Ltd., London, 1925.)

Asphalt Roads. P. E. Spielmann and A. C. Hughes. (Arnold & Co., London, 1936.)

Modern Road Emulsions. F. H. Garner (Editor). (Carrier's Publishing Co., London, 1939.)

Asphaltic Bitumen. Science of Petroleum, Part III, Section 40. (Oxford University Press, London, 1938.)

Modern Petroleum Technology. (Institute of Petroleum, London, 1946.)

Standard Methods for Testing Petroleum and its Products. (Institute of Petroleum, London, 1948.)

XXXII

SPECIAL PRODUCTS

IN addition to the main products described in previous chapters, many special products of great variety are made in increasing numbers and quantities. Some of these, such as the special boiling point spirits, are merely special, narrow-cut fractions of hydrocarbons ; some, such as naphthenic acids, are separated out in the refining processes ; and some, such as the various chemical derivatives, are made from hydrocarbons by chemical processes and bear the same relation to petroleum as drugs and dyes to the coal tar from which they are made.

SPECIAL BOILING POINT SPIRITS—WHITE SPIRIT
These petroleum solvents are obtained as special cuts, to specified distillation ranges, since controlled volatility is their most important property. While wider boiling range solvents, such as 150° C.–200° C. white spirit, may be prepared during direct distillation of suitable crude oils using modern fractionating columns, narrow-cut S.B.P. spirits, such as 60° C.–80° C. cut, are usually prepared by rectification of a wider boiling once-run fraction (*vide* chapter XVII). The odour of the unrefined products is sweetened and reduced to a minimum by suitable chemical treatment.

These S.B.P. spirits are characterized by their distillation range, which may be narrow (60° C.–80° C.) or wide (30° C.–130° C.), and their aromatic content, which depends on the nature of the base material from which they are derived. Certain individual grades of S.B.P. spirits are designated by reference to their particular application, e.g. extraction benzine and rubber solvents ; the general practice is to specify the boiling range, e.g. S.B.P. 60° C.–80° C.

S.B.P. spirits are broadly divisible into three categories, i.e. :—
  (1) Low-boiling ;
  (2) Medium-boiling ;
  (3) High-boiling.

The low-boiling spirits (petroleum ethers) are of narrow boiling range (70° C.–80° C.), of high degree of purity and low aromatic content. These are used for pharmaceutical and surgical purposes (salves and adhesives) ; also for the extraction of perfumes, essential oils and edible oils. The majority of the S.P.B. spirits marketed for industrial purposes (rubber solvents, extraction benzines, lacquer diluents) fall within the medium boiling range and may be either of narrow or wide cut.

Extraction Benzines may have a low or high aromatic content, depending on the nature of the product (vegetable oil, essence, etc.) to be extracted. Good extraction solvents should have the narrowest possible boiling range for the maximum efficiency, and where these are used for extracting vegetable oils, the aromatic content should be low in order to avoid extraction of undesirable materials such as resins and vegetable pigments. These benzines are used for the extraction of oil from ground nuts, palm kernels, linseed, castor beans, soya beans etc., and of grease from bones for glue manufacture. They are also employed to extract fish, animal and fat residues for the preparation of foodstuffs, fertilizers etc.

Rubber Solvents should be non-toxic, of good odour and even evaporation, not too volatile on account of losses and fire risk, nor too heavy, with consequent incomplete evaporation. Solvents of high aromatic content are required for rubber-proofing and dipped rubber goods in order to obtain high viscosity rubber solutions, while a low aromatic content is desirable in solvents required for cements for use in the construction of boots and shoes.

For **lacquer diluents** the boiling range of the S.B.P. spirit must be selected according to the nature of the other true and latent solvents present in the lacquer. The S.B.P. spirits are not themselves solvents for nitrocellulose but are used to adjust the solid content and viscosity of the lacquer and to cheapen its cost. The high aromatic S.B.P. spirits are preferable since they possess a higher dilution ratio with respect to nitrocellulose and also have better solvent powers for the resins used in lacquer composition.

In the **paint and varnish industry,** solvent naphtha is generally used ; this is an S.B.P. spirit of high aromatic content (45–70%) with a boiling range in the region of 115° C.–160° C.

For **dry cleaning** purposes, white spirit (or Stoddard solvent) is normally used, but there is a demand for a more volatile spirit (30° C.–110° C. or 115° C.–160° C.) for use in conjunction with a non-inflammable solvent of the chlorinated type.

Other uses for medium boiling S.B.P. spirit include the degreasing of leather, metal type, textile printing, and cleaning spirits of the clear soluble oil type.

White spirit and Stoddard solvent, mentioned above, come within the high boiling type of S.B.P. spirit, with a boiling range of the order of 140° C.–210° C., and with flash points above 73° F. (22·8° C.). White spirit replaces turpentine as a solvent in most paints and varnishes and is a more powerful solvent and more consistent, besides being non-corrosive. The solubility properties can be improved by using a white spirit of high aromatic content.

Other uses are in the production of furniture creams which are based on waxes and white spirits, and the manufacture of metal polishes, which are mixtures of white spirit with abrasives.

APIEZON PRODUCTS

"Apiezon" products were specially developed from petroleum, their particular virtue being that they are much less volatile even than mercury, and the amount of vapour which they give off, even under high vacuum, is exceedingly small. The range of Apiezon products includes the Apiezon oils which can advantageously replace mercury in the special diffusion and condensation pumps, with minor adjustments, used to obtain these high vacua. They are also available in the form of greases and waxes suitable for lubricating taps or sealing joints of high-vacuum apparatus.

Apiezon products find application wherever a high vacuum is to be created. Apart from laboratory research work carried out under high vacua, there are many everyday articles for the manufacture of which a high vacuum is required at some stage in the process. This list includes such things as wireless valves, neon signs, "daylight" lighting, X-ray tubes and cathode ray oscillographs.

NAPHTHENIC ACIDS

Naphthenic Acids are the cyclo-carboxylic acids which occur naturally in petroleum and are extracted from various fractions such as kerosine and gas oil (*vide* chapter XVII). They are similar in general properties, possessing the characteristic chemical properties of carboxylic acids, and resemble the fatty acids, such as oleic acid, in many of their chemical reactions. For example, they readily form metallic salts or soaps when reacted with a solution of caustic alkali, and the main applications of naphthenic acids are in the form of metallic salts or soaps. Cobalt, manganese and lead salts are extensively used as paint driers, while the copper and zinc compounds are very important as rot-proofing materials. Sodium and potassium soaps are powerful emulsifiers and are widely used in the manufacture of cutting oils, disinfectants and related materials.

Paint Driers. The introduction of metallic soaps into drying oils accelerates the rate of drying and improves the properties of the paint film. The cobalt, manganese and lead soaps of the fatty acids (linoleates and resinates) are steadily being replaced by the corresponding naphthenates prepared from the high acid value naphthenic acids. The naphthenates have several distinct advantages over the fatty acid soaps, such as higher acid value, and consequently higher active metal content. They are also very stable on storage and retain easy solubility in oil whilst preserving their high active metal content. In contrast, fatty acid soaps tend to polymerize on storage, and consequently there is a reduction in the active metal content.

The metal present in the soap has an important influence on the properties of the driers. Cobalt produces a rapid surface drying which is utilized in the production of "wrinkle" finishes. Manganese yields a more abrasion-resistant film, while lead and zinc are slow drying, but the dried film is tough and durable. Calcium naphthenate is also "through" drying, similar to lead, and is of light colour. Iron naphthenate gives a tough greasy film, but in view of its staining effect is restricted to use in dark colour baking enamels.

In the formulation of paints it is usual to incorporate a blend of driers into the paint vehicle in order to obtain a "balanced" drying effect.

Rot Proofing. Investigations have shown that while many copper compounds have rot-proofing and preserving properties,

the naphthenate is the most effective.   This copper soap is generally applied in white spirit solution.   Zinc and iron naphthenates
are sometimes used in conjunction with copper, and where a
colourless preparation is required zinc alone is used, although
these other metal naphthenates are less effective in intrinsic rot-
proofing properties than the copper compound.   Further investigations into the pronounced superior fungicidal capacity of copper
naphthenate have shown that it has good protective power against
the growth of the copper-tolerant fungus *Aspergillus Niger*.   For
this application, a high acid value material is desirable so as to give
as high a metal content as possible in the finished naphthenate.

Emulsifiers.   The sodium, potassium and ammonium salts of
naphthenic acids have valuable properties as emulsifiers.   For this
purpose, the low acid value material gives the best results.   These
alkali metal naphthenates are readily soluble in water and have
very good solubility in oils, solvents, cresylic acids and the like.
Naphthenic soaps can be used in the formulation of both
mayonnaise-type emulsions and in the soluble or miscible oil
types, although in the case of the manufacture of miscible oil type
emulsions it is sometimes necessary to use a mutual solvent
(''coupling agent'') such as cresylic acid or an alcohol.

Miscellaneous Applications.   The naphthenic acids act as dispersing agents, this property being made use of in the manufacture
of lithograph printing inks, i.e., as a good dispersing agent for
carbon black ; they are also used in the manufacture of printers'
ink to increase the fluidity and decrease the clogging and gumming
tendencies.

In the rubber industry, the low acid value naphthenic acid can
be used as a softener in natural rubber mixes, as a processing aid
in reclaim mixtures for dispersing the crumb, and as a reclaim agent
for scorched neoprene.

ALBINO BITUMENS

These materials are obtained from the distillation of special crude
oils which contain very small quantities of asphaltenes, which are
dark coloured.   They are used in the same industries as Dutrex
(*vide infra*) and, particularly in the paint industry, they are valued
because of their light colour.

DUTREX (AROMATIC EXTENDERS)

Petroleum resins obtained during the refining of certain fractions (*vide* chapter XVII) are marketed under the name of "Dutrex". They are brown, mobile oils which are compatible with vegetable and mineral oils, and are solvents or vehicles for many resins, and consequently find a number of industrial applications.

Rubber Industry. Dutrex was originally used in the rubber industry as a processing aid and softener, replacing pine tar and stearic acid. It may also be used to increase the hydrocarbon content of rubber mixes, in which case the quantity used is greater than when it is used as a processing aid. The actual amount of Dutrex incorporated in the mix depends upon the characteristics desired of the finished product. The synthetic rubber, GR–S, differs from natural rubber in being more difficult to process ; also, its inherent physical properties are poorer. The addition of Dutrex effects improvement in both respects. While the major improvement in physical properties is obtained by the incorporation of reinforcing carbon blacks, the addition of Dutrex facilitates its incorporation as well as producing further improvement in the properties of the GR–S mix. It makes processing easier, especially in the milling stage, where much less carbon black falls off the rolls. As the milling is easier, it reduces power consumption and the risk of "scorch". As in the case of natural rubber, Dutrex may be used entirely as a processing aid. However, when used as an actual component of a GR–S mix it affords an all-round improvement in the physical properties of the vulcanized product.

Paint Industry. Dutrex can form part of the oil medium in the formulation of paints, thus reducing the quantity of linseed or other drying oil required. For straight oil paints, the amount of Dutrex which can be used depends upon the weathering properties desired of the finished paint.

Considerable quantities of Dutrex have also been used in emulsion paints, both of the varnish and distemper* types. The varnish type gives a glossy film and is compounded of linseed oil and copal resin or other similar material. Up to 20% of Dutrex, calculated on the oil phase, can be incorporated with success in this type of paint. The distemper type of emulsion paint, which gives a matt surface, is normally based on linseed oil, bitumen emulsions or mixtures of the two. Dutrex can replace 50% of the linseed oil in the paints based on this material, and can completely replace the bitumen emulsion as a base, in which case the lighter colour of the Dutrex results in a considerable saving in expensive pigments where light, bright colours are required. Paint films containing Dutrex are impermeable to water and have high resistance towards acids, alkalies and lime, also good adhesion to rough surfaces, which is of particular importance with regard to application to concrete surfaces.

Foundry Industry.   In the foundry industry the moulds or cores are made from sand mixed with core oil as a binder. The formulation of core oils varies from foundry to foundry, but, generally speaking, starch, sulphite lye or molasses and a drying oil are used. By virtue of the film-forming properties of the linseed oil the particles of sand are held together and can be baked to give a good core. After use, the core is broken up and the sand reclaimed by burning off the core oil residues. The linseed oil of these core oils can be replaced up to 40% by Dutrex, without appreciably affecting the crushing strength of the final core. The inclusion of Dutrex in core oils does not affect the stripping qualities of the sand mixes.

Plasticizers for Vinyl Resins.   At the beginning of the war much work in the cable industry was carried out upon materials suitable for the replacement of rubber, particularly with reference to the use of polyvinyl chloride incorporating Dutrex as a plasticizer*. Dutrex is compatible with polyvinyl chloride and gives improved electrical properties combined with satisfactory mechanical properties, except where flexibility at exceedingly low temperatures is required. The amount of Dutrex incorporated depends upon the use to which the material is to be put, but in general is in the range of 20-40 parts of Dutrex to 100 parts of polyvinyl chloride.

CRESYLIC ACIDS

The wide variety of the phenolic (carbolic acid) type of compound covered by the term ''cresylic acids'' occurs as such in certain cracked distillates. They are separated as the sodium compounds by extracting with soda, after which the free acids are recovered by treatment with mineral acid (*vide* chapter XVII). Methods are being developed for the production of individual cresylic acids by synthesis from petroleum chemicals such as acetone.

Phenol-formaldehyde Resins. Cresylic acids find application in the manufacture of phenol- or cresol-formaldehyde resins, which are made by reacting phenolic compounds with formaldehyde*. Bakelite* articles are well known, but for each particular formulation of finished resin the type of phenolic compound has to be carefully selected, and this tends to make these industrial applications highly specialized.

Flotation* Processes. These processes are frequently used for the separation of materials of the same density. Cresylic acids find extensive use as frothing agents in the mining industry, especially of gold, silver, copper, zinc and lead. Zinc blende (a zinc ore) is not wetted by water, whereas galena (a lead ore) is. These minerals frequently occur together, and to effect a separation the mixture, as mined, is ground to a fine powder and agitated with water containing cresylic acid. The zinc blende forms a scum on top while the lead sinks. For this application the mining industry does not require such a highly purified product as does the resin industry.

Disinfectants. Cresylic acids find a large outlet as disinfectants. They have the fresh, clean smell associated with carbolic acid and may be used as such or as the starting material for the finer types of antiseptics, such as mouth washes and gargles.

SODIUM NAPHTHA SULPHONATES

Sodium naphtha sulphonates are obtained from the refining of technical and medicinal white oils by treatment with oleum (*vide* chapter XVII). The acid sulphonates are recovered as the sodium soaps by neutralization with soda. There are two types of soaps ; the technical white oils produce what are known as ''mahogany soaps'', which are oil-soluble, while the ''green soaps'' from the medicinal white oil treatment are water-soluble.

The mahogany soaps are good emulsifying agents, and it is in this capacity that they find their main application for the manufacture of cutting oils, soluble oils and special products based on emulsion formulæ, and for crude oil emulsion dehydration.

The water-soluble sodium naphtha sulphonates find applications in the textile industry because of their wetting properties.

ESTER SALTS

Ester Salts is the generic name covering synthetic detergent and wetting agents consisting essentially of sodium higher alkyl sulphates of the type

$$\begin{array}{c} R \\ \diagdown \\ \diagup \\ R_1 \end{array} CH. O. SO_3Na,$$

R and R_1 being alkyl radicles (*vide* chapter VII). The commercial product normally marketed is an aqueous solution of a mixture of compounds of this type and is known by the trade name of " Teepol".

Teepol is made by sulphation of a specially selected olefin fraction, providing the optimum balance for wetting and detergent properties in the finished product. After sulphation, purification and neutralization of the fraction, a pale amber-coloured liquid is obtained which can be spray-dried to give a powder with similar wetting and detergency properties when re-dissolved in water. Teepol is also available in paste form (*vide* chapter XVII).

Teepol falls into the class of water-soluble wetting agents, its solubility in water being high. Its property of making water "wetter" can be demonstrated as follows. If water is poured on to a perfectly clean sheet of glass, it spreads completely over the surface as a thin film. However, if the surface of the glass is at all greasy, the water remains on the glass surface as small globules and not as a film. If a small quantity of Teepol is now added to the water, it is found that even on the greasy glass the water completely wets the surface and spreads over the surface in a uniform film. Associated with this property of wetting are the foaming characteristics of Teepol.

A solution of Teepol in water is in itself neutral, but is stable in the presence of acids, alkalis and salts in the concentrations that are applicable in practice. Also, as the calcium and magnesium alkyl sulphates are soluble and are in themselves detergents, the normal scumming effects which obtain in hard water with the ordinary fatty acid soaps do not occur. Associated with their wetting properties is their power of dispersing fatty acid scums. Such scums are dispersed finely and do not re-aggregate.

The very wide range of applications of Teepol depends upon its two-fold function. In some applications it acts as a wetting agent, and in others as a detergent.

Domestic Applications. Three-quarters of the total production of Teepol goes to manufacture products used in the domestic field, where synthetic detergents have now found a permanent place alongside the traditional soap products. Here the detergency, odour and colour of Teepol are in general of more importance than its wetting power. For household washing, many products are now marketed which are based on Teepol, and these may conveniently be divided into three main categories. Firstly, neutral or slightly alkaline products, which are recommended mainly for woollens, silks and rayons. They are in general superior to the neutral soap flakes of which they are the synthetic equivalent. Secondly, there are more strongly alkaline products for washing cotton goods. These products can be used in those fields where the alkaline soap powders are normally used. By suitable additions of builders these products will successfully wash white cotton, which formerly was one of the chief difficulties with synthetic detergents. Thirdly, there are a variety of products for dish-washing and general cleaning which may vary in the degree of alkalinity. The alkali, if any, which is used in wool-washing products is usually sodium sesquicarbonate. The cotton-washing and dish-washing products may contain sodium phosphates, silicates or carbonates. There are also some products recommended for all purposes which generally contain sodium carbonate. These Teepol-based products are sometimes sold as liquids, but normally as powders, the latter being generally produced either by spray-drying or drum-drying.

Another, and older, important domestic application of Teepol is in the manufacture of shampoos. This is a very obvious outlet for Teepol, particularly in hard water areas, as the formation of lime soaps is very objectionable in shampoos. Here the products are marketed either as neutral liquids or as powders. A very high proportion of the total world shampoo market is now based on synthetic detergents, since their use in this field commenced well before their application in domestic products generally.

Textile Industry. The textile industry is an exceedingly complicated one technically, since not only is it concerned with an exceedingly wide range of natural and synthetic fibres, but processes them in a large variety of ways.

Each of the properties of Teepol, and of those related products which have been prepared or compounded for specific purposes find application in the textile industry. Teepol is used in the scouring and preparation of the whole range of textile fibres, wool, cotton, silk, linen, jute, rayons and other fibres. These fibres adsorb Teepol in greater or lesser degree, depending on the conditions of treatment, the effect being more marked in the case of wool than with any of the other fibres. Not only does the adsorbed Teepol impart a soft ''handle'' to the finished goods, but it also has a beneficial effect in the subsequent dyeing process. Its properties as a wetting agent are also used in carbonizing, which is a process for removing cellulosic material from wool, in bleaching operations, and in the wet chlorination anti-shrink treatment of wools.

Teepol finds parallel applications in the leather industry.

Engineering. There are many aqueous processes in the engineering industry in which Teepol finds application. After operations such as turning, milling and grinding, where a coolant or lubricant is employed, the oil and swarf have to be removed prior to assembling or subsequent processing. Treatment is by dipping, brushing or spraying the metal with an alkaline Teepol solution, the quantity and type of alkali depending upon the type of grease and the metal being treated.

Subsequently the metal is rinsed. Articles which are to be electro-plated are de-greased before plating in some such manner, as perfect cleanliness is one of the essentials in the formation of a uniform protective film.

Acid pickling—the immersion of metal parts in dilute acid for the removal of surface corrosion—is generally applied to iron and steel. The acid attacks the steel with evolution of hydrogen, the bubbles of which play a mechanical part in dislodging the scale from the surface. Addition of Teepol increases throughput by giving better penetration of liquid to the metal surface, especially when dealing with oily or greasy metal.

Paper Manufacture. The manufacture of paper from straw and other similar materials depends upon the breaking down of the fibre by boiling, usually under pressure, with caustic alkali. It has been found that the addition of Teepol in this process, by promoting better penetration of the fibre, reduces considerably the time required for boiling, which means that more time can be devoted to rinsing, thus ensuring the thorough removal of alkali. The pulp is then bleached and re-washed, and in the bleaching process, too, the addition of Teepol results in a less stringy pulp of a better colour.

Rubber Industry. Teepol is used as a dispersing agent in rubber mixes and as a reclaiming agent for both natural and synthetic rubbers. It is also used as a wetting-out agent for textiles prior to and during impregnation with latex.

Paint Industry. In water paints and distempers the pigment is dispersed in an aqueous medium, so that there is an obvious outlet for Teepol as a dispersing agent. Teepol aids in the grinding of the pigment. Where the pigment is initially in a fine state of division, it is advantageous to use Teepol to paste the pigment. This gives good dispersion, and hence higher covering power and increased fluidity, which means that more pigment can be incorporated if desired.

Food Industry. The importance of extreme cleanliness in the food industry is obvious, and Teepol is employed in processes which range from general factory cleaning to the washing of the heat exchangers of pasteurizing equipment. In dairy work, it is generally necessary to remove dried milk residues from bottles, churns etc., for which purpose a suitable alkaline form of Teepol is available. In the case of heat exchangers, however, deposits of milkstone have to be removed, so that a specially compounded material has been evolved for this purpose. In food canning, great success has been obtained in the cleaning of meat cans with a jet washing type of machine using Teepol solutions. In these practices it is desirable to use warm solutions.

The uses of Teepol cover such an extensive range that many can only receive a passing mention. In the cosmetic industry, Teepol is used in the formulation of cold creams and vanishing creams, where it has the effect of reducing particle size and acts as an emulsion stabilizer auxiliary. It is also used in the formulation of liquid stockings, where it acts as a dispersing agent for the pigment.

In cement mixing, the addition of Teepol to the gauging water improves the workability, with the result that for specific amounts of cement, sand and water, the mix has more fluidity and gives a better cast when poured into moulds. It means also that the amount of gauging water can be reduced if desirable.

In photography, the addition of small quantities of Teepol to the developer enhances wetting of the paper or film and prevents tear stains forming on drying.

CHEMICAL PRODUCTS

Organic chemicals derived from petroleum are finding extensive industrial applications as intermediates for synthesis and as solvents in numerous industries. These solvents include aliphatic alcohols, ketones* and ethers*. The starting points for most of these chemicals are alcohols (*vide* chapter XVIII) made by the hydration (addition of H_2O) of olefin hydrocarbons which are obtained as by-products from oil-cracking processes.

Iso-propyl Alcohol—$(CH_3)_2CH.OH$. Iso-propyl alcohol (I.P.A.) is made by hydration of propylene ; it is marketed in the anhydrous form and contains more than 99% of I.P.A., boiling at 82° C. It has wide application in nitrocellulose lacquer thinners because of its high latent solvent power for cellulose esters ; it has a satisfactory rate of evaporation, and, in addition, it has a low rate of absorbing water from the air. Iso-propyl alcohol has certain advantages over ethyl alcohol and is used to replace it in many applications. The main uses for iso-propyl alcohol are in the synthesis of other chemicals, perfumes, pharmaceutical products and as a pectin precipitant.

Secondary Butyl Alcohol—$CH_3.CHOH.C_2H_5$. Secondary butyl alcohol is made by the hydration of α and β butylene, and has a purity of more than 98% and a boiling range of 97°–100° C.

It is used in lacquers to promote flow and levelling, its rate of evaporation being intermediate between iso-propyl and normal butyl alcohols. It is also a good solvent for natural and synthetic resins, besides being miscible with vegetable oils and aromatic hydrocarbons. It finds application as a component in aeroplane dopes, base lacquers, thinners, leather softening and penetrating agents and as a synthetic resin solvent.

Secondary butyl alcohol is used in the manufacture of hydraulic brake fluids and in the preparation of secondary butyl xanthate, an ore flotation agent.

Tertiary Butyl Alcohol—$(CH_3)_3C.OH$. Tertiary butyl alcohol is prepared from iso-butylene, with a purity of more than 99% and a boiling range of 78°–85° C. It is used as a solvent in the extraction of drugs, in paint and lacquer removers, in the manufacture of perfumes, germicides, wetting agents and in the synthesis of alkylated phenols* for use in the plastics industry.

Acetone—$CH_3.CO.CH_3$. Acetone is made by dehydrogenation of iso-propyl alcohol. It is a colourless stable liquid with a boiling point of 56·5° C. and a high rate of evaporation. It is an excellent solvent for animal and vegetable oils, for cellulose acetate, nitrocellulose and synthetic resins. For this reason, it is used in the acetate rayon industry, in the lacquer industry, and as an ingredient of paint and varnish removers. Acetone is also used in extraction processes, the manufacture of synthetic leather, celluloid and safety glass, and as a solvent for storing acetylene. It is used as a chemical intermediate in the production of rubber chemicals and in the manufacture of acrylic type resins.

Methyl Ethyl Ketone—$CH_3.CO.C_2H_5$. Methyl ethyl ketone is obtained from secondary butyl alcohol and is an almost pure compound containing more than 99% methyl ethyl ketone and has a boiling range of 78° C.–81° C. It has high solvent power for nitrocellulose and affords solutions of low viscosity for all grades of nitrocellulose. The low viscosity of solutions of synthetic resins and nitrocellulose in methyl ethyl ketone make it possible to formulate lacquers of high solid content. It is widely used in vinylite lacquers, nitrocellulose lacquers and thinners, artificial leather dopes and as a solvent for resins and waxes.

Diacetone Alcohol—$(CH_3)_2.C.OH.CH_2.CO.CH_3$. Diacetone alcohol is produced by combining two molecules of acetone, and has a boiling point of 168° C. It has a slow rate of evaporation and is a good solvent for nitrocellulose, cellulose acetate, resins and certain gums, and it is miscible with the usual lacquer ingredients. It is widely used in aeroplane dopes and lacquers, its lack of odour making it especially suitable for brushing lacquers which are applied for interior decoration. It has the property of reducing the consistency of viscous liquids, and this property has been utilized in the manufacture of hydraulic brake fluids. It is also used as a solvent for the pentachlorophenol type of fungicides, which are used for preserving wood.

Mesityl Oxide—$(CH_3)_2.C:CH.CO.CH_3$. Mesityl oxide is an unsaturated ketone, boiling at 128° C.–130° C., prepared by dehydrating diacetone alcohol. The material is water-white in colour and has an odour resembling peppermint. It has high solvent power for gums and resins, particularly for vinylite resins, giving films which have high gloss and excellent flow. High concentrations of vinylite resins in mesityl oxide can be sprayed without ''cobwebbing'', such solutions tolerating large amounts of aromatic hydrocarbon diluents. Its rate of evaporation is slightly less than that of normal butyl acetate and its solvent power for nitrocellulose is very similar. The nitrocellulose solutions have low viscosity, excellent tolerance for hydrocarbons and high resistance to humidity.

Methyl Iso-butyl Ketone—$(CH_3)_2.CH.CH_2.CO.CH_3$. Methyl iso-butyl ketone can be prepared by the hydrogenation of mesityl oxide and is a water-white liquid of pleasant odour with a boiling range of 113° C.–119° C. Its evaporation rate is slightly greater than that of normal butyl acetate, and its properties as a lacquer solvent are very similar to mesityl oxide. The advantages of this ketone are its excellent solvent properties for a variety of natural and synthetic resins and its ability to produce low viscosity solutions of high solid content.

Iso-propyl Ether—$(CH_3)_2CH.O.CH(CH_3)_2$. This solvent has similar properties and uses to ordinary ethyl ether, but it has a higher boiling point and slower evaporation rate. Its main uses are in extraction processes in the pharmaceutical field.

Hexylene Glycol—$(CH_3)_2COH.CH_2.CHOH.CH_3$ (boiling point

198·3° C. at 760 mm.). Hexylene glycol (2-methyl-2-4-pentane-diol) is prepared from diacetone alcohol. The chemical structure of this compound makes it an excellent blending and coupling agent for immiscible substances. Its compatibility with castor oil, combined with good viscosity characteristics and little effect on rubber, make it a valuable ingredient of hydraulic brake fluids. It is used in flash-dry printing inks, where its steeply sloping vapour pressure curve and solubility for ink resins are advantageous. Hexylene glycol is also used in industrial cleaning compounds, as a coupler, penetrant and humectant* in textile treating, in ''soluble'' cutting oils, grinding aids and pre-spotting cleaning soaps.

Allyl Alcohol—$CH_2 : CH . CH_2 OH$. Allyl alcohol is a colourless liquid completely miscible with water. This material is very reactive and it is consequently particularly interesting as a base for the synthesis of other organic chemicals, certain flavourings, pharmaceuticals and perfumes and in the manufacture of synthetic resins and plastics.

Allyl alcohol is poisonous and should be handled carefully in well ventilated rooms, as the vapours are irritating to the eyes and respiratory passages.

Allyl Chloride—$CH_2 : CH . CH_2Cl$. Allyl chloride, from which allyl alcohol is made, is a water white liquid and is chiefly used as a chemical intermediate for the synthesis of certain pharmaceuticals and anæsthetics, such as nephal and allonal, for essences and flavourings. It is prepared by the high-temperature chlorination of propylene gas. New developments include its use, combined with starch, in the form of allyl ether of starch, as a surface coating in the paint industry.

Allyl chloride is also poisonous and should be handled with care. If spilt on the skin these allyl compounds should be washed off immediately with large volumes of water.

Glycerol Dichlorohydrin is a high boiling liquid which is prepared by hypochlorination of allyl chloride. The commercial mixture consists of about 70% 2,3-dichloropropanol-1 and 30% 1,3-dichloropropanol-2. Both isomers may react either through the reactive carbon-to-chlorine bonds or through the reactive hydroxyl groups to produce a variety of glycerol derivatives.

Glycerol dichlorohydrin is of interest as a starting material in the manufacture of synthetic resins, dyes, fine chemicals, surface-active agents, pharmaceuticals, cements, and adhesives.

Epichlorohydrin—CH$_2$(O)CH.CH$_2$Cl. Epichlorohydrin is obtained by the dehydrochlorination of glycerol dichlorohydrin. The presence of the epoxide* ring and the chlorine atom in one molecule makes epichlorohydrin valuable as an intermediate for organic syntheses. Epichlorohydrin has been successfully used as an intermediate by manufacturers of adhesives, dyestuffs, plasticizers, cosmetics and pharmaceuticals. When included as a stabilizer in the formulation of various industrial chlorinated compounds, epichlorohydrin removes free acidity developed by decomposition of the compounds during ageing.

NEW DEVELOPMENT CHEMICALS

Other products, some new to industry and as yet only available in limited quantities, include unsaturated alcohols and ethers, di-ketones, chlorinated unsaturated hydrocarbons, mixed tertiary ethers, high molecular weight alcohols and ketones.

The development work in hand on **Diallyl Phthalate** is of particular interest. This compound (C$_6$H$_4$(COO. CH$_2$. CH : CH$_2$)$_2$) is a colourless liquid of similar viscosity to kerosine. When heated with a few per cent. of an organic peroxide, such as benzoyl peroxide, it polymerizes, resulting in a progressive increase in viscosity, terminating in the formation of a clear, insoluble, infusible solid. As a result of this reaction, in which there is no evolution of volatile materials, a thermosetting plastic is obtained. On account of these properties diallyl phthalate has been developed for the production of clear castings in sheets and other forms, and also for the production of laminates of outstanding physical and chemical properties, from paper, wood and fabrics of all kinds, including glass. The development during the past twenty years of a chemical industry using petroleum as a raw material has been remarkable, and we find such chemicals increasingly used in connection with the manufacture and utilization of synthetic resins, plastics, coating materials, films, printing inks, lubricating oil, flotation agents, pharmaceuticals, insecticides, photographic products, explosives, detergents, and in many other fields.

The industry, however, is still in its infancy and may be expected to expand at a rapid rate, since the possibilities for the synthesis of compounds from petroleum raw materials is unlimited, and many new products now only in the exploratory stage will eventually attain commercial production.

AGRICULTURAL AND PEST CONTROL CHEMICALS

Historically, fertilizers have constituted the bulk of chemicals used in agriculture ; however, during the past several decades, as the factors governing production of crops and healthy herds have become better understood, a very large increase and diversity in the use of chemicals in agriculture has occurred, the products involved including insecticides and insect repellents, fungicides, herbicides, nematicides*, rodenticides and growth regulators. A survey made by Shell Oil Company, U.S.A., showed that consumption of such chemicals, other than fertilizers, in that part of the U.S.A. east of the Rocky Mountains, was $36,500,000 in 1941. That there is opportunity for considerable increase in this figure is evidenced by the estimate that the annual loss to farmers in the U.S.A. through pests and diseases of crops and herds is estimated to be greater than $2,000,000,000 per annum.

Many different organisms can act as pests to a crop—weeds, rodents and other vertebrates, insects of many kinds, fungi, bacteria and virus diseases. Control of these pests frequently may be accomplished by application of chemicals toxic to the pests but harmless to the hosts, or by applying the chemicals at times when the hosts are in the dormant or over-wintering state and so less susceptible to damage. In the past, the greatest use of pesticidal sprays in temperate and sub-tropical countries was in orchards, glasshouses and, occasionally, on high-priced crops such as tomatoes and potatoes, but in recent years the rapid increase in the occurrence of various pests has resulted in the extension of such usage to most vegetables grown on a commercial scale. At present, the development of more effective chemicals and more efficient means of application is leading to the economical use of pesticides and growth-regulating chemicals on field crops such as maize, wheat, flax, and even on pastures and forests. Outside the field of agriculture, large-scale operations for the control of mosquitoes and other disease-bearing insects are being undertaken widely in the temperate zone, as well as in the tropics, aeroplanes frequently being employed for the application.

The earliest use of chemicals for pest control involved mainly inorganic compounds such as lead arsenate, lime-sulphur and copper sulphate. Later, botanicals such as nicotine, pyrethrins* and rotenone were introduced. The Group entered the field some years ago with oil emulsions of various types for the control of pests on fruit trees in both temperate and sub-tropical zones and by developing Malariol for controlling mosquito larvæ. Since then, the use of petroleum oils in agriculture and horticulture has increased very rapidly. During the last decade, a considerable number of synthetic organic chemicals have come into use in this field, and it is now apparent that such compounds will play a major part in pest control in the future. Some of these are already being manufactured in whole or in part from petroleum derivatives, e.g. D-D (chlorinated propylenes), a soil fumigant*, and Ester Salts (sodium higher alkyl sulphates), the latter being useful as wetting and spreading agents.

Perhaps the most extensive ultimate use of petroleum in this field will be as a vehicle or carrier for chemicals which are active in dosages smaller than can be applied conveniently in the pure state. For this purpose, specially selected or refined petroleum fractions serve as solvents for the active chemical, the solution being applied either as an emulsion in water or by atomization either from aircraft or ground equipment capable of applying uniformly over the vegetation as little as one-half to five gallons of liquid per acre. Similarly, for the treatment of farm animals the oil solution of the toxicant may be diluted with water and used in a dipping bath or sprayed on the animal to control such pests as ticks on cattle and blowfly larvæ on sheep.

Among the synthetic organic chemicals used as pesticides, D.D.T. (dichloro-diphenyl-trichloroethane) is by far the best known at the present time. Dissolved in various solvents, ranging from conventional or specially refined kerosines, fuel oils and light lubricating oils to a variety of aromatic solvents, many of which are obtained from petroleum, it is useful as a household insecticide and for the control of mosquitoes and similar insects in their breeding areas, as well as for the control of many pests of agricultural crops and forest insects. Such solutions are sometimes applied undiluted with hand or power atomizers, but the more concentrated ones, containing usually 25% to 30% D.D.T., are first emulsified in water. Unlike most of the insecticides previously available, D.D.T. is frequently effective against insects coming in superficial contact with it long after it has been sprayed on plant foliage or on the walls of buildings or other surfaces. This persistent action makes possible the economical control of many pests previously not susceptible to practical attack in this manner. The use of formulations and techniques of application particularly adapted to the problem at hand is desirable in most cases.

Among other synthetic organic chemicals which have in recent investigations shown great potentials as insecticides are : hexachlorocyclohexane, variously known as benzene hexachloride, Gammexane, or 666 ; tetraethyl phosphate, which was first used together with a group of chemically similar but insecticidally inert compounds produced simultaneously as a mixture termed hexaethyl tetraphosphate ; chlordane, a chemical compound having the empirical formula $C_{10}H_6Cl_8$; chlorinated camphene, and diethyl-p-nitrophenyl thionophosphate, now known as parathion.

Other organic chemicals being used in increasing quantities are the so-called plant hormones, especially derivatives of naphthalene acetic acid and chlorinated phenoxy acetic acid. Appropriate concentrations of various of these compounds are used in some cases to promote plant growth as in the rooting of cuttings or the retention of fruit on the trees when it would otherwise drop prematurely, and, also, as a means of inducing the setting of fruit from blossoms which would otherwise fall. Some of these compounds are selective in their action and are used to destroy weeds among agricultural crops or in pastures without injuring the crop itself. In a few instances certain petroleum fractions have been observed to have similar herbicidal properties.

The development of new chemicals for use in agriculture is in the hands of the large research organizations of the Group in the U.S.A., Holland and Great Britain, but testing of new materials and development of methods of application require to be done in the field in the climatic zones in which each is to be used. Centres for development and demonstration of agricultural and horticultural products have therefore been set up, one, for the subtropical zones, in California, and one for the temperate zones in England. At these centres the new materials can be tested under controlled conditions and the best methods of spraying, the proper formulation of the spray and the best type of oil base, and so on, can be determined.

Spray Oils

Lubricating oils applied as emulsions are used extensively on citrus and deciduous* fruit trees and on ornamental trees for the control of scale insects, leaf rollers and other pests, and also as wetters, stickers and spreaders for solid insecticides which are applied as suspensions in water. The specifications for oils to be used in any particular instance depend on the pests to be controlled, the sensitivity of the host plant and the weather or climatic conditions prevailing. The oils may be sold as such without any additives, in which case the user must add suitable emulsifying agents at the time of application. Usually, however, the oils are compounded, suitable emulsifiers being added to produce the desired degree of emulsibility. In some instances a small amount of water, 25% or less, is added and the product thoroughly emulsified before sale so that the user has only to dilute the emulsion in his spray tank.

(1) **Winter Grades.** These are usually spindle oils of medium to low viscosity. Formerly, it was thought that relatively low unsulphonated mineral residue (UMR) was desirable in oils for application during the dormant period. Recent investigations, however, indicate that more highly refined oils are more effective as insecticides. Where they are available, paraffinic oils having unsulphonated residues upwards of 85% are to be preferred for this use.

In some instances oil alone will not control all of the insects present on the dormant trees and it is necessary to supplement the oil with dinitro-ortho-cresol (D.N.O.C.) or one of its salts. The dinitro compounds can be applied separately, when the trees are completely dormant, the oil being applied in the delayed dormant or green tip stage of development of the tree. Alternatively, combinations of dinitro-ortho-cresol with the oil can be used when the trees are dormant. The use of the dinitro compounds has largely displaced in some areas the tar oils formerly employed.

(2) **Summer Grades.** These are used on citrus fruit trees and on deciduous fruit trees in foliage. The base oils employed are more volatile than those used for spraying dormant deciduous trees, usually being slightly heavier than mineral seal oil and falling in the range of oils used as transformer oils. For spray oil purposes such oils are refined to have an unsulphonated mineral residue of 90% to 95%, the heavier oils being of the highest UMR.

On citrus, summer oils are used largely for the control of scale insects and mites. Prior to the discovery of D.D.T., summer oils were used extensively in many areas on apples and pears, in combination with lead arsenate, for the control of codling moth, scale insects and mites. Now the latter two pests are attacked principally in the delayed dormant stage as indicated above, although summer oil sprays are still important.

(3) **Mist Sprays.** The wartime use of solutions of D.D.T. in oil applied from aircraft for the control of mosquitoes and other disease-bearing insects has stimulated interest in the use of oil-borne insecticides for other purposes.

Equipment for the application of small amounts of liquid, viz., one-half to five gallons per acre or the equivalent, is largely in the developmental stage. Fixed wing aircraft, helicopters and a considerable variety of atomizers and mist blowers mounted on wheels are being used. High-temperature air and steam are both being employed for the atomization of liquids in this field, but it is yet too early to make any conclusive statements as to the relative efficacy of the different types of equipment.

Two series of products are being manufactured by members of the Group for this type of application. The first of these employ specially selected and refined oils in the mineral seal range as vehicles for the toxicants or other active agents, such as D.D.T. and pyrethrins, and are preferred when the material is to be applied to valuable vegetation such as agricultural crops or valuable ornamental shrubs or trees. In large-scale operations such as the treatment of forest trees, in which cost of materials and rate of application are of vital interest, more concentrated products are employed. These use oils of the same viscosity and volatility characteristics, but in order to provide greater solvency for the active components, as well as lower cost, oils of the light fuel oil type are used as vehicles. Sometimes additional solvent materials are added to the oil base in order to increase still further the solvent power for the toxic agent. The latter series of products are rarely applied at rates higher than 1 gallon per acre, while the former may be applied at rates from 2 to 5 gallons per acre.

Fertilizers

The world demand for fertilizers is immense and growing. World production of nitrogenous fertilizers, for example, is now over three million tons.

At the present time the production of fertilizers by the Group is restricted to Holland and the U.S.A. and is concerned only with nitrogenous fertilizers (*vide* chapter XVIII). In California, at Shell Point, the ammonia produced from hydrogen obtained from natural gas is converted either into ammonium sulphate, aqua ammonia or into anhydrous liquid ammonia. Two new techniques, ''nitrogation'' and ''nitrojection'', have been developed by Shell to enable liquid ammonia to be used by the farmer. In ''nitrogation'', the ammonia is passed directly into irrigation water ; in ''nitrojection'', the liquid gas is discharged into the soil at a depth of from four to eight inches, using special injection equipment. Both processes are economical and very successful in California, and the use of the ''nitrojection'' process is now spreading elsewhere.

Soil Fumigants.

The history of Shell D-D is a romance in itself but cannot be adequately dealt with here. Shell D-D is a mixture of chlorinated C_3 hydrocarbons, primarily dichloropropene and dichloropropane. It is a dark brown liquid and has been shown to be one of the most effective soil fumigants known for the control of plant nematodes, which are minute worms very widely spread in soil throughout the world and responsible for much serious plant disease. Potato, tomato, sugar-beet, citrus and pineapple are some of the important crops attacked, the economic loss being very great. D-D is injected into the soil, in the absence of the plant, by means of specially-designed equipment, at the rate of 200–400 lbs. per acre. It volatilizes, kills many nematodes and other soil-inhabiting pests, such as wireworms, and leaves the soil in such a condition that plant growth is greatly stimulated. Shell D-D is a typical example of a new and promising petro-chemical with valuable and, until recently, unsuspected properties. Its value to the farming community is already great, although only the fringe of its possibilities has been explored.

Growth-regulating Substances.

Alpha naphthalene acetic acid in oil solution is effective both for the control of premature dropping of apples and pears at harvest time and for the setting of fruit in the spring; 2,4-dichlorophenoxy acetic acid at low concentrations is effective in retarding the dropping of Stayman and Winesap varieties of apples over a longer period of time than the alpha naphthalene acetic acid. Beta naphthoxy acetic acid has been found effective for promoting the setting and development of tomato fruits; this latter compound is formulated with a percentage of Teepol to facilitate wetting of the plants. Still another application of growth-regulators is to delay bud burst in various fruits in the spring to protect them from late frost damage.

Weed-Killers.

In the last decade very important progress has been made in the use of weed-killers or herbicides. Weed competition and growth probably cost the farmer more than all insect and fungus attack combined, but hitherto few chemical herbicides have been available. The most useful weed-killers on the farm are those which are selective, that is, those which will kill one unwanted plant while leaving the crop plant uninjured. On the other hand, non-selective herbicides are valuable for use on roads, rail-tracks, yards, and the banks of canals and irrigation ditches.

Certain petroleum oils can act either as selective or non-selective herbicides. Thus, the use of naphthas in the white spirit range having 15% to 20% aromatic content has extended considerably since the discovery that these petroleum fractions will kill many weeds in the earlier stages of growth but are without effect on young carrots, parsnips and related plants, so that they can be used as selective weed-killers with these crops. Further, diesel oil is coming into wide use as a non-selective herbicide, especially in connection with the clean weeding of citrus groves. The most notable advance in weed-control technique, however, arises from the use of 2,4-dichlorophenoxy acetic acid (2,4-D). This is a plant growth regulator which functions as a highly selective weed-killer when used at relatively high concentrations and will then effectively control most broad-leaved weeds in pastures, lawns and in wheat and other grain fields. The use of oil as a carrier for 2,4-D and for other toxicants such as pentachlorphenol and, possibly, isopropyl-*n*-phenyl carbamate, is a development which is only now at its beginning.

Household and Industrial Insecticides.

Oil is an important constituent of the insecticide preparations used to control those destructive, disease-carrying or annoying insects which are commonly found in buildings, on livestock and in any place where food or animal products such as hides and furs are stored. There are many uses for these insecticides in homes, warehouses, hotels, restaurants, food factories, ships' holds, transport vehicles, farm buildings and flour mills for the control of such pests as flies, mosquitoes, ants, cockroaches, bed-bugs, lice, weevils and moth larvæ*. The specially refined petroleum bases used for this purpose not only exert their own insect-killing and repelling properties, but also serve as almost universally-used carriers for insecticides such as pyrethrum* and D.D.T.

(1) **Space Sprays.** These are the common fly sprays with which everyone is familiar. They are so called because they are normally sprayed into an enclosed space to form a floating mist which will quickly knock down and kill flying insects. Shelltox is, therefore, a space spray.

(2) **Residual Sprays.** These preparations are designed to be sprayed on to walls, ceilings, carpets, sacks and similar areas to

render the sprayed surface deadly to insects for long periods. They contain a fairly high percentage of a persistent insecticide such as D.D.T. dissolved in suitable, relatively odourless petroleum solvents and are virtually stainless. Where a visible residue is of little importance (e.g. barns and stables), a less highly refined oil carrier may be used or, alternatively, a wettable powder such as a D.D.T. preparation, containing Ester Salts powder as the wetting agent. These residual sprays are of very great importance in the fight against malaria, since, used in conjunction with larvicides, they offer the possibility of complete eradication of the mosquito in certain areas. They are also being used to control tsetse fly, the carrier of sleeping sickness.

(3) **Livestock Sprays.** These preparations contain special ingredients to enhance the natural killing and repellent action of the highly refined light oil which serves as a base. They are used to kill lice, ticks and fleas on cattle, horses, sheep and pigs and to repel flies and mosquitoes. Used on dairy cattle at milking time, they quieten the animal and help to maintain peak milk production.

Larvicides.

Special petroleum oils or blends of petroleum oils have been used for many years throughout the world in malarious areas for the control of the larval stage of the mosquito which transmits this disease. Thus Shell ''Malariol'' is a well-established preparation which has long been officially recognized and conforms to the official specification for larvicidal oils. The use of this material is fully described in the ''Handbook of Malaria Control'', written by Dr. R. Svensson, Assistant Director of the Ross Institute of the London School of Hygiene and Tropical Medicine and published by the Shell Group.

Malariol is sprayed over the water surface at the rate of 15–20 gallons of oil per acre and forms a surface film toxic to mosquito larvæ which come to the surface periodically to breathe. In recent years a second product, Malariol H.S., has been developed, which contains D.D.T. and in which the oil acts primarily as a carrier for this insecticide. Malariol H.S. is simply poured on the water surface at intervals and does not require to be sprayed. It spreads over the water surface very effectively owing to the incorporation of special spreading agents and forms a very thin film which is virtually invisible and yet carries sufficient D.D.T. to ensure larval kill. The use of Malariol H.S. greatly reduces the cost of application of a larvicide and renders malaria control possible in areas where, hitherto, economic considerations have prevented proper measures being taken.

BIBLIOGRAPHY

Solvents. T. H. Durrans. (Chapman & Hall, London, 1944.)

Varnish Constituents. H. W. Chatfield. (Leonard Hill, London, 1947.)

Surface Active Agents. C. B. F. Young and K. W. Coons. (Chemical Publishing Co., New York, 1945.)

Chemistry of Petroleum Derivatives. Carleton Ellis. (Chemical Catalog Co., New York, Vol. I 1934, Vol. II 1937.)

Scientific Principles of Plant Protection. H. Martin. (Edward Arnold & Co., London, 1940.)

Handbook of Pest Control. A. Mallis. (McNair Corland Co., U.S.A, 1945.)

TABLES

TABLE I

INTERRELATION OF UNITS OF MEASUREMENT

MEASURES OF LENGTH

IMPERIAL

1 Inch	=	2·540	centimetres.
1 Foot	=	0·30480	metres.
1 Yard	=	0·91440	metres.
1 Mile	=	1,609·3	metres.
1 Nautical Mile	=	1,853·2	metres.

METRIC

1 Centimetre	=	0·39370	inches.
1 Metre	=	39·370	inches.
	=	3·28084	feet.
	=	1·09361	yards.
1 Kilometre	=	1,093·61	yards.

MEASURES OF WEIGHT

IMPERIAL AND AMERICAN

1 Ounce (oz.)	=	28·35	grammes.
1 Pound (lb.)	=	0·453592	kilogrammes.
1 Hundredweight (cwt.)	=	50·802	kilogrammes.
1 English or Long Ton	=	2,240	pounds.
	=	1·1200	short tons.
	=	1·01605	metric tons (tonnes).
1 Short Ton	=	2,000	pounds.
	=	0·892857	long tons.
	=	0·907185	metric tons (tonnes).

METRIC

1 Gramme	=	0·035	ounces.
1 Kilogramme	=	2·20462	pounds.
1 Metric Ton	=	2,204·62	pounds.
	=	0·98421	long tons.
	=	1·10231	short tons.

MEASURES OF VOLUME AND CAPACITY

IMPERIAL

1 Cubic Inch	=	16·387	cubic centimetres.
	=	0·0163865	litres.
	=	0·00360463	Imperial gallons.
1 Cubic Foot	=	28·316	litres.
	=	0·0283167	cubic metres.
	=	6·2288	Imperial gallons.
	=	7·4805	American (U.S.) gallons.
	=	0·178106	American (U.S.) barrels.
1 Pint	=	0·56825	litres.
1 Imperial Gallon	=	277·42	cubic inches.
	=	0·160544	cubic feet.
	=	4·54596	litres.
	=	0·0045461	cubic metres.
	=	1·20094	American (U.S.) gallons.
	=	0·028594	American (U.S.) barrels.

METRIC

1 Litre	=	61·0258	cubic inches.
	=	0·0353158	cubic feet.
	=	1·7598	pints.
	=	0·219975	Imperial gallons.
	=	0·264178	American (U.S.) gallons.
	=	0·00629	American (U.S.) barrels.
	=	1,000·03	cubic centimetres.
1 Cubic Metre	=	35·3148	cubic feet.
	=	219·97	Imperial gallons.
	=	264·17	American (U.S.) gallons.
	=	6·2898	American (U.S.) barrels.
	=	999·97	litres.

1 American (U.S.) Gallon	=	231·00	cubic inches.
	=	0·133681	cubic feet.
	=	0·83268	Imperial gallons.
	=	0·0238095	American (U.S.) barrels.
	=	3·78533	litres.
	=	0·00378543	cubic metres.
1 American (U.S.) Barrel	=	9,702·0	cubic inches.
	=	5·6146	cubic feet.
	=	34·9726	Imperial gallons.
	=	42·00	American (U.S.) gallons.
	=	158·984	litres.
	=	0·158988	cubic metres.

NOTE : The litre is defined as the volume of one kilogramme of pure water at 4° C. and under normal atmospheric pressure. When this volume is compared with the cubic decimetre it is found that—

1 litre = 1·000027 cubic decimetres.

The litre and its 1/1000th part, the millilitre (ml.), are ordinarily employed as the units of volume in the measurement of capacity ; the ml. is often improperly designated as the cubic centimetre (c.c.). The cubic decimetre and its multiples and submultiples are employed in determinations of volume derived from the linear dimensions.

TABLE II

EQUIVALENT WEIGHTS AND VOLUMES

NOTE: The figures in these tables are abbreviated and approximate, and the long tons and metric tons are both assumed to be "weights in air". Full tables for these weights and volumes equivalents are contained in the Company publication *Oil Measurement Tables* by H. Hyams.

WEIGHT OF UNIT VOLUME OF LIQUID

Specific Gravity	Weight in Long Tons per			
	Cubic metre	Imperial gallon	American gallon	American barrel
0·650	0·638	0·00290	0·00242	0·101
0·700	0·687	0·00312	0·00260	0·109
0·750	0·736	0·00335	0·00279	0·117
0·800	0·786	0·00357	0·00297	0·125
0·850	0·835	0·00379	0·00316	0·133
0·900	0·884	0·00402	0·00335	0·141
0·950	0·933	0·00424	0·00353	0·148
1·000	0·982	0·00447	0·00372	0·156

Specific Gravity	Weight in Metric Tons per			
	Cubic metre	Imperial gallon	American gallon	American barrel
0·650	0·648	0·00295	0·00245	0·103
0·700	0·698	0·00317	0·00264	0·111
0·750	0·748	0·00340	0·00283	0·119
0·800	0·798	0·00363	0·00302	0·127
0·850	0·848	0·00386	0·00321	0·135
0·900	0·898	0·00408	0·00340	0·143
0·950	0·948	0·00431	0·00359	0·151
1·000	0·998	0·00454	0·00378	0·159

VOLUME PER UNIT WEIGHT OF LIQUID

Specific Gravity	Volume per Long Ton in			
	Cubic metres	Imperial gallons	American gallons	American barrels
0·650	1·57	345	414	9·9
0·700	1·46	320	384	9·2
0·750	1·36	299	359	8·5
0·800	1·27	280	336	8·0
0·850	1·20	264	317	7·5
0·900	1·13	249	299	7·1
0·950	1·07	236	283	6·7
1·000	1·02	224	269	6·4

Specific Gravity	Volume per Metric Ton in			
	Cubic metres	Imperial gallons	American gallons	American barrels
0·650	1·54	339	408	9·8
0·700	1·43	315	378	9·0
0·750	1·34	294	353	8·4
0·800	1·25	276	331	7·9
0·850	1·18	259	312	7·4
0·900	1·11	245	294	7·0
0·950	1·05	232	279	6·6
1·000	1·00	220	265	6·3

Approximate Specific Gravity Ranges of Petroleum Products

In order to calculate the volume equivalent to a certain weight, or vice versa, the specific gravity of the product must be known with a fair degree of accuracy. As the table below shows, crude oils and commercial petroleum products vary widely in specific gravity. The examples following the table demonstrate the degree of error which may be involved by assuming approximate specific gravity figures.

Product	Specific Gravity Range	Product	Specific Gravity Range
Crude Oils ..	0·800/0·970	Diesel Fuels ..	0·820/0·920
Aviation Gasolines	0·700/0·780	Lubricating Oils	0·850/0·950
Motor Gasolines..	0·710/0·790	Fuel Oils ..	0·920/0·990
Kerosines	0·780/0·840	Asphaltic Bitumen	1·000/1·100
Gas Oils	0·820/0·900		

Examples.

(i) Assuming that a crude oil has a specific gravity of (*a*) 0·850, (*b*) 0·950, what would be the equivalent weight in long tons of 125,000 American barrels ?

(*a*) 0·133 × 125,000 = 16,625 long tons.

(*b*) 0·148 × 125,000 = 18,500 long tons.

(Difference 11·3%)

(ii) What is the equivalent volume in Imperial gallons of 67,500 metric tons of motor gasoline, assuming a specific gravity of (*a*) 0·720, (*b*) 0·770 ?

By interpolation we find that 1 metric ton equals 306 Imperial gallons with a specific gravity of 0·720, and 286 Imperial gallons with a specific gravity of 0·770.

Therefore :

(*a*) 67,500 × 306 = 20,655,000 Imperial gallons.

(*b*) 67,500 × 286 = 19,305,000 Imperial gallons.

(Difference 7%)

TABLE III

CONVERSION OF A.P.I. GRAVITY TO SPECIFIC GRAVITY 60°F./60°F.

Degrees A.P.I.	Sp. Gr. 60° F./60° F.	Degrees A.P.I.	Sp. Gr. 60° F./60° F.	Degrees A.P.I.	Sp. Gr. 60° F./60° F.
0·0	1·0760	30·0	0·8762	60·0	0·7389
1·0	1·0679	31·0	0·8708	61·0	0·7351
2·0	1·0599	32·0	0·8654	62·0	0·7313
3·0	1·0520	33·0	0·8602	63·0	0·7275
4·0	1·0433	34·0	0·8550	64·0	0·7238
5·0	1·0366	35·0	0·8498	65·0	0·7201
6·0	1·0291	36·0	0·8448	66·0	0·7165
7·0	1·0217	37·0	0·8398	67·0	0·7128
8·0	1·0143	38·0	0·8348	68·0	0·7093
9·0	1·0071	39·0	0·8299	69·0	0·7057
10·0	1·0000	40·0	0·8251	70·0	0·7022
11·0	0·9930	41·0	0·8203	71·0	0·6988
12·0	0·9861	42·0	0·8156	72·0	0·6953
13·0	0·9792	43·0	0·8109	73·0	0·6919
14·0	0·9725	44·0	0·8063	74·0	0·6886
15·0	0·9659	45·0	0·8017	75·0	0·6852
16·0	0·9593	46·0	0·7972	76·0	0·6819
17·0	0·9529	47·0	0·7927	77·0	0·6787
18·0	0·9465	48·0	0·7883	78·0	0·6754
19·0	0·9402	49·0	0·7839	79·0	0·6722
20·0	0·9340	50·0	0·7796	80·0	0·6690
21·0	0·9279	51·0	0·7753	81·0	0·6659
22·0	0·9218	52·0	0·7711	82·0	0·6628
23·0	0·9159	53·0	0·7669	83·0	0·6597
24·0	0·9100	54·0	0·7628	84·0	0·6566
25·0	0·9042	55·0	0·7587	85·0	0·6536
26·0	0·8984	56·0	0·7547	86·0	0·6506
27·0	0·8927	57·0	0·7507	87·0	0·6476
28·0	0·8871	58·0	0·7467	88·0	0·6446
29·0	0·8816	59·0	0·7428	89·0	0·6417
30·0	0·8762	60·0	0·7389	90·0	0·6388

Degrees A.P.I.	Sp. Gr. 60° F./60° F.	Degrees A.P.I.	Sp. Gr. 60° F./60° F.	Degrees A.P.I.	Sp. Gr. 60° F./60° F.
90·0	**0·6388**	**110·0**	**0·5859**	**130·0**	**0·5411**
91·0	0·6360	111·0	0·5835	131·0	0·5390
92·0	0·6331	112·0	0·5811	132·0	0·5370
93·0	0·6303	113·0	0·5787	133·0	0·5350
94·0	0·6275	114·0	0·5764	134·0	0·5330
95·0	0·6247	115·0	0·5740	135·0	0·5310
96·0	0·6220	116·0	0·5717	136·0	0·5290
97·0	0·6193	117·0	0·5694	137·0	0·5270
98·0	0·6166	118·0	0·5671	138·0	0·5250
99·0	0·6139	119·0	0·5649	139·0	0·5231
100·0	**0·6112**	**120·0**	**0·5626**	**140·0**	**0·5212**
101·0	0·6086	121·0	0·5604	141·0	0·5193
102·0	0·6060	122·0	0·5582	142·0	0·5174
103·0	0·6034	123·0	0·5560	143·0	0·5155
104·0	0·6008	124·0	0·5538	144·0	0·5136
105·0	0·5983	125·0	0·5517	145·0	0·5118
106·0	0·5958	126·0	0·5495	146·0	0·5099
107·0	0·5933	127·0	0·5474	147·0	0·5081
108·0	0·5908	128·0	0·5453	148·0	0·5063
109·0	0·5884	129·0	0·5432	149·0	0·5045
110·0	**0·5859**	**130·0**	**0·5411**	**150·0**	**0·5027**

This table is based on the recognised formula :

$$\text{Sp. Gr. } 60^\circ \text{ F.}/60^\circ \text{ F.} = \frac{141\cdot5}{\text{A.P.I.} + 131\cdot5}$$

TABLE IV

CONVERSION OF SPECIFIC GRAVITY 60°F./60°F. TO A.P.I. GRAVITY

Sp. Gr. 60° F./60° F.	Degrees A.P.I.	Sp. Gr. 60° F./60° F.	Degrees A.P.I.	Sp. Gr. 60° F./60° F.	Degrees A.P.I.
0·500	151·50	0·600	104·33	0·700	70·64
0·505	148·70	0·605	102·38	0·705	69·21
0·510	145·95	0·610	100·47	0·710	67·80
0·515	143·26	0·615	98·58	0·715	66·40
0·520	140·62	0·620	96·73	0·720	65·03
0·525	138·02	0·625	94·90	0·725	63·67
0·530	135·48	0·630	93·10	0·730	62·34
0·535	132·99	0·635	91·33	0·735	61·02
0·540	130·54	0·640	89·59	0·740	59·72
0·545	128·13	0·645	87·88	0·745	58·43
0·550	125·77	0·650	86·19	0·750	57·17
0·555	123·45	0·655	84·53	0·755	55·92
0·560	121·18	0·660	82·89	0·760	54·68
0·565	118·94	0·665	81·28	0·765	53·47
0·570	116·75	0·670	79·69	0·770	52·27
0·575	114·59	0·675	78·13	0·775	51·08
0·580	112·47	0·680	76·59	0·780	49·91
0·585	110·38	0·685	75·07	0·785	48·75
0·590	108·33	0·690	73·57	0·790	47·61
0·595	106·32	0·695	72·10	0·795	46·49
0·600	104·33	0·700	70·64	0·800	45·38

Sp. Gr. 60° F./60° F.	Degrees A.P.I.	Sp. Gr. 60° F./60° F.	Degrees A.P.I.	Sp. Gr. 60° F./60° F.	Degrees A.P.I.
0·800	45·38	0·900	25·72	1·000	10·00
0·805	44·28	0·905	24·85	1·005	9·30
0·810	43·19	0·910	23·99	1·010	8·60
0·815	42·12	0·915	23·14	1·015	7·91
0·820	41·06	0·920	22·30	1·020	7·23
0·825	40·02	0·925	21·47	1·025	6·55
0·830	38·98	0·930	20·65	1·030	5·88
0·835	37·96	0·935	19·84	1·035	5·21
0·840	36·95	0·940	19·03	1·040	4·56
0·845	35·96	0·945	18·24	1·045	3·91
0·850	34·97	0·950	17·45	1·050	3·26
0·855	34·00	0·955	16·67	1·055	2·62
0·860	33·03	0·960	15·90	1·060	1·99
0·865	32·08	0·965	15·13	1·065	1·36
0·870	31·14	0·970	14·38	1·070	0·74
0·875	30·21	0·975	13·63	1·075	0·13
0·880	29·30	0·980	12·89	1·076	0·01
0·885	28·39	0·985	12·15		
0·890	27·49	0·990	11·43		
0·895	26·60	0·995	10·71		
0·900	25·72	1·000	10·00		

NOTE. This table is based on the formula :—

$$\text{Degrees A.P.I.} = \frac{141·5}{\text{Sp. Gr. } 60° \text{ F.}/60° \text{ F.}} - 131·5$$

GLOSSARY

Words in this Glossary are indicated by the
*sign * where they first occur in the text*

Acetylene. A gas, C_2H_2, largely used in industry for cutting and welding metals, also for lighting. It is a highly unsaturated hydrocarbon usually made by the action of water on calcium carbide.

Activated. The condition of a substance which has been treated in a special manner to increase its activity in promoting reactions which may be physical, such as decolorizing or adsorption, or may be chemical, such as in the behaviour of catalysts.

Alcohols. A class of organic compounds containing oxygen, of which ethyl alcohol (the alcohol of potable spirits and wines) is the best known. They can react with acids to form "esters". They are largely used as solvents.

Alkylation. A process in which an olefin hydrocarbon is combined with either an iso-paraffin or an aromatic hydrocarbon. Examples are the combination of butylene (C_4H_8) with iso-butane (C_4H_{10}) to form iso-octane (C_8H_{18}), or ethylene (C_2H_4) and benzene (C_6H_6) to form ethyl benzene (C_8H_{10}).

Alkyl (Alkylated) Phenols. Chemical compounds derived from phenol by replacing one or more of the hydrogen atoms by saturated radicles of the paraffin series.

Alluvium. Geological term for the fine mud and other sediments laid down by rivers in flat valleys or in deltas.

Amorphous (without form). A term applied to such bodies as glass and glue, which do not show a crystalline structure.

Anaerobic. Term applied to microbes or bacteria which live in the absence of oxygen.

Anhydrite. A natural form of calcium sulphate occurring in large quantities in Italy, the U.S.A. and elsewhere.

Annealing. The process of re-heating materials such as glass or metals and cooling slowly to remove, or avoid the setting up of, internal strains.

Anticline. When beds are upfolded into an arch-like form (with the lower beds within the upper) the structure is called an anticline because the beds "incline away" from the crest on either side.

Anti-knock. An adjective signifying resistance to detonation (pinking) in spark-ignited internal combustion engines. Anti-knock value is measured in terms of Octane Number (*q.v.*).

Anti-larval. Term applied to a substance or operation to kill the larvæ of insects.

A.P.I. American Petroleum Institute. An association incorporated in the United States, having as its object the study of the arts and sciences connected with the petroleum industry in all its branches and the fostering of foreign and domestic trade in American petroleum products.

A.P.I. Gravity. In the U.S.A., an arbitrary scale known as the A.P.I. degree is used for reporting the gravity or the density of a petroleum product. The degree A.P.I. is related to the British specific gravity scale (60° F./ 60° F.) by the formula :

$$\text{Degree A.P.I.} = \frac{141 \cdot 5}{\text{Sp. Gr. } 60° \text{ F.}/60° \text{ F.}} - 131 \cdot 5.$$

The degree Baumé is an antiquated form of the degree A.P.I.

Aromatics. A group of hydrocarbons, of which benzene is the parent. They are called "Aromatics" because many of their derivatives have sweet or aromatic odours. These hydrocarbons are of relatively high specific gravity and possess good solvent properties. Certain aromatics have valuable anti-knock characteristics. Typical aromatics are : benzene, toluene, xylene.

Aromatization. Term applied to the formation of aromatic compounds from aliphatic or straight-chain hydrocarbons, which involves the formation of cyclic compounds and subsequent dehydrogenation to aromatic compounds.

Arrester. An arrangement often consisting of a vessel with baffle plates whereby the removal of a liquid or solid from a stream of gas or vapour can be effected.

A.S.M.E. American Society of Mechanical Engineers.

Asphalt. This term has two meanings : (1) in the United Kingdom it refers to a mixture of bitumen (*q.v.*) and mineral aggregate, as prepared for the construction of roads or for other purposes ; (2) in the United States it refers to the product which is known as bitumen in the United Kingdom.

Asphaltenes. That portion of asphaltic bitumen which is insoluble in aromatic-free petroleum spirit.

Asphaltic Bitumen. The full name for "bitumen" (*q.v.*), formerly adopted by the Permanent International Association of Road Congresses.

A.S.T.M. American Society for Testing Materials. An association incorporated in the United States for the promotion of the knowledge of the properties of engineering materials and for the standardization of specifications and methods of testing.

Athwartships. Extending from one side of the vessel to the other.

Autoclave. A heated pressure vessel for carrying out chemical reactions involving the use of liquids. In general, the pressure obtained therein is due to the vapour pressure of the constituents when raised to the desired temperature.

Back-filling. This refers to the replacement of earth to the position from which it was originally excavated, e.g. back-filling a pipeline trench.

Backwash. Term used in solvent extraction processes to designate the extract or partially processed extract fraction which may be returned to the tail end of the extraction system to increase the efficiency of the extraction process.

Bakelite. A type of artificial resin first made by Baekeland from formaldehyde and phenol. When heated in a mould under pressure it sets to a hard insoluble resin. A great industry, making many familiar objects, has developed.

Barytes. A heavy mineral consisting essentially of barium sulphate of high specific gravity which is mixed in powdered form in drilling fluids to increase their weight and so to prevent an oil or gas well from blowing out.

Bean. *Vide* Flow-Bean.

Beeswax. A wax excreted by bees, consisting mainly of esters of palmitic acid. Used commercially in polishes, etc.

Bentonite. A naturally occurring earth used in treating petroleum products to improve their colour.

Benzex. A fraction distilled from aromatic extracts and which boils within the range of a motor spirit.

Bitumen. A non-crystalline solid or semi-solid cementitious material derived from petroleum, which gradually softens when heated, consisting essentially of compounds composed predominantly of hydrogen and carbon. Bitumens are black or brown in colour. They may occur naturally or may be made as end products from the distillation of, or as extracts from, selected petroleum oils.

Blown Bitumen (Oxidized Bitumen). A type of bitumen prepared by the oxidation of petroleum, normally by air blowing at an elevated temperature.

Boundary Lubrication. The condition in which bearing surfaces are separated by a film of lubricant only a few molecules thick. The coefficient of friction in these circumstances is higher than is the case with fluid lubrication (*q.v.*), where the surfaces are separated by a comparatively thick film of oil. Special properties are required in a lubricant which has to function under boundary conditions.

Breathing. When a storage tank containing volatile products becomes warmed by solar heat, the vapours inside expand and blow out to atmosphere. On cooling, a slight vacuum is created, causing air from outside to be sucked into the tank. This double action is referred to as ''breathing''.

B.Th.U. British Thermal Unit. The quantity of heat required to raise the temperature of 1 lb. of water through 1° F.

Bubble Cap. An effective method of ensuring contact between the vapour and reflux of a fractionating column is by the use of plates and bubble caps. The object of the bubble cap is to obtain an even diffusion of vapour through the liquid. Bubble caps are made in a variety of designs, the more common type consisting of a circular cap inverted over a vapour riser of smaller diameter than the cap. The periphery of the cap, which clears the plate by a short distance, is slotted to cause the vapour to pass into the liquid as streams of small bubbles.

Bumped. A vessel or tank having a slightly convex or, less usually, a concave end or bottom is said to be bumped or dished.

Calibration. The process of measuring or calculating the volumetric contents or capacity of a receptacle. Also the determination of fixed reference points on the scale of any instrument by comparison with a known standard, and the subsequent sub-division or graduation of the scale to enable measurements in definite units to be made with it.

Calorie. The amount of heat required to raise the temperature of 1 gram of water through 1°C. (from 0°C. to 1°C.).

Calorific Value. The calorific value of a combustible material is the quantity of heat produced by complete combustion of unit weight of the material. The units in which the calorific value is usually given are (a) calories per gram and (b) British Thermal Units per pound. The systems may be converted by the relationship :
1 calorie per gram = 1·8 B.Th.U. per lb.

Candelilla Wax. A yellowish brown wax obtained by boiling the leaves and stalks of a certain South American tree (Euphorbia antisyphilitica) with water and a little sulphuric acid.

Capillary. The inside bore of a tube when the diameter of the bore is extremely small.

Carnauba Wax. A wax obtained as exudation from the leaves and berries of a South American palm tree (Copernicia cerifera). Used in the manufacture of polishes etc.

Casinghead Gas. *Vide* Natural Gas.

Catalyst. A substance added to reacting chemical compounds causing an acceleration of the chemical reaction, thus enabling such reaction to take place at a lower temperature. A suitable catalyst will also prevent the formation of undesired products.

c.c. Cubic centimetre. *Vide* ml.

Centipoise and Centistokes. A centipoise is 1/100th of the absolute unit of viscosity, the poise. The viscosity of water at 20° C. is approximately 1 centipoise. The centipoise is derived from the kinematic unit of viscosity, the centistokes, by multiplying the latter by the density of the liquid, i.e. 1 centipoise = 1 centistokes × density of liquid.

Christmas Tree. A multi-way fitting at the head of a well which carries the valves, beans and gauges by which an oil or gas well is controlled at the surface ; named from the complex arrangement of these resembling a Christmas tree.

Coaming. The raised edge round hatch openings upon which the hatch covers are fixed.

Coir. A tough, resistant fibre made from the outer cover of the coconut.

Compression Ignition (C.I.). The combustion which takes place when fuels are injected in a fine spray into the hot compressed air (500° C.) in the cylinder of a diesel (compression ignition) engine. The heating of the air is due to its rapid compression by the piston.

Counter-current. The description of any process involving the treatment of one gas or liquid by another liquid in which the two materials flow in opposite directions.

Courses (Tanks). Each continuous ring of plates in a tank. Also known as " strake".

Cresylic Acids. Chemical compounds of the same family as phenol or carbolic acid. They are derived mainly from coal tar, but can also be extracted from certain cracked distillates. They are used as gasoline inhibitors (*q.v.*).

Curb. The angle iron round the bottom or top of a tank to which the side and bottom or top are riveted.

Cut. Refinery term for a fraction of oil made when distilling ; an oil which has a narrow boiling range as distinct from a product, such as kerosine or gas oil, which has a wide boiling range.

Cutback Bitumen. Bitumen which has been rendered fluid at atmospheric temperatures by the addition of a suitable diluent, such as white spirit, kerosine or creosote. The abbreviation "cutback" is often used.

Deadweight. The amount of cargo, stores and fuel which a vessel carries when loaded to the appropriate draft allowed by law. The difference between deadweight and displacement represents the actual weight of the vessel.

Deciduous. Term applied to trees which shed their leaves each year.

Dephlegmator. That part of a distillation apparatus in which a portion of the vapours is condensed and returned to the main fractionating column as reflux to improve the efficiency of the fractionation.

Derris Root. A tropical root containing highly toxic components (including rotenone), which can be extracted or used in the powder form for insecticidal purposes.

Dewpoint. The lowest temperature at which a small quantity of any liquid contained in a closed vessel will evaporate and remain in the vapour state without condensation. Cooling of the vapour below its dewpoint results in condensation of part of the vapour as liquid. The dewpoint of a normal gasoline approximates to the temperature at which 70% volume distils over in the A.S.T.M. distillation test.

Diatoms. Microscopic plants having silica skeletons, found floating in salt and fresh water. Their remains on the ocean floor form deposits of diatom ooze.

Dielectric Properties. Those properties which relate to the value of a material as an electrical insulator.

Dipping. A process of measuring the height of a liquid in a storage tank. This is usually done by lowering a weighted graduated steel tape through the tank roof and noting the level at which the oil surface cuts the tape when the weight gently touches the tank bottom. *Vide* Ullage.

Distemper. A paint compounded of a pigment with water and an adhesive such as size, glue, casein, etc.

Distillate. The liquid obtained by condensing the vapour given off by a boiling liquid.

Distillation (Fractional). The process of separating components of different boiling points by evaporation and condensation of the lower boiling components. When applied to the separation of gasoline, kerosine, etc., from a crude oil, to leave a residual fuel oil or asphaltic bitumen, the process is frequently called "topping". Distillation is normally carried out in such a way as to avoid decomposition (cracking) ; in the case of the higher boiling distillates, such as lubricating oils, this is accomplished by distillation under vacuum.

Dope. A general name for a product which is added in small quantities to a petroleum fraction to improve quality or performance.

Double-bottom Tanks. In general cargo vessels the frames at the bottom of the hull are plated over internally, forming an inner bottom. The space between this and the bottom is divided into tanks which may be used for water ballast or bunker fuel storage. Tankers are not built with double bottoms in the cargo tanks, but only under machinery spaces.

Dyke. An igneous intrusion ; in this case the magma has been injected up a vertical fissure, forcing the walls apart, and on cooling has become a vertical sheet of rock with parallel sides cutting across the bedding planes.

Emissivity. The degree to which a substance absorbs or radiates heat.

Emulsion. A liquid in which is suspended another immiscible liquid in a very fine state of division.

Entomologist. One who studies the life and habits of insects.

Epoxide Ring. A type of chemical compound (cyclic oxide) in which two adjacent carbon atoms are also connected to the same oxygen atom.

Escarpment. A ridge in the landscape caused by the outcrop of a relatively hard rock which stands up because it is not eroded away as quickly as the rocks lying above and below it.

Esters. Compounds formed by the combination of an organic acid with an alcohol. Thus, acetic acid and ethyl alcohol give ethyl acetate.

Ethers. Organic compounds in which two hydrocarbon radicles are united to an oxygen atom. The best known ether is C_2H_5—O—C_2H_5 (di-ethyl ether).

Exploitation. The development or drilling up and producing phase of an oilfield, following the phase of exploration.

Exploratory. The phase in which an oil region or oilfield is being explored, either by technical surveys or by exploratory drilling. Exploration is followed by exploitation.

Extract. The portion of an unrefined petroleum product (generally a kerosine or a lubricating oil) which is removed by solvent refining. The extract, after removal of the solvent, consists largely of aromatic hydrocarbons. Those from lubricating oils are known in the paint trade as Aromatic Petroleum Residues.

Extrusive. Molten rock (or magma) generated in the sub-strata may force its way through the crust and be extruded in volcanic regions in the form of lavas, basalts, etc. *Vide* Intrusive.

Fatty Acids. Organic acids containing carbon, hydrogen and oxygen, which in combination with glycerine constitute fats or fatty oils.

Fatty Oils. Oils which occur naturally in plants and animals. Typical vegetable oils are castor, rapeseed and olive ; typical animal oils are lard, neatsfoot and whale oil.

F.B.P. Final Boiling Point. The maximum temperature observed on the distillation thermometer when a standard A.S.T.M. distillation is carried out on gasoline, kerosine or gas oil.

Flash Distillation. The process of heating a liquid to a temperature above the boiling range of the liquid or some of its components, preventing substantial evaporation taking place by keeping the liquid under pressure and then releasing the pressure by passing the heated liquid into a large receptacle, which causes the evaporation of all or part of the liquid. The vapours are then condensed or fractionated.

Flotation. The process of treating a powder, such as a powdered metallic ore, with a liquid and blowing in air so as to cause a foam. Differences in the degree of wetting of the components by the liquid used (generally water containing some special chemical) cause the ore component of the powdered mineral to rise to the surface with the foam, while the other remains at the bottom.

Flow-Bean. The apparatus installed in a Christmas Tree for controlling the flow of oil or gas from a well—in simple form, a nipple with central hole drilled through, which is inserted in the flow line of a well to reduce the oil and gas flow to the required figure ; hence to "bean up" or "bean down".

Fluid Lubrication. The condition in which bearing surfaces are separated by a relatively thick film of lubricant.

Foraminifera. Very primitive animals living mostly in the sea, or in brackish water, having a skeletal structure of lime or other substance often preserved in sediment, very useful for determination of geological age of rocks and correlation thereof. Existed from Cambrian times until the present day.

Formaldehyde.   The first member of the class of organic substances known as aldehydes.   It is a gas normally used in solution known as formalin.

Fumigants.   Gases or volatile liquids which are toxic to insects and can be used, therefore, for their destruction.

Furfural.   A colourless organic compound—liquid at ordinary temperatures—having a boiling point of about 160° C. and specific gravity 1·2. It is made by the action of dilute acids on bran, corn cobs and similar materials.   Its chemical formula is $C_5H_4O_2$.

Gabbro.   One of the many varieties of igneous (fiery) deep-seated (plutonic) rocks corresponding in chemical composition to the volcanic lavas and basalts.

Gasex.   A fraction distilled from aromatic extracts, and which boils within the range of a gas oil.

Geomorphology.   The study of the surface features of the earth and their inter-relations from both the genetic and historical aspect, and, in particular, the investigation of the constructional and destructional agencies giving rise to them.
Gr.—Geo—earth ; *morpha*—form ; *logos*—discourse.

Glycerol.   Chemical name for glycerine.   It is a type of alcohol.

Grout.   A liquid or a suspension of a powdered solid in a liquid which is injected into the interstices between a collection of solid fragments in order that it may form a binding medium to hold the solid materials together.   Grouting work is also often referred to as "penetration macadam".

Gudgeon Pin (Wrist Pin).   The hardened steel pin connecting the piston with the connecting rod of an internal combustion engine.

Gun Perforated.   Holes and perforations made by a "gun" or casing perforator in oil well casing with a view to admitting the oil in adjacent strata.   The holes are made by bullets electrically fired from the "gun" suspended in the casing by a line from the surface.

Hæmatite.   Naturally occurring red oxide of iron, Fe_2O_3.

Heave (Heaving Shales).   The habit of certain strata, notably clays and shales, to absorb water and so increase markedly in volume.   Heaving clays will close up a hole drilled through them, by plastic flow.

Homologue. A member of a series of hydrocarbons or of any series of organic chemical compounds, the members of which bear close chemical relation to each other.

Humectant. A chemical compound which readily absorbs moisture, such as glycerine, and is used for preventing substances from drying out.

Hydroforming. A conversion or "reforming" process, in the presence of a catalyst and excess of hydrogen, whereby gasoline fractions of low octane rating are converted into those of high octane rating. This result is obtained mainly by the conversion of naphthene hydrocarbons into aromatic hydrocarbons.

Hydromatic. A term which is somewhat loosely applied in the U.S.A. to a transmission system which usually incorporates a fluid flywheel in conjunction with an automatic gear change system generally controlled hydraulically.

Hydrostatic Head. The pressure caused by the weight of a column of water.

Hygroscopic. Capable of absorbing water readily from the atmosphere.

Hypoid Gear. A combination of the spiral bevel and worm type, which is very quiet in operation. The motion of the teeth is a combination of rolling and sliding, causing high loading pressure on the tooth faces, together with high rubbing speeds, and so demanding exceptional qualities of the lubricant.

I.B.P. Initial Boiling Point, that is, the temperature at which the first drop of distillate appears on commencement of distillation in a laboratory apparatus.

Inhibitor. A substance, the presence of which in small amounts in a petroleum product, prevents or retards undesirable changes taking place in the quality of the product, or in the condition of the equipment in which the product is used. In general, the essential function of inhibitors is to prevent or retard oxidation. Examples of uses include the delaying of gum formation in stored gasolines and of colour change in lubricating oils ; the prevention of corrosion is also included—e.g. rust prevention by inhibitors in turbine oils.

Intrusive. Molten rock (or magma) generated in the sub-strata may be forced into the earth's crust but fail to reach the surface. These deep-seated (or plutonic) intrusions may take the form of batholiths, laccoliths, etc.

I.P. Institute of Petroleum. The organization in Great Britain primarily responsible for the advancement of the study of petroleum and its allied products in all their aspects. It is the recognized British standardization authority for methods of testing petroleum products.

Isomerization. The conversion of a compound into another compound containing the same atoms in the molecule but arranged in a different way. For example, butane may be converted into iso-butane by isomerization.

Kerex. A fraction distilled from aromatic extracts and which boils within the range of a kerosine.

Ketones. A class of chemical bodies containing the group CO which are much used in industry as solvents and in the manufacture of artificial resins.

Laccoliths. A plutonic or deep-seated intrusion of molten rock (magmatic melt) injected between the bedding planes of strata, resulting in arching of the overlying beds in the shape of a mushroom.

Larvæ. The intermediate stage in the development of insects between the egg and the winged insect.

Latent Heat. The quantity of heat (measured in British Thermal Units or calories) which is required to change the physical state of unit weight of a substance, without alteration in temperature, from solid to liquid, or from liquid to vapour.

Latent Solvent. A constituent of a nitrocellulose lacquer which has little solvent properties of its own, but which can improve the solvent properties of a true solvent present in the lacquer.

Laterite. A superficial deposit found generally in tropical countries. It consists of red-brown mottled clays and is a decomposition product of rocks of various kinds.

Lithology. Science of the nature and composition of stones and rocks. *Gr.—lithos—*a stone.

Loess. A soft rock of wind-borne origin occurring as large deposits, particularly in China and in Central and Eastern Europe. Geologically, a deposit of fine yellowish-grey loam, consisting of quartz particles with lime and clay as binding materials, the product of glacial erosion during Ice Ages.

Look Box. A device usually located in the receiving house of a distillation plant, whereby the product stream from the plant is kept under observation by the operator. The look box is usually connected to a manifold leading to the receiving tanks, one or more tanks being provided for each "cut" or product desired from the distillation.

Lubex. An aromatic extract from a lubricating oil.

Macadam. A collection of broken stone or similar material arranged in such a manner as to form a road surface in which the fragments of solid are interlocked and mechanically bound to the maximum possible extent.

Magma. Fluid strata under the solid crust of the earth which may be extruded at the surface by volcanic activity or intruded into the strata of the crust on its way to the surface. *Vide* Extrusive, Intrusive and Laccoliths.

M.E.K. Methyl ethyl ketone.

Mercaptans or hydrosulphides. Organic compounds of carbon, hydrogen and sulphur. They have a bad odour and frequently occur in unrefined gasoline. Mercaptans must be removed from gasoline or converted to the unobjectionable disulphides by suitable refining (e.g. by "doctor" treatment).

Metamorphism. Term applied to the changes in structure of rocks which have been subjected to high temperatures or pressure during geological time, e.g. limestone to marble.

Methanol or methyl alcohol, CH_3OH. The simplest member of the class of organic compounds known as alcohols. It is a liquid boiling at 66° C. Methanol is inflammable and poisonous.

Micron. One-millionth of a metre. Abbreviation μ.

Miscible. Capable of mixing with.

ml. Millilitre. The millilitre is one-thousandth part of a litre, the metric unit of capacity. Its size is very nearly equal to one cubic centimetre (c.c.). Whereas, however, the millilitre is the volume occupied by 1 gram of pure water at its maximum density, the cubic centimetre is the volume of a centimetre cube.

$$1 \text{ ml.} = 0 \cdot 999972 \text{ c.c.}$$

Naphthenes. A class of saturated cyclic hydrocarbons of the general formula C_nH_{2n}.

Naphthenic Acids. The organic acids which are present in petroleum fractions rich in naphthene hydrocarbons.

Natural Gas. The gas which occurs naturally with many crude oils, and issues from the top of the casing of a producing well. It consists mainly of the lighter paraffin hydrocarbons. The term ''Casinghead gas'' is also used.

Nematicide. A substance which will kill nematodes, minute thread-like worms infesting the roots of plants.

Nipple. A short length of pipe screwed at both ends.

Nitrobenzene. Compound made by treating benzene with nitric acid.

Nitrogen Bases. Organic compounds containing nitrogen which are capable of combining with acids to form salts.

Octane Number. The octane number of a fuel is numerically equal to the percentage by volume of iso-octane in a mixture of iso-octane and normal heptane having the same resistance to detonation as the fuel under consideration in a special test engine. It is a measure of the anti-knock value of a gasoline, and, in respect of the special test engine, the higher the octane number the higher the anti-knock quality of the gasoline.

Oiliness. The coefficient of friction under boundary conditions can be reduced by certain lubricants or by incorporating small quantities of additive in mineral lubricating oils. This property of reducing the coefficient of friction is termed oiliness. Fatty oils and fatty acids are examples of substances possessing this property.

Olefins. A class of unsaturated hydrocarbons of the general formula $C_nH_{2}n$.

Olein. A fatty oil which is a constituent of many vegetable and animal fats and fatty oils, such as olive oil and beef fat. The term is also frequently applied to oleic acid, which is an unsaturated fatty acid.

Oleum. A specially strong sulphuric acid containing free sulphur tri-oxide, used in the refining of white oils.

Orifice Meter. A meter for measuring the flow of a gas or a liquid in a pipe. The rate of flow is measured by the pressure drop across a constriction in the pipe. This constriction usually takes the form of an orifice plate, which is a metal plate having a circular hole of known diameter cut in it (*vide* Venturi Meter).

Outcrop. The emergence at the surface of a stratum, vein or rock.

Outstepping. A location or well drilled beyond an existing well, whether for purposes of exploration or exploitation, is said to be an outstep well.

Overlap. Strata overlap when each successive stratum of the upper formations extends beyond the limits of the stratum lying below. An unconformity may or may not overlap.

Oxidizing Flame. Term applied to a flame in which there is an excess of air or oxygen.

Ozokerite. A naturally occurring micro-crystalline mineral wax related to petroleum, also known as earth wax. After refining it is frequently termed ceresin.

Palæontology. The study of ancient animals, the remains of which exist only as fossils. *Gr. palaios*—ancient.

Paraffin. Chemical name of the series of saturated hydrocarbons of the general formula C_nH_{2n+2}, the first member of which is methane. The paraffin waxes are high molecular weight members of this series. The term ''paraffin'' in the U.K. is often misapplied to kerosine.

Partial Pressure. That part of the vapour pressure of a liquid mixture which is contributed by one of the components of that mixture.

Penetration. A measure of the hardness or consistency of asphaltic bitumen in terms of the distance in tenths of a millimetre which a weighted needle will penetrate the sample in five seconds, the temperature, unless otherwise stated, being 25° C. or 77° F.

Petrolatum. A semi-solid material obtained from petroleum and consisting essentially of micro-crystalline waxes in association with oil.

Petrology. The study of the mineral and chemical composition of rocks· *Gr. petra*—a rock.

Phenol. Chemical name for carbolic acid.

Pinking. One of the names applied to knocking or detonation in gasoline engines.

Plasticizers. Solvents of low volatility which are added to paints in order that they may dry to a stable flexible film.

Polymerization. The combination of two or more molecules of an unsaturated compound to give a compound of higher molecular weight. Polymerization processes are largely used for the production of high octane gasoline, synthetic rubbers, etc.

Promoter. A substance which may considerably increase the activity of a catalyst. For example, the catalytic action of iron is greatly increased when the catalyst contains a small amount of oxides of aluminium or silicon, etc.

Pyrethrins. Chemical compounds which are the active toxic principles of the pyrethrum plant.

Pyrethrum. A plant, a species of the genus Chrysanthemum. Only a few of the species are toxic to insects ; the important one is Chrysanthemum Cinerariæfolium, which looks somewhat like the ordinary field daisy.

Quebracho. An extract of the wood of certain trees (Aspidosperma Quebracho) which are found in South American forests. The extract is rich in tannin and is used in the tanning industry.

Raffinate. The refined product resulting from a solvent refining process.

Rectifying. The separation of fractions of different boiling range from a liquid mixture by distillation. The term is used chiefly when one particular liquid is the main product and is, therefore, being purified by this process.

Reducing Flame. Term applied to a flame in which there is insufficient air or oxygen for complete combustion.

Reforming. The operation of cracking straight-run or cracked petroleum fractions, boiling largely within the gasoline range, in order to increase the anti-knock value.

Revetments. Protective layers placed on sea walls or river banks to prevent their being washed away by erosion.

Saponification. The splitting of fats or fatty oils by alkali to form soaps. Sometimes applied to the neutralization of fatty acids with alkali.

Seepage. A naturally occurring escape of crude oil or gas to the surface.

Settling Tank. A tank employed for separating two liquids which are not miscible. If the liquids are not miscible and do not form an emulsion they separate into layers according to their specific gravities, and the layers can be drawn off from different levels in the tank.

Shell Method Series (S.M.S.). A private publication of the Group setting out the methods and apparatus to be used in carrying out laboratory tests on petroleum products.

Shower Decks. Perforated plates, often used in fractionating columns in place of bubble trays. They may be used in vacuum fractionating columns where only a small pressure drop is permissible, or in columns where the degree of fractionating is not important.

Side-Stripper. A vessel which enables the initial boiling point of a liquid drawn off a tray in a fractionating tower to be raised by bubbling steam through it before running it to storage.

Sill. Molten rock (or magma) forced for great distances between more or less horizontal bedding—planes of sedimentary strata forming sheet-like masses, much greater in their lateral than in their vertical thickness. Such igneous masses are known as sheets or sills.

Smoke Point. The maximum height of flame measured in millimetres at which a kerosine will burn without smoking when tested in a standard lamp used for this purpose.

Sour Gas. Natural gas which contains objectionable amounts of sulphuretted hydrogen and other corrosive sulphur compounds. The sweet, or sulphur-free gas is, in the U.S.A., by conservation law, reserved for sale only to commercial and domestic fuel users.

Stabilizer. A fractionating column designed to separate efficiently very volatile products from components of gasoline boiling range in crude oil, casinghead gasoline or pressure distillate, thus controlling the vapour pressure.

Static Electricity. Static or frictional electricity may be generated from handling materials, by the flow of certain liquids through pipelines or from the operation of equipment such as belts.

Straight-run. A term applied to a product of petroleum made by distillation without cracking.

Strapping. The measurement of the external diameter of a vertical or horizontal cylindrical tank by stretching a steel tape around each course of the tank's plates and recording the measurement.

Stratigraphy. Science dealing with geological formations, in particular of sedimentary rocks, their stratification and their correlation by means of palæontology and related sciences.

String. Derived originally from the suspended cable and tools of the cable tool drilling method ; but now applied equally to ''strings'' of drill pipe, casing, tubing, etc., in rotary drilling.

Surface String. The topmost section of well casing to which the well head fittings are attached.

Surface Tension. The force exerted by the particles of a liquid at its surface which maintains a continuous surface. The surface tension is measured by the force required to tear apart unit length of the surface.

Sweating. The operation of submitting crude paraffin wax to a very gradual increase of temperature with the twofold object of (1) removing the contained oil, which slowly oozes or ''sweats'' out and is drained away, and (2), preparing from the wax so obtained fractions with successively higher melting points.

Syncline. A geological structure, bowl-shaped or trough-like in form, the beds dipping towards the centre or axis of the syncline, and due to compression of the earth's crust ; contrast anticline.

Tectonics. Science of structural morphology or of movements within the earth's crust, and giving rise to tilting, folding, thrusting, over-thrusting, and faulting, leading to earthquakes and mountain building.

Therm. Unit of heat equivalent to 100,000 British Thermal Units or 25,200 kilo (K.) calories.

Tonnages. These are of three categories—gross, under-deck and net. The word "tonnage" has no relation to weight, but is purely a marine measurement term, being expressed in tons of 100 cubic feet, or approximately 2·83 cubic metres.
Gross tonnage is the total internal volume of the hull and all superstructures, such as deck houses, etc.
Under-deck tonnage is the internal volume of the hull below the upper or tonnage deck.
Net tonnage is the gross tonnage less the statutory allowances for spaces occupied by machinery, crew accommodation and ballast tanks other than double-bottom tanks.

Top Dead Centre. The position of the crankshaft when the piston is at the top of its travel in the cylinder, i.e. at the finish of the compression stroke.

Topographic. Detailed description, representation on map, etc., of natural or artificial features of a country or region. Topographical mapping is an essential basis to geological mapping. *Gr. topos*—place.

Tops. The lightest fractions obtained when distilling a mixture of oils.

Traverse. Essentially a connected series of lines of constant bearing, on the earth's surface, the length and bearings of which have been determined. Usually this word includes topographical or geological detail, or both, observable along and to either side of the traverse.

Tuff. A sedimentary rock composed of fine material—volcanic dust, so-called ash and cinders and lapilli (small stones)—explosively ejected from a volcano. It may or may not be deposited in water.

Turbulence. Indiscriminate movement of air or fuel mixture in the combusion chamber of an engine.

Ullage. The volume of available space in a container unoccupied by contents. Hence ullaging, a method of gauging the contents of a tank by measuring the height of the liquid surface from the top of the tank. *Vide* Dipping.

Unsaturated. A term applied to organic compounds in which some carbon atoms are held together by double bonds, so that these compounds are capable of combining directly with other elements or compounds.

Up-dip. Proceeding or lying upwards in the direction of inclination of strata to the horizontal.

Vapour Lock. Stoppage in the gasoline feed to a carburettor, or in the carburettor itself, owing to the evolution of vapour from a gasoline too volatile for use in the existing conditions.

Vapour Pressure. The vapour pressure of a liquid is the equilibrium pressure developed in a closed vessel containing only the liquid and its vapour at the test temperature. In the petroleum industry, the Reid vapour pressure apparatus is commonly used, the results being given in lb. per square inch at 100° F., although normally reported simply as ''Reid V.P. in lb.''

Venturi Meter. A specially designed tube for measuring the rates of flow of gases or liquids, having a constriction or throat with convergent upstream and divergent downstream walls, the angles of which are such that streamline or almost streamline flow through the tube is achieved. The rate of flow is measured by the pressure drop across the throat. *Vide* Orifice Meter.

Viscosity Index. A method of indicating the viscosity/temperature relationship of an oil.

Volatile. Term applied to materials which have a sufficiently high vapour pressure at normal temperatures, causing them to evaporate readily at normal atmospheric pressure and temperature. It implies a high degree of volatility.

Water Bottom. Water accumulated at (or sometimes added to) the bottom of the oil in a storage tank. In cases where the tank bottom is very uneven, the water level assists in the accurate measurement of the oil content of the tank.

Water Finder. A graduated rod, usually of metal, to which water-finding paper or paste can be applied. This paste or paper is discoloured on contact with water, and thus affords a ready means of measuring the depth of water in a tank when the water finder is lowered to the tank bottom.

Water Gauge (W.G.). Term applied to the measurement of pressure or vacuum in terms of the height of a column of water which can be supported, i.e. measurement of pressure by water barometer.

Wildcat. A well drilled without reference to technical surveys or with little or no knowledge of the chances of striking oil.

INDEX

Where more than one reference is given, the more important are printed in heavier type. Explanations of the terms indicated with the sign * are given in the Glossary.
